Dykes, Peter (3)

Edsell, Mark (4)

Evans, Jim

Evans, Kevin (1)

Filer, Richard (1)

Fisher, Joe (1)

Fletcher, Ron (3)

Forster, Pete (11)

Gallagher, Carla (1)

Gompertz, Nick (1)

Green, Ian (3)

Hale, Dan (1)

Harlow, Tim (1)

Harrison, Ginette (4)

Harris, Steve (1)

Harvey, Tim (6)

Hawkesworth, Chris (1)

Haydock, Ron (1)

Hext, Faye (1)

Hillenbrand, Peter (3)

Hoar, Helen (5)

Howell, Tony (1)

Imray, Chris (9)

Jensen, Jörgen (1)

Johnson, Brian (7)

Jones, Gron (4)

Joseph-Lester, Barry (1)

Joyce, Kelsey (1)

Kalson, Nick (2)

Keohane, Kate (1)

Kewley, Emily (2)

Birmingham Medical Research Expeditionary Society

Bhutan 2012

Kanchenjunga east face at dawn

Gasping *Thin* Air

Mountain adventures by The
Birmingham Medical Research
Expeditionary Society

—

Jo Bradwell

With contributions from John Simmons, Alex Wright,
Peter Forster, Ian Chesner, John Delamere and
line illustrations by Barry Joseph-Lester

Published by the Birmingham Medical Research Expeditionary Society, B15 2TT, UK. Registered Charity No. 277893. info@bmres.co.uk.

This book was produced by AR (Jo) Bradwell.

Proof reading by Ian Jones, Jinja Publishing Ltd, 39 Newtown Road, Bishop's Stortford, CM23 3SB, UK.

Layout and typesetting by Kate Farrell Visual Communication, 55 Hamilton Road, Evesham, Worcestershire WR11 2XE

Maps by Matt Preston, iDC Graphic Design and Digital Agency, The Bond, 180-182 Fazeley St, Birmingham B5 5SE

Printed in Slovenia on behalf of Latitude Press Limited.

ISBN 978-1-5272-6297-3

Contents

Preface

The silken veil of air that mantles the Earth quickly rarefies on the great mountain ranges, frustrating life at the highest altitudes. Above 3,000 m, the effects of the thin air are immediately apparent as shortage of breath, weakness and headaches. At more than 6,000 m, permanent habitation is impossible while beyond 8,000 m, in what is chillingly dubbed the 'death zone', humans only survive for a few hours. Into this thin air, visitors travel at their peril; some suffer acute mountain sickness while indigenous peoples have shortened lives because of long-term oxygen deprivation (chronic mountain sickness).

Much is now understood about the causes of these conditions but in 1976 the canvas was largely blank. Areas of the great mountain regions remained unknown and acute mountain sickness was a medical mystery waiting to be explored. Into this arena stepped the Birmingham Medical Research Expeditionary Society. It was formed by a group of young doctors in the academic Department of Medicine at the Queen Elizabeth Hospital, Birmingham, and its members were looking for excitement. They were inquisitive, energetic and fearless. Having gathered ideas and borrowed some medical equipment, they took a plane to Kathmandu. From there they trekked to the north side of Annapurna, exploring and testing the effects of low oxygen levels on their bodies and minds.

After the first expedition there was a second, then another and eventually 15 in total to the great mountain ranges of the world. Trips to the Alps provided short experimental test beds for more ambitious escapades, while tough winter and summer hikes welded the members into an expeditionary force. On sometimes serious, occasionally farcical but always challenging trips, society members hiked, climbed and suffered their way around the world, contributing significantly to medical knowledge in the process.

This book is about the adventures of this unique Society as it enters its 45th year. Each chapter describes a large expedition while other sections cover the minor projects. A separate volume collates its research papers (ISBN 978-1-5272-0087-6). Before minds become vacant and perils hyperbolised beyond reality, details of the exploits and follies of these intrepid pioneers are documented for others to enjoy.

This publication is of course a personal account. Others have contributed substantially to several chapters but the words are mine. More expressive or lucid members may recollect a different assortment of facts and emotions, but memories fade, suffering pales to pleasurable adversity and serious illness to minor inconvenience. Even diaries may romanticise, exaggerate or belittle the good and the bad.

Finally, an apology to friends who may feel ignored, disregarded, or even irritated by incidents that I have described incorrectly or overlooked. I could not include all adventures and, anyway, your recollections may be as mistaken as mine.

Jo Bradwell
Founding member, Birmingham Medical Research Expeditionary Society
January 2020

Dedication

———

To Barbara, the family and comradeship from
members of the Birmingham Medical Research
Expeditionary Society

Acknowledgments

———

The Birmingham Medical Research Expeditionary Society is grateful to The Arthur Thompson Trust, The Wellcome Trust and The JABBS Foundation for financial support. Furthermore, a host of smaller charities, pharmaceutical and other companies plus numerous individuals contributed generously to research projects. In particular, my thanks go to the many mountain equipment suppliers that allowed us to suffer in reasonable comfort at high altitude. Finally, our heart-felt gratitude to numerous institutions including the University of Birmingham and the Queen Elizabeth Hospital, Birmingham that have allowed time off service.

My special thanks to the patrons who have supported us over the years: Professor Sir Melville Arnott, Sir Chris Bonington, Joe Brown MBE, Kenton Cool, Professor Sir David Eastwood, Professor Donald Heath, Professor Sir Raymond Hoffenberg, Professor MJ Irvine, Sir Alex Jarrett, Professor Prem Kumar, Professor Sandy McNeish, Dr James Milledge, Doug Scott CBE, Sir Peter Scott, Professor Michael Sheppard, Dr Michael Stroud, Mr Michael Ward and Professor Tom Whitehead.

I am most grateful to Amy Cogswell for all her hard work helping to prepare the manuscript over seven and a half years.

Beginnings

PER ARDUA AD ALTA

"Great things are done when men and mountains meet;
This is not done by jostling in the street."

– William Blake

I lay shivering in my sleeping bag, listening to the assorted sounds in the darkness: soft snores in neighbouring bunks, the sighing of the wind and the fitful breathing of Frank Davies lying next to me. I feared for him and how much more suffering he could take. What if he should die? A spike of anxiety stabbed my chest. It would be my responsibility; it would be on my shoulders. He could have descended two days ago if I had only pressed him harder. Yesterday, looking awful, he had briefly come into the dining room of the hut. Clutching his head in pain, he passed us by and disappeared outside into the blizzard to vomit repeatedly. I thought about the 1976 article in the The Lancet on acute mountain sickness. 'See Nupste and die', it had been titled. Perhaps Frank's epitaph would be 'See Chimborazo and die'.

Frank turned in his thick goose-down bag and groaned. Because he was suffering the most, I had deliberately chosen to be next to him. If he needed an emergency descent then I hoped I would be sleeping lightly enough to awaken and offer help. His sporadic breathing became lighter with brief gasps and then stopped. I waited for him to breathe again. The seconds ticked by; then half a minute. Silence. "Come on Frank, breathe, breathe!" I said to myself. "Frank, breathe!" My fear increased. "BREATHE!"

I reached over and, shaking his body, whispered, "Frank, Frank." He rolled over towards me, took a small breath and mumbled, "What's the matter?"

Thank God he was still conscious.

"It's okay, just checking you were not suffering too much," I whispered back.

He turned away. His breathing gradually increased to a noisy crescendo then stopped once again. After another anxious minute of waiting, I heard him lightly inhale then exhale again. Shallow inhalations rapidly gave way to deep sighing breaths, only to stop once again in the next cycle.

I lay back gently taking care not to bump my aching head on the pillow. What bizarre cause had brought 20 of us to this forbidding place 5,000 m up the Andes?

It had started in the glorious summer of 1976. Day after day the sun rose into a clear blue sky and shone into the evening, desiccating England and the English hills. A group of us in our early thirties were badly overworked in the medical mayhem of junior doctor imprisonment and needed to escape. We toiled at the University of Birmingham Teaching Hospital known as the Queen Elizabeth Medical Centre. Tim Harvey, John Delamere and I had known each other for several years. We had shared patients, listened to one another's presentations at medical meetings, enjoyed parties in the hospital mess and had a common interest in mountains. John had audaciously (for those days) taken six months' leave of absence during his junior doctor years to cross the Andes. He had taken a boat up the Amazon into Peru, climbed challenging mountains and crossed the Altiplano. He had also climbed in the Kulu region of northern India. Tough, resolute and obsessed with mountains, he was aching to return to the Himalaya. My exploits were trivial in comparison but I had climbed a little in the Pyrenees and Britain and I liked long distance walking. For a student bet with school friends Willie and Angus, I had walked 52 miles from my home town of Stoke-on-Trent to Sheffield. On a ward round at the children's hospital the next day, the head of paediatrics, Professor Sir Douglas Hubble, was convinced that I had Still's disease (a form of juvenile rheumatoid arthritis) because of the way that I was walking. When I embarrassingly explained the reason for my abnormal gait, he thought it was a jolly good story and directed his hostile inquisitions at other students. However, my exploits were surpassed by those of Tim Harvey. Tough, wiry, resolute and fiercely intelligent, he had completed the 58 miles of the London to Brighton walk five years in a row between 1962 and 1966. The route, mostly along main roads, is fraught with danger. Vehicles thunder by only inches from the walkers, leading to the occasional fatality.

During those long hot days of 1976, members of the doctors' mess organised some big weekend walks. The first I attended was the Lyke Wake Walk, which takes its name from the act of watching over (wake) a corpse (lyke). The route takes a direct line across the North York Moors for 42 miles. There were a dozen of us from the hospital and inevitably it developed into a race, which I completed in a respectable 8 hours. This gave me membership of the Lyke Wake club and I became the proud possessor of the club tie – black with coffins. It was not entirely suitable for hospital use or for my parents, who were horrified that their medical practitioner son should be so morbid.

On a subsequent walk, Tim joined us for the Yorkshire Three Peaks (Pen-y-ghent, Whernside and Ingleborough) commencing at the Crown Inn in Horton in Ribblesdale. It was a beautiful day and I remember running back to the pub from the top of Ingleborough with Hans Wordle, an Austrian friend.

The experience was exhilarating. What a contrast from the stifling atmosphere of the hospital; what a joy to be free of the responsibilities of managing very ill patients. I was young (31), fit, strong and enjoying the great outdoors as never before. I bumped into Tim the following day in the hospital secretaries' office. He was limping badly. He was wearing only socks on his feet as his blisters were too painful for shoes. He had struggled to finish the walk in 12 hours. Driven on by the humbling experience, he repeated the Three Peaks a few weeks later in a much better time.

We were walking or climbing most free weekends of that blissful summer. We climbed the Snowdon Horseshoe at least three times as well as many lesser peaks.

Early in September 1976 we took up the challenge of the 'Three Peaks in 24 hours race'. This entails the ascent of Snowdon, Scafell Pike and Ben Nevis, Britain's three biggest peaks, within 24 hours. Tim Harvey, Neville Richardson (Department of Chemistry), Gron Jones (Department of Physics), Phil Gamlin (a research chemist) and I set off at 4.00 pm in two cars from Birmingham for the exploit. By late on Friday evening, we had knocked off Snowdon and we then drove overnight to Wasdale Head to ascend Scafell Pike. Tired muscles, sleep deprivation and excitability were a recipe for disaster. Nevertheless, we scrambled unharmed onto the summit of England's highest peak in the early light of Saturday morning. The next drive was the most dangerous, with fast traffic on the narrow, winding Scottish roads. To speed up the drive north, we adopted a procedure for overtaking. The lead car would stay on the right-hand side of the road if it were clear for the second car to pass slower vehicles. Blind corners were in the hands of the leaders. We dodged and weaved our way through Glasgow, overtaking everything as we raced past the sweeping vistas of Rannoch Moor, and watched the clock ticking by on the frustratingly narrow roads up to Fort William and Ben Nevis. Anxious and agitated, we arrived at the start of the Ben Nevis path with only 4 hours of our 24-hour deadline remaining.

By chance our final climb coincided with the annual Ben Nevis fell race. Rushing up the lower slopes, Neville and I caught up the back markers as we entered the clouds. We mockingly offered them sweets and water while the race leader, the legendary Joss Naylor, raced down past us, leaping from rock to rock in giant 50-foot strides, winning in 1 hour 28 minutes. We reached the summit surrounded by fell runners and, jogging down with the slowest, made it back to the cars with 90 minutes to spare. However, this was a team event, not just an exploit for Neville and me. Looking back up the mountain, Phil and Gron could be seen below the mist and soon arrived. That left only Tim as we anxiously watched the minutes tick by. The cloud base was by now only a few hundred feet so it was hard to see far. But with half an hour remaining, we spotted a lonely figure staggering down the path. We walked up to encourage him over the remaining few hundred yards. Refusing all help with his pack, he stumbled in with 10 minutes left on the clock. We were very pleased with ourselves and celebrated in the appropriate manner in the pubs of Fort William.

The conditions had been perfect and the timing excellent, for the 4-month drought broke dramatically the following day. It was a marvellous climax to the summer. Our confidence was sky high. What challenge could we face next? Why not a trip to the Alps?

In late October, Tim and I drove to Chamonix and took the cable car up the Aiguille du Midi. As we arrived, we watched a man nonchalantly vault the safety barrier and plunge towards Chamonix 7,000 feet below. We thought it was suicide until his parasail opened and he soared around the peaks. This had be the theatre for our future mountain adventures.

We walked up the lower slopes of one peak in the early snows of November. It was cloudy, isolated and cold with threatening weather. Suddenly Tim stopped, held his chest and lay down. His pulse was weak, fast and chaotic. My first fearful thought was a heart attack as I questioned him on his symptoms. My thoughts raced ahead. Would I be able to carry him down? Would he survive long enough?

Thankfully, when we had overcome the initial shock, we realised that it was only fast atrial fibrillation and not a serious problem. It slowly settled and we descended deep in thought. Did he have an underlying problem? Although it was the first time it had happened, it has plagued him ever since – with serious consequences on a later expedition to Mt Everest (chapter 7).

The towering snow-capped Alpine peaks inspired even bigger ideas. Why not an expedition to the Himalaya? By chance, Lufthansa Airlines were planning a new route from Frankfurt to Kathmandu and were looking for customers to advertise their new flights. Hans Worndle, an advertising executive who I had run with on the Lyke Wake Walk asked if we might be interested. The dream of a lifetime unfolded before us. Indeed, why not an expedition to the Himalayas?

There were numerous immediate problems. We had no money, we were in thrall to our liege lord, Sir Raymond Hoffenberg (Professor of Medicine) and his acolytes, and we were allowed only two weeks' holiday in any six-month period. How could we possibly take four weeks away from clinical service and medical research for mere fun? Tim, John Delamere and I were discussing what to do one evening at my house in Harborne, Birmingham. Ted Olive, a friend from student days, lived nearby. He was now training to be a psychiatrist, was lively and enterprising. We wondered what he would think. We walked down the road and invited ourselves in. "Do you fancy going to the Himalayas?" we asked. "Fantastic," he instantly replied. "It would be wonderful."

His enthusiastic response spurred us into action. Since cost was a fundamental limiting factor, our thoughts turned to sponsorship. Rather than only trekking and climbing, perhaps we could also study an important medical question. After all, we were all research doctors and supposed to be full of ideas. We merely needed something to investigate.

The society was formed in the doctors' mess of the Queen Elizabeth Hospital, Birmingham, in the autumn of 1976. That was the place we naturally met when we were off duty. The early members of the expeditionary group were myself and Tim Harvey (lecturers in medicine), John Delamere (registrar in medicine) and Ted Olive (senior registrar in psychiatry). Our proposed Himalayan adventure attracted colleagues such as Tony Howell (lecturer in medicine), and Bob Stockley and David Cove (medical research fellows). Climbing friends from the Three Peaks race such as Neville Richardson and Gron Jones joined in and, much to our surprise, three consultant physicians, Alex Wright, Ron Fletcher (endocrinologists) and Ian Green (respiratory medicine), were very enthusiastic. Their seniority would lend much-needed influence in our request for leave of absence.

What we needed next was a society name, a logo, a constitution, rules and medical research projects to justify our time away. After much debate, the rather long-winded title of the Birmingham Medical Research Expeditionary Society (BMRES), affectionately pronounced as 'BumRes', was agreed. It most accurately described our shared aims. The 'medical research' component would mollify our professors and 'expeditionary' would allow us to go anywhere in the world. Because of our climbing interests, we settled on a logo of an ice axe with a rope spiralling around its handle. This mirrored the medical staff and snake of Aesculapius (used by many medical societies). For good measure we added the Greek symbol omega (Ω) to imitate the logo of the British Medical Association.

To add gravitas to our exploits, we also needed important patrons for our headed notepaper. The Chancellor of the University of Birmingham, Professor Sir Peter Scott (son of the Antarctic explorer), graciously agreed. With this in the bag, the dean of the faculty, Professor Tom Whitehead, followed suit as did our own professor, Sir Raymond Hoffenberg.

We then came to the thorny issue of society rules and constitution. As might be expected from a group of opinionated and enthusiastic young professionals, this was contentious. As the old maxim goes, 'if you ask four doctors for an opinion on a patient, you will get five different answers.' We were free-spirited, independent and didn't much like the hospital rules, so why should we be hide-bound by some of our own making? After much debate, we settled on the following:

Rule 1. There are no rules
Rule 2. There is no waiting for others
Rule 3. If in doubt about rule number 2, see rule number 1.

Finally, there was the important question of research projects. In July 1976, Dr Peter Hackett and colleagues had published an article in The Lancet entitled 'The incidence, importance, and prophylaxis of acute mountain sickness'. It described the little-recognised condition in considerable detail and suggested that its occurrence was common in people ascending to Everest base camp. An accompanying editorial, 'See Nuptse and die', made riveting reading. The medical condition seemed far more common than had been previously thought. Nearly 50% of trekkers on the normal route to Everest, from Namche Bazaar to Pheriche, suffered adverse effects of altitude such as nausea and headaches. Importantly, around 4% experienced severe problems with fluid on their lungs (pulmonary oedema) or brain (cerebral oedema).

Could these numbers really be true and, if so, what was the explanation? Lack of oxygen was clearly important at altitude, but was dehydration relevant or ascending too quickly or even poor food? Since the article demonstrated considerable variation between individuals, we wondered if there were underlying biochemical mechanisms that might disadvantage one person over another. Careful scrutiny of the paper and others on acute mountain sickness suggested that the illness was poorly understood.

We now had our project: 'Investigations into the clinical and laboratory features of acute mountain sickness'. We also had a destination – the Himalaya.

Over the winter and spring months of 1977, we met on a regular basis to discuss our plans. The big question of course was funding. Our salaries were around £2,000 per year so we could each contribute very little to the £12,000 project. We agreed on £200 per person but we desperately needed sponsors.

The most obvious route was to write to charities and companies. The Medical School library had books listing every possible source of support so we wrote thousands of letters to every address we could find. We begged for expedition equipment from all the climbing shops and pleaded with company directors for a few crumbs off their tables.

One letter, sent in February by Barbara Scott my PhD student, alighted on the desk of John Simmons, owner and managing director of TOC Ltd, an engineering company in Coventry. He was interested in our plans and might offer some support. Four weeks later, Ted, Neville and I arranged to meet him in a pub on the Coventry Road. What did he want? How much could we ask for? Over a pint of beer, we explained our important medical projects and our needs. He seemed supportive but non-committal. We explained that we were interested in research, particularly high-altitude problems, and wished to climb in the Himalaya. He said he quite liked hill walking and could understand that huge mountains would be exciting. We exchanged pleasantries for 10 to 15 minutes. He talked about his engineering company with 200 employees. And he said he could make just about anything.

Ted and I waited for the moment to ask the all-important question. We exchanged glances, emphasised the importance of the studies and how trekkers were dying, at the same time trying to play down our enthusiasm for climbing and trekking. Eventually, I could hold back no longer: "Could you contribute £3,000 to support the expedition and perhaps fund a short film?" I blurted out. We had never met him before and we were asking for a small fortune. His reply was the last thing we expected: "I will give you the money but only if I can come with you."

I glanced at Ted in amazement. My heart raced with exhilaration. This would guarantee the expedition and he seemed calm, thoughtful and reflective, just the sort of person we could get on with. We were sure there would be no need to ask the others for confirmation. We agreed to his terms and shook hands, barely able to contain our delight.

We left the pub so excited. We now had sufficient financial support for the whole expedition. As we drove back to the hospital, our minds were in overdrive as we chatted about the possibilities – the mountains, the research ideas and what we would tell the others.

When I look back at over 40 years of expeditions, I realise what an enormous debt of gratitude we all owe John. That single generous donation guaranteed the first expedition and hence all those that followed. We quickly became close friends and he went on more expeditions than anyone else.

But we now had work to do. In barely six months, we would be going to Nepal.

Tiger's nest monastery

Everest 1993
Left to right back row: *Gelzen, Ian MacLennan, John Simmons, John Milles, Ian Chesner, Martin Cooper, Brian Johnson, John Delamere, Maggie Beazley, Graham Mead, Pete Forster, Alex Wright, Ron Haydock, Bill Unertl, Peter Dykes.*
Front row: *Jo Bradwell, Simon Morrissey, Patrick Cadigan, Seamus Mulholland, Sharu, Helen Hoar, Chris Imray, Jim Evans, Steve Boyer*

Parinacota 2008
Left to right back row: *Andy Luks, John Delamere, John Simmons, Hannah Rhodes, Andy Davies, Emily Kewley, Faye Hext, Brynn Bird, Susannah Patey, Nick Kalson, Alison Stubbings, Ian MacLennan*
Left to right front row: *Colin Chan, Chris Imray, Tim Clarke, Steve Brearey, Damian Bailey, Kevin Evans, Adam Booth, Brian Johnson*

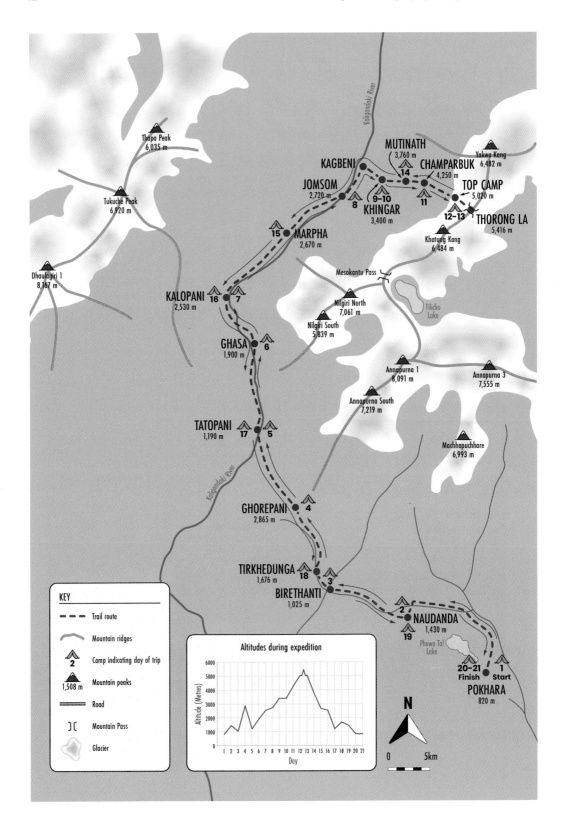

Chapter 1
Thorong La, Nepal – September 1977

Mountains above Thorong La

Sickness at 5,000 m

"Let the fool persist in his folly and he will become wise."

– William Blake

Summary: We chose a trek to the Thorong La at 5,416 m on the north side of Annapurna, a route that had only just been opened to tourists. There we undertook a series of measurements on the clinical, biochemical and other features of acute mountain sickness. Somewhat to our surprise, we discovered that acute mountain sickness was a very real disease with several expedition members becoming ill. Despite a huge effort, we failed to analyse an important blood hormone in collected blood samples. Other results were published in a special supplement of the *Postgraduate Medical Journal*.

Expedition members: Jo Bradwell (leader), David Cove, Frank Davies (quartermaster), John Delamere (deputy leader), Ron Fletcher (medical officer), Ian Green, Tim Harvey (secretary), Chris Hawkesworth (film cameraman), Tony Howell, Gron Jones, Ted Olive, Mike Reynolds, Neville Richardson, John Simmons (engineer), Bob Stockley, Norman Waterhouse (student), Alex Wright (figure 1).

It was Tuesday 25 October 1977. There was a cacophony outside. Shouting, barking, chanting, horns honking, engines roaring. Where was I? What was that banging at the window? Noises of the city slowly suffused my thoughts. I was in Kathmandu. In the downmarket Hotel Asia. In charge of an expedition. And the banging at the window was a monkey. Yes, I did have jet lag and a slight hangover, but the banging was definitely a monkey. The oriental sounds flooded in as I lay reflecting on the previous few months. Ted Olive lay in the bed next to me breathing quietly. He was our expedition psychiatrist. I would need one over the next four weeks.

Six months earlier, John Simmons's generosity had been the final ingredient that guaranteed our Himalayan expedition (see Beginnings). John Delamere, Tim Harvey, myself and others had pulled together a series of research projects and an accomplished team. At Easter, we had agreed on the legendary Tashi Lapcha pass as our trek/climbing itinerary in Nepal. This route offered several ideal features. It provided a gradual ascent, so scientific measurements could be made at progressively higher altitudes. It was remote and rarely used by trekkers. It was among huge mountains, with Everest Base Camp as the final goal. Importantly, it provided a round trip with a rapid descent to Namche Bazaar and Lukla, where blood samples could be flown back to Kathmandu. There was also historical interest, as it was the route taken by Sir Edmund Hillary on his return from climbing Everest in 1953.

News of our plans had attracted considerable interest at work. Nowadays, such expeditions are commonplace but at that time they were quite a novelty. As word spread, many asked to join us. Eventually, we ended up with 17 members, 10 of whom were doctors at the teaching hospitals in Birmingham. Our number also included a third-year medical student, Norman Waterhouse, and two friends we had climbed with over the previous summer, particle physicist Gron Jones and research chemist Neville Richardson. Another showing an interest was Mike Reynolds, an outdoor pursuits instructor from the university sports science department. He introduced us to Frank Davies, who owned climbing shops in Birmingham and Ambleside. He was keen to accompany us, and secured his place by offering us generous discounts on mountain equipment. We also wanted to capture our exploits on film, and through colleagues we contacted Chris Hawkesworth. He had produced an adventure film of canoeing down rapids in Nepal. Such experience of moving equipment to remote locations would be useful. Finally, there was our generous benefactor, businessman John Simmons, who was funding the film. With the team assembled, Lufthansa finally agreed they would fly the 17 of us to Kathmandu for a discounted price.

At one memorable meeting we decided the organisation of the society and the expedition. We were not short of leadership potential, with several eminent consultants among our number. It was put to a vote, and I found myself elected chairman of the society and leader of the expedition – positions I accepted with a mixture of gratitude and anxiety. Awkwardly, this put me in charge of those who until recently had been my tutors, and indeed I had been Ron Fletcher's houseman seven years earlier. However, it was a democratic vote and all seemed happy with the arrangements. I immediately proposed Tim as secretary and John Delamere as treasurer. Tim was ideal as secretary for he had excellent writing skills; witty, acerbic and a flowing style, talents he put to good use over the following years. John was also central to our plans and, being anti-establishment and with much mountaineering experience, he provided us with the necessary confidence that what we were attempting was achievable.

* * *

Acute mountain sickness was to be our principal research topic, and we spent considerable time discussing suitable research questions. One particular feature of the condition, it seemed from our reading, was that some climbers were unaccountably struck down while others were unaffected. Susceptibility was not related to age, gender, strength, fitness or other simple factors. It was clearly dependent upon speed of ascent and altitude, while the worst type of acute mountain sickness was associated with fluid retention in the lungs or brain (pulmonary and cerebral oedema, respectively). We wondered whether this might be related to hormones that regulate fluid balance (aldosterone, vasopressin and antidiuretic hormone, ADH). They had not been measured in people with mountain sickness, partly because they were fragile molecules, particularly ADH. Test samples had to be collected first thing in the morning before people got up. In hospital, this was a simple matter, as blood could be taken while patients were lying in bed. But on an expedition, it would be tricky. We set up the following schedule. As soon as they awoke, Tony and David (medical academics in the department of medicine who would lead the project) would take blood from each other while lying down in their sleeping bags. They would then get dressed and take samples from a few other team members, who could in turn get up and take samples off everyone else. Fortunately, there were ten doctors in the team (plus a medical student), so we would rapidly be able to collect all the samples.

However, sample collection was only part of the challenge. Serum had to be separated from the whole blood by clotting and centrifugation for 20 minutes. Serum samples then had to be stored frozen for the remainder of the expedition to keep the molecules stable. Each processing stage had to be carefully considered. The air temperature during the day at high altitude would be $-10°C$ or lower, so samples would have to be kept warm during clotting and then promptly centrifuged. Fortunately, there were several small, portable centrifuges in my laboratory so we borrowed two. To power them, we needed to generate our own electricity. We eventually settled on two 1.5 kW Honda generators – one as a back-up. At altitude they would be less powerful because of reduced atmospheric pressure but would still produce 0.75 kW each at the top camp. Each weighed 42 kg so potentially they would be too heavy for the porters. John Simmons, our engineer, was quite happy that they could be split into two roughly equal pieces and then carried separately. He also obtained special carburettors that enabled the generators to function at high altitude by allowing more air to enter the engines.

We were therefore confident that we could collect serum samples. The biggest problem, however, was how to store the serum samples after they had been taken. They would have to be kept frozen throughout the expedition, on the return journey to Birmingham and during their delivery to a university laboratory in Chicago for analysis. It was a toss-up between solid carbon dioxide (CO_2), also known as dry ice, which freezes at $-80°C$, and liquid nitrogen, which has a temperature of $-178°C$. Solid CO_2 would be relatively easy to transport on a trek. By contrast, liquid nitrogen is dangerously cold, can easily be spilt and has to be carried in a fragile thermos flask. Early enquiries revealed that Lufthansa Airlines would not allow it on board. This, fatefully, restricted us to dry ice.

The next step was to design and build special insulated boxes. With the help of a manufacturer in Stourbridge, near Birmingham, we designed four two-foot cube polystyrene boxes with four-inch walls and a thick lid that slotted tightly onto the top. Each could carry

20 kg of dry ice with room to spare for blood samples. As the dry ice evaporated, we planned to top up the one containing the blood samples so eventually there would be only one box for the return trip.

Laboratory tests suggested our dry ice would last about three weeks. Since it was a four-week expedition, we would need extra for the last few days. The tour operator suggested that dry ice might not be available in Kathmandu, and there were certainly no local manufacturers. However, it can be generated from CO_2 gas in a cylinder by using a small metal gadget that attaches to the pressure valve. When the gas is released, it expands through a tiny nozzle, cools rapidly and precipitates as dry-ice snow. We located a company that made the gadget and were reassured that it was very simple to use. This would allow us to top up the polystyrene boxes just before we went to the mountains, rather than take a huge amount from Birmingham. Finally, we persuaded Lufthansa that dry ice posed no threats and they agreed to take the four full boxes in their cargo hold.

Because of the complexity of the studies, we decided to have a practice run on the weekend before departure. So, on a cool, misty afternoon in October, 15 doughty members of the team drove up to the 350 m high Waseley Hills, just outside Birmingham city limits, and camped for the night. Next morning, we rehearsed our blood collection routine. We waited in our sleeping bags while others took bloods and separated the sera using the centrifuges powered by a Honda generator. Then we packed up and went home. The 350 m hill was our altitude preparation for the Himalayas. Few of us had ever left Europe before, and only one had been to a developing country.

* * *

One week later, on 22 October 1977, 17 of us set out from the Medical School for Kathmandu. We couldn't have chosen a worse time. By sheer bad luck, our departure coincided with the climax of the biggest criminal and political showdown that Germany had experienced since the Second World War – Der Deutsche Herbst or 'the German Autumn' as anxious Lufthansa cabin staff described it.

Just four days earlier, a Lufthansa plane hijacked by members of the Baader–Meinhoff terrorist group had been stormed by elite army forces at Mogadishu airport. When we arrived at Heathrow, we walked right into its aftermath. Having previously been fairly relaxed about excess baggage because they were supporting the expedition for publicity purposes, Lufthansa was now very apprehensive. They quizzed us about each item and were argumentative about the generators and the masses of climbing equipment. Then we showed them the polystyrene boxes containing the smoking CO_2 containers…

After a very fraught hour, they finally allowed it all to go on the weighing machines. We thought the excess weight might be the final straw but thankfully Chris put his boot under the scales, causing them to substantially under-read. The 300 kg excess passed without comment onto the plane. So much for airport security in those early days of terrorism.

Much relieved, we boarded the plane and, after the short flight to Frankfurt, headed overnight to Delhi and thence to Kathmandu. Distant views of the western Himalayas greeted our eyes as we came in to land at 9.30 am. Inevitably our medical equipment was the main topic of conversations as we landed. We were soon met by staff from the tour company to assist our transit through the little airport's primitive security procedures. The dry-ice boxes and generators were waved through after appropriate diplomatic niceties (financial assistance). However, to our consternation, much of our personal and climbing equipment failed to appear. We learnt later that they had detected our 'boot under the scales' ruse and sent it as unaccompanied baggage on another plane.

There was nothing else to do as we dejectedly emerged from the airport into the midday tropical heat. In 1977 Kathmandu was a medieval city reminiscent of London in 1666, immediately before the great fire. Extraordinary new sights assaulted our naive Western senses. Shrines with rats in them – we saw one merrily eating scraps of food in a magnificently ornamental stupa. Pieces of goat, chicken and possibly yak being dried in the sun. A rotting pig lying at the entrance to a restaurant ('The Upper Crust'), feral dogs gnawing at its intestines. Fruit stalls so infested with flies we wondered if anything would be suitable for our feeble Western stomachs. A flock of guinea fowl walking across the main road. And lots of hippies. In its favour, there was no air pollution – it was still the pre-car era.

Our residence for the next few days was the pretentiously named Hotel Asia. Small, scruffy and insignificant, its name belied its modest quality, with bedrooms separated by thin bamboo walls and toilets in the middle of the showers.

But our day was by no means finished. The tour company called a 5 pm meeting. We were introduced first to Jackie, an English woman who had lived with the Sherpas for some years, then to our sirdar (head Sherpa) and his second-in-command, the chief cook. We gradually realised that Jackie would be our guide throughout the expedition. To her credit, she and the Sherpas all looked fit and tough, and clearly had experience of numerous expeditions.

The question of our missing luggage then arose. We were informed that the security authorities in Delhi had been very alarmed by the Lufthansa hijacking and were impounding all unaccompanied baggage from Lufthansa jets. This included our 300 kg of personal items and all our climbing equipment. Hopefully, they explained, it would be delivered before we departed for the trek but we would have to keep visiting the airport. We spent several days hanging forlornly around Kathmandu airport baggage arrivals, to no avail. Chris was particularly concerned that he had lost an expensive camera.

To cap it all we were informed that permission to trek over the Tashi Lapcha pass had been refused because it was too near the border with China and politically unstable. This came as a real shock, as it was the route we had been planning for the previous nine months – a route that we had carefully chosen to satisfy our research requirements. We were jet-lagged, sleep-deprived, travel-weary, had no personal clothes, sleeping bags, or toiletries, and now the viability of the whole expedition hung in the balance. The meeting ended with the shock realisation that all our hopes and plans for the last 12 months could be shattered.

* * *

That night, we went to the famous KC's restaurant in Tamil for drinks. With all the sights, sounds, smells and great companionship, our fears were temporarily put aside as we breathed in the exotic oriental ambience. Then, we heard mention of a tourist who had died of acute mountain sickness at a high camp. The illness really did seem to exist. We yearned to see our first case.

Next morning, we learned that our gear would probably not arrive. We would have to improvise. Thankfully, Tamil market had everything we needed. We were soon dressed in second-hand (or third-hand) clothing and boots that were mostly tatty discards from past climbing expeditions – British, Russian, American. We looked like a band of grubby down-and-outs rather than the smart young doctors we imagined ourselves to be. I had no walking shoes, only the heavy-duty climbing boots I had worn on the aeroplane to reduce the baggage weight. I located a pair of thin, well-used plimsolls which would have to make do. We reflected on what is known as the 'butterfly effect'. The fallout from political murders in Germany ripples across the world, leading to lost baggage, dilapidated footwear and bad blisters for a group of doctors in the Himalayas. If only the Baader–Meinhof gang had realised the serious consequences of their actions on our poor feet, surely they would have had second thoughts?

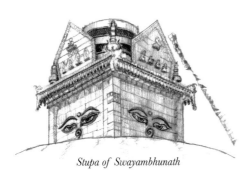

Stupa of Swayambhunath

The main objective on our second day in Kathmandu was to source dry ice. Needless to say, it was not available in Kathmandu so we needed some CO_2 cylinders to generate our own. A group of us searched the city and eventually located some at Dr Pander's shop. Congratulating ourselves on our foresight, we went along with our dry-ice-producing gadget.

It did not go well. In spite of repeated efforts, it proved impossible to persuade the CO_2 gas to turn into dry ice. We tried changing the size of the gas jet, different bottles, big ones, small ones, but all in vain. The released CO_2 would not cool enough to condense. After an initial burst of gas, it gradually slowed then stopped. We noticed that the bottom end of the cylinders became coated in ice, condensed from the surrounding moist air. The gas expansion was cooling the remaining CO_2 so it could not expand properly. We put the bottoms of the cylinders in hot water but again without success. After several hours, we returned, disheartened, to the hotel.

Back at Dr Pander's next morning, we tried wrapping rags around the cylinder valve and pouring warm water over it to encourage the release of gas. Again to no avail. I remembered making solid CO_2 as a child with just this technique, but it eluded us all now. It was hopeless.

We departed worrying about the outcome of our planned experiments. How were we going to maintain the samples in a frozen state? We briefly considered flying dry ice from Delhi, but the logistics were beyond us. We eventually concluded that we would have to monitor the dry ice carefully during the trek and ensure that none was wasted. We would minimise the opening of the boxes and wrap them up in blankets to keep them cool. Perhaps we could eke out the dry ice long enough. But the evaporation rate calculations could not be denied, as we were to discover to our cost.

* * *

By the afternoon of the second day, we were informed that the excess baggage would not arrive. Miraculously, however, Chris's missing Bolex cine-camera appeared in its black bag. Re-motivated, the film crew busied themselves with the sights and sounds of Kathmandu. Neville and Ian acted as sound crew, while Chris enjoyed himself and handled the equipment with professional ease. They dutifully recorded the developing fiasco with the dry-ice generation at Dr Pander's.

By then we had also settled on an alternative itinerary. We had finally agreed on a trekking route going to the north side of Annapurna and Thorong La (5,416 m), one of the highest trekking passes in Nepal. A few months earlier it had been reopened for tourist travel, so we would be one of the first groups for a long time to enter the fabled Kali Gandaki Gorge. It did not quite hold the cachet of Everest Base Camp, but it promised to be a memorable trek to a spectacular Himalayan destination. And, most importantly, it would enable us to carry out all the scientific studies we'd planned back in Birmingham.

Chris Hawkesworth

After two days in Kathmandu, we were reasonably prepared for departure. We longed for cool air and the mountains, which were tantalisingly visible poking above the surrounding foothills. We all piled into two clapped-out buses and left the anxieties of the city in our second-hand clothes and worn footwear. Chris filmed from the bus roof as we coursed through Kathmandu and into open country, with terraced rice fields stretching to the distant mountains. Every few miles we were stopped by soldiers at heavily armed barriers demanding road taxes of 2½ rupees. Western Nepal was like a police state, with repeated scrutiny of all traffic. The areas closer to neighbouring China were completely forbidden in order to stop communist incursions. Annapurna had only just opened to tourists, while neighbouring Mustang and Dhaulagiri were still out of bounds.

The drive to Pokhara proved eventful. As we turned a bend at high speed, one of the tyres exploded. We had not thought to check the tyres but on inspection the rupture was hardly surprising since all tyres were worn down to their webbing. John Simmons helped change the tyre. Our engineer was becoming very useful.

It was dark when we reached the city of Pokhara, little more than an elongated village. The campsite was located in a large dirty enclosure on its outskirts. In the middle sat some flimsy tents and on one side the Sherpa cook was preparing our dinner. We were paired off into nine tents plus a large mess tent for meals. John Simmons started one of our generators which he connected to a set of lights. At least that was one thing that worked. In this inauspicious location we began our experiments – urine collections at 5 pm. From then on, fluid intake and urine volumes had to be measured and the total amounts recorded each 24-hour period. In the morning would come the first blood tests.

That night it rained continuously. We had been repeatedly assured that the monsoon was over but there is often a final flourish, and we caught it. By morning everything was soaked and the campsite was awash. Peering through the early gloom, we belatedly realised our encampment was in the middle of a pigsty. We were surrounded by ample evidence of the problem of dysentery in Nepalese pigs. From our sleeping bags we looked out on the filth as blood was collected from cold arms in wet air smelling of defecating farm animals. Breakfast was kerosene-flavoured porridge and the tea was cold. We had every reason to be miserable and indeed we were. It was a dismal, grey, boggy, shitty place (figure 2).

Hundreds of indolent Nepalese men were standing around our sunken quagmire, sheltering under the dripping roofs of wretched shacks. Many were combing among our tents and medical equipment or talking to the Sherpas. These people, we presumed, were in our employment. The medical equipment had all been contained in cardboard boxes, many of which were now soaked and falling apart. I could see the expedition failing on its first day.

I approached the sirdar, hoping for some reassurance. Wisely he suggested that we buy some large polythene bags to cover everything, including the porters. We purchased several dozen and shared them around. The porters hung them over their panniers and heads and wrapped up our precious equipment, the food, the dry-ice boxes and our second-hand personal gear. On the sirdar's bidding, we trudged out of the pigsty and past our 60 bedraggled porters sheltering under overhanging roofs in the downpour. Gradually the sky brightened, the storm cleared and we were in the countryside among rice paddies and thatched huts. Frank bought some levity to a dire situation by suggesting a prize for the best photo of copulating cattle. The temperature rose, mountain slopes appeared below the clouds, and we started to believe in ourselves again.

* * *

Over the next three days we travelled through the foothills of the Himalaya via Naudanda, Birethanti and Ghorepani. We wandered along age-worn paths, through ancient paddy fields fertilised with human manure, ascended through small villages with their Hindu shrines, and overtook long lines of men, women and child porters as we climbed towards the low clouds. We forded rushing rivers, as many bridges had been washed away. The first night we camped in a basic school under thick cloud. We were still miserable. Then quite suddenly the cloud lifted and the skies cleared. In front of us was an enormous shimmering peak. It was Machhapuchhare – the Fish Tail mountain – and it was beautiful (figure 3). Importantly, it was the last rain of the expedition.

From then on, we rapidly settled into the daily routine of early morning shouts for blood to be taken followed by a leisurely breakfast as the samples were centrifuged and stored. Ian and Bob ran the breathing tests and could often been heard arguing about its importance in their tent late at night. Ian, a consultant respiratory physician, was very mild while Bob was short, argumentative, forceful, lively, combative and amusing. They got on very well.

After packing our own items followed by the medical equipment, we trailed along overtaking the porters and Sherpas. After two hours, we stopped for lunch. We were a fast group and had to wait an hour or more for the cooks to prepare the food. Lunch was followed by another rapid walk to the night's camp. Arriving by 3 pm, we had a siesta then carried out a few tests such as measuring lung volumes and collecting and measuring urine samples. We had dinner in the mess tent around 7 pm followed by an evening conference then bed. The conferences were an important time when everything was discussed – experiments, how everyone was feeling, where help was needed, anticipated problems, individuals' expectations, difficulties, and the looming question of acute mountain sickness. Was it a real disease? Would any of us suffer from it? Would one of us become seriously ill? Were we at risk of dying? These questions repeatedly entered the conversations and became more intense as we ascended.

On the second day, we entered a semi-tropical forest with rhododendron and magnolia trees, leeches and spiders but no rain. Scattered houses became more substantial and we enjoyed the exercise, the banter and the daily race to lunch stops and evening camps (figure 4). The trail followed wide paths with innumerable steps, for seemingly the wheel had yet to be invented. We clambered over suspension bridges, jumped overflowing streams and swam below waterfalls in clean clear pools. Repeatedly we had distant views of Annapurna and Machhapuchhare (figure 5). The drama of the Himalayas, the excitement of the expedition and the fellowship of great companions was a magical concoction.

But all was not perfect with our health. Naturally, we were meticulous with the fluids we drank as we had been repeatedly warned about drinking polluted water. Everything was sterilised with chlorine pills or a drop of iodine and left for half an hour before being imbibed. But it was to no avail. We all developed diarrhoea. Gradually, we developed suspicions about the cook. He was often last into camp with his cronies and on occasions seemed to stagger. Was he drunk? The food was of poor quality, often cold and late to be served. Lots of small hands had fingered half-cooked chapatis and rice which was handed to us by dirty fingers. The cups and plates were washed in the puddles and wiped on filthy dishcloths or left to dry in the sun. On one occasion when the cook was absent, we had a very tasty meal of sausage, beans and potatoes cooked by Jackie.

Machhapuchhare

One by one we became ill. Norman collapsed on the trail and had to be helped along for a while and Chris was too ill to do any filming. I vividly remember him rushing belatedly into one camp, gasping for help then vomiting violently. While the 11 medics watched on in disgust, Jackie rushed over to assist. We were not nurses and showed little compassion, and he had become unpopular. During the first days in Kathmandu he had been bossy and a know-all during filming, but now we were on the expedition proper, when filming was important, his poor fitness made him surly and unhelpful.

Then there were the leeches. As we brushed past the undergrowth, they snuck through the webbing of our shoes, through socks, shirts and jackets. They could be seen as tiny threads, barely visible on leaves and grass. But when they had extracted their fill, their bloated dark brown bodies were unable to get back out the way they had come in. As soon as we took off any clothing, we discovered them lying sluggishly against bleeding skin, barely able to move in their corpulence. Squatting in the undergrowth to relieve diarrhoea became a hazard. We discretely checked each other's bottoms, and many a leech was flicked back to the night soil from whence it had come.

* * *

One might imagine that a Himalayan trek would involve gentle meandering among the ancient forests admiring distant mountain views, exotic birds and plants. Not a bit of it. Ours was not a contemplative stroll. It was a daily race to the finish. We were a competitive lot, and being first to arrive at camp was highly prized. Most of the time was spent looking at where one's running feet would land or at the heels of the person in front. The pace would start slowly enough after a leisurely breakfast but then a few would head for the front of the pack and the speed would increase. Normally, I would wait until everyone had left camp to ensure that all the medical equipment was on the move, that the camp was packed up and that the sirdar was happy. Then I would race to catch up. This was a particularly useful strategy because it provided an opportunity to see who was struggling. Some had gut problems, others blisters, and there were lots of aches from the strenuous daily walks. I had the chance to talk to each person individually, to find out what they thought of the expedition so far and how they were coping. Gradually, I would work my way past each one, past the porters with their heavy loads and up to the front. There the sirdar would control the pace by walking in the lead with a light day sack. Since we did not know the route it was difficult to go ahead. But some days we would make a rendezvous for the lunch or night stop so that he did not hold us back.

On the third day we raced up the 3,000 steps of the Gurung Staircase to Ulleri, passed Banthati and pressed on towards our campsite at Ghorepani (2,865 m). Gasping for breath in the thin air, none of the front runners would give up as the race developed. For two hours we challenged each other, with the leaders arriving at the campsite by lunchtime. We then spent the afternoon waiting for the long trail of porters, Sherpas and poorly members of the team. Thankfully, the altitude reduced the day temperature and it was cool at night. We camped on a wooded campsite near Poon Hill. That evening around a wood fire we were surrounded by monkeys, and the night sounds of the jungle sang us to sleep. Interestingly, a few walkers complained of headaches. Was this a hint of mountain sickness?

During the walks, although brisk, we finally got to know each other, talked about the expedition, the experiments and how mountain sickness might affect us. It was the first expedition for nearly everyone. Many were here by chance, especially those who had joined more recently. Hence it was not clear who would be agreeable companions. In particular, there had been no plan about who would share the double tents. After a few days, I floated the idea of rotating tent mates so that we could get to know each other better. This was not a comfortable concept for many. It was Ted who articulated it most clearly: "I only want to sleep with Jo," he shouted, to roars of laughter. We had shared a tent for three nights and I thought a change might be appropriate. But that was my position settled and there was no further talk of swapping. Gradually pairings developed that everyone seemed to be happy with.

Early on Ted showed his true colours. He was an articulate, extrovert and noisy character who felt very positive about himself and his role. He would talk to anyone about the expedition. He chatted up a 'colonial sahib and his memsahib' who were taking the 'airs' around the Himalayas. They were properly spoken, had been to the right schools and done Colonial service. Ted rabbited on about BMRES and what a brilliant group of top doctors we were. How we would sort out acute mountain sickness plus other diseases in the Kali Gandaki valley. They were most impressed with the talk, but less so with our actions. When Norman developed diarrhoea and lay vomiting in the roadside the next day, splattered with excrement, we all rushed by. It was another race day so there was no time to stop. Our compassionate qualities were clearly not apparent and they told Ted in no uncertain terms that we were a bunch of scallywags.

We may not have observed much of the flora and fauna but we did notice the stinging nettles beside the tracks. Superficially they were similar to those in England, just with slightly larger leaves. Innocently we brushed past them, but only once. Their touch was agony. When stung you stayed stung. Even two or three days later the wounds were intensely irritating. Poor Norman tripped and fell among them early on, screaming in anguish. His distress from the awful pain was palpable. One might have expected a remedy from ten doctors but none was forthcoming.

Himalayan nettles

Over the next few days the terrain and weather changed dramatically as we traversed into the magical Kali Gandaki river valley. In one long plunge, we descended from Ghorepani at 2,860 m to Tatopani at 1,190 m. In five hours we cast aside the 1,600 m we had so laboriously gained over the previous three days. The descent comprised innumerable steps built of heavy rocks that led out of the wet jungle down to an arid paradise. Innumerable trickling streams ran through a land of sun, fruit and honey with pretty thatched hovels and wooden water wheels fed by wooden pipes – a vision of 16th-century England. In the evening, fireflies flickered above the camp as we revelled in the hot sulphurous springs at Tatopani. In 1977, there were only a few thatched cottages and no road. The beautiful snow-covered peak of Dhaulagiri Himal glimmered in the distance. We never imagined that many years later a member of our group would die on its slopes.

* * *

The contrast between the first few days in the subtropical jungle and the days in the Kali Gandaki valley could hardly have been greater. The gorge cuts through the Himalayas, linking Tibet with India. From its origin as a tiny spring beyond the forbidden city of Mustang on the Tibetan plateau of northern Nepal, the river has carved out the deepest valley in the world. It lies between Dhaulagiri at 8,167 m (the seventh highest mountain in the world) and Annapurna at 8,091 m (the tenth highest) with the valley floor at an average height of only 2,300 m. A height difference of nearly 6 km separates summits a mere 10 km apart (figure 6).

No place on Earth has such a large change of altitude and it has a startling effect on the weather. It is like a giant air leak on the Earth's surface between the Tibetan plateau and the plains of India. During the day, the Tibetan plateau, devoid of all cloud cover, warms rapidly and the hot air rises. This sucks air up the Kali Gandaki valley which becomes a wind tunnel. It starts in the early morning and reaches a crescendo in the heat of the afternoon then rapidly stops as the sun sets and the air cools. Moist, misty air, sucked up from the warm jungle, enters the lower reaches of the valley and promptly evaporates. As we walked north of Tatopani the next morning, we were pushed along by a rush of foggy warm air. A quarter of a mile further on, we were in clear air and could look back at this cloudy curtain, evaporating as it came towards us. Higher up the valley the rising moist air forms clouds that march up towards Tibet in a long line. Shortly after sunset there is a brief moment of calm as the high plateau cools. The heavy cooling air, mixed with freezing air from the glaciers, then rushes back down the valley. Throughout the night, this wind whipped up sand and dust which buffeted and pummelled the tents.

Yet those three days in the valley were the most tranquil of the expedition. After the hot springs at Tatopani, we passed through a string of villages, Ghasa, Kalopani and finally

Jomsom, ascending from 1,190 m to 2,720 m. It was dry and sunny in the day, the epidemic of diarrhoea lessened and we were getting fitter. The experiments were going well, the morning blood routines were fast and efficient, and we settled into a daily routine starting with tea in bed. Around us were some of the greatest mountains in the world.

We also began to make progress with the expedition film. Chris was beginning to overcome a host of minor ailments – diarrhoea, stiffness from the exercise and bad blisters, exacerbated by his lack of fitness and excessive weight. We were sympathetic and supportive, but the demands of filming and his rather dictatorial manner created tensions. One morning Chris, Ian and Neville with several porters departed early to set up a film sequence. We were filmed walking over a suspension bridge, rather like the Seven Dwarfs going logging. It was not very natural and not good enough, so we had to do it again. Intermittently over the next few days we were filmed – on the valley floor, through tunnels, near waterfalls, over bridges and through the villages. There was good footage of the experiments, including blood taking, exercising, electro-cardiograms and others. I finally began to believe that we might return with a decent film.

The Kali Gandaki river valley ascends through several climatic zones: initially moist rice and millet terraces then fields of hardy grains and bamboo which turn to pine forests and finally the wind-swept desert of the Himalayan rain shadow. The first day took us through Dana and Titre to Ghasa at 1,900 m. The path passed high up on the valley wall to avoid the unpredictable meanderings of the river. Barely two metres wide in places, it had been hacked out of the cliffs where it traversed tunnels, passed precarious overhangs and edged along dangerous landslips, forcing us to cling to the rock walls. That night we camped in a football field, 5,000 m below the dramatic white peaks of Nilgiri, which shone golden red as a perfect sky finally smiled on us.

* * *

All the while we were conscious of the experiments. Urine was a particular preoccupation. Others had shown protein leakage from the kidneys during the development of mountain sickness, but little was known about changes in urine volume, pH or salt concentrations. Our studies could reveal more about what happens to these parameters when ascending to 5,000 m.

To make these measurements, everyone had to save all their urine in two-litre plastic bottles during a 24-hour period, every day of the trip (figure 7). Collections went from 5 pm to 5 pm, when every bottle was lined up in alphabetical order, perhaps on a dry-stone wall or beside the loo tent. John Delamere and Gron Jones were our urine-ologists and responsible for measuring their volumes, then assessing their pH, protein content and so on using dipsticks before finally saving a small sample to be analysed in Birmingham. The remaining urine was then tipped away, a preservative added to each empty bottle, and the following day's collections started.

Needless to say, the whole process caused much amusement. As we trekked, other groups quizzed us about the half-full bottles of urine hanging from our day sacks. Individuals would disappear behind a bush or wall and emerge smiling in the happy knowledge that the process had been successful.

The urine bottles had a capacity of two litres. This was generally enough. Little urine was passed in the sweaty jungles leading up to Ghorepani or on a hot day's walk in the dry winds of the Kali Gandaki valley while suffering from diarrhoea. But leading up to Thorong La, many passed more than two litres – and, of course, there was the occasional beer-drenched evening. Then the bottles filled up. John Delamere would have to scurry around to locate the plaintive shout and provide an extra bottle – he carried several extra ones for just such emergencies. Meanwhile the culpable individual would be forced to carry two bottles of urine for the rest of the day.

In the daytime heat, we drank several litres of fluid to rehydrate. At night, particularly at the higher altitudes, the thin air caused us to breathe rapidly with our mouths open, so many people put drinking water beside their sleeping bags. These one-litre water bottles, although smaller in size, were of similar shape to the urine bottles so one had to be vigilant. On going to bed, the urine bottles were normally put just outside the tent while the water bottles were placed beside the sleeper's head. However, as the nights became very cold, the urine in the bottles started to freeze. After some discussion, it was agreed that they should be brought inside the tents because their fragile plastic might crack as the ice expanded. It was logical to leave the urine bottles at the tent entrance for easy access and to avoid any possibility of confusion with the water bottles. But the nights were pitch black. It was a misfortune waiting to happen.

One night, Gron, who was tenting with John Simmons, put his urine bottle at the head end of his sleeping bag. In the dark hours, poor John reached out for some water, opened a bottle and to his horror drank some of Gron's urine. To much amusement, next afternoon at 5 pm, John Delamere had to enquire delicately as to how much he had swallowed so that he could accurately estimate Gron's 24-hour urine volume.

* * *

Because we had lost considerable altitude since leaving Ghorepani, we were anxious to proceed quickly up the valley. A typical morning started as early as possible. On awakening, samples for the ADH measurements were taken while we were in our sleeping bags. Anyone who woke and wanted to pass urine wasn't allowed up until their blood had been taken. As the round proceeded there were plaintive cries from those with full bladders pleading to be next or threatening a watery disaster. With completion of the blood collection, 'tea sahib' echoed around the camp as the cook's assistants bought welcome refreshments (figure 8). Their smiling happy faces, as they opened the tent flaps, are an abiding memory of those halcyon days. Meanwhile, the bloods were clotted, centrifuged and the residual serum put into the dry-ice boxes.

Power for the centrifuges came from the two 1.5 kW Honda generators. We only needed 0.75 kW to power the centrifuges but took a spare centrifuge for security. At night we had a set of lights that John Simmons had supplied. Since the Sherpas had only provided candles, night-time electricity was most welcome.

The generators weighed around 42 kg each. The porters' loads were set at a maximum of 30 kg plus their own personal kit. They managed this with the aid of a small walking stick shaped like an elongated letter 'T'. As they stopped, they rested the pack on to the top of it and leant against a wall, usually panting hard. The strongest porters on the trail we met carried up to 120 kg. Our porters carried much less but still used their sticks and stopped frequently, but could carry much more if they were paid appropriately. We presumed there was some sort of porters' union that restricted their carrying capacity so that more could be employed. However, we saw evidence of their enormous strength with the generators. Each one was split into two to reduce the weight to 21 kg but invariably both pieces were put together by the porters, who then added their own kit plus rice and other items until the pannier was full. It was impossible for any of us to carry these huge weights more than a few yards.

We all expected to lose weight and were interested to see if this was in any way connected to the development of acute mountain sickness. The weight loss could be fat, muscle or fluid, and to find out we needed to make several measurements. Overall weight was recorded on a set of scales calibrated against a urine bottle containing two litres of water. Fat tissue was measured from skin thickness on several body sites using skin-fold callipers handled by Ron and ably assisted by Alex (figure 9). Ron was an expert having written a PhD thesis on the subject. Measurements were made on several occasions during the expedition. Fluid balance was more difficult but we could measure the amount of fluid in blood by measuring packed red blood cells. A small sample of whole blood was put into a special centrifuge (micro-haematocrit) and the percentage of fluid compared with the packed cells measured against a simple scale.

* * *

From the hot lowland entrance to the Kali Gandaki valley we walked into high alpine scenery, with Tukuche Peak (6,920 m) rising above us. We walked through the very attractive village of Kalopani, passing underneath houses huddled together from the winter cold. There were walls containing prayer wheels and square buildings with oriental roofs with turned-up corners and spikey brass turrets. The impact of centuries of trading between India and China was apparent in the intricate wood carvings on the houses and robust mud and stone buildings with roofs covered in drying wood, to provide warmth for the winter. Pleasant though it might be in the autumn sun, those houses were built for bitter weather. Above the village, inaccessible caves were carved into the cliffs and more shrines dotted the hills. Surprisingly, we were the only people for miles around except for the occasional heavily clothed Thakali trader accompanied by his mules.

As we ascended, the valley bottom became flatter, sometimes extending up to two miles across and all the way into the Mustang valley. It was a long, tiring third day but we were pushed upwards by the afternoon wind from India at our backs through the beautiful village of Marpha and its fruit orchards. By evening, we reached the windy squalor of Jomsom, a barrack town that controlled the flow of goods to the fabled walled city of Mustang. Near Tibet and with its own Emir, Mustang was strictly off limits to Western tourists. This was conflict territory and millennia of struggle showed in ruined castles scattered up the valleys and on cliff tops (figure 10). Whatever had made this barren wasteland worth fighting over was hard to imagine.

We camped within a tiny square of stable buildings

Prayer wheels

on dry dirt with one of the rooms replacing our mess tent. After dinner an intense debate developed. We were very concerned about the lack of mountain sickness. The ascent profile had not been nearly fast enough. We had now been on trek for a week and were only at 2,720 m. Ghorepani, four days previously, had been at 2,860 m and the few headaches observed there might have been the earliest signs of acute mountain sickness. Since then we had been much lower. Our original climbing plans had been for a steady ascent throughout the first 12 days but so far our ascent rate had been too slow. None of us had experience of acute mountain sickness but we knew we needed to provoke it much more to make our trip worthwhile. The current plan was to spend two days ascending from Jomsom to Muktinath at 3,760 m and then another couple of days to the pass at Thorong La. We agreed a faster ascent profile was needed. If we could reach the village of Khingar at 3,400 m, 800 m higher, the next day, then that would be a good start.

We brought in the sirdar. Acknowledging our concerns, he thought our plans might be possible. However, it would be difficult to persuade the porters to cram a day and a half of load-bearing into one day. Difficult but not impossible. Extra payments were discussed. The main problem was that the loads the porters carried were very heavy, and they were lowland porters – recruited in Kathmandu and many with no exposure to altitude since the spring trekking season four months earlier. Eventually, after much discussion, an increase in the ascent rate was agreed by everyone.

Then the discussion turned to personal ambitions. The mountaineers in the group, such as John Delamere and Neville, wanted to stay at Thorong La for a few days and climb a peak. I was not in favour of this, as it would compromise the blood and urine collections. I began to worry that we were seeing the first sign of an expedition rebellion that I had read so much about and feared. The discussion was amicable enough but I was wary of individual's yearnings and hidden agendas. This was my first mountain leadership experience and there were a lot of strong personalities in the group.

Importantly, we still hadn't solved the blood sample refrigeration issue and the potential shortage of dry ice. Some people thought we should book a flight back from the small Jomsom airport to Kathmandu. However, the flights were unpredictable because of the high winds and normally were severely over-booked. Many of us went to bed somewhat anxious about whether the next and most important phase of the expedition, the provocation of acute mountain sickness, would be successful. And, even if we were successful, whether we would be able to preserve our precious samples.

Our fitful attempts at sleep were not helped by the local dogs. In the villages they were everywhere, lying in the dust and following us on the trail, sometimes for several days. They were mangy, ugly, flea-ridden and dirty. They would sleep all day and bark all night. They showed not a hint of movement in the day as we strode by except for the occasional tail flick to remove a particularly irritating insect, but at dusk they would erupt in a cacophony of barking, howling and yapping. One would start, setting off the others. Dogs from neighbouring houses would pitch in until the whole village was barking. Yowls from nearby villages would echo back, the dreadful racket lasting an hour or so until peace gradually descended. Then some unknown canine provocation would spark the whole dispute again. No wonder the mutts slept all day. We shouted or pushed them awake in the futile hope that they might sleep a little more at night. We learned our lesson, though: on later expeditions, we made sure we camped away from the villages, ideally beside a noisy stream or waterfall.

Unfortunately, the Sherpas and porters always wanted to be in the villages. That way they could see their mates, chat up the girls and get drunk.

* * *

To add to our miseries, we ate the cook's food again. We had been spared for a few days by using supplies of fresh fruit and vegetables from the valley's produce, but now he was back and again drunk. In the middle of the night, I awoke with stomach cramps and knew the worst. Not those cramps where there is time to think leisurely about getting up. Not the cramps where there is time to find a decent toilet. The cramps that demand immediate attention. In a flash, I unzipped my bag, the inner tent and the outer tent and rushed into the bitterly cold, dusty wind. Just in time. I hoped I had not woken Ted, but looking to my left I saw that he had beaten me to it. He was already crouching over the river in agonising spasms. In the gloom I could make out the shadowy figures of a dozen others each suffering their own private miseries, bottoms facing downwind. The cook had to go.

The next morning, I confronted our sirdar, who showed little concern for our suffering. We had spoken to him before about the cook but some family relationship prevented him from finding a solution. As leader, I was pressed to sort it out and Jackie was supportive. I checked his whereabouts in the cooking tent and found the culprit – drunk. He understood enough English to know what I was saying and came out aggressively as I stood in the entrance. After a brief shouting match, he hit me several times. In defence, I grabbed him by a shoulder and pushed him to one side. This was no act of great strength by me as he was barely five feet tall and plastered, while I was over six foot, twice his weight and sober. With looks of horror on their faces, other Sherpas held him back. "Him bad man, him bad man," the cook kept shouting at me.

I demanded his dismissal. Jackie and the sirdar rapidly intervened and calmed everyone down. The team watched on with amazement. Apparently, hitting a sahib gave me the right to flog him down the hill. I again insisted that he be sacked. Jackie confirmed that he would be fired and that she would take charge of the cooking. Thank goodness for that, we all thought. The most difficult part of the whole expedition was just ahead of us. To be properly fit, we had to be properly fed.

This was all a big distraction from our purpose that day, which was to reach Khingar. We had wasted enough time and had a long day ahead. The cook looked balefully on from the edge of the camp. He was very angry and I hoped he would not seek revenge. Ted teasingly said that he might stab me and that I should look over my shoulder at all times. He helpfully imitated an assassin wielding a sharpened kukri knife slashing open the tent canvas followed by a stab to the heart. He promised to watch my back for the next few days.

* * *

Finally, we departed. The porters struggled under their loads in the thinning air while we struggled with diarrhoea. The expedition was again on a knife-edge. Perhaps a first expedition never goes smoothly; after all, few of us had any experience of these situations and we were performing complex research.

Before moving far, we reported to the Army post and had our trekking permits checked, signed the visitors' book and set off. The track followed the Kali Gandaki for a few miles then turned steeply upwards. Previously sparse vegetation was reduced to a few small bushes except where glacial melt water fed bright green patches. The intense sun bore down on us and the strong wind pushed us up. It was a harsh environment. Occasional tourists with ponies loaded with goods stumbled down from Thorong La and Muktinath.

By mid-afternoon we had reached our Khingar camp at 3,400 m where nearby ruined castles topped barren grey hills. The village was an oasis of greenery supplied by a small reservoir and irrigation channels full of clear rushing water. There were a few tea houses while an enormous lime tree in the centre of the village provided shade from the hot sun. Rows of aspen trees in their yellow autumn colours flanked the roadside. Ahead were the twin summits of Thorong Peak (Yakawa Kang) at 6,482 m on the north side of the pass (figure 11) and Khatung Kang at 6,484 m on the south side. We walked into the camp delighted with our progress and lazed about in the warm afternoon sun as the rest of the team and porters gradually arrived. The camp was made (figure 12), the sun set and it became cold. Our second-hand clothes were in bad shape and our shoes were falling apart. Bob Stockley's only shorts had lost their legs and become a skirt. It was time for duvet jackets and the additional clothing purchased in Kathmandu. Interestingly, some people had slight headaches: the altitude was beginning to tell.

* * *

One of our many questions concerned the clinical features of acute mountain sickness and how they should be measured. We had read articles about cerebral and pulmonary oedema (fluid on the brain and lung, respectively) with well-defined symptoms such as headache, nausea, vomiting, weakness and ataxia (uncoordinated walking). But milder forms of the condition were poorly described. American studies had used a scoring system based on an environmental symptoms questionnaire (ESQ). This comprised dozens of features which individuals marked for themselves each morning and evening.

To help our understanding of acute mountain sickness, Ron and Alex met each person every day to quiz them on any altitude-related symptoms. This was followed by a clinical examination for signs of fluid retention in the legs or lungs. They also checked for ataxia, asking team members to walk along a straight line touching heel to toe. There was an eye examination for retinal bleeding and routine examinations such as pulse rate.

As the expedition progressed above Khingar, we began to see the adverse effects of altitude in our colleagues. People awoke with severe headaches, their faces were puffy (oedematous) and they felt weak. Tent mates were a personal cause for concern as we could see their deterioration at first hand. A particular worry was intermittent or periodic breathing at night. Also known as Cheyne–Stokes respiration (after John Cheyne and William Stokes, two Dublin physicians who first described it in the mid-19th century), it is a common feature in people who have had strokes. Breathing rates in individuals affected varied dramatically during a one- to two-minute period, becoming faster and deeper over a series of breaths and then stopping for half a minute or more. It was apparent above 2,500 m and became more frequent as we gained height. In some individuals it was so pronounced, and the period of non-breathing so long, that we feared their breathing might cease altogether. Initially we awoke people to see how they were feeling, but our concerns lessened as we all became familiar with its features.

* * *

That evening many porters failed to arrive. One generator appeared but wouldn't work properly despite Neville swapping the carburettor jet. Anxiously we waited for the other but it soon became dark and there were still no people visible on the trail below. After the evening meal, excellently supervised by Jackie, we sat glumly around a camp fire. If the other generator arrived mid-morning, after we had all got up, then it would be impossible to get the early morning blood samples.

Before bed I looked back down the path. There, alone and barely visible in the moonlight, was a small, dark figure creeping up the track. The Sherpas had seen the shape earlier and were chattering excitedly. There were robbers in the area and vigilance was necessary. But, they explained, it was the cook. He sneaked to within 200 yards and stopped. He was like Gollum following the Hobbits up Mt Doom. I wondered if he would come into the camp that night for food and me! Later one of the cook's assistants took him some food and he stole back to Jomsom.

We awoke with the sun at 6 am but still no porters. Over a rather depressed breakfast, we kept scanning the path. At 10.30 am we sent two porters down to try and find the missing equipment. Eventually, at 1 pm the generator arrived, together with the blood tubes and syringes. A cheer went up and we excitedly gathered around, eager to start. We decided to spend one hour lying down, to provide some sort of horizontal rest period, and then take the blood samples. Thankfully, the generator worked perfectly, the samples were separated and stored. Then it was on to exercise, breathing and other tests, by which time we were ready for the urine collection at 5 pm. The day was nearly gone and we had gained no altitude. It was pointless to move to Muktinath at that late hour so we agreed to stay the night.

After the urine collection, the sun set, it rapidly cooled and a biting wind picked up. We huddled over the camp fire swathed in our duvet jackets and discussed the next day. We resolved to go past Muktinath, which was only 270 m higher than our current camp, and ascend to the last habitable building at Champarbuk (4,250 m), an 850 m height gain. It would be a challenging day and the higher altitude should be more provocative of acute mountain sickness. We would need an early start.

The remaining persistent worry was the continuing decline in dry-ice levels. Nights were very cold and evaporation was slow, but we were down to less than half our starting quantity. Maybe we could fly the samples out of Jomsom with just one or two people – it would be impossible for the whole group to go. If we developed more mountain sickness over the next few days, the blood collections would be valuable and we should make a huge effort to get them back intact.

We started early. Bloods were taken, breakfast eaten, the last of the diarrhoea sufferers were prescribed antibiotics (Septrin) and off we set by 7.30 am, soon to arrive at Muktinath (3,760 m). Lunch was taken outside the famous temple walls with beautiful panoramic views of Dhaulagiri and its long ridges (figure 13). We were now leaving the walls of the Kali Gandaki and heading towards Thorong La and its peaks which shone above us in the afternoon sun (front figure). The path was good, with high alpine pastures all around sustained by melting snow and glacier run off. The harsh sun beat down upon us as we ascended. The altitude was showing. We needed frequent rests to gain breath. This was not a day to rush. There was no chance of keeping up with the fully acclimatised Sherpas.

By 3 pm we had reached the campsite alongside the last shepherd's hut. The porters filed in, the generator arrived and it worked perfectly. However, the team was exhausted; they sprawled around in the warm sun, many complaining of headaches. Every activity was hard work. I suggested that we should do some filming but Chris was too unwell.

As we had ascended above 3,500 m, it had become apparent that some individuals were deteriorating, with morning headaches, lethargy and poor appetite. Ted, for example, who was usually noisy and first in the food queue, had atypically been last up and last to want food. Chris and Frank were also uncharacteristically quiet. Were these symptoms of acute mountain sickness? We were not sure. Diarrhoea and dehydration had caused some symptom confusion earlier, but these were now settling thanks to Jackie's cooking. At our evening meeting, Ron and Alex discussed the features at some length and the results from their daily interviews. It did seem that we were seeing the first genuine signs of acute mountain sickness.

As doctors we watched each other for signs of illness and listened to colleagues' comments or complaints, wondering if they were becoming ill. However, it was a confusing picture. The hardened climbers were a tough bunch who were used to suffering while climbing and were least concerned about themselves. In contrast, novices complained more about any discomfort, unsure whether it was a normal feature of the expedition experience. There was also a competitive element, none wanting to appear the worst affected and certainly not to let it be seen by others. This led to some expressing their views more than others or wishfully projecting their symptoms onto the less popular members of the group. By contrast, the 'hard men' were in denial and were prone to dismiss the trivial symptoms of others when they were clearly in difficulties themselves. Ron and Alex's job during the clinical interview was to sort out the denials from reality and rank individuals as to how they were performing.

* * *

The following day was 'the big one', the final push to the top camp just below Thorong La: another jump of around 800 m to over 5,000 m. I was willing people to be ill. Obviously, that was not what I ever thought about patients, or friends and certainly not myself. But this was different – we'd put so much effort into this expedition and we needed people to be ill. Some people had had a rough night with headaches and periodic breathing, and they had difficulty eating. Chris and Frank in particular seemed to be suffering. Was this the real thing? Could we finally be certain that it was acute mountain sickness? I felt well, as did several others – perhaps a little lethargic but we were exercising hard and we had been ill with diarrhoea. This final push would make it clear. The distance was not far, it was only altitude gain.

Again, we started before the sun was up. Tony and Dave efficiently collected the bloods. We wandered around in all our high-altitude clothes waiting for the sun to rise. It was bitterly cold. Frost covered the tents and the bubbling stream had frozen solid. A large frost-covered tarpaulin near the cooks' tent moved and then lifted. Underneath were a dozen porters, huddled together for warmth. They wore only thin shirts and trousers and had slept beneath a thin canvas sheet – unlike us 'hard men' who had slept fully clothed, in feather-down bags and still felt the cold. The sun rose, we shivered over breakfast and headed upwards at 7.30 am towards the snow line.

After three hours we stopped at a height of 4,600 m on a rock terrace with grand panoramic views to Dhaulagiri and beyond. Lemon juice and orange mixed with snow from a glacier was passed around while tea was brewed in huge pots, slowed by the need to melt the snow. It took a long time in the thin cold air. Much to my surprise, everyone just lay in the sun on the warm rocks. This would not have happened lower down. It had not even been a strenuous morning. It must be the altitude.

We stopped for two hours, during which time Bob coerced us into yet another exercise test. This produced a pulsating headache in many people that persisted for the rest of the day. Frank and Chris had seemed to be walking very slowly and both lay on the ground and slept. Frank's breathing came intermittently as he developed typical Cheyne–Stokes periodicity. Individuals watched each other anxiously, mindful of pulmonary and cerebral oedema. At about 1.30 pm we set off to the top camp wondering how those who were starting to develop mountain sickness would fare with another 400 m of ascent. Many had headaches and were off their food. They could only become worse.

With spectacular views of the great Himalayan chain to the west, we wound our way up a steep ridge of glacial moraine and trudged up to a campsite on a gently sloping scree slope at 5,020 m. Progress for everyone had become very slow, with many suffering from headaches and weak legs. The lowland porters were in a similar state, stopping frequently with their heavy loads. One poor chap fell off the moraine ridge and plunged 30 metres down the icy scree with his load. Resolutely he replaced his pannier and climbed back up. It was hard on us but it was even harder for them, dressed in inadequate clothes, walking in light flip-flops and carrying 30 kg or more.

As we neared the camp, groups of porters came jogging down, singing and chatting with excitement having delivered their loads. They would descend to Muktinath and return when our studies were completed in two days' time. Only Jackie and four Sherpas were to stay with us.

After tents were pitched and with the sun still quite hot it became quite obvious that Ian Green was seriously unwell, with Frank and Chris little better. Tim also felt quite weak. I consulted with Ron. He reported back that Ian had a severe headache. He was barely coherent and ataxic. We agreed that he had severe acute mountain sickness and that he should descend immediately. Tim was asked if he would accompany him, together with a Sherpa. Ian and Tim strenuously denied being ill but the clinical directive was that they should descend. We clustered around the two, giving them our sympathies and assurances that they would recover rapidly on descent. Their belongings were gathered together and they set off down the moraine slope (although not before we had taken blood samples and their urine collections). I was cast as the bad guy. "Bloody Hitler," Ian shouted back up the slope.

Who would be sent down next? Several others lay in their tents with splitting headaches. Ted had additional symptoms. He was very emotional. He felt a great sadness over those who were ill and burst into tears.

In contrast, others appeared mostly unaffected, including John Simmons, John Delamere and myself. Maybe, we suggested, our hormone levels were different. Our reward was further blood samples. Thankfully, the generator started perfectly and the samples were quickly taken and stored. It must have been the highest laboratory in the world.

The conference that evening had a serious air. Everyone was anxious about Ian and Tim and how people would fare over the coming hours. Alex and Ron made a 'tent round' and reported that everyone was well enough to survive the night. Few were without headaches. I had little appetite and took care to move slowly because of a dull ache in my temples.

Before bed, I took a final glance at the night sky, with the Milky Way painted across the heavens, brighter than I had ever seen it. I went to sleep happy that my friends were ill! We should have good research results – provided the generator started and we could get the blood samples home safely. Ted had recovered a little but was still miserable and complained bitterly about his headache. He hated the place.

* * *

Next morning, no one rose until the sun had touched the tents and warmed the air. It had been an uncomfortable night, though we had kept most of our clothes on to stave off the cold. Frank, Ted and Chris were a little better, although Frank had been bitterly cold again during the night. His sleeping bag was a relic from the 1953 Everest expedition. All those he had supplied with discounted sleeping bags from his shop were warm enough but he had badly overestimated the quality of his historical artefact.

The blood collections took a long time as the generator would not power the three centrifuges simultaneously and then some samples froze and had to be re-taken. An early morning delivery of yak dung from Muktinath provided a meagre fire.

The plan at the highest camp was to take photographs for the sponsors (figure 14) then walk to the pass. One at a time, we had ECGs, stripping off all our layers of clothes in the bitter wind. Just before we set off for the top, Tim arrived with a tale of woe from the previous night: "Ian and I spent an extraordinary evening in a dismal hovel at around 3,800 m surrounded by drunken Tibetan muleteers all milling around with mules, pigs, dogs, chickens and filth; there was a lot of scratching and coughing with a great deal of noisy expectoration. I slept with a donkey for warmth. No wonder I elected to climb back up the 1,700 m next day." He had done it to prove that he did not have acute mountain sickness. We were delighted to see him back.

Everyone had prepared their crampons and ice axes and John Delamere wore boots for the first time. We left the tents and travelled light for the col. The climb took us two hours to reach 5,416 m, 400 m above our camp. There was a huge cairn and we all took photographs. Chris was too ill so I took the camera and inexpertly managed a few minutes of filming. It was very windy and bitterly cold. The view the other side was towards Gyaji Kang, Chulu West and numerous other 6,000 m peaks. They were covered with glaciers that flowed down to the pass.

A few wanted to climb a peak and Khatung Kang, the southern of the two, was selected. John Delamere and Neville donned their crampons and started up the steep ice. The rest of us were too inexperienced or too tired and I was filming so after venturing a few metres on the hard ice I turned back. We watched as the two climbers moved slowly upwards. They barely had an hour before sundown when they would have to turn back. A few of us hung around in the strong wind before moving back to the col. The sun began to drop and so I followed Ron and Mike down to the camp. John and Neville were still climbing as we left. They had no provisions to stay out for the night. No doubt they would not be long.

Back at camp it was 5 pm urine collections for the penultimate time. The Sherpas had cooked a meal but most of us were not hungry. John and Neville staggered in at dusk completely exhausted. They had only climbed 300 m before turning back with headaches, feeling sick and ataxic. John had never felt so ill on a mountain and struggled to walk. Ron gave then painkillers and they collapsed into bed.

The condition of people varied quite a lot – everyone was having headaches except John Simmons, who said that he felt marvellous; but he was the only one. I was suffering from the altitude and the effort. The pass was a desolate, albeit beautiful place, but I couldn't help finding it an anti-climax. The pressure of the expedition, the problems that we had encountered, the illnesses and the research expectations had taken their toll. And all the bravado about climbing one of the peaks – it was sheer fantasy. The truth was we were nowhere near acclimatised. We needed a week at this height to manage a serious attempt. If there had been an accident, no one was in any fit state or sufficiently experienced to mount a rescue.

* * *

That evening we discussed the important issues facing us over the next few days: clinical evaluation of acute mountain sickness in the group, remaining blood and urine samples, persisting illness and the thorny issue of getting the frozen blood samples to Kathmandu. We potentially had some good results but the next few days would be critical.

It was another bitterly cold night and by morning most were ready for the descent to Muktinath. Thankfully Neville and John were better but Ted was not at all well and set off soon after breakfast. His headache was worse and while discussing his plight he cried again, although later he had no recollection of any emotional upset. He had facial and ankle oedema and clearly had acute mountain sickness (figure 15). Tim followed soon after and the camp started to break up.

On his way down, Ted met a group of Nepalese accompanying an English climber intent on climbing a peak. The two chatted about the various mountains, with Ted offering advice about which were possible and appropriate equipment. He explained about acute mountain sickness and how to manage fluid balance, food and so on. Ted was in full flow. He later explained how much he had helped the climber. We subsequently discovered that it was Peter Boardman (of Everest fame). Good for Ted – it was like telling Sherpa Tenzing how to climb Everest. Once revved up, Ted could offer advice to anyone.

I checked the amount of dry ice in the polystyrene boxes. On the way up the Kali Gandaki valley, it had disappeared at an alarming rate. To conserve it, only one box of the four was opened at a time and, as soon as it was possible, the shrinking ice blocks were put into three boxes and then two. By contrast, at the top camp it was freezing hard at night and the ice blocks had hardly changed. But we were down to about 30% of the initial amount and there was no way that it would survive another 10 days of subtropical heat.

Looking around the campsite we were surrounded by ice, at −20°C. Why not use some to keep the samples frozen? During the night we had heard the heavy roar of an avalanche so I asked John Simmons if he might go with a porter and find where the ice had fallen. They found some in a small frozen pool set a good distance from the glacier base. An hour later, John struggled back into the camp wearing the porter's leather and rope head strap and carrying the blocks of ice in a pannier. He had taken it from the porter and insisted on lugging it back. Gratefully we filled the boxes with the largest pieces. It would evaporate the dry ice rapidly since that was at $-80°C$ but it would buy us valuable extra time. I quietly worried that all the blood samples would be ruined, especially the samples for ADH testing; the hormone that was so fragile and would be destroyed if the samples thawed, yet they might hold the secret of acute mountain sickness.

Generally, I felt well and had adapted to the altitude. It seemed a shame to leave the top camp too early so I asked the fittest, John Simmons, John Delamere and Mike, if they fancied a scramble up to a high ridge ledge. By 12.30 pm we had climbed a steep scree and ice slope to a castellated crumbling ridge at around 5,500 m. Magnificent views opened all around: north into Tibet with snowy mountains 100 miles away and south to Dhaulagiri, Nilgiri and to the plains of India covered in cloud. Below was our campsite with the sirdar awaiting our return. We now realised that we had camped on a glacier with a deep layer of rocks covering its surface. No wonder it had been cold. I ran down the uneven scree with John Delamere, returning in a fifth of the ascent time, and by 1.30 pm we were with the Sherpa. From there we retraced our ascent path to Muktinath – a total descent of 1,700 m. It was much further than we had imagined. Our extra climb took its toll and we struggled into the camp in late afternoon.

The Sherpas had set a wood and yak dung fire and were cooking the evening meal. We all felt much better in the thicker air and were able to think again. Many had already visited the famous temple – the most important Hindu and Buddhist shrine in the whole of Nepal. A large walled complex contained the 'everlasting holy flame', a jet of natural gas that burns just above a spring of sacred water. The spring fills a pool with 108 brass waterspouts (a sacred number in Tibetan Buddhism), cast in the shape of cows' heads, from where the water can be collected. We filled our bottles while a nun lit a yak butter lamp to speed us on our return journey. Prayer wheels, wind-powered by Maxwell House coffee lids, completed the holy scene.

Brass water spout

* * *

Now was time to reflect on our experiences at high altitude and all the symptoms and signs of acute mountain sickness. Since self-questionnaires and clinical interviews might be biased by people denying their sickness, we suggested a third assessment method – peer review. We debated whether each individual should rank everyone else in order of susceptibility to acute mountain sickness. The discussion was lively, then became heated. Many claimed that they had not taken sufficient notice of others to form any judgements; others felt that the more vocal members had expressed their illness more than quieter members so they could be assessed more easily. Nevertheless, 17 pairs of eyes and ears, and mostly doctors, can gather more information than two clinicians seeing people for only a few minutes. We finally agreed to have a peer review ranking score. Interestingly, subsequent analysis showed that it was in good agreement with other scoring systems and it correlated better with arterial oxygen concentrations (chapter 2) than the other methods. At the top camp it was apparent that some were in clear denial of their suffering to the questioning physicians. One person stated he was perfectly well during the evening meal and appeared to eat heartily but was seen vomiting behind the tent shortly afterwards.

The animated discussions continued over beers at the evening conference. A major concern was how to determine who was ill and who wasn't. No one objected to the assessments but rather to their accuracy. A mild headache to one person is a severe headache to another. The tough people wanted to be ranked low, while the more neurotic and expressive thought they had suffered badly. All the medics pitched in with their opinions. The non-medics watched on in silence, baffled at our indecision and disagreement. Eventually, we decided that Ron and Alex should interview each individual to provide a ranked clinical score.

* * *

The following morning, we re-checked the ice containers. The dry ice was nearly gone and the glacier ice was starting to melt – as presumably were our precious samples. I was becoming increasingly concerned that our sacrifices might all have been in vain. Again, we considered a flight from Jomsom but, as the sirdar explained, the flights were irregular and unreliable, the wind could be a major problem after mid-morning, and they were usually over-booked. Fickle weather often led to delays of several days, leaving a backlog of irritated trekkers and climbers. Even so, it was worth a try but we would have to descend quickly.

Thankfully, no blood collections were required which saved at least an hour. Everyone packed quickly and we set off. In less than an hour we had reached Khingar where we had stopped for two nights on the ascent. From there we followed the long sloping track to the Kali Gandaki valley, finally reaching Jomsom around 1.30 pm in the harsh afternoon winds.

The sirdar, Neville, Ted and I headed straight to the airport where, by chance, there was a plane about to depart for Kathmandu. A German, wanting to return early because of illness, had hired the plane for himself leaving two spare seats; perhaps one for the samples and one for me or Neville? Nev talked to him in fluent German while the rest of us stuck to broken English. We explained our dilemma, the importance of the samples, how the success of the whole expedition rested on their analysis, how they could thaw any day. But to our surprise and gathering anxiety, he said no. He was irritated, pompous and not remotely interested. He had hired the plane for himself. We emphasised that it was the first time this study had ever been attempted and how we had spent thousands of pounds and weeks of work undertaking this vital research. He was unmoved. No was his final answer. "Nothing to do with the war then?" Ted muttered to himself.

By then it was late afternoon and we needed to join the others down the valley at Marpha for the night's camp. We left a Sherpa and porter with the samples to try putting them on another plane in the morning. We thought that the ice would last about four more days, while our return trip would take six days, three to Tatopani then three more to Pokhara. Half an hour later we saw the small plane speed off towards Kathmandu. A plane was surely our only chance to save the samples and all our hard-won research.

Over the next two days we saw the occasional early morning plane flying to Jomsom and return an hour or so later. Although we worried about the thawing samples and whether they were on one of the flights, trekking down the valley was a very pleasant way to spend the remaining days of the expedition. A couple of exercise tests and the urine collections were the only studies remaining. And, of course, there was filming to be done – better late than never.

Some of our spare time at lunch stops and in the evening was spent assessing mountain sickness scores. Ron and Alex put a lot of thought into how each person had performed. Each day a few more of us would be interviewed and we completed the forms that ranked individuals from 1–17 according to their mountain sickness symptoms.

But the blood samples were always at the back of my mind. Clearly, we had achieved a lot. There had been a good degree of acute mountain sickness, we had developed a clinical scoring system, we had loads of urine samples but the bloods were important. But there was no news.

Mani stone

* * *

In the early afternoon on the third morning, as we were approaching the hot springs at Tatopani, there was a commotion among the Sherpas. A bedraggled porter came into view carrying two large polystyrene boxes. We were most surprised to see him. I thought maybe the samples had been put onto a plane in another box, or perhaps they were still in Jomsom in a fridge; if they were still in the boxes then surely they were ruined. We gathered around and opened them anxiously. There were several large lumps of glacier ice in the first one but no samples. The second contained more ice and there, underneath were the samples. We examined them with deep apprehension. Remarkably, they were still frozen.

With a Sherpa translating, we quizzed the porter. He explained that for two successive mornings they had tried desperately to put them onto one of the planes but to no avail. Finally, they realised that the last possibility of saving them was to walk with them to Pokhara. The previous afternoon they had set off to catch us up. They had travelled overnight and completed a two-and-a-half-day trek in just 16 hours. We were hugely grateful for their effort and astonished at their achievement. A two-and-a-half-day trek in only one day?

We carefully examined the remaining ice blocks. We reckoned that the ice would last only another day, but it was three days to Pokhara: up the steep climb from Tatopani to Ghorepani then two further days through the warm forests via Birethanti and Naudanda to Pokhara. From there it could be put on a bus to Kathmandu. But there was no way the ice could survive that long.

The discussions then turned to the possibility of a hotel in Pokhara having a freezer and Jackie thought it was likely. We realised that if porters and Sherpas could travel without stopping then it might be just feasible. However, they would have to be accompanied by one or two of us to persuade a hotel to freeze the samples. Nev and I were the fastest in the group and now that we were fit it would be worth a try. If we took two porters and a Sherpa we might be able to get to Pokhara by the morning. It would mean travelling overnight with only brief rests over a total distance of around 35 miles. That did not seem so bad. Two of the fastest porters were chosen and we finalised our plans as we briefly stopped at the night's camp at Tatopani. Neville and I borrowed head torches; the porters set off and 15 minutes later we followed them with a Sherpa. It was Pokhara by morning or bust.

Neville and I carried day sacks with minimal content while the porters carried an ice box each, along with their personal items. Their loads were much heavier than ours so we could easily keep up in the beginning. Up we went past Ghara, Sitka, Phalante, Chitre and finally Ghorepani for a brief stop near our campsite from two weeks earlier, 1,700 m above Tatopani. Then down we headed through the high forest as the short tropical twilight embraced us. We rushed on in the blackness, head torches on, the leading Sherpa out front with his twinkling Tilly lamp. We stopped briefly at 9 pm at a tea house, surrounded by jungle noises of bull frogs, crickets and heavy trampling animals. Then on again in silence, stumbling in the shadows, down and down then up and up completely unaware of our location. Tiredness gradually bore down and by 3 am exhaustion was fighting our minds and legs.

There was a complete language barrier between us and our guides but they could sense our fatigue. Incomprehensible Nepali talk was followed by knocking on the doors of forest houses as we plunged on by. After an hour or so it was apparent that there was going to be a rest stop. The porters too were exhausted from their loads and were starting to stumble. They had no head torches and were wearing flip-flops. They had carried 25 kg for the past 12 hours with barely a stop. Then a light appeared up ahead at a small shack. We entered to warm-hearted greetings, a cup of chang and some biscuits. Shortly afterwards we were led to a couple of small beds with thin filthy mattresses. We were going to stop for two hours until first light. I lay in bed in the dark marvelling at the journey, the excitement of our desperate race against time, surrounded by unknown people speaking an incomprehensible language. I drifted into a dreamless sleep to the buzz of the crickets and cattle stomping in the room below. Most houses contain sheep, goats, buffalo or chickens or a combination of them all. Thankfully, the cockerels were quiet.

In a moment, two hours had passed; there was a faint dawn light and movement in the house. Aching legs greeted my awakening. We had to leave soon; a hurried breakfast of chapatis and biscuits then down the mountain trail with the porters. The movement, scuttling down the endless steps and dodging past other early travellers, eased the leg pain. We were all very tired by now. We had camped earlier at the village of Birethanti, leaving only 20 miles remaining. We descended into the river valley, past Naudanda, and the rice paddies, with towering Machhapuchhre shining in the sun's early rays. In the distance was Pokhara. The rest of the morning passed in silence, the sirdar leading, then us, followed by the porters with their peculiar shuffling gait from a lifetime of carrying heavy loads.

With aching feet, legs and backs, it was early afternoon when we finally arrived in the shabby outskirts of Pokhara and hailed a taxi. It drove us to a beautiful hotel with golden griffins adorned with erect phalluses either side of a huge wooden entrance door. The manager came out, looking warily at us covered in filth from the long journey and two weeks in the mountains. The Sherpa explained our predicament and we were welcomed heartily. Neither he nor the porters were allowed inside but we were treated like kings. We carried the boxes with their valuable contents into the kitchen and stood before the deep freeze. In simple English we conveyed the idea of putting the blood samples on their food shelves. We opened the boxes and exposed the lumps of clear ice carried from the far side of Annapurna, and our precious samples. Meat, bread and an assortment of other items were removed from the fridge and replaced with our miraculously still frozen serum tubes. But the staff's interest was more in the ice blocks. None had ever been to Annapurna. None had seen such huge lumps of transparent ice from its glaciers. They were amazed. With the language barrier and our slight exaggeration, they probably thought that we had climbed the mountain and taken ice from the summit. We were received as conquering heroes and they were only too eager to please us.

A grand twin room overlooking Pokhara lakes was arranged and after a brief meal we had hot baths and slumped into bed, happy, relieved and exhausted but thrilled with our adventure and success. Three days of walking in one single night's push; 35 miles over 20 hours, with nearly 4,000 m of ascent and descent. We fell asleep in a blissful buzz of contentment.

Hunger pangs awoke us in time for an evening meal. It was a good hotel with fine food and half a dozen different wines, including half-bottles of Calvet Bordeaux at £10 each. We ordered one, much to the amazement of the waiters. It was a fortune to them. Their annual salary was around £20. We had just spent six months' worth. Even for us it was a considerable amount. Gingerly the head waiter pulled the cork – it was delicious. We ordered another and sat in a happy haze of success, enjoying the wine, good food and the admiring babble of the staff marvelling at our heroism and wealth.

The next morning we met the sirdar and arranged to go to Kathmandu by minibus. The ice boxes were packed with ice from the freezer, preserving the frozen samples. The two porters were rewarded with generous tips, and with the Sherpa we headed back along the bumpy highway to the noisy bustle of Kathmandu and security for the serum samples in a freezer at the Hotel Asia.

* * *

Neville and I kept ourselves busy in Kathmandu. We had three days before the others would arrive. Neville had a ring made for his future wife Caroline. We went around the markets, bought rugs and trinkets, and had sizzling buffalo steaks at KC's. We checked to see if the Lufthansa flight was arranged and whether there had been any other hijackings.

Our colleagues' story was a little different. John Delamere took charge as deputy leader, but with little to worry about. There were odds and ends such as filming to be completed, clinical interviews and Bob's exercise tests but no blood or urine tests. A holiday ambience took over as the now fit and lean group took up the daily race. The first was the ascent from Tatopani to Ghorepani, which was completed by midday even though it had been intended as the night's stop. Since it was cold and drizzling, many wanted to carry on, particularly as the fastest porters were agitating to return to Kathmandu. By contrast, Chris was trying to organise more filming – much to people's irritation – while the slower members wanted a rest. A heated debate was resolved by some porters heading down towards Pokhara. That was the trigger for the next race, a run down the 3,000 steps of the Gurung Staircase, as the path from Ulleri to Tikhedhunga is called, and the night's camp.

The next day followed a similar pattern, some members wanting a leisurely walk to admire the countryside, others pushing for the finishing line while Chris wanted to film. Lack of focus on a clear objective, a relaxed time schedule and different personalities gaining confidence led to the first serious argument. Mike, a lecturer in sports medicine, thought the group was too competitive and became irritated with Chris bossily trying to organise filming after the event.

Hay carrier

Often, at the end of expeditions, emotional safely valves are released. Personal expectations, hopes, pressures, worries and fears are ended. But failures are clear for all to see and scores may need settling. Petty animosities and frustrations that have simmered over the weeks boil over. Around the evening camp fire, below the path to Annapurna base camp, tensions finally erupted. Across the burning logs, Mike criticised Chris's inadequate filming in front of everyone. Others watched in quiet amusement, trying to ignore the developing argument, and carried on eating. Then Mike threw a film canister at Chris and suddenly they were upon each other, fists flailing. Multiple strong arms pulled them apart and the brief spat was over. The general hubbub of contentment returned. John Simmons, who had paid £3,000 towards the film, watched on but said nothing.

Next morning all was forgotten, so with fine weather and good humour filming continued. But it was all low-level photography; the real action had been 10 days earlier. This frequently happens with expedition films. It is easy at low altitude but when the going gets tough the film crews need to be tougher.

The day passed uneventfully with the final night on trek spent at Naudanda, the same campsite as on the ascent. There followed two leisurely nights at Pokhara lakes, where the early morning mists cleared to reflect Annapurna in the still waters. Ethereal snows, 7,000 m above, shone above the clouds and upon the deep green forest that surrounded the town. Bliss.

There was canoeing in dug-outs, a few final clinical interviews with Ron and Alex, plus thoughts of Neville and me with the precious samples. They had no news of our dramatic walk and success. Porters disappeared home while the Sherpas and Jackie looked after everyone.

We finally met up with everyone in Kathmandu on the afternoon of 17 November, 23 days since we had departed together. We swapped stories over beers and sizzling steaks at KC's restaurant. We excitedly told them of our adventures with the blood samples and how all had successfully been put into a deep freeze at the hotel. That night we dined out royally and told our story time and again until well into the night. We reckoned that, at around 36 hours, it was the fastest ever overland journey from the airport at Jomsom to Pokhara.

* * *

On our last day in Kathmandu, we returned our rental equipment and shopped. There were (and still are) several camps for Tibetan refugees from the Chinese invasion in 1950. Their much-admired metal craft, jewellery, wood carvings and rugs were a magnet for our unspent dollars.

But thoughts turned to home, Lufthansa, hijacked planes and our lost luggage.

Thankfully, our plane was available and on time. We had a final dinner at the Hotel Crystal in Kathmandu, accompanied by Jackie and Dr John Dickinson who worked at the Shanta Bhawan Hospital in Kathmandu. He had seen many cases of cerebral and pulmonary oedema. He showed great interest in our research and we tentatively invited him to the UK.

At the airport next morning there were still no sign of our missing baggage. We felt a twinge of anxiety as our equipment and blood samples, packed in ice, disappeared past the ticket desk. We boarded a modest-sized plane crammed with people desperately trying to get home to Europe. Then we were diverted to Patna followed by Lucknow and finally Delhi. With all the chaos around us, we had little confidence of getting home on time.

From Delhi we flew to Frankfurt in an empty plane. Travellers had been frightened off Lufthansa by the Baader–Meinhoff murders. Just before departure, the captain brought John Simmons his knife that he had handed in at the security check. How times have changed.

We stretched out in luxury – five seats each – and slept the peace of kings for the overnight flight. Then on to London where we bade farewell to mountain-forged friendships and boarded a hired bus to the Medical School in Birmingham. Alongside us lay the samples, still frozen solid after their long, long journey.

That was quite some trip.

* * *

However, the saga was not quite finished, for a sting remained in the tale. The fragile ADH samples, collected with such difficulty and carried with such heroic effort, still had to be analysed. In 1977, no laboratory in the UK had the necessary capability so we kept them frozen over the winter months and in the following June they were dispatched to a specialised laboratory in the USA. We used an American Airways cargo flight, which landed at O'Hare International Airport in Chicago – right in the middle of a strike by baggage handling staff. The plane was taken to a corner of the airport and left on the tarmac for a week. A heat wave enveloped the city, and the refrigeration on the plane failed. Our ADH samples thawed, then cooked. All that effort had been in vain. In the depths of the Indian subcontinent, against all the odds, we had managed to keep the samples frozen but back in supposed civilisation we had been thwarted.

Postscript:

Nothing can quite recapture the novelty and delight of that first trip. Kathmandu was relatively unvisited in the 1970s. There was little traffic, no air pollution and few roads outside the main towns. The overland route from Pokhara to Jomsom was travelled only on foot except for the occasional army four-wheel-drive vehicle. Mustang was a forbidden city. Within a generation, that had changed: traffic lights, flyovers and underpasses, roundabouts, computers, flash restaurants, nightclubs, coups d'état, pollution, corruption – two centuries of development rushed through in 20 years.

In later years, when asked which expedition I preferred, my answer is always "the first one". The magnificence of the mountains, historic exotic Nepal with all its tropical sensations and mysterious culture – nothing can compare with that heady first experience.

Over the next few months we analysed the samples. As we were all in full-time day jobs, it had to be done in evenings and at weekends. Although our hopes of assessing ADH changes had been dashed, many other substances were measured and produced interesting results. Ron and Alex thought it would be important to hold a conference in Birmingham to showcase our findings. This was held in the Medical School on 14 July 1978 and invitees included well-known experts in the field such as Professor Donald Heath, Dr John Dickinson from Kathmandu and Dr Charlie Houston. The latter was famed for a desperate mountain rescue attempt on K2 when a colleague eventually died. He never climbed again but instead had dedicated himself to understanding high-altitude physiology and had become a world authority.

On commencing his lecture, he looked up at the audience and saw that most of us were hirsute – not what he expected of doctors. We had kept our beards from the expedition. Regrettably, he lectured in a monotonic American accent, and requested that the lecture theatre lights be dimmed. It was the final straw: we put our heads to the benches and fell asleep. After the hour, on went the lights and with horror, he saw that many of us were dead to the world. Years later, he mentioned this to me at a conference. He had felt dishonoured by the experience and thought we were a rum lot. The word 'scallywags' came to mind.

We published eight papers in the Postgraduate Medical Journal the following year. We had justified our efforts to our peers and sponsors. Several years later I noted with pride several copies of the journal in a Tamil book shop in Kathmandu.

And the film? Four years later, with help from the University film department, we had 30 minutes of our adventure worth watching.

Publications from the expedition:

1. Bradwell AR. Birmingham Medical Research Expeditionary Society 1977 Expedition. Serum and urine proteins during a high-altitude trek. Postgraduate Medical Journal 1979; 55, 478–481.
2. Delamere JP, Jones GT. Birmingham Medical Research Expeditionary Society 1977 Expedition. Changes in renal function observed during a trek at high altitude. Postgraduate Medical Journal 1979; 55, 461–463
3. Fletcher RF. Birmingham Medical Research Expeditionary Society 1977 Expedition. Signs and symptoms. Postgraduate Medical Journal 1979; 55, 461–463.
4. Harvey TC, James HM, Chettle DR. Birmingham Medical Research Expeditionary Society 1977 Expedition. Effect of a Himalayan trek on whole body composition, nitrogen and potassium. Postgraduate Medical Journal 1979; 55, 475–477.
5. Howell A, Cove DH. Birmingham Medical Research Expeditionary Society 1977 Expedition. The diuresis and related changes during a trek to high altitude. Postgraduate Medical Journal 1979; 55, 471–474.
6. Olive JE, Waterhouse N. Birmingham Medical Research Expeditionary Society 1977 Expedition. Psychological aspects of acute mountain sickness. Postgraduate Medical Journal 1979; 55, 464–466.
7. Stockley RA, Green ID. Birmingham Medical Research Expeditionary Society 1977 Expedition. Cardiopulmonary function before, during and after a twenty-one-day Himalayan trek. Postgraduate Medical Journal, 1979; 55, 496–501.
8. Wright AD. Birmingham Medical Research Expeditionary Society 1977 Expedition. Thyroid function and acute mountain sickness. Postgraduate Medical Journal 1979; 55, 483–486.

Fig 1. **Back row:** *Ted Olive, Frank Davies Gron Jones, Neville Richardson, Ron Fletcher, Alex Wright, David Cove, Ian Green, John Simmons, Tony Howell;* **Front row:** *Mike Reynolds, John Delamere, Jo Bradwell, Tim Harvey, Bob Stockley, Norman Waterhouse;* **Photographer:** *Chris Hawkesworth.*

Fig 2. *First night in Pokhara*

Fig 3. *Machhapuchare*

Fig 4. *Evening camp*

Fig 5. *Annapurna*

Fig 6. *Kali Ghandaki valley*

Fig 7. *John Delamere with urine collection*

Fig 8. *Tea sahib?*

Fig 9. *Alex measuring skin folds on Frank*

Fig 10. *Khingar*

Fig 11. *Yakawa Kang from Khingar*

Fig 12. *Camp at Khingar*

Fig 13. *Muktinath with Dhaulagiri*

Fig 14. *Damart underwear advert*

Fig 15. *Ted with acute mountain sickness*

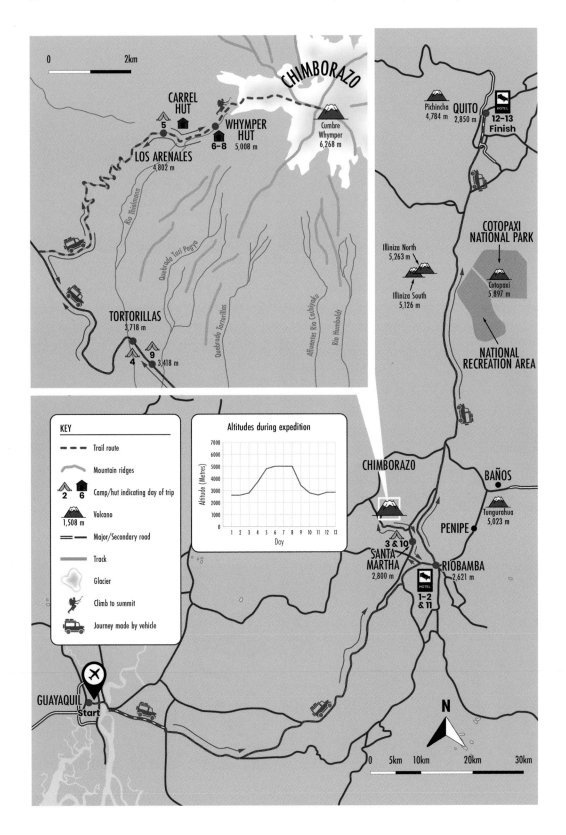

Chapter 2
Chimborazo, Ecuador – September 1979

Chimborazo from the Pan-American Highway

A new pill to make you feel lower

"In about an hour I found myself lying on my back, along with both Carrels, placed 'hors de combat' and incapable of making the least exertion. We knew that the enemy was upon us, and that we were experiencing our first attack of mountain-sickness. We were feverish, had intense headaches, and were unable to satisfy our desire for air, except by breathing with open mouths."
  – Edward Whymper at the site of the future Whymper Hut on the flanks
      of Chimborazo. In: *Travels Amongst the Great Andes of the Equator;* 1892.

Summary: Our second expedition investigated the role of acetazolamide (Diamox) in the prevention of acute mountain sickness. We undertook a double-blind, randomised trial of 500 mg of acetazolamide versus placebo in 20 people. During a rapid ascent to the Whymper Hut, at 5,000 m on the southwest flank of Chimborazo, we demonstrated clear clinical and biochemical benefits of the medication. An elegant paper in The Lancet brought BMRES widespread recognition in the medical and national press.

Expedition members: Jo Bradwell (leader), Dave Burnett, Bernard Coles, Frank Davies (quartermaster), John Delamere (deputy leader), Norman Dorricott, Ron Fletcher (medical officer), Pete Forster, Ian Green, Gron Jones, David Lort (medical student), John Mackintosh, John Milles, Simon Morrissey, Ted Olive, John Simmons, David Thomas, Malcolm Walker, Norman Waterhouse, Alex Wright (figure 1).

 Himalayan expedition had generated a lot of interest. Our work on acute mountain sickness was published as 12 scientific papers, eight of which filled a supplement of the Postgraduate Medical Journal. They had been published within a couple of years, thanks to the Trojan efforts of Ron and Alex. Our results justified our absence from hospitals in Birmingham and obtaining them had been a thoroughly enjoyable experience.

After the expedition we met on a regular basis to analyse the results but there was no sense that another expedition might follow. I discussed closing the society's bank account with John Delamere since our 'trip of a lifetime' was over. However, he counselled caution because maybe, just maybe, one day we might go again. I doubted we could pull off a similar month of 'study leave', and what research could we possibly do?

Coincidentally, the Sunday Times ran an article about medical charities and how tax could be reclaimed from donations. I wondered if this might apply to us. We had each personally paid £200 for the first expedition but if we continued with annual subscriptions, we could make a tax reclaim that effectively increased the amount to £300 per year. Could we be eligible? In retrospect this appears impossibly naïve but at the time it was a revelation. We knew many huge medical charities such as the Cancer Research Campaign and the Wellcome Trust accepted tax-exempt donations but we had not made the connection with our work. Our publications proved we were carrying out useful medical experiments but it had also been a lot of fun rather than 'serious research' on cancer or heart disease. Was what we were doing serious enough? We sent off an application form for charitable status and, much to our delight, a few weeks later discovered we were successful. The realisation that we had 'noble status' spurred our interest in another mountain trip.

On reviewing Peter Hackett's important paper in The Lancet (see Chapter 1), it was clear that we had found similar clinical features to his observations. He had also demonstrated that acetazolamide (Diamox) reduced the symptoms of acute mountain sickness. On close examination, it was clear that the study had several limitations. First, the participants had self-assessed their symptoms which, as we had shown on the Thorong La expedition, may be inaccurate. Second, nearly 50% of participants had failed to enter or complete the study correctly. And third, treatment was started at 3,000 m when ill people might have already descended, thereby limiting the population studied.

These unsatisfactory aspects would not occur in a prospective, randomised controlled trial. We realised that such a project could be possible if we evaluated ourselves. We would need a placebo group and the study would have to be double-blinded (when neither subjects nor investigators know who is receiving active medication). Also, we thought the results might be 'cleaner' if interfering factors such as exercise and gut infections were avoided.

As our knowledge of acute mountain sickness developed over the ensuing months, we realised that its cause was not properly understood – in particular, the role played by oxygen (O_2) and carbon dioxide (CO_2). For many years CO_2 had been considered important because it is the main controller of breathing. Indeed, as stated by Miescher-Rusch (1885) in a poetic phrase: 'Over the oxygen supply of the body, carbon dioxide spreads its protecting wings'.

The theory goes as follows. At sea level, CO_2 produced by the body stimulates the breathing centres in the brain and elsewhere. Anyone can easily demonstrate this by over-breathing. After taking 20 or so deep breaths, there is a period of apnoea (no respiratory movement). This is because CO_2 has been 'blown off', leaving low blood levels. Gradually, as CO_2 levels increase again, breathing restarts but during that time O_2 levels in the blood may fall below those required to sustain the brain's normal function, leading to unconsciousness.

At altitude, where oxygen levels are much lower than sea level, breathing rates greatly increase. CO_2 concentrations are reduced as a result, which in turn switches off the breathing centres. Consequently, people breathe erratically at altitude – the periodic breathing known as 'Cheyne–Stokes respiration'. Frank Davies had suffered from this badly (see Beginnings). Fortunately, with acclimatisation the brain gradually readjusts its response to lower CO_2 levels and regular breathing patterns are re-established.

However, in 1979 it was unclear whether low O_2 levels or inadequate control of CO_2 influenced the development of acute mountain sickness. Could we resolve this issue by measuring blood levels of CO_2 and O_2 during ascent to high altitude? Perhaps surprisingly, in the 1970s, instruments for measuring blood gases were rather unsophisticated and consistent results difficult to obtain.

We therefore settled on two projects as the main aims of our second expedition: a drug trial of acetazolamide and measurement of blood concentrations of O_2 and CO_2 in people with acute mountain sickness. The requirements would be a rapid ascent to around 5,000 m and no hard exercise. A high hut would be ideal for the complex experiments and a location close to the equator would provide warm weather. These restrictions ruled out the Himalayas and the Karakoram because they all required long treks to high base camps, so we turned our attentions to the Andes. It was not long before we settled on Ecuador. By chance, it was the centenary of Edward Whymper's 1879 expedition to Ecuador.

In 1865, Whymper had found fame and infamy in a single step. He was an intrepid climber who, after many attempts, conquered the Matterhorn. Disastrously, four of his seven team members fell to their deaths on the descent. The controversy over the climb rumbled on, with Whymper saying little until he published his account in Scrambles Amongst the Alps in 1872.

He was one of the first professional mountaineers and regarded as cold and somewhat ruthless. This in part was because he was from the wrong class, not a gentleman climber as Victorians preferred their heroes. His climbing was focused on getting to the summit. After the Matterhorn, he looked further afield than the Alps for his adventures as all the major peaks had been climbed. In the 1870s, the Himalayas were ruled out because of political sensitivities, as were Chile, Peru and Bolivia. But the Republic of Ecuador was accessible. His goal became Chimborazo (6,268 m). In 1745, it was believed to be the highest mountain in the world, a belief that persisted until the discovery of Dhaulagiri (8,167 m) in 1808.

As a result of simple physics, Chimborazo remains the world's highest point – in the sense that it is furthest from the Earth's core. The Earth's spin produces an equatorial bulge, and Chimborazo's summit, 6,384.4 km from its centre, is 2,168 m higher than the top of Mt Everest. However, since sea and atmosphere bulge similarly, from a climber's viewpoint, its summit is really 6,268 m, well below Everest's 8,848 m.

In 1879, Whymper made the first ascents of Chimborazo, Cotopaxi, Sincholagua,

Antisana and Cayambe. He concluded with a second ascent of Chimborazo, during which a violent eruption of Cotopaxi, 60 miles to the north, covered him in volcanic ash.

To commemorate the centenary of his first ascent, a mountain hut had been built at 5,000 m on the south-west shoulder of Chimborazo. It was a perfect location for our studies. To add even more historical context, Whymper had entitled his research: 'Studies into the causes of mountain sickness'.

Organising this second expedition was much easier than the first – indeed, too easy to be true. As the old adage goes, 'hubris before nemesis'.

The evening of 14 September 1979 found us at the departure gate of Iberia Airlines at Heathrow Terminal 2, and that was when the problems began. This trip had been trouble-free to that point. No trouble collecting the money; £1,000 here, £500 there. Tax returns on the basis of the charity association had bought in another £4,000, while the Arthur Thompson Trust (Birmingham Medical School charity) had given us £3,000 in support of David Lort, a final-year medical student.

The success of the Himalayan adventure had attracted considerable interest, with many people keen to come with us if we had a subsequent expedition. Consultant friends such as Norman Dorricott (general surgeon at the General Hospital) and David Thomas (neurologist at Queen Square in London) joined BMRES, as did three junior doctors at the Queen Elizabeth Hospital – John Milles (endocrinology), Pete Forster (rheumatology) and Malcolm Walker (cardiologist). David Burnet (immunology) and John Mackintosh (physiology) were friends from the Medical School. Last but not least was Simon Morrissey, a medical student friend of Norman Waterhouse and son of the well-known surgeon Denis Morrissey, with whom I had been a houseman 10 years earlier.

A major success in the run up to the expedition had been obtaining a blood-gas analyser. Initially we had assessed several methods of obtaining O_2 and CO_2 measurements. Pete Forster had thought of snap-freezing capillary blood samples in solid CO_2 at $-80°C$ but the expansion of ice in the blood cracked the tubes when they were full. Then we found a laboratory instrument that made all the measurements automatically. Pete went to the company in Manchester to evaluate its use. The staff looked after him really well – big lunch, full sales pitch. But when Pete explained that we only wanted to borrow the equipment, their conviviality rapidly dissipated. But there was still the possibility of borrowing it if we paid for the insurance costs.

Meanwhile, a sales representative from VA Howe Ltd came to see Bob Stockley, who thought we ought to try their blood-gas saturation machine. This was not quite what we wanted but they also had another analyser that measured ten parameters automatically, including barometric pressure. I asked the sales rep to discuss its suitability for high-altitude studies with the managing director and owner, Richard Brown. I also offered a tempting lure by suggesting we might purchase a large centrifuge for my laboratory if they were cooperative.

The next day the sales rep returned to discuss the centrifuge proposition. I eventually turned the conversation to our Andes expedition and how it might be of interest to their company. "Could we perhaps borrow a blood gas analyser?" I suggested. "No, they are not suitable," was his reply. I demanded to speak to his boss on the phone and explained the novelty of our research and the importance of our trip. This was the turning point. He was definitely interested from a marketing perspective and would lend us an instrument provided we could operate it. Next day it arrived, with one week remaining before our scheduled departure to Ecuador.

The person who came to demonstrate it was Bernard Coles. He was the chief technical salesperson for the instrument and an expert on its operation. He had spent the previous five years demonstrating it around the country, taking it apart and putting it together again. He knew all about the sensitive electrodes, the tubing, the gas mixtures – everything. He would be the ideal person to take with us as he would produce the best results we could possibly obtain. Bernard had also heard that there was a spare place on the expedition and was interested in coming along. He seemed very amiable although there were similarities with Chris Hawkesworth, in that he was rather overweight and unfit. If he wanted to come, I suggested we phone his boss again. Nervously, he got him on the phone. I spoke first, strongly supporting his membership, while Bernard anxiously followed my conversation. The discussions were persuasive enough to allow Bernard to join us. We were all delighted. Within a couple of hours, he had been tested on our exercise bike and had received all the advice anyone would need for their first trip to big mountains.

With the blood-gas analyser and an expert to run it, we had every chance of linking the acetazolamide trial with O_2, CO_2, pH measurements (acid/base concentrations in the blood) and the development of acute mountain sickness. We were convinced it would be the best study ever undertaken at altitude.

There were other major successes, but first I must return to the hassle we were having at the airport. I had negotiated 700 kg of total baggage allowance, which included 20 kg extra per person, but the exact amount had always been rather vague. Twickenham Travel, with whom we had booked the tour, had not indicated the exact amount but had merely said it would not be a problem. So we arrived at Heathrow two hours before departure with everything we needed and anything we might need. Frank Davies, our quartermaster, started processing all the bags and equipment, 63 pieces which together weighed 950 kg – 250 kg over our negotiated allowance. There was no chance of this going through unnoticed.

Jennifer Moir, the representative from Twickenham Travel, explained that Iberia had accepted the 700 kg but any more was impossible. The Iberia airline manager was insistent. No more baggage allowance.

I remember remaining quite cool, almost as if I were standing outside the problem. I explained that it was impossible to pay the full amount, and since the equipment had all been loaded on board, we were all set to go. I stayed unflustered while watching other members of our group. The diplomats (Ron and Ian, for example) stayed back while the businessmen – Frank, John Simmons, Norman Waterhouse and Norman Dorricott – moved in. They knew how to force the issue. Waterhouse was the most irascible: "There is no way you can stop us boarding," he insisted. "We will write to every climbing magazine unless you let the baggage go free. You will go out of business." Others were adamant that we must not pay a penny more.

"You have to be firm, Jo," said Norman Waterhouse. "Tell them to get lost and we will take our £13,000 to another airline." This was the cheque we had just signed for the whole trip. "This is business they cannot afford to lose." He is a fiery, intense, passionate character, and meant every word of it.

By now I was beginning to get rattled. I asked Jennifer Moir if I could speak to her superior, but she had already done so and said we had to pay an additional £1,480 (£6 per kg excess). Time was running out – we only had 45 minutes before departure. I spoke to the owner of Twickenham Travel, Hedde Lyons, who was very sympathetic but said we would have to pay unless the baggage could go as freight, which would cost only £300. The Iberia manager said it was too late to do this because it had already been signed in. The only way to change its status was to take it off the plane and then we would miss the flight. It was an impasse.

I was the first to blink. I explained to the team that we had to pay. We signed a cheque for £1,480 to Twickenham Travel who then paid Iberia, and with much grumbling we went to the departure lounge. Little did we realise that are troubles were far from over.

We thanked Jennifer, who gave us the 20 boarding passes and tickets and went to the customs control desk. However, there were only 19 of us since we had arranged for Alex Wright to meet us at the first stop in Madrid. He had been attending a conference in Bratislava but had been delayed at the last minute trying to leave Czechoslovakia (still part of the Soviet Union in those days) and was flying from Vienna to Madrid. The first security officer saw my collection of 20 passes, but I managed to ignore him and in we went to the departure lounge. The next official spotted the discrepancy. "There is a passenger missing," she said, counting all the passengers again.

"That must be Alex Wright," I said, producing his spare pass. "He went through ages ago."

"We never saw him."

"He is quite small," I replied hopefully.

"Ok, then you can get on board," she replied to my amazement.

As we boarded, to my dismay, I saw them counting the passengers again. I had to confess Alex was missing.

"You again!" They did not know about the baggage excess, thankfully.

"Yes, me again." I winked, smiled, confessed, apologised and explained our dilemma. Finally, we departed, still anxious about Alex.

Our arrival at Madrid was at 11 am local time. We filed into the transit lounge but there was no sign of Alex. After a tense hour, he appeared beyond the barrier, having been stopped from entering the departure lounge because he had no boarding ticket. At a discussion across the security desk, we showed him the missing ticket and all were happy. What a relief! We were called, boarded at 2.55 pm and we were off. Surely nothing else could go wrong?

The flight to Guayaquil was a long one on a DC10. Surrounded by friends on the 'second trip of a lifetime', the conversation turned to our luggage, the next four weeks and what other problems we might face. It was the culmination of six months of effort by 20 people (albeit with other jobs). Hundreds of hours of thought and effort.

Our first stop was Puerto Rico after 7 hours, then Bogota in Colombia, where the cabin was de-pressurised before we disembarked, since it is at 8,000 ft. We stopped for 45 minutes in a superb modern terminal, hardly the drug capital of the third world that we had expected, then climbed back in. Next stop Guayaquil. On the way we flew over Chimborazo, our target mountain, and its neighbour Cotopaxi, both of which were clearly visible. These are huge snow-covered volcanoes (in Cotopaxi's case, still active).

Our next hurdle was customs. We had no import permits for the medical equipment and no documentation. Months earlier we had made several abortive attempts to obtain the correct certificates but having acquired the blood-gas analyser only a few days earlier, documentation would have been impossible anyway. The more risk-averse members of the group were very worried. We might be fined, equipment could be confiscated, held in bond or a bribe might be necessary. It was a tense time. We descended from the plane onto the tarmac of the runway and were unexpectedly enveloped in a wall of tropical heat.

After collecting our baggage, we came to the customs desk. We explained we were an important medical expedition investigating mountain sickness and had sophisticated equipment that was essential for the research. But that was not enough for them. They wanted to check all the baggage – we refused.

"Where is the official documentation?" they demanded. Instead I showed him a copy of the Postgraduate Medical Journal containing our publications from the previous expedition. Then I produced the Society's headed notepaper and pointed out such luminaries as Sir Peter Scott who was Chancellor of the University of Birmingham and one of our patrons. Whereupon he looked through our passports and, noting his name was absent, demanded, "Where is his passport?" I then showed him my name at the bottom of our notepaper as chairman of BMRES. There were smiles all around and much to our surprise they waved us through.

Beyond customs we were met by Marco Cruz, our guide for the expedition (figure 2). We had booked a package tour that would provide accommodation, tents, food and transport for the next ten days. He ran a trekking company that would look after all our needs. He was a very amiable and experienced climber and knew Chimborazo well.

Outside the airport buildings, a pre-World War II bus awaited to take us to Riobamba. Frank organised all rucksacks and equipment boxes to go on the roof while we were packed inside in the sweltering heat. It was our first experience of the equator. We rattled out of the airport and through a shantytown with houses of wood and corrugated metal on stilts, across the Guayas River and into banana plantations. It was very tropical – bamboos, birds of prey, papaya, pineapples, coconut trees. We stopped for Inca Kolas, beers and passion fruits to the sound of camera shutters clicking as the team captured the local scene.

Then abruptly we were in the mountains, with steep-sided passes. The driver, of Quechuan descent, clearly suffered from a mild form of Monge's disease (chronic mountain sickness). He had a red, suffused face and bloodshot eyes. It was either that or too much booze, for he sipped aguardiente (fire water) as he drove into the night. We had stopped at a scruffy café to try this sugar cane-derived spirit served up in a filthy Castrol 20-50 oil container. It was 40% alcohol and completely undrinkable. We tried a drop while the driver had a full glass. Papayas, watermelons and huge pineapples were more to our tastes.

We gradually ascended a most impressive road up to 3,800 m. The driver was very good in spite of the booze. With one hand on the horn, he continuously passed other cars, lorries and buses at great speed as we rattled alongside yawning chasms. The vegetation and climate over the pass were very much like the Lake District – peat bogs and reeds with a cold drizzle. We then descended to Riobamba through small towns crowded with diminutive Quechua Indians, some on horseback. All had deep red faces and were gaily dressed in boater hats. At one small village, a band of drunken musicians started playing brass instruments and clarinets. The aroma of aguardiente suffused the air as we stopped briefly to enjoy the cacophony – after all, it was Saturday night. There followed a steep descent and by 5 pm we were at the Hotel El Galpon – at $12 a day, the best in Riobamba. Our altimeter showed 2,621 m.

It was a beautiful modern building with spacious bedrooms containing en-suite showers plus a communal sauna and pool. Ted and I shared a room for three. We were all very tired having slept little on the plane or bus. But after a drink at the modern bar and our first meal together, we were ready for more beer. Marco welcomed us to Ecuador and, to honour our arrival, musicians played Andean music on hand-made bamboo flutes.

We were naturally very concerned about the route up to Chimborazo over the next few days. The ascent profile needed to provoke acute mountain sickness so it had to be similar or faster than our previous trip to the Himalaya. Ron and I thought that a three-day ascent from the hotel to the Whymper Hut at 5,000 m would be about right. Since we would be travelling by bus, except for the final ascent, we could choose any speed we wanted. After a few more beers and some potent aguardiente, we staggered off to bed at 10.30 pm, 3.30 am Birmingham time.

The next day, we had a relaxed morning. Just across from the hotel were palm trees and exotic plants in a maze of small streets with stalls selling every consumable imaginable, including large slabs of raw meat. It was market day where everything was for sale, including pet sheep. The native Indians were tiny. At 6ft 1in, I towered over them all by at least 18 inches.

Sheep to market

At the back of the hotel, there was a large grassy area that overlooked the swimming pool, which made an ideal place to set up the experiment tent. A tropical sun, a swimming pool, a sauna and lashings of beautiful fruit – that was the proper sort of research. One experiment was a suntan lotion trial for a company called Boehringer Ingelheim. We had been given two tubes of cream, one for each side of the body with the nose classified as the right-hand side. Both creams were applied at the same time, and at time zero, 30 minutes and 3 hours the degrees of erythema (redness), blistering and suntan were assessed. We were soon all lying around the pool covered in grease. We needed some results; the company had given us £1,000.

The most important study was the clinical trial to determine whether acetazolamide could prevent acute mountain sickness. This had started three days earlier, with ten of us taking active drug (500 mg slow release daily) and the other ten taking placebo pills.

These contained lactose and looked identical to the active drug. None of us knew who was taking which medication in order to avoid any subjective bias in reporting symptoms. Pete had a sealed envelope that contained the medication code. This would be opened when we were back at the Hotel El Galpon in nine days' time.

In parallel with the drug trial was the blood-gas analysis, undertaken by Bernard Coles (with Ian Green assisting). His fragile instrument was carefully packed into a protective box specially made by John Simmons. Setting up the instrument took 3–4 hours, after which we all had small ear-prick blood samples taken that were collected into capillary tubes (figure 3). There were also venous blood and urine studies. Collected samples were stored in dry ice as in the first expedition.

Half-way through the experiments, a rainstorm lashed the town. We dived into the hotel where we completed some exercise tests in the main corridor. This provided a source of great amusement to guests and staff alike. The rest of the tests continued in the mess tent that we had erected in the garden (figure 4).

This was quite a heavy workload. As leader, my job was to ensure that everyone had what they needed but I had no direct responsibility for a project. Hence, I became the official (self-designated) photographer and took dozens of pictures (film cameras in those days) using various settings and filters while watching the group working. It was only when they were developed four weeks later that I discovered that many were hopeless.

The tests continued until 11 pm. I took over the ear-prick tests for the blood gases but Malcolm Walker and David Lort became the experts. I finally lay in bed happy and relaxed and thought about how well the expedition was going. I had a slight headache and pins and needles in my feet. Perhaps I was on acetazolamide?

The next morning was a 6 am start, with blood samples taken lying down for antidiuretic hormone analysis as we were trying to repeat the study that had failed on the Thorong La. Norman Waterhouse came into the bedroom, took my blood, I then took Ted Olive's followed by several others in neighbouring rooms.

We also had early morning urine collections. Stupidly, I got up and peed into the toilet, having forgotten it had to be saved. Right in front of my eyes was a measuring cylinder sitting on the toilet but I just used a very inviting loo. Ted was talking, of course, but it wasn't his fault. Fortunately, I had stopped early enough to leave 30 ml for the titratable acidity assay and 2 ml for proteinuria measurements.

Because we had been in Riobamba for only two nights, we were not yet acclimatised to the altitude, plus we were still jet lagged. We thought another control day at the same altitude would be useful to allow our bodies to settle to the local environment before the ascent. Marco's cousin owned a hacienda four km away on the road to Chimborazo, so we set off by foot for the short walk. Meanwhile, experimental gear and rucksacks were packed up and loaded onto a lorry together with tents, cooking equipment and everything we needed for our time on Chimborazo.

We wanted to avoid excessive exercise but Simon and Norman Waterhouse were young, irrepressible members of the team and wanted to carry their full rucksacks. Not to be outdone, I carried my rucksack plus all the camera equipment. A race inevitably developed but I held back, determined to take some photographs of the mountains. We wound our way out through Riobamba, past the local football stadium and a bull ring. Finally, we entered the countryside, passing crop fields and eucalyptus woods until we arrived at an idyllic campsite. Beside it was an irrigation channel containing water running down from the high Andes. In the camp, our cooks, Henrietta and her sister, were already preparing lunch.

I chose a three-man tent with Ted and Frank. While most were familiar with camping, some struggled with the concept. The Andes is perhaps not the ideal place for a first experience. Dave Burnett quietly asked Pete Forster, his tent partner, what he should wear in his sleeping bag. "Please don't tell anyone I have never camped before," he pleaded. Pete was not the right person to ask. Within minutes the debutant was subject to ribald mocking from the group. Poor Dave.

The afternoon experiments started below beautiful views of the volcano Altar, which towered over us; in the distance, Chimborazo remained swathed in clouds. There were exercise tests by the brook to the clicking of a metronome, blood gases in the mess tent and urine collections alongside a dry-stone wall. As we stopped for supper, a beautiful tropical sunset unveiled itself, blues, greens and reds over Tungurahua and Altar (figures 5 and 6). After a supper of fruits and meats, I went to bed contented.

It was not a relaxing night. Three people in a three-man tent is a squeeze. I was in the middle between Frank and Ted. We were awoken at 6 am for resting blood samples followed by all the other studies. The previous day they had taken 9 hours to complete, but this time we were finished by lunch.

The water-load test was the most unpleasant experiment. John Milles was in charge and he needed all the charm he could muster. His plan was to check serum and urine osmolality (which is related to antidiuretic hormone production) after a water-load test. We had to drink 20 ml of water per kg body weight. This amounted to two litres for poor Bernard, 1,650 ml for me and 1,100 ml for the smallest person. We all sat around and drank water that had been collected from the Hotel El Galpon the previous day. To prevent bacterial contamination, it was sterilised with chlorine tablets, which made it taste foul – like drinking over 1.5 litres of swimming pool water. Afterwards we collected blood samples every hour for four hours. Most of us felt terrible with nausea and headaches, presumably related to the combination of chlorinated water and high altitude. John Milles was not popular. We lay around like battle casualties and were unable to eat lunch as we nursed our aching heads. We looked a pathetic lot when the transport arrived to take us back through Riobamba to our next camp at Tortorillas (3,719 m).

On his expedition 100 years earlier, Edward Whymper had stopped at Tortorillas and we proposed to follow the same route. The altimeter marked our rapid ascent towards a great mass of cloud that hid Chimborazo.

Eight kilometres before the camp site, Norman Waterhouse and Simon decided to carry full packs and quickly sped off up the track. Older members, John Delamere, Pete Forster, Malcolm and I carried little, fearing headaches from the rapid gain in altitude. Norman and Simon had a good start, but by cutting corners we soon caught up, much to their annoyance. We found them lying down beside the track holding their heads and opening a bottle of Panadol (paracetamol) painkillers. Pete dubbed them the Panadol kids and the soubriquet stuck.

Despite concentrating on the race, none of us missed the huge impact of the massive volcano. Its destructive powers were everywhere. Along the eroded track, metre-thick bands of lava and black volcanic ash were layered beneath sods of grass (figure 7). All around were large boulders (lava bombs) that had been explosively ejected by the now dormant volcano. There were even cliffs of lava, frozen solid in some distant age. On this stark landscape, a dotted patchwork of scrubby agriculture was visible to the horizon.

We arrived at 4 pm to the welcoming sight of beers in the half-assembled camp beyond an eight-foot ravine full of black run-off water from Chimborazo. At the narrowest point, we bridged it with the wooden tailgate from the lorry and unloaded the medical equipment. John Simmons, our hard man, staggered across carrying the generator. Remarkably, a hummingbird flitted among the tents in the dank fog.

The remainder of the walkers arrived in dribs and drabs. Ron and Frank were slow, similar to their performance in the Himalaya, but everyone arrived safely and joined in with the experiments. Since the weather was poor, with intermittent rain and wind, we rested in our tents, many still nursing headaches from the water loading in the morning.

The exercise tests were performed using the generator boxes. The two Honda E1500 AC generators weighed about 40 kg each but were cumbersome to transport. To help, John Simmons had built two wooden boxes, each with two wheels and carrying handles. Furthermore, he had made them the same height as that used for the Harvard step test (a standardised exercise test protocol). To the timing of a metronome sounding once a second, we stepped up and down. Our fitness could then be assessed with pulse rates taken every 30 seconds for the five minutes of the test and for two minutes after stopping.

Dinner took an age, being cooked with great labour by our two cooks over three gas stoves. After eating, most of the group went to bed, some with altitude headaches. I broke our tent zip trying to enter in a hurry to escape from the cold dank fog. I must ensure someone else gets this tent tomorrow night, I thought. Some selfishness is frequent at altitude, although we all try to put on a public face of generosity. We called it self-preservation, for camping in the freezing cold and wet was horrible without having to cope with a broken tent.

Frank Davies was not well and lay next to me in the tent complaining of headache and nausea. A generator coughed in the thin air while providing some lighting for the continuing experiments. It had played up all evening and we noticed it had been dropped and damaged in spite of being in the box. John Simmons cleverly fixed it with some washers, which immediately improved its performance. Our engineer was again proving very helpful.

That night I slept well, probably from the hard exercise, but outside all was not well. A dank, driving cloud enveloped the campsite and sleet filled the air. According to our expensive altimeter, we had been at 3,718 m overnight. In contrast, Edward Whymper had recorded 3,900 m using a mercury barometer 100 years earlier. Which one was correct?

We soon had all the bloods completed with the blood-gas analyser producing consistent results in Bernard's capable hands. This crucial instrument, containing water-based buffers, would be irretrievably damaged if it froze. John Simmons had therefore constructed a special metal box containing a double layer of thick polystyrene with gaps for three 2-litre plastic bottles, which were filled with water at 50°C in the evenings. Inside the box, the maximum and minimum thermometer showed that the temperature had fallen to only 34°C overnight whereas outside the tent, water was frozen hard. The water bottles had kept the analyser almost ready for use (37.4°C).

While waiting for the ear-prick tests, we performed reaction time tests led by John Macintosh and assisted by Ted. John had acquired two Cambridge reaction-time meters to assess brain function. Individuals pressed a button with an index finger whereupon a random number generator would cause one of five lights to come on between one and five seconds later. Then, as fast as possible, subjects would press the off button and the time delay was recorded. Reaction times varied hugely between subjects – from 170 to 270 milliseconds – but were remarkable consistent for any individual. One might have imagined that age would have been a determining factor but Ian Green, almost the oldest, was lightning fast. I was little better than average. Testing was each morning and evening. Each person took about 5 minutes for 40 recordings.

By midday, the camp had been packed and all boxes placed in the lorries. With their heavy loads, the vehicles struggled to move across the thick scrub of the camping area in the thin air. In the mist and rain, our bus headed steeply upwards on dirt tracks towards the Carrel Hut at 4,802 m on the Great Arenal (Spanish for a sandy area). We had agreed that such a large altitude gain (nearly 1,100 m) was necessary to ensure that some developed acute mountain sickness. Because the camp site was located at the top of the road, an emergency evacuation to lower altitude would be simple if needed. The Whymper Hut was another 200 m higher along a rough path.

With 5 km to the camp, the rain turned to snow but even so several of us decided to walk the final stage. We bent forward into the wind and against the steep ascent. I felt good and much to my surprise had soon left the others far behind. I again wondered whether acetazolamide accounted for my energy.

Soon I met others who had decided to walk from higher up the road. John Simmons was struggling with an enormous pack – entirely his own doing – while Frank was moving slowly. I talked to them and others as I walked on. In spite of the mist and snow I was hot from the exercise and, removing cagoule and jacket, I was down to shorts and T-shirt as I strolled into camp. Today the yellow jersey was mine by a margin of 15 minutes.

The Carrel Hut (named after Whymper's guide, Jean-Antoine Carrel) lies at 4,802 m on one edge of the Great Arenal. This large, grit-covered plateau whistled in the snowstorm and all was hidden in the cloud. Snow clung to the few tents that had been erected. I scrambled onto the bus and watched the others as they came into camp. Everyone seemed reasonably well but this could not last. It always takes a few hours for fast ascents to high altitude to have their full effects.

The rest of the tents were erected (figure 8) with Ted carefully checking that ours had a good zip, having remembered our previous night's experience. Two of the tents were broken and we did not fancy a cold and windy night with snow blowing in. The mess tent was erected and the experiments slowly started.

Acute mountain sickness was starting to take its toll. Several members were not to be seen. Frank, Pete and David Burnett had disappeared into their tents. Ted was very talkative – always a bad sign – and most of us had headaches. The exercise test proved difficult. Norman Dorricott vomited, and he had a bad headache. Ron Fletcher sat glumly in a dark corner of the mess tent hardly moving. It was getting cold. I crept into my tent with Ted and into my sleeping bag. Bliss. I got out Travels Amongst the Great Andes of the Equator by Edward Whymper (1892) and read to Ted who gradually became less and less responsive.

Supper, comprising fresh fish bought up in boxes of ice, was slowly cooked in the thin, cold air. Water boiled at a little above 80°C which meant hot drinks were disappointingly cold. Appetites were poor for many; Frank, Bernard and Norman ate nothing while Ted ate a little food but had a terrible headache. Some individuals were really incapacitated; five hours at altitude had decimated the group. The rate of ascent was greater than the first expedition and deliberately much faster than recommended to determine whether acetazolamide was protective.

After supper we congregated in the mess tent but there was no warm place. Many stood, well wrapped in duvet jackets and glumly holding tepid cups of tea or coffee in the gloom of head torches. Then, to much delight, there was rum-tea, beer and lights powered by the generator. With cold noses and frozen fingers, we completed all the experiments. As the evening wore on, the wind abated and the sky cleared, revealing Chimborazo for the first time, silhouetted against the stars.

That third night camping was the coldest night of the expedition. The thermometer read a low of −6°C. In the night I had to put on all the clothes I possessed, including my duvet jacket and two pairs of gloves, to keep warm. I slept poorly, partly because Ted kept waking me up to explain how awful he felt. He even threatened to walk down in the night. That would have been impossible because there was now a foot of snow on the road below us. He moaned and groaned all night and was very thirsty. I had a mild headache but felt fine as long as I was not disturbed

Thankfully, the awful night turned to a beautiful morning (figure 9). We were above the clouds, with superb views of Chimborazo glowing red in the early sun. Cougar prints were visible around the tents. Snow was knocked off the outsides of the tents, causing icicles from inside to fall onto the occupants. I passed 500 ml of urine into my solidly frozen bottle. My feet and hands stung with parasthesiae (tingling) that was intolerable at times and lasted several minutes. It must be the acetazolamide!

Cougar

We were a glum lot emerging from the tents, many feeling worse than the evening before, but there was work to do. The generator kicked into life and slowly we started the experiments with ear pricks for the blood gases and urine analysis that revealed proteinuria in many. The blood tubes were frozen and had to be thawed. Pete and Malcolm ably completed all the blood collections and their storage in little more than an hour. Then it was breakfast. Half the group were not hungry but I had three helpings of porridge and two of eggs and bacon. Appetite must relate to acute mountain sickness and my reaction times were my fastest yet.

But others such as Ted and Dave were poorly. Dave was hardly able to walk while Ted had become very emotional and said he had never felt so ill in his life. Marco agreed to take them back to the Hotel El Galpon in Riobamba.

At 11 am, three horses and a dozen mules arrived, with several muleteers urging them on. It was time to move to the Whymper Hut, 200 m higher. Our group slowly started up the track alongside the mules, boxes skilfully lashed to their backs. They were carrying food plus a few rucksacks while the medical equipment was left for a second trip. We had to restrict the loads to essential items for the first day. The fittest members, Malcolm, John Delamere, Pete Forster, John Milles and myself, stayed back to ensure that the medical equipment was loaded carefully. The blood-gas analyser, in its box, was nearly as large as one of the small mules. At least it was fairly light, while the centrifuges were heavy but compact. The generators were just too big and there was a lot of gear we would not need for a few days so that could come up later. This was packed into boxes and put back on the lorry for safety. Ian Green insisted that the toilet tent was taken up as the toilets in the hut were broken.

The bus was made ready for the descent. Dave Burnett was slumped over a rock feeling wretched with a headache and nausea (figure 10). Ted looked poorly but was noisy and full of advice for the other ill individuals, clearly pleased to be descending. He didn't get much sympathy. We helped them onto the bus and they left, not to be seen again for six days. I watched them go, wondering how quickly they would recover on the descent and how much of their illness was due to the altitude or the harsh weather.

The mules descended from the hut and were skilfully loaded for a return trip. That left the two generators. They were too heavy for the mules. John Simmons came to the rescue. He put a wide harness around his shoulders and pulled one very slowly across the Arenal. We thought it was impossible and crazy to try – a Superman complex as Frank described it. Also, he was not well, had had a headache for the past two days, but was in denial. A very tough guy. The other generator we tied behind a large white horse, and with Pete helping we adjusted the handle and got underway. The lead was too long but after some adjustments we managed to guide it, with the horse pulling hard and us lifting the front from the dirt. John had made the boxes superbly; they were robust enough to take the battering while we gasped to keep up with the horse in the thin air, pulling and pushing for a few yards then stopping for several minutes.

The hut came into view 300 metres away with most of our group around it. No one came back to help. Again and again we moved a few yards but the horse became exhausted and wouldn't move. We released the strap attaching it to the generator allowing it to speed off down the slope. The two of us could not possibly move it. I shouted to the hut to get help but all refused. We sat for a few minutes and started walking dejectedly upwards. Then, suddenly, two horses and three men descended from the hut shouting and waving. We scrambled back to the generator. This time it was attached to two horses, which proceeded to drag and slide the generator the last 300 metres over the snow. My pulse was up to 180 beats per minute as we pulled again. Pete claimed 200 beats per minute – he was working harder. Finally, we arrived, to be greeted with cheers and an enormous plate of fresh pineapple slices – beautiful. I staggered into the Whymper Hut completely knackered. We were at 5,008 m.

The Whymper Hut was of alpine style and had been partly designed by our guide

Marco Cruz. It had cost £50,000 and was comfortable, with 100 bunk beds (figures 11 and 12). We were spread over four rooms, rather unwisely as there was talk of thieves, but many of us were too poorly to care, just lying in bed with nausea and bad headaches. I had a bunk next to Frank, who was lying down feeling very miserable.

John started the generator and cleverly powered up all the lights in the hut. Since the toilets had been vandalised, the toilet tent was erected on the edge of the slope facing the sunset (figure 13). A simple supper was rustled up at 8 pm but none of us ate much and soon went to bed ill or exhausted. Outside clouds hid the summit and avalanches rumbled through the night. Then the wind picked up, whistling past the closed windows.

That first night was very cold. I crept into my sleeping bag next to Frank and slept reasonably for the first time in two nights, largely because Ted wasn't there to wake me up. Before dawn I awoke bursting to go to the loo but needed to wait to give an early morning urine sample. After what seemed an age, someone turned on the lights. Many complained of headaches and lack of sleep. We gave our bloods and got up. Outside it was a clear, beautiful morning. With teeth chattering in the wind, we stared up at the beauty of Chimborazo towering above us with its glaciers and rocky outcrops. To the west was an abyss all the way to the Pacific Ocean.

By 9 am the blood gases had been completed and it was time for breakfast. We then performed the rest of the tests, went for a short walk and had lunch. Many of the group were still poorly. All of us had headaches and many needed painkillers. Frank felt terrible and we hardly saw him all day. I kept popping up to the dormitory to see if he was still alive. He was a tough nut. Norman Dorricott was also poorly in the night but most people felt much better after being up for a few hours. Remarkably, some felt well with only slight headaches.

In the beautiful afternoon sun, we took photographs for the sponsors – Uvistat sun cream, Damart underwear, sunglasses, the centrifuge. John Macintosh took most of them but he had a bad headache and was confused.

I got out Whymper's book. The pictures were very like the mountain we were looking at, including the aiguilles (rocky outcrops) on the ridge. That evening the sun went down in a blaze of yellow over the Pacific Ocean, the mountain's face glowed back a golden reflection and the temperature plummeted.

Frank was not to be seen, Norman Dorricott was in bed early, as were many others, and John Simmons was unwell. The sudden climb to altitude had caused a lot of illness. Frank's arterial oxygen concentration was only 29%. Ron Fletcher's was not much higher. Mine was 44% and few were better. If such low readings had been recorded in a hospital setting, patients would have been put in intensive care immediately or even on ventilators. They were desperately low.

We had supper, completed all the tests and went to bed. I slept next to Frank again, somewhat fearful as to what the night might bring. But after strong painkillers, his headache abated and he felt a little better. We gave him a Mogadon sleeping tablet to help.

I lay in bed listening to the others breathing deeply and coughing in the darkness, and wondered if we had come up too quickly. There were soft snores a few bunks away, the sighing of the wind and the fitful breathing of Frank next to me. I feared for him and how much more suffering he could take. What if he should die? A spike of anxiety gripped my chest. It would be my responsibility; it would be on my shoulders. He could have descended two days ago if I had only insisted. Yesterday, looking awful, he had briefly come into the dining room of the hut. Clutching his head in pain, he passed us by and disappeared outside into the blizzard to vomit. I thought about the article in The Lancet on acute mountain sickness: 'See Nupste and die.' Perhaps Frank's epitaph would be 'See Chimborazo and die'.

Frank turned in his thick goose-down bag and groaned. Because he was suffering the most, I had deliberately chosen to sleep next to him. If he needed an emergency descent, then I hoped I would be sleeping lightly enough to awaken and offer help. His sporadic breathing became lighter with brief gasps and then stopped. I waited for him to breathe again. The seconds ticked by; then half a minute. Silence. "Come on Frank, breathe, breathe!" I said to myself. "Frank, breathe!" My fear increased. **"BREATHE!"**

I reached over and, shaking his body, whispered, "Frank, Frank." He rolled over towards me, took a small breath and mumbled, "What's the matter?"

Thank God he was still conscious.

"It's okay, just checking you were not suffering too much," I whispered back.

He turned away. His breathing gradually increased to a noisy crescendo then stopped once again. After another anxious minute of waiting, I heard him lightly inhale then exhale again. Shallow inhalations rapidly gave way to deep sighing breaths, only to stop once again in the next cycle.

On the second day at 5,000 m, most were busy with experiments. The bloods were taken efficiently and Bernard powered up the blood-gas analyser. He had done very well. He had been cyanosed (blue) for three days, with terrible headaches and had hardly eaten, yet had always managed to run the blood-gas analyser. We were all impressed. Under the circumstances, he had achieved more than anyone else.

Frank had slept soundly but was clearly still in poor shape. He managed to get up and pass a minimal amount of urine – 200 ml, the first for two days. I was keen for him to descend. It was unfair to subject him to any more suffering. He refused. I suggested he saw Ron (our physician) for a medical opinion. Thankfully, after weighing the evidence, Ron persuaded him to descend. He considered that the rest of us were well enough to remain at the hut but many thought Ron was probably more ill.

Centrifuge

Alex had noticed that Ron's ears were pulsating. This, he realised, was due to swollen jugular (neck) veins transmitting heart beats to his ears as a consequence of right-sided heart failure. He had the lowest blood oxygen concentrations (30%), was remarkably cyanosed with a fast heart rate and very breathless. He had failed to notice his own illness. We then realised that he was quite confused and had even given the wrong medication to someone. Alex prescribed him a 20 mg tablet of frusemide (a diuretic) but it had no effect. An hour later he was given an 80 mg intravenous dose of frusemide, which produced a four-litre diuresis (increased urine flow) over the next 24 hours. The scales showed he had put on 4 kg in two days as a result of fluid retention. He should have gone down with Frank, but he was the medical officer and had refused. We were unable to persuade him otherwise.

I accompanied Frank to Riobamba. This gave me chance to see Dave and Ted and perhaps stop my headache for an hour or two. I promised to bring back beer, mineral water, chocolate and other goodies – after a final ear prick and a reaction time test. We helped Frank organise his personal effects and walked down the track to the Carrel Hut with Marco Cruz as our guide. Reaching the truck, the three of us occupied the front while a boy sat in the open rear with our bags, desperately hiding from the freezing wind as we descended.

As we drove back over the Arenal with beautiful views of Chimborazo, Marco talked about his climbing career. "There are ten routes on Chimborazo, two by Whymper and eight by me," he boasted. He claimed to be the first to climb Altar, Illiniza Norte and many other volcanoes. He had spent three years as a guide in Chamonix and then climbed all over the world, including the Hoggar mountains, Mt Kenya, the Rwenzori range, Greenland and even the Himalaya. He spoke Spanish, English and Quechuan, the local language. Frank chatted him up as he slowly felt better but didn't believe a word he said. After two hours, we arrived at the Hotel El Galpon. Ted and Dave were not there but a row of urine bottles outside their bedroom was evidence of their recent activities.

I went to the bar with Frank and drank a beer – bliss – then had a shower – further bliss. Perhaps this, rather than ensuring Frank's survival, was the real reason for coming to the El Galpon! We walked around the market, with Frank clearly hugely improved, and on returning to the hotel found Ted and Dave. They were suntanned, in high spirits and had felt well within an hour of starting the descent. It was a relief to see them so happy after their miseries on the mountain. We sat by the swimming pool with Cokes and talked about the others suffering at the Whymper Hut and Ted's bull fight (see below).

It was soon time to return to the hut. Marco picked me up and we wound up the slopes to Chimborazo, which shone in the bright sun. Within the hour we were at the Carrel Hut, with the sun setting on the summit. We waited for 20 minutes as three groups of trekkers descended. Marco was afraid of his truck being stolen. Even a small remote sign in the middle of the Arenal directing visitors to the hut had been vandalised. The night before I had found a youth attempting to enter our bedroom,

Aiguilles and summit of Chimborazo from Whymper's 'Travels amongst the Great Andes of the Equator'

creeping quietly in with a lighted match. He fled when challenged. From then on, one of us constantly guarded the rooms and equipment, with Marco, guides and Henrietta (our chief cook) sleeping on the top bunks.

In the morning several people climbed up the ridge of the mountain towards the aiguilles, benefiting from perfect weather and great views. Tourists arrived, including some children. One developed acute mountain sickness, repeatedly vomiting, and had to descend. We were not the only sufferers.

On the final evening, we had an intense debate about the experiments, the oxygen results and how people were performing. The controversial peer ranking of each person's illness led to an animated discussion (as on the previous expedition) but eventually all agreed to participate. It was surprising how many were in denial of their illness, including Ron. Lying in bed, I found it curious that going back to the Hotel El Galpon had not been a particular pleasure. I was happier at the hut with friends and the harsh, beautiful mountain.

We awoke on the final morning in the hut to another beautiful day and warm sunshine. It seemed that half the group were happy and had acclimatised while the remainder were not well. Ron needed another dose of diuretic and several members were sitting by their beds holding their heads (figure 14). I suspect Ron would have gone into severe heart failure if we had not descended that morning. He departed early with Ian, who was also only too keen to descend. He left his jumper at the hut and we shouted down to him but he wouldn't even walk 50 m for it. He had had enough.

John Milles wanted five of us to undertake a water load test for his wretched antidiuretic hormone measurements. This meant an early morning blood sample, a urine sample and no breakfast but instead 1,650 ml of chlorinated water. I drank it so quickly that it induced headache and nausea, as it did for others (figure 15).

Other experiments were completed (figures 16, 17 and 18), then we started packing up all the equipment with a wary eye on personal items in the rooms for fear of theft. The gear was assembled and everyone mobilised. The mules arrived at 9.30 am and were loaded up. One of the generators was towed down by two muleteers while five of our group were allocated to the other one. The mules descended fully laden and returned for the remaining equipment. Once at the Carrel Hut, the lorries were loaded, with most people on the bus.

Several, however, decided to walk down to the next camp. From the hut we climbed a small ridge then descended a gradually sloping snowfield, glissading down the lower half. John Milles did it in style, reflecting his Cambridge Blue for skiing. Deep red pumice stones littered the path as we traversed steep scree slopes that had been gouged by huge tumbling boulders. Other recent volcanic activity was obvious from the huge bands of stratified volcanic ash and lava plugs shaped like human guardians. Well below us we could see Totorillas, our lorries and bus, and tents being erected.

As we descended, the rubble turned to alpine meadows and we followed ancient irrigation channels, reputedly constructed by the Incas. Collecting snowmelt from high up in the mountains, they contoured for miles, delivering water to the low-lying crop fields. Just above the campsite we passed a small enclosure of sheep, corralled for the night to protect them from wolves.

We arrived to beer, dinner and final tests for the day. At night we snuggled up in our warm sleeping bags with plenty of oxygen and no headaches for we had descended to 3,418 m with immediate recovery from acute mountain sickness. I shared a tent with John Milles who talked about his family, skiing and travelling across Afghanistan to India. He had done a lot in his life. I always thought he was quiet but not a bit of it. My experiences did not compare. I never imagined that many years later he would be my best man, and me his.

The next morning, our eighth day, a few tests remained. Water-loading, reaction times, cerebral function tests and the penultimate ear pricks and oxygen saturations. We were mostly feeling fine but Ron, Bernard, Gron and Ian had still not fully recovered and many preferred to ride on the bus to the last camp even though it was not far. The walkers enjoyed a beautiful hike in the sun to Santa Martha, our ascent camp huddled beside the river, with Chimborazo clear of all cloud in the afternoon sun (figure 19).

As we arrived, the final exercise tests were underway, easy in the thick air. We gathered driftwood from beside the river for a campfire to provide welcome heat as the sun set. Although we had descended 2,200 m from the hut, it was still cold in the evenings.

Marco provided aguardiente and Gron whisky, helping us to bask in the euphoria of descent and our recovery form acute mountain sickness. But it was disappointing that the expedition was coming to an end. A great adventure on the biggest mountain in Ecuador. Tomorrow we would be in Riobamba and would break the code for the acetazolamide trial. Would we show that it reduced acute mountain sickness?

At the Hotel El Galpon, Frank, Ted and Dave were there to meet us, looking tanned, fit and clean, compared with the rest of us, who had hardly washed in nine days. After showers, clean clothes, lunch and beers on the terrace, we embraced the pleasures of good food, beer and clean surroundings in the warmth of the equator.

Ted told us about his bull fight. With Frank and David, he had gone to a small bull ring near Riobamba where military bands had trumpeted the arrival of the crowds and bull fighters. The sport had persisted from Spanish colonial days but a particular attraction on this occasion was the attendance of a well-known matador from Madrid. The show commenced with a series of small bulls being released into the ring. Several spectators showed their bravery by jumping over the barrier and escaping from the bull by hiding behind protective gates. The bull was then dispatched by the matador with a thrust of his sword. Standing behind the surrounding seats, Ted practised holding a red handkerchief at his side. Seeing that the bulls were tiny and almost tame he fancied demonstrating his prowess. He climbed over the wooden barrier and into the ring to await the next bull. The gate opened and in rushed a huge bull, twice the size of the earlier ones and in a frenzy of anger. It charged. Spectators fled to the protective gates but there was not enough space for everyone. Ted was spotted. Desperately he ran to the side wall and scrambled up, just in time to avoid the bull's horns. The crowd roared their approval.

After lunch we had a few final tests, sold generators and other equipment that wasn't worth taking home and had discussions about the next week – a holiday week – before the flights home.

Over dinner we announced the results of the trial, which showed that those on acetazolamide had felt better than those on placebo. We were jubilant but full analysis would need O_2 and other measurements that would have to wait until our return. Then we all adjourned to the bar. Whisky, beer, spare dry ice in the whisky, liqueurs – the works. Through the foolish wonders of alcohol, we managed to acquire nearly all the signs and symptoms of mountain sickness that we so recently had been at great pains to treat – headache, nausea and semi-consciousness.

Our next hotel was the Embassy in Quito, a three-hour bus journey along the Pan-American Highway from Riobamba. Along the so-called Avenue of Volcanoes, we passed Cotopaxi, which was like a Japanese painting, Illiniza, Pichincha and others, then descended over a ridge to Quito. I sat next to Ron. He was not communicating well; he had not yet recovered from acute mountain sickness. At the hotel we were met by Francisco Salazar from the Metropolitan Touring Office. He would help us plan the rest of the trip and sort out the return flights plus our excess baggage requirements.

The expedition had been completed within two weeks. Most of us had booked three or four weeks leave of absence but with curiously little idea about what to do. Many had expected the society to organise their holidays. Six of us had always intended to climb some volcanoes and had sufficient climbing equipment for the purpose but others were less organised.

At the hotel, I handed out our passports, which had been held by Francisco's trekking company while we were on Chimborazo. This act galvanised everyone's thoughts. Repeatedly, I was asked what might be done in the remaining two weeks. I explained that I was not a tourist guide but the Galapagos or climbing were good options. Furthermore, I was feeling ill from a gut infection picked up at the Hotel El Galpon and retreated to bed. With lack of leadership and no focus on experiments, many became anxious and awkward. Some of our group were consultants and, used to telling their juniors what to do, tried to exert their authority. I and other climbers were told we were irresponsible: "I will make sure you never get a job in London," David Thomas warned. Petty irritations, suppressed during the expedition, came out in harsh words. It was time the group split up. Fortunately, David took charge of organising a week in the Galapagos while Ted, Malcolm and Pete headed to the coast, leaving six of us to go climbing.

Staying at the Embassy Hotel was the wife of an Ecuadorian general. Her husband had suffered from a peptic ulcer for many years and was planning to have a gastrectomy (stomach removal). Norman was a well-known surgeon at the Birmingham General Hospital and an expert on surgical treatment of peptic ulcers. After visiting the military hospital, Norman agreed to perform a highly selective vagotomy and pyloroplasty, a surgical procedure that was not available in Bolivia. The operation was fixed for the following week, it was successful and Norman became a local hero. Unfortunately, he had to provide post-operative care for the week, so he missed our post-expedition climbing trip.

The three Johns, Norman, Simon and I planned to 'knock off' some of the volcanoes that Edward Whymper had climbed 100 years earlier. We hired a jeep, filled up with food and camping equipment, and headed south to our first peak, Illiniza. This dormant volcano had two summits, an easy north peak at 5,126 m and a rather steep south peak at 5,284 m, both hardly higher than the Whymper Hut. We camped on the saddle between the two summits and watched a beautiful sunset on Cotopaxi 30 miles away (figure 20).

Early next morning we awoke for the climb only to find that John Delamere had already left camp. He had decided to climb the more difficult south summit alone, leaving us to climb the 'tourist' north summit. Looking upwards, we could just see John climbing the steep snow cone at the top. We agreed that perhaps it was beyond our skills but the Panadol kids were most upset. Needless to say, we ascended the north peak with little difficulty, although rock fall was a continuous danger.

Cotopaxi (5,897 m) was next. We drove high up the mountain on a tiny track to a refuge, ate our meagre rations and went to bed early. We arose at 3 am, ate a quick breakfast and walked up in the dark to the edge of the summit glacier. With little idea of the route, we milled around for an hour trying to climb an ice barrier. In the distance, the dawn rose on Chimborazo (figure 21). John Milles, John Simmons and I became dispirited and returned to the hut, only to meet a lone Japanese climber starting his ascent. As our three colleagues eventually reached the summit, they met the Japanese climber eating oranges. Perhaps it would have been wiser to start later! However, descending the ice barrier was tricky, requiring an abseil. Although our Japanese climber had beaten them to the top, and in style, he had no rope and had to appeal to our chaps to help him climb down.

Poor John Simmons was most disgruntled with the whole affair, particularly the lack of organisation and leadership. Many years later, the very mention of Cotopaxi set him off moaning about the whole fiasco.

Tungurahua (5,023 m), to the south, was our next peak. Since it was late in the day, we stopped at the small town of Penipe for the night. We found the central square bustling with people, for it was the Festival of San Francisco (St Francis of Assisi). Our modest hotel overlooked a square built in Spanish Colonial style. It contained temporary shops and open stalls manned by Quechuan Indians dressed in their finest. A huge bonfire dominated the centre with massive fireworks tied to wooden frames. A brass band trumpeting military tunes marched around town repeatedly interrupting our much-needed siesta. Volcanoes loomed in the distance.

We fell asleep only to be awoken by a huge BOOM and the room shook. My first thought was a volcanic eruption but there were loud cheers and another BOOM. We peered beyond the curtains to see rockets and roman candles showering in the sky. The night-time festival had started.

We entered the noisy throng amid dancers, bands and revellers. A firework maestro stood next to a car-sized wooden frame covered in large fireworks. A sheaf of rockets protruded from his pocket while his hands were full of gunpowder-packed tubes. A lighted cigarette drooped from his mouth; two fingers were missing from his left hand.

Harvey's gunpowder

He explained in broken English that he had constructed the frames, and all explosives had continuous fuses so that they went off in sequence. To prove his credentials as the munitions' chief, he took a rocket from his pocket, held it between his fingers, tapped the ash off his cigarette and lit the fuse. I looked on with horror as it hissed then roared skywards. The drunken crush around us roared in approval. He let off another to confirm his bravery, then offered me one. We moved on to less dangerous parts of the town square (figure 22).

The festival finale came on the stroke of midnight, with a noisy crescendo from the band, a huge explosion, then silence. We went to bed relieved that we were only mountaineers. Next morning, the devastation of minds and bodies from alcohol was all too apparent and the smell of gunpowder hung in the air (figure 23).

The climb to Tungurahua started in the jungle headwaters of the Amazon. We trekked upwards in drizzle through spectacular vegetation to a hut shrouded in mist. That night it poured with rain. John Delamere, Simon and Norman arose early to climb the steep cinder cone while I stayed in the hut but cloud denied them the summit.

After Tungurahua we needed a good clean up. Nearby was Baños, a town with thermal springs heated by magma from the active volcano. A two-sucre entry fee (5p) allowed us into the dilapidated, sulphurous green pools. Not quite bliss, and probably smellier than we already were, but very pleasant. They had known better days.

That night John Milles insisted we stayed at a cheap hotel. Eventually we found one for 25 sucre. Needless to say, the mattresses were smelly, sheets unchanged and pillows dirty. I dared not take off my clothes. We all got fleas, which infested us for a couple of weeks after our return.

After Tungurahua it was back to Chimborazo. We drove up the same track to the Carrel Hut as before and walked to the Whymper Hut. This time it took only 20 minutes rather than 40. We were fit and well acclimatised. The same three, John, Norman and Simon, climbed while the rest of us scrambled up to the aiguilles. In good weather, they managed to reach the Whymper summit at 6,268 m, the very top of the mountain. It was an extremely taxing climb at high altitude over deep wet snow. They had done well.

We returned to Quito, and with one day remaining, Ted, Frank and I knocked off Pichincha (an active 4,784 m volcano on the outskirts of the city) in a massive lightning storm. The others returned from their expeditions to the Galapagos and the coast. We had all enjoyed challenging but ultimately enjoyable mixtures of work and holiday.

Over the months following our return, we analysed the trial data. Our initial thoughts had been correct; those on acetazolamide had less mountain sickness than those on placebo. By stimulating breathing, the drug increased blood oxygen levels by 15–20%, simulating a reduced altitude. Results were published in The Lancet. This was followed by articles in the Sunday Telegraph colour supplement, the Birmingham Post and Mail, and the Guardian. To make a comparison with the poor economic state of the UK in 1981, the front page of The Times had a cartoon alongside a column titled:

'Mountain pill conquers sickness.
Drug's effect is to lop 6,500 ft off Everest.'

The scientific results established the reputation of BMRES. This, in turn, provided a springboard for many subsequent expeditions. We were invited to give many lectures and write articles for newspapers and journals.

Postscript:

One unexpected consequence of the expedition occurred at the Hammersmith Hospital in London. Not long after returning I attended a lecture in Birmingham given by Professor Keith Peters. He was a top medical research professor and a fierce intellect who later became Regius Professor of Physic (medicine) at Cambridge and a knight of the realm. He had been the Welsh junior chess champion and had a reputation of being a bad loser. I made some mild, considered comments at his lecture and pointed out that he was wrong on a minor detail. I did not know him well but I could see that he was somewhat taken aback and he approached me after the session. We exchanged pleasantries and he invited me to the Hammersmith Hospital to provide advice on some of the research he was conducting. I fell into the trap like a fly to a spider.

Two weeks later I walked in trepidation up the steps to the Immunology Department and met Keith Peters. He had arranged for me to see his academic colleagues, one at a time, so I could comment on their research. I was sat down at a desk and they filed in to hear my wise words. Unfortunately, my knowledge was trivial. I had only recently joined Immunology from the Department of Medicine and had a student-level understanding of the subject. The doctors I was introduced to were kings in their fields; international stars. My humiliation was complete. It was obvious to one and all that I knew very little and could not possibly comment intelligently on any aspects of their research. This torture went on for three hours. Keith Peters had got his revenge – in spades.

He then led me on a brief tour of his department, clearly very pleased with his victory. Eventually, and after a further 30 minutes of embarrassment, he allowed me to leave. We approached his secretary, "How much shall we give him? £20 or perhaps £30, with travel expenses?" he mused aloud.

The secretary looked on, guessing what I must have been through. "Yes, give him £20," Keith finally decided.

"Who shall I make out the cheque to?" the secretary asked with a slight smirk.

"Jo Bradwell," I replied quickly, hoping my shame would soon be over.

"Not the Jo Bradwell?" she exclaimed. Even the secretary was mocking me. "Are you really the Jo Bradwell who wrote in the Guardian today?" she continued.

I looked on in bewilderment as she opened the newspaper. There, covering most of one page, was an article that I had written some weeks earlier about our trip to Chimborazo and the value of acetazolamide. It was an extraordinary coincidence.

Keith's jaw dropped, the secretary fawned over me and asked for an autograph as she filled out the cheque. I gently eased it from her hand and headed for the exit. I smiled sweetly back at Keith as the door closed. Grinning, I fled down the stairs and into the street. I had escaped from the jaws of death smelling of roses, all because of a climbing trip to Ecuador.

Publications from the expedition:

1. Bradwell AR et al.; BMRES mountain sickness study group. Acetazolamide in control of acute mountain sickness. The Lancet 1981; 1(8213): 180-183.
2. Bradwell AR, Delamere, JP. The effect of Acetazolamide on the proteinuria of altitude. Aviation, Space and Environmental Medicine 1982 53(1): 40–43
3. Delamere JP. Prophylaxis of acute mountain sickness. BMJ 1982; 284: 743.
4. Milles JJ, Baylis PH, Howell A. Effect of altitude on water excretion. Clinical Science (London) 1980; 59(3): 11p.
5. Mackintosh JH, Thomas DJ, Olive JE, Chesner IM, Knight RJE; BMRES. The effect of altitude on tests of reaction time and alertness. Aviation, Space and Environmental Medicine 1988; 59: 246–248.

* * *

All the team feeling peaky
Said its only just a hill
One stride --- we'll make it to the top
And! We gotta test that pill.

Diamox -- the wonder drug
To stop us feeling queasy
Or others who are FAR BEHIND
Who think it's all so easy.

We conquer Andes Mountains
Leviathan can't stop us
And the Sherpas reputation
We know has never topped us.

In any case we cannot fail
We must be strictly fair
And give the credit where tis due
Our Damart UNDERWEAR.

We never feel the cold at all
No! we don't need a bed
Tis the best thing ever marketed
Since the advent of sliced bread.

– James Brougham

Fig 1. Back row left to right: *Jo Bradwell, Ron Fletcher, Alex Wright, Malcolm Walker, David Thomas, Ian Green, David Lort, Pete Forster, Dave Burnett, Gron Jones, Simon Morrissey, John Delamere, Norman Waterhouse, Bernard Coles.* **Front row:** *Ted Olive, Frank Davies, John Milles, John Mackintosh, John Simmons, Norman Dorricott.*

Fig 2. *Marco Cruz*

Fig 3. *David Lort, and Ian Green giving blood*

Fig 4. *Experiments at night*

Fig 5. *Tungurahua*

Fig 6. *Altar*

Fig 7. *John Milles and lava bands*

Fig 8. Camping near the Carrel hut

Fig 9. Chimborazo from the Great Arenal

Fig 10. Dave with mountain sickness

Fig 11. Whymper hut with mules

Fig 12. Whymper hut plaque

Fig 13. Highest loo tent in the world

Fig 14. Headaches at the Whymper hut

Fig 15. Water load test at 5,000 m

Fig 16. Blood pressure at 5,000 m

Fig 17. John Delamere measuring 24-hour urine volumes

Fig 18. Bernard measuring blood gases

Fig 19. Chimborazo from Santa Martha

Fig 20. Cotopaxi at dawn

Fig 21. Chimborazo from Cotopaxi

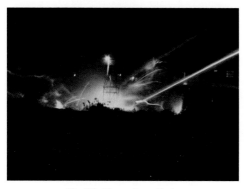

Fig 22. Fireworks at Penipe

Fig 23. Post-festival drunk at Penipe

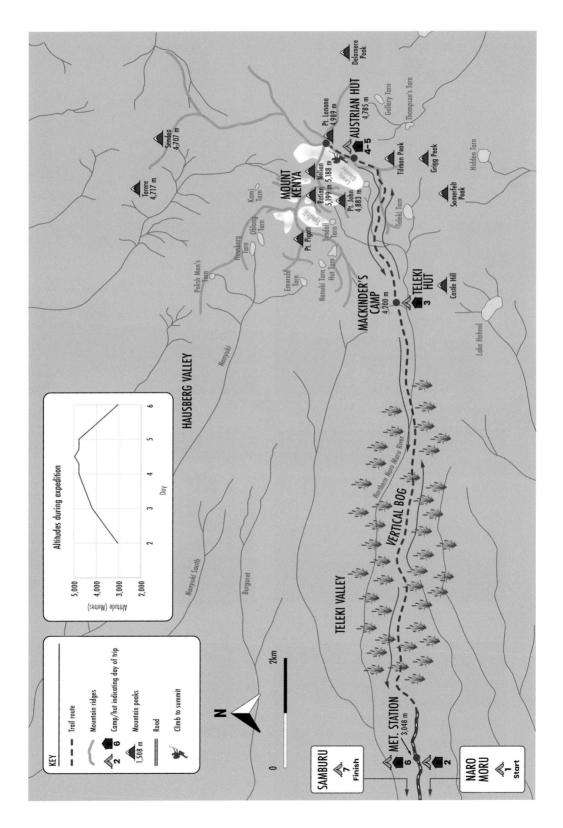

Chapter 3
Mount Kenya – January 1982

Mt Kenya showing Nelion, Batian and Point John

No Picnic on Mt Kenya

"Perhaps more than any climbing story, 'No Picnic on Mount Kenya' captures that strong underpinning of revolt common to most mountaineers. The men and women I know drawn to the hills are mavericks whose principal loyalty is to the individual's right to take his own risks and discover his own truths, and as much as anyone, Benuzzi applauds that right and condemns those who might curtail it."

– Rick Ridgeway in an introduction to No Picnic on Mount Kenya
by Felice Benuzzi, 1952

Summary: Acetazolamide has a variety of analogues that could prove better in preventing acute mountain sickness. For instance, methazolamide is faster acting and better absorbed. Hence, we compared the two drugs in a double-blind manner during a rapid ascent to Point Lenana on Mt Kenya (4,985 m). The results, however, showed no significant differences in efficacy. Six members climbed Nelion, the lower of the twin summits.

Expedition members: Jo Bradwell (deputy leader), Ian Chesner, Bernard Coles, Frank Davies, Norman Dorricott, Ron Fletcher (medical officer), Ian Green, Tim Harlow (medical student), Ginette Harrison, Tim Harvey, Gron Jones, David Milles, John Milles, Simon Morrissey, David Parker (medical student), Neville Richardson, John Simmons (engineer), Neil Smith, Norman Waterhouse, Alex Wright (leader) (figure 1).

In the year following the acetazolamide studies on Chimborazo, BMRES had a high public profile. But we were soon itching for another mountain expedition. The general view of society members was that we should first decide where we wanted to go and then design the experiments to fit our selected mountain. Clearly, we needed to go high again – preferably around 5,000 m. To satisfy our desire for somewhere different, we discussed the possibility of Africa, which has two big mountains: Mt Kilimanjaro and Mt Kenya. Although relatively close to each other geographically, they were worlds apart in terms of our needs. Kilimanjaro, at 5,895 m, was the first choice because of its greater altitude but the authorities restricted time on the mountain to one week and there was an expensive fixed peak fee. Mt Kenya, rather lower at 5,199 m, was not far from Nairobi, had fixed camps near the top and was cheaper. Furthermore, an intriguing climbing book written by an escaped convict, No Picnic on Mount Kenya, had captured our imagination.

Felice Benuzzi, an Italian climber from Trieste, had been interred as a British prisoner of war in Camp 354 near Nanyuki, facing Mt Kenya. In January 1943, with improvised equipment and meagre rations, he escaped with two colleagues to climb the mountain. Their only 'map' was a sketch on the label of an Oxo tin. Two of them reached a point above the Petit Gendarme, at about 5,000 m on the north-west ridge. After an eventful 18 days, and to the amazement of the British, the three adventurers broke back into the camp. As a reward for their exploits, they each received 28 days in solitary confinement, commuted to seven days by the camp commandant in acknowledgement of their 'sporting effort'.

After some months of indecision and failure to negotiate two weeks on Kilimanjaro, we agreed that Mt Kenya would be our objective. We could all ascend the easy peak of Point Lenana at 4,985 m to conduct our experiments while climbing members could attempt the difficult twin summits of Nelion and Batian.

Since the earlier expeditions, those members who were climbing enthusiasts had much improved their skills and thought the peak would be relatively easy. Simon and Norman regularly climbed in north Wales and the Lakes and could lead E1 and E2 grades. Tim Harvey and Neville had climbed extensively in the Mont Blanc area (including some epic misadventures) with John Delamere. However, the most serious climber was Ginette Harrison, a trainee general practitioner from Bristol and our first female recruit. She had extensive experience on the rocks of the Avon gorge and was very intent on scaling the two peaks of Mt Kenya.

On the morning of Sunday 16 January 1982 in the middle of Birmingham, I climbed off my narrow boat, Calstock, where I was living. The canal was frozen hard in the coldest snap of the winter and there was a bitter wind. With Frank Davies, I drove to the Medical School and took a bus with 12 others to London Heathrow airport. As we passed the white landscape, canals, fields, ponds and water pipes were frozen hard. We would emerge from our plane 24 hours later into the heat of the equator.

The build up to the expedition had been gradual over the previous year, with much discussion about research. In particular, the success of the acetazolamide trial had made us wonder whether we could improve on our discoveries. The 20% increase in oxygen levels in those taking the drug was most useful but side effects of tingling, nausea and drowsiness prevented use of higher doses that might have provided more benefit.

We therefore turned our attention to a similar drug, methazolamide. Because of its slightly different structure, it is absorbed into tissues faster than acetazolamide, an effect that might produce a greater stimulating effect on respiration while having fewer side effects. Lederle Laboratories, who made the drug, agreed to give us financial support and supply the medication. To demonstrate greater efficacy, we would need to compare it with acetazolamide in a double-blind manner. Furthermore, as on Chimborazo, we would need to measure blood oxygen levels, and we would need at least 20 subjects to produce statistically meaningful results.

I was too busy at work to organise the final details of the trip so Alex Wright agreed to be expedition leader. Recruitment was a simple matter. Many of the previous members were keen and had spread the word to colleagues. John Milles persuaded his brother David (who spoke with an even posher accent); we had support from the Arthur Thompson Trust for two medical students, David Parker and Tim Harlow, while Neil Smith, a young haematologist, replaced someone who withdrew at the last minute.

The night before departure, we all met at the Medical School to collect baseline urine samples, fill in medical questionnaires and finalise the packing. There were the usual worries about whether the generators would work properly and how we would get up to the top camp. In contrast to Chimborazo, there were no roads to the summit, so all our equipment would have to be carried. Since Kenyan porters would not carry the same weights as the Nepalese, we were concerned about the heavier items of equipment.

By 8 pm we were all lined up in front of the ticket office at London Heathrow with 200 kg of scientific equipment. By agreeing to reduce personal baggage from 20 to 15 kg (by wearing big boots and layers of clothing), we had 100 kg excess for 'negotiation' with Kenya Airways. With scarcely a word from the ticket handler, the bags were weighed, counted and pushed through onto the conveyor belt. There were no hassles, no excess baggage charges and no complaints about what we were carrying: what a relief after all the troubles at previous departures. Wearing heavy boots and several layers of clothes, we climbed into a Boeing 747 with the next stop Rome.

At 1 am the plane briefly landed to take on half a plane-load of Italian holidaymakers bound for Mombasa, which seemed an extraordinarily exotic place to go for a mere holiday. Dawn came at 6 am to reveal the silhouette of Mt Kenya against the lightening sky. Formed from the remnants of a giant volcanic plug, it stood high above all else, its twin black summits and white glaciers clearly visible. At 7 am we touched down at Nairobi's Jomo Kenyatta International Airport. The doors opened and we descended into the smells, tropical heat and brightness of the equatorial sun. The contrast with freezing, leafless England could not have been greater. Our heavy boots and layers of clothing were rapidly exchanged for trainers, shorts and T-shirts.

As we ambled over to two waiting lorries to load the equipment and rucksacks, we realised that Alex and David Parker had not passed the police barrier. A rumour spread that they had been detained by customs for illegal entry and trying to smuggle equipment. I suppose we had got through Heathrow lightly. What was wrong? Alex was such an honest person.

Back in the baggage hall, we found him talking anxiously with two police officers who were demanding money. Completely unexpectedly, they wanted a deposit of £300 in Kenyan currency to allow the two generators into the country to ensure they were not sold. Fearing we would never see the money again, we forcefully argued our case and eventually they relented. We had been warned of fraud at the airport and thankfully had not given in.

As we drove from the airport, we were met with lines of flags and flowerbeds stocked with gorgeous red, white and blue bougainvillaea. We sat in the rows at the back of the lorries relishing the refreshing breeze and bright sunlight as we drove around the outskirts of Nairobi towards the distant Mt Kenya. The folded green landscape, cultivated by Kikuyu people, gave way to a high windswept plain of prickly shrub and cactus. Afternoon clouds gradually descended, causing the upper parts of the mountain to disappear, and it started to drizzle.

Our first stop was a camp near the Naro Moru River Lodge to the north of Nairobi. It was beautifully positioned by a river. Nearby were English-style country houses with red-tiled roofs and stucco walls. Fenced-off gardens full of English flowers enclosed white people relaxing under verandas. We could have been in a Surrey suburb of London – apart from flashes of exotic birds. We wondered how long their paradise could last with the changing politics of the country. At an altitude of 1,980 m, the local climate could not be more attractive to Europeans. Water run-off from Mt Kenya's glaciers and the fertile volcanic soils provided all that was required to recreate luxuriant English gardens.

The afternoon was spent on experiments – blood-gas analyses, symptoms questionnaires, urine tests – until dinner. Our cooks provided an evening meal of steak and mash, and afterwards we walked over to the River Lodge for beers to discuss the forthcoming journey up the mountain. The tropical rain fell heavily outside, suggesting we were in for a wet expedition. Later in the camp, I lay thinking of the soaking start to the first expedition when we had camped in a flooded pigsty. At least we were more comfortable in the lodge.

Another concern was the rate of ascent as we planned to be at 4,785 m in a mere three days. The Rough Guide to Kenya was emphatic in its advice: do not climb that high within 72 hours as it could lead to severe mountain sickness with cerebral or pulmonary oedema. We were all on acetazolamide or methazolamide so I hoped we would be safe. We were soon going to find out.

By the morning the clouds had cleared, giving a clear view of Mt Kenya, a mere 20 miles distant (figure 2). But first we had an important routine to follow: resting pulse rates, overnight urine collections, daily weights, baseline symptoms questionnaires for acute mountain sickness (morning and evening), and reaction times (twice a day). After a breakfast of porridge, bacon and egg with tea or coffee, we took blood samples, which were stored without centrifugation in our white polystyrene boxes packed with dry ice. We would wait until the evening for the blood gases and clinical examinations by Alex and Ron Fletcher. Tim Harvey was in charge of the eye examinations (to assess retinal bleeding) while Ian Green's lung tests were a sit-down affair which produced an ink trace. That was much better than the handheld gadget we had used previously.

Of particular concern was the transport of the generator up the mountain. We had bought two sizes: a 500 W lightweight generator that was quiet and could run lights during the evening and a 1,500 W generator for the blood-gas analyser. This could produce a steady power output at high altitude but at 35 kg it was too heavy for an individual Kenyan porter. Furthermore, the generator had to be carried over a notorious obstacle – 'the vertical bog', a very wet area of sloping moorland high up the mountain. Stories abounded about its difficulty. We were familiar with bogs on the hills of Wales and Scotland and imagined it would be similar but we needed an engineering solution so we naturally turned to John Simmons.

His practical mind provided a possible answer. The device comprised a chest and shoulder harness with a light frame so that the generator could be carried on a person's back. Attached to the base was a long pole with a large wheel that reached the ground and could carry a proportion of the weight. John walked comfortably with it around the campsite for a quarter of an hour (figure 3). We wondered how much the wheel helped, so while in use it was run over some scales, which gave a read-out of 13 kg. The burliest members of the group – the Milles brothers, Simon Morrissey, John Simmons, Tim Harlow and Ian Chesner – were then recruited as generator porters.

That afternoon we drove to the equator line near Nanyuki. It was marked by a wooden sign at the end of a layby alongside a shabby tourist shack. The village itself was impoverished, with shops selling all sorts of cheap goods of little interest. However, we did find some personal items we might crave on the mountain – chocolate and whisky.

By the time we were back at camp, it was getting dark and blood taking time. The large generator powered up the blood-gas analyser, which Bernard dutifully worked on through the evening while the small generator powered the lights. We talked excitedly until late into the night about the anticipated ascent of the mountain. The next day required an early start and an ascent to the meteorological station at 3,048 m in the Mount Kenya national park.

At first light, the twin peaks of Mt Kenya, Nelion and Batian, stood out dramatically on the horizon. These had been named by Sir Halford Mackinder after two 19th-century Maasai leaders. He had been the first to climb Batian, the higher of the two, in 1899, but it was another 30 years before the more difficult summit of Nelion was conquered. Surprisingly, the peaks had not been seen by Europeans until 1849, and even then few believed the German missionary Johann Krapf that snow existed at the equator. It was only in 1883, when the Scottish explorer Joseph Thomson saw Mt Kenya, that others were finally convinced.

The 26 km journey started well enough as our lorries collected us, our baggage (figure 4), and 27 porters from Naro Moru. As we drove to the mountain, the tarmac rapidly changed to muddy roads, soaked by overnight rain. The shambas (household vegetable plots) gave way to tall African trees, which in turn became conifer plantations as we approached the national park. We all signed in at entrance gates, fees were paid and we drove on with the lorries struggling upwards in the thinning air. We stopped to allow their engines to cool a little but our total weight had been too much so they wouldn't restart. Excited with the prospect of some exercise, we all scrambled out in order to walk to the meteorological station, our camp for the night. John Simmons, keen to suffer more than the rest of us,

Baobab tree

hauled out the heavy generator from underneath our baggage. We strapped it on and left him trailing behind alongside Tim Harlow as an assistant. Neville and I marched uphill, keen to be first into camp. The Milles brothers followed closely on our heels but we gradually outpaced them, much to their annoyance, and arrived after an hour and a half. At full speed, with heads down, we hadn't noticed the change from conifers to deciduous forest and a zone of colossal bamboo. The others told us afterwards.

All arrived in dribs and drabs, followed eventually by the lorries carrying John, Tim and the generator. They had had a strenuous walk hauling it, changing over every 30 minutes. It had not been easy. The generator was also full of petrol, which not only added weight but also sloshed around and spilt. Fortunately, the lorries came by after a couple of hours to carry them the rest of the way, saving an hour. It had been exhausting and was clearly going to be very hard 1,000 m higher up through the vertical bog.

The meteorological station camp was surrounded by jungle (figure 5), which was reputed to contain big animals such as elephants, lions, buffalo and even the occasional leopard, although it looked benign enough to me. However, we did see numerous Sykes' monkeys, which were fed potato peelings by our cooks. John Simmons pulled an 18-inch black snake out of the grass by its tail end. We were all very impressed since he had no idea whether it was poisonous.

At dusk several of us went for a walk in the forest with a guide, hoping to see some big game. A muddy circle suggested a buffalo wallow, and the guide indicted a leopard lair under a rock, but we saw and heard nothing. Afterwards, it was back to the hut for blood oxygen measurements then dinner. At 10 pm it was bedtime, with Bernard arranging overnight transcutaneous (through the skin) oxygen monitoring. It was well known that oxygen levels at altitude were lowest at night, which probably accounted for mountain sickness being worse in the morning. However, few measurements had been reported in field experiments so we thought it would make an interesting study. The monitors could work using the small generator, which was quiet and would not disturb anyone's sleep.

The camp comprised a hut that we could use for experiments plus several wooden cabins. Most of our group were keen to sleep inside but I decided to camp nearby, where I was joined by Frank and Alex in neighbouring tents. I didn't fancy being in a noisy bunkroom with the blood-gas team working late plus assorted snoring and grunting. A clearing in the forest with no one else in the tent promised blissful peace and quiet.

I lay in the quiet of the tent reflecting on the walking race, the momentum of the expedition and tomorrow's vertical bog. Then the noises started. Not squeals or trumpeting or roaring but sounds of something heavy moving, loud and close. We were a few metres from the edge of the jungle but I was convinced we were surrounded by elephants or buffalo, or even leopards. The tent shook with the loudest vibrations. I called to Frank who was equally alarmed. I unzipped the tent flap and peered out but it was completely black, with no moon, stars or light from the hut. Then it started to rain, while the trampling, crushing, stomping noises continued, accompanied by the occasional sound of breaking branches and the earth shaking. Without a head torch, I groped my way over to the hut, heading for the quite hum of the generator. I thought I might stay inside after all, but it had been locked for the night. I carefully felt my way back to the tent, fearful of over-shooting and ending up in the jungle. Eventually, I fell asleep and at first light the forest was once more completely quiet.

Alex had organised breakfast for 6.30 am since we had a long hard day ahead of us to reach the Teleki Hut at Mackinder's Camp. The porters agreed to carry our main rucksacks while we carried a small day sack containing warm clothes and wet gear because afternoon rain was expected. The generator team minimised their bag weights and, with John Simmons making the first carry, they began walking up the steep zigzag path that led beyond the camp, each person carrying for 15 minutes at a time. Within a mile, the path widened to enter the steep bog. A muddy trail with deep foot imprints swept upwards towards Mt Kenya.

The extra weight of the generator meant that each foot sank deeply into the peat. With no stable surface under it, the wheel sank even deeper. Also, because of the generator's inertia, it was difficult to do anything but walk in a straight line, so there was no way to dodge round deeper-looking puddles (figure 6). The carrier's assistant tried bending down to lift the wheel to relieve some of the generator weight but it was hard work. Then it started to drizzle. In spite of scouting far out on each side of the route, we couldn't find any drier firmer ground. It was unrelentingly tough. The six strongest members of the group took 15-minute rotations in their exhausting struggle upwards. Fortunately, I was not classified as a strong member. I briefly helped carry the wheel and even that was gruelling.

Giant lobelia

As we ascended, the vegetation changed to a land of peculiar giants: giant groundsel (figure 7), giant lobelias and giant heather. Curiously, there were no proper trees. After five hellish hours the vertical bog finally changed to firm ground on a ridge above the Teleki valley and the clouds cleared. After crossing the Naro Moru stream, Nelion, Batian and Point John came into view. In the clear air of the mountain, they seemed close enough to touch (figure 8). By mid-afternoon, we had reached Mackinder's Camp at 4,200 m (figure 9). Two hours later, we watched John Simmons bravely carry the generator for the final walk into the camp, surrounded by his assistants. We cheered and plied them with welcoming mugs of hot chocolate as they arrived.

We had booked the vole-infested Teleki hut (figure 10) for the experiments and accommodation but tenting was preferable. A fire of wood and dry parts of the giant plants was most welcome in the cool of the evening. Experiments followed, with the generators working perfectly, and we endured a rather unpleasant dinner.

I tented for the first time with Frank Davies. He had been poorly on Chimborazo so I chose to be near him in case he became ill again, although this seemed unlikely since everyone was on an active drug. What I had not anticipated was that he snored loudly. Early in the night was no problem because I slept but with a hard Karrimat, a degree of altitude hypoxia and unfamiliar surroundings, I was repeatedly awakened by his snoring.

Nevertheless, it did give me chance to try a small experiment. A mathematics colleague at the University had described a sure-fire way of stopping a person snoring. He proceeded to produce a quiet high-pitched whistle through slightly pursed lips. "It is so quiet that it doesn't wake the sleeper but activates the unconscious brain to stop the snoring," he explained. He had described this technique some years earlier, so now was the time to put it into practice. Indeed, it was an outstanding success. After a few seconds of quiet soprano music from my lips, the snoring stopped and I fell asleep. A good practical experiment, I mused, not just academic theorising. During the night, the general discomfort caused me to awaken many times and if Frank was snoring, I used the trick with unfailingly good results.

In the morning, I was rather tired having slept poorly but thankful as it could have been much worse. Frank was already awake and asked me how I had slept. I explained that I found it difficult because he had snored most of the night. In turn, I politely enquired how he had slept, to which he replied vehemently, "Terribly! Because you were bloody whistling all night!"

Nearly everyone had slept badly. The hut was too small and noisy, several people had mild gut infections with diarrhoea in the night, while others suffered from altitude headaches. There was a layer of hoar frost in the tents, which was melted by the rising sun and dripped onto our faces. However, outside it was beautifully clear, giving perfect views of the mountain, while the vertical bog was hidden under low-lying fog.

The guidebook firmly advised staying in Mackinder's Camp for a day to acclimatise but we had other plans. We needed to ascend fast to test the difference between acetazolamide and methazolamide. We planned to stay at the Austrian Hut (4,785 m) nearly 600 m above our current encampment and slightly below the peak of Point Lenana (4,985 m).

Experiments were swiftly completed, and after a breakfast in the rapidly warming sun, we headed steeply upwards towards Point Lenana (figures 11 and 12). The route started with a scree slope followed by rocks surrounded by more giant groundsel. It was slow but easy walking. The occasional rock hyrax peered at us from nearby burrows (figure 13). Remarkably, the closest relative of those small animals is the elephant. Such is evolution.

Inevitably, the generator team had a tough time as the air thinned, and Neville and I pitched in to help. Unfortunately, we all strayed off the path, heading right to Teleki tarn rather than to the left. We paid for the error with an exhausting clamber over sloping rocks and boggy ground. With straining legs, aching lungs and many changes of hauler, we were finally close to the Austrian Hut. John Simmons persuaded me to take over for the last carry, with Simon holding the wheel. We arrived to cheers and welcome drinks from our colleagues. The generator had arrived so the highest altitude research could be completed.

Around us was a scene of great beauty – Batian, Point Lenana (figure 14) and Point John, below us the Lewis Glacier and in the distance the vertical bog and the jungle.

We paused to enjoy warm drinks and a snack, and then it was to work. First we carefully fixed tents on the rocky ground with boulders, then started on the experiments. We had booked the hut, a meagre affair with 20 bunks, but groups of Italians and French had taken occupation and refused to budge. Fortunately, there was room for the blood-gas analyser so Bernard moved in, despite complaints from the squatters about the noise of the generator. We collected water from the Lewis Glacier, strung out lights around the mess tent, and our two cooks rustled up dinner in a corrugated iron shed next to the hut.

During the evening, talk turned to climbing. The serious rock climbers – the two Tims, Ginette, Simon, Neville and Norman Waterhouse – planned to leave before dawn to climb Nelion and Batian. The route comprises a steep, relatively easy series of rock pitches, but at very high altitude, while the crossing between the two summits is a difficult ice traverse. Their excitement made an entertaining spectacle for the non-climbers; jangling of fancy-coloured carabiners and rock jammers, repeated coiling and uncoiling of ropes, donning and adjusting of helmets and harnesses. "All the gear and no idea," was one uncharitable comment. We would know tomorrow. The rest of us planned to climb Point Lenana – the 'tourist' peak 200 m above us, which comprised a gentle rock and snow slope.

Altimeter

As the sun set, Nelion developed a cloud trail and the air became very cold (figure 15). We donned thermal underwear and duvet jackets. There was no fuel for a fire so we migrated to our sleeping bags. The generator hummed as Bernard pressed on with blood-gas measurements well into the night. While lying in my bag to think about the expedition, it seemed that the research was almost complete yet we had been out less than a week. No one seemed ill, despite the rapid altitude gain. We presumed the drugs were being effective. The trip was proving easy so far.

At 5.30 am there were sounds of movement in the dark. The climbers were getting prepared, waking everyone in the process. Although itching to start, they first had to aliquot overnight urines, give blood samples and test reaction times. The cooks kindly supplied them with hot drinks and corned beef sandwiches.

The camp quietened again until 6.30 am when sunlight touched the frozen tents. It was cold and windy as we looked over to the rocky peak of Nelion wondering about our colleagues. They had first to cross the Lewis Glacier followed by steep screes before arriving at the almost vertical rock face that looked rather like the Milestone Buttress on Tryfan in north Wales. Three-quarters of the way up the face is a metal refuge called

Bailey's Bivvy. On the top of Nelion peak there is another, slightly larger hut, providing just enough protection from storms for six people.

After breakfast we started for Point Lenana. Many opted for full equipment, with crampons, ice axes and ropes. To begin with, the snow was fresh and fairly soft but there was ice beneath. As we climbed up, it became obvious that Ron and David were struggling while Bernard fell, only avoiding a serious slide with his ice axe. With help from Frank, who even cut some ice steps, we all made it to the summit. Across on Nelion, we could see the climbers steadily ascending the cliffs.

We were back at the Austrian Hut by midday, leaving time for John Simmons and myself to explore the Lewis Glacier (figure 16). We roped up after ascending the bergschrund (deep crevasses where glaciers abut against mountainsides) and tramped across ice and deep crevasses to reach the scree slope below Nelion. A ridge led to the base of the rock climb, and high above us we could see our friends slowly ascending to the top hut. It was clear they would make that first peak but it seemed too late to cross the snow slope connecting it to Batian, 11 m higher. With the altitude and the effort, I was exhausted and headed back to camp. After about an hour John followed, tracking my footprints for safety.

Experiments were completed (figures 17-21) well before the climbers' return. Just as the light was failing, they staggered into camp looking exhausted. As we had suspected, they had reached the summit of Nelion but it was too late for Batian. The rapid ascent from Nairobi meant they were poorly acclimatised for climbing at over 5,000 m and it was very cold. Ginette had led the route, leaving the men trailing in her wake. We were very impressed. No mountain sickness, no headaches, no tiredness. She was awesome. On one occasion she complained of a headache, so Tim thought finally there was some evidence she was suffering from the altitude. But no, her helmet was just a little too tight. The climbers ate their fill of beans and sausages with mugs of soup while recounting their adventure. This included assisting one of the Italians into Bailey's Bivvy since he was suffering from acute mountain sickness.

That second evening was our last at the high hut. With remarkable speed the expedition – the shortest so far – was coming to an end.

The next morning we were greeted with a bitter wind and a hard frost. Blood and urine samples were collected and packed, and the final measurements of oxygen levels, weights, reaction times and so on were taken. By 8 am we had started down, with John carrying the generator. The path down the scree was still frozen, allowing the wheel to take much of the weight. The porters trotted ahead while our group stretched out in a long line in typical BMRES 'no waiting' style.

We descended through the giant groundsel, past frightened rock hyraxes and Mackinder's Camp before reaching the Teleki Hut. After a brief early lunch, we tackled the dreaded vertical bog. Although still very wet and slippery, with people falling in the mud, it was nothing like the challenge we faced during our ascent.

We stopped the night at the meteorological station camp. We had a good bathe from a standpipe producing clean water – our first for three days – and felt much better. We met Neil, our New Zealand-born safari leader for the next three days, and discussed options for the forthcoming post-expedition holiday.

It was a jolly evening with serious amounts of beer and whisky consumed as we recovered from the hard few days at high altitude. Accommodation was free in the tents or an extra £1 for a bunk in the cabins. I opted for Frank's Gore-Tex igloo tent again, wondering about animals in the jungle. But the night was silent. Had I imagined all those noises the time before?

From the meteorological station we drove to Samburu game reserve for an evening safari adventure. Giraffes, elephants, impala, zebras and leopards greeted our eyes. What a contrast with the freezing rocks of Mt Kenya just a few miles distant. No wonder the early travellers had not believed tales of snow on the equator.

The medical research side of the expedition was not quite over. There were a few final urine samples and clinical questionnaires to be completed before full holiday mode kicked in and partners arrived from England – Barbara for me, Frank's girlfriend Kate, plus Norman's wife Judith, Ron's wife June and Gron's wife Kris.

After two days of morning and evening safaris we bade farewell to our support team of cook boys, porters and Neil before splitting into several groups. The six climbers went to Lake Naivasha in the Rift Valley and its steep cliffs known as Hell's Gate Gorge. Others went to safari parks or Mombasa beaches. David and John Milles visited Lord Delamere and his wife – old acquaintances from school. They were surprisingly impoverished, living in a small hut on the edge of their old estate, which had been taken over by native Kenyans. They didn't stay long.

Barbara and I, Frank and Kate, and John Simmons trekked back to the east side of Mt Kenya, even climbing back to Point Lenana. After a week on the mountain, we drove back to Nairobi across the desert landscape. Red volcanic ash plumed out from the car wheels as we raced over the dry dirt roads. It got in our eyes, ears, noses and mouths and penetrated all our clothes. We had never been so filthy. The receptionist at the Excelsior Hotel could not believe that such dirty people were staying at such a nice hotel.

After recovering for a day, we took the overnight train to Mombasa. This was one of the world's great train journeys – the Orient Express of East Africa. The British built it at the end of the 19th century to connect Lake Victoria with Mombasa, with Nairobi only a railway construction camp in the middle of a swamp. (It is now a city of three million and the capital of the nation.) It cut the travel time from three months to two days and was a great success, but it had a dark history. The construction was held up for several months at the Tsavo River by two man-eating lions, which repeatedly attacked the camp. Before the lions were eventually shot by the army chief Lt Colonel Patterson, 28 Indian construction workers and 135 African labourers had been killed. In addition, 2,493 of the Indians died from other causes; the Africans were not considered important enough for an accurate record to be kept. 'Health and safety' was not a top priority in those days. We were slightly worried about the railway journey since the death toll had continued. In half-a-dozen separate incidences, nearly 200 people had died over the past 20 years.

We walked to the station, which had a lingering colonial atmosphere, reinforced by the butler welcoming us to our first-class couchettes. The train was a British Pullman classic with drop-down bunks, enamelled hand basins and brass knobs, labelled 'MADE

IN BIRMINGHAM' in large letters and dating back to the 1920s. The waiter service was impeccable, all staff being dressed in black suits and white shirts, while the cabins contained neat piles of freshly washed sheets, towels and pillows.

The train departed on the stroke of 7.30 pm then slowly accelerated to its maximum speed of 30 mph, jerking and wobbling on its narrow gauge. In the wood-panelled dining car, we were greeted by Edwardian splendour. The soup was served from a silver-plated tureen, while the vegetables and lamb lay on huge silver-plated dishes. All was elegantly scooped onto decorated china plates made in Stoke-on-Trent. The food quality was not quite as good as the service but we were transported to a bygone colonial era. Well lubricated with French wine, we lurched back to our cabins for a noisy night. The train stopped intermittently for no apparent reason but then tried to make up for lost time. It raced the downhill stretches to the coast at well above the speed limit and by morning was chugging through suburbs, passing occasional skeletons of derelict steam locomotives on the sidings. An elegantly served full-English breakfast was just the job. We had had a safe journey, with no signs of man-eating lions.

Our Mombasa sojourn was for three days. The self-styled hard men of the mountains had been reluctant to loaf around at a beach resort but it did us all good. We had lost a lot of weight and were very tired. At lunch I realised how starving I was. After two main courses from a huge buffet, I ate 10 puddings without stopping. It was like pouring food down an open-ended pipe. We soon replaced our 7 kg weight losses.

A visit to the old port of Mombasa was a revelation. With a history going back to Roman times, it didn't disappoint. Traditional Arabian dhows were moored at the quayside. Directed by Arabs in flowing white garments, black stevedores unloaded hessian bags full of grain. Hugely muscled, they were bent under massive loads as they struggled back and forth from the ship's storerooms to nearby warehouses. It was a scene from the 14th century. We wondered if they were free men.

After Mombasa, we returned to Nairobi on the overnight train, again in grand style. We passed through a game park at first light, catching sight of ostriches, herds of wildebeest, eagles, giraffe and gazelle. It was a great end to a wonderful journey. Sadly, the train no longer operates.

Carrying our bags from the station to the hotel we were involved in a sting. We had been offered black market money many times as we wandered the streets of Nairobi but we were warned that many traders were dishonest. Neil, our courier, insisted that we changed our English money at the banks even though the rates were kept artificially low by the government. Black market rates were double. We decided to give it a go believing that with care there was little chance of being cheated. When the next person approached us, we would weigh him up and exchange £25 between us.

Within a few minutes two men approached offering black market money. We took the bait. Initial exchange rates were too low but they followed us to the hotel and by the time we were about to enter they doubled their offer. They showed us the Kenyan money we would receive in return for our sterling. The game was on. One of them counted out the Kenyan currency while I showed him ours. All seemed to be correct. Our money was in £5 notes while theirs was a collection of different denominations but added up to the agreed value. He proceeded to put the notes in an envelope with the ends protruding. Concentrating on the swap. I reached out for the envelope while one of them reached out to hold the corner of my wodge of notes. I looked at my colleagues – they nodded their approval and I released my notes and held onto their envelope.

At that moment there were shouts from a bunch of youths running past us. They banged sticks on the ground and made a huge row. I looked around feeling slightly threatened, although there was no direct aggression. The two money exchangers ran off with them, shouting and hooting, passing our money between them. Unclear as to what was happening, I looked at the envelope held tightly in my hand. In disbelief, I looked again to see it contained only a few scraps of newspaper. "Chase them!" Gron shouted, but wiser voices stayed our impulse. There were 10 of them and we had all our luggage from the train journey.

I laughed nervously, apologising to my friends. We had been done. I could not understand how he had taken the currency but that moment of raucous confusion was clearly a deliberate distraction. The Excelsior Hotel was across the street. We wandered in agitated and animated. The receptionist looked up and said he had seen it all. If he had known we were guests he would have come out to warn us. He thought we were lucky to have lost so little. Annoyed though we were, we could afford it, we hadn't been beaten up – and we had to concede it was a rather clever trick.

Our flight home was in the evening so we hung languidly around the hotel or visited local shops in the heat of the day. We were now keen to get home. There were only the remaining doubts about the flight being on time and whether the excess baggage would be a problem. We spent our remaining Kenyan currency as it was forbidden to take any out of the country and it was of no value in the UK. After dinner at 7.30 pm we climbed onto a Kenya Airways bus for the airport. As the expedition was all but over, we reflected on our adventures mingled with talk of a Himalaya expedition in a couple of years' time. But there was one final sting.

Our personal baggage weights had to be no more than 20 kg per person, for any excess led to punitive charges. We had to wear or put the remainder in our hand luggage. Furthermore, an 80 Kenyan shillings (£7) airport departure tax had recently been introduced – a tax on being in the country.

As we approached the conveyer belt leading to the security police check, we were redirected to an X-ray scanner (which we doubted actually worked). However, before loading our bags, we were asked for extra payments. I handed over 20 shillings then passed the message back to the others. The amount required for 'checking luggage' was unclear, with the maximum demanded being 100 shillings. Attempts to put the two generators on the belt were stubbornly resisted despite us having all the export paperwork. The police feigned a lack of English language. Finally, the penny dropped. I opened my wallet and passed over $20 but seeing more they demanded more. Another $20 was persuasive. We were then asked if we had any remaining Kenyan money. Those saying yes were asked to 'give it to our friends' – the Kenyan officials behind a nearby desk. It disappeared into a drawer and there was no receipt. We were through.
A noisy bunch of Italians following us had the same treatment. The plane was full, we drank our fill and via Rome ended up in London Heathrow airport the following cold winter's morning, Monday 7 February 1982.

Postscript:

We achieved our main research aim. The comparison study of methazolamide with acetazolamide was well-conducted and generated good data, but there was little difference in the effectiveness of the two drugs. We had half hoped that methazolamide would have been better, as had its manufacturers, Lederle Laboratories. It was still on patent and might have led to useful sales. Nevertheless, we were most grateful for their financial support.

Publications from the expedition:
1. Wright AD, Bradwell AR, Fletcher MD. Methazolamide and acetazolamide in acute mountain sickness. Aviation, Space and Environmental Medicine. 1983; 54(7): 619 621
2. Wright AD, Black EG, Fletcher RF, Bradwell AR; BMRES. Thyroid function at high altitude. New England Journal of Medicine. 1984; 310: 1334.
3. Fletcher R. Acute mountain sickness revisited. Aesculapius 1982; 2: 36-37.

*Fig 1. **Top row: left to right**. Ian Green, Alex Wright, Neville Richardson, David Parker, David Milles, Neil Smith John Milles, John Simmons. Middle row: Bernard Coles, Ron Fletcher, Tim Harlow, Ginette Harrison, Tim Harvey, Simon Morrissey, Norman Dorricott, Norman Waterhouse. **Front row**: Jo Bradwell, Ian Chesner, Frank Davies, Gron Jones.*

Fig 2. Mt Kenya

Fig 3. John Simmons with generator

Fig 4. John Milles, lorry and loads

Fig 5. Met station

Fig 6. *Vertical bog*

Fig 7. *Giant Goundsel*

Fig 8. *Mt Kenya from vertical bog*

Fig 9. *Mackinder camp ranger station*

Fig 10. *Teleki hut*

Fig 11. *John Milles, John Simmons and Simon*

Fig 12. *Mackinder camp*

Fig 13. *Rock Hyrax*

Fig 14. *Point Lenana*

Fig 15. *Nelian at night*

Fig 16. *Lewis glacier*

Fig 17. *Clinical examination*

Fig 18. *Ian Green, Gron & respirometer*

Fig 19. *Bernard, John Milles and blood gases*

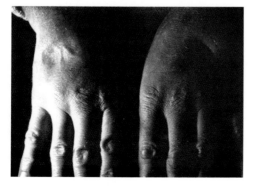

Fig 20. *Hand oedema*

Fig 21. *Reaction time test*

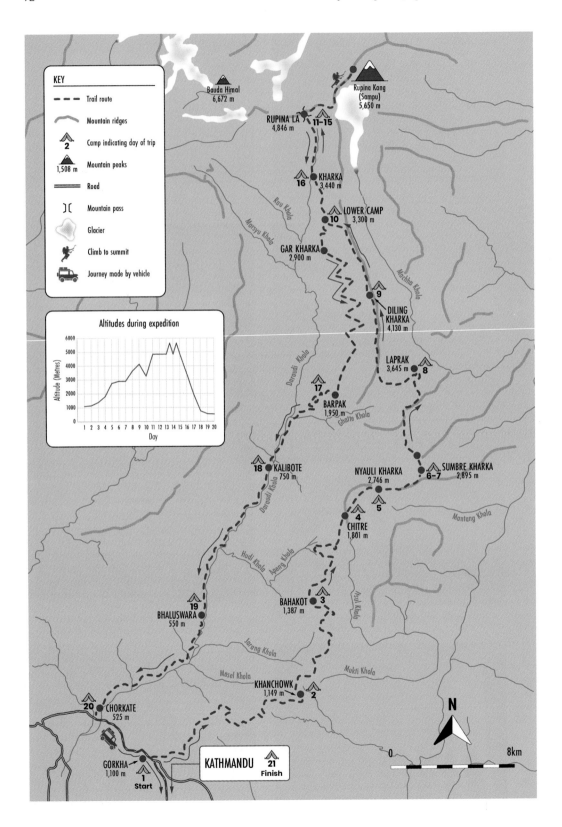

KEY

- - - - - Trail route

Mountain ridges

Camp indicating day of trip

1,508 m   Mountain peaks

Road

)(Mountain pass

Glacier

Climb to summit

Journey made by vehicle

Altitudes during expedition

Altitude (Metres)

6000
5000
4000
3000
2000
1000
0

Day 1 2 3 4 5 6 7 8 9 10 11 12 13 14 15 16 17 18 19 20

Bauda Himal 6,672 m

Rupina Kang (Sampu) 5,650 m

RUPINA LA 4,846 m

11–15

KHARKA 3,440 m
16

LOWER CAMP 3,300 m
10

GAR KHARKA 2,900 m

Rau Khola

Marsya Khola

Machha Khola

9

DILING KHARKA 4,130 m

LAPRAK 3,645 m
8

Daraudi Khola

17

BARPAK 1,950 m

Ghatte Khola

KALIBOTE 750 m
18

NYAULI KHARKA 2,746 m

SUMBRE KHARKA 2,895 m
6–7

Daraud Khola

5

CHITRE 1,801 m
4

Mantang Khola

Hudi Khola

Apeng Khola

Prsul Khola

BAHAKOT 1,387 m
3

BHALUSWARA 550 m
19

Jarang Khola

Masel Khola

Mukti Khola

KHANCHOWK 1,149 m
2

CHORKATE 525 m
20

GORKHA 1,100 m
1
Start

KATHMANDU
21
Finish

N

0   8km

Chapter 4
Rupina La, Nepal September – October 1984

Himalchuli and Bauda

Monsoon blues

"Gradually I acquired a reputation for being quite unperturbed by flogging, a delusion I was careful to foster for reasons of pride. In fact, I was always terrified."
– Eric Shipton on early conditioning for the mountains,
in his autobiography, *"That Untravelled World"* (1969).

Summary: Because of the increasing use of acetazolamide, questions were raised about possible side effects, including its impact on exercise performance. After a slow ascent to a remote location in the Himalayas, we showed that, compared with placebo, acetazolamide increased maximum exercise and reduced muscle loss. The results, published in The Lancet, further enhanced the society's profile. We also assessed sleep, weight loss and proteinuria at altitude.

Expedition members: Nick Binns (medical student), Jo Bradwell (leader), Martin Bradwell, Ian Chesner, John Coote, Frank Davies, Peter Dykes (expedition doctor), Jonathan Evans (medical student), Pete Forster, Ginette Harrison, Tim Harvey, Gron Jones, Kate Keohane, John Milles, Simon Morrissey, Neville Richardson (deputy leader), Dave Siviter, John Simmons, Pete Smith, John Taverner, Mike Winterborn (figure 1).

Why do people climb? Many answers are hocus-pocus, written by climbers who confuse hypoxia-driven insanity with philosophy and deep thought. George Mallory's "Because it is there" deliberately avoided a considered response but was as good an answer as any reporter from the New York Times deserved.

The 'why' is asked by those who are not climbers and who have not experienced the simple joy of moving in the hills, the thrill of adventure, the buzz of being in a beautiful place with stunning views, the fresh smells of ice and mountains, the great outdoors and being with friends – perhaps best friends. "Friends on the mountains are friends for life," it is often said.

In over a dozen expeditions, I have spent a year in tents with mountaineering friends in the most exciting of environments, including the Himalaya and the Andes. We have raced to peaks and mountain passes joined only by a rope lifeline for survival. It is exciting. Not the limited excitement of seeing a good movie or making a bungee jump in complete security, or even driving at 150 mph on an open road, but a total body excitement. The physical and mental struggle of dealing with crevasses, ridges, rock and ice faces; the rewards of a successful descent – peace, calm, tired legs and satisfied weariness; and the alcohol-fuelled camaraderie that follows.

The flipside to the pleasure is the pain and suffering that typifies mountaineering. Founder members of BMRES were schooled in the hard days when beatings by Christian Brothers or Jesuit teachers were commonplace. The ability to suffer yet still enjoy the physical pain of severe exercise or the fear of difficult summits and exposed ridges has selected many members. As Eric Shipton had noted, childhood exposure to flogging at the hands of sadistic teachers was probably helpful in his acceptance of pain.

Does this childhood experience mature into the more complex pleasures arising from exposure to life-threatening danger? The psychologist Paul Rozin identified a syndrome of acquired tastes he called benign masochism.

"These paradoxical pleasures include consuming hot chili peppers, strong cheese and dry wine and partaking in extreme experiences like saunas, skydiving, car racing and climbing. All of them are adult tastes, in which a novice must overcome a first reaction of pain, disgust, or fear, on the way to becoming a connoisseur. And all are acquired by controlling one's exposure to the stressor in gradually increasing doses. What they have in common is a coupling of high potential gains (nutrition, medicinal benefits, speed, knowledge of new environments) with high potential dangers (poisoning, exposure, accidents). The pleasure in acquiring one of these tastes is the pleasure of pushing limits: of probing, in calibrated steps, how high, hot, strong, fast or far one can go without bringing on disaster. The ultimate advantage is to open up beneficial regions in the space of local experiences that are, by default, closed off to others from innate fears and cautions."

Stephen Pinker wrote more technically: "The brain circuits for sexuality and aggression may be linked to benign masochism. They are intertwined in the limbic system and both respond to testosterone." (In: The Better Angels of Our Nature, p. 670).

Competition is integral to climbing and testosterone with it. There is also a selection process. Not all are physically strong enough to ascend big mountains. Others acclimatise poorly to high altitude and are unlikely to return because of the risk of acute mountain sickness. These traits are partially genetically determined. There is also the issue of risk and risk tolerance. Non-climbers usually consider climbing too risky, but risk is a personal assessment. I do not believe in taking risks but I am very concerned with risk assessment. Most risks can be determined and mitigated by analysis, experience and training. But there are risks that cannot be anticipated and prepared for: the random strike of a lightning bolt; a collapsing ice serac; an unexpected rock fall or avalanche. This is the arena that is frightening. This is where extreme climbers die.

Himalayan climbers gradually become numbed to high risk. They have survived so far; the gods must be with them. They have always made good decisions about what they have climbed; naturally, because they are still alive. But these are the climbers who have survived against the odds not just because they are skilful, as they come to believe, but also because they have been lucky. Eventually, the ball on the roulette wheel lands on their number. A generation of British climbers died in this fashion: Joe Tasker, Pete Boardman, Al Rouse, Dougal Haston, Nick Estcourt, plus the best of the female mountaineers, Alison Hargreaves, Julie Tullis and our own dear Ginette Harrison.

* * *

Nearly three years had passed since our last expedition. We wanted a return trip to the Himalayas. The scale and beauty of the mountains is unsurpassed, and we had not climbed there for seven years. While the weather is better on Mt Kenya early in the year, the Himalayas are best visited in the autumn, from October to December. With the monsoon finished, the countryside is green and lush, while the air is sparklingly clear, allowing the peaks to shine in the cold air. September is a little close to the end of the monsoon but we set a departure date of 12 September. We had little choice. Several of us had teaching commitments in October at the start of the university term. We hoped the monsoon would finish early.

In addition to a research base camp at 5,000 m, we wanted a nearby mountain as a climbing target. We approached Mike Cheney who ran the well-known Nepal-based Sherpa Cooperative. He had been a Gurkha army officer for many years but on retirement had teamed up with Colonel Jimmy Roberts to pioneer tourist trekking and had been involved with several Everest expeditions. With his extensive knowledge of the region, we felt confident that we would easily identify an ideal location for our expedition. Chulu West at 6,419 m, near Thorong La, was suggested as a relatively easy peak with a possible high camp.

Our main research plans were twofold. The first was to investigate the effect of acetazolamide on exercise at altitude. We had been in discussions with the climber Chris Bonington about its use. He had organised several trips to Everest, including the successful ascent of the south-west face by Dougal Haston and Doug Scott, but had personally struggled above 8,000 m. We thought that the extra oxygen levels in the blood from acetazolamide might help him reach the summit, since we had shown that 500 mg daily increased blood oxygen levels by about 15%, equivalent to reducing the height of Everest by over 1,200 m; down from 8,848 m to perhaps 7,500 m. This had been the subject of the cartoon on the front page of The Times newspaper in 1982 (Chapter 2). It was, of course, a theoretical calculation based on extrapolation from 5,000 m. Nevertheless, it was food for thought.

I contacted him, explained what we had in mind and invited him to our laboratory in Birmingham. He was already acquainted with acetazolamide but had heard that it might impair exercise performance. Either way, both of us were keen to assess his exercise capacity at an oxygen concentration of 10%. This is equivalent to an altitude of 5,700 m (figure 2).

The test showed that he was fit, although not as fit as some of our group, but had a relatively modest hypoxic ventilatory response (the increase in breathing caused by low oxygen levels) that might be increased with acetazolamide. However, there were no published data on the effect of the medication on climbing rates, so he was unwilling to try it without further studies.

This became the main focus of our next expedition – to compare the effect of acetazolamide with placebo on exercise ability at altitude. Since Everest expeditions lasted for many weeks, we wanted to have a prolonged high-altitude exposure period before assessing exercise. The plan was to ascend slowly so that everyone acclimatised properly, for any acute mountain sickness would impair performance. We thought that ten days of slow ascent to 5,000 m would be suitable.

Exercise bike

However, there was an issue with finding the appropriate equipment. Cycling is an excellent method of assessing exercise performance but bikes used for laboratory-based physiological studies are too heavy to carry up a mountain. Thankfully, Jim Milledge allowed us to borrow the lightweight model designed by Griffith Pugh for the Silver Hut studies of 1960–61. It still weighed 43 kg in its protective wooden box but was just about manageable by a single porter.

A second research question was how to improve sleep at altitude. Because sleeping is often difficult, climbers frequently take sedatives. Since hypoxia is greater at night, we were concerned that drug-induced sleep might make hypoxia worse still. In discussion with Dr John Coote, from the Department of Physiology, we found a common interest in the problem. He had extensive knowledge of adaptations to altitude, including exercise, was an expert on sleep and an experienced mountaineer. (He had wide climbing experience that included a disastrous accident in the Andes. A head injury from a bad fall had left a huge scar on his forehead while his climbing partner was paralysed and confined to a wheelchair.)

The sedative we chose was temazepam, as it was thought to cause no reduction in brain function. It has even been said that temazepam won the Falkland's War. Apparently, by helping Harrier Jump Jet pilots to sleep well between combat missions, it maintained their critical fast reaction times. Dr Tony Nicholson at RAF Farnborough had been instrumental in its use and was well-known to John Coote. After an introductory visit, we agreed on a joint research programme. Furthermore, the manufacturer of temazepam, Wyeth, liked our proposals so much that they offered to underwrite the whole of the next expedition, including baseline sleep studies. Over the next few weeks, many of us visited the RAF laboratory at Farnborough aerodrome for baseline EEG (electro-encephalograph) studies of our brains during sleep (figure 3). Pete Smith, one of the technicians helping with the study, was invited to come on the expedition with us.

One of the minor projects was a study of the origin of altitude proteinuria (protein in urine), which we had observed on Chimborazo. Mike Winterborn, a consultant renal paediatrician at Birmingham Children's Hospital, was the lead investigator. He was of rather short stature and an agonisingly slow walker, but a very pleasant mild-mannered individual.

We were also joined by Peter Dykes, a well-known senior gastroenterologist at Birmingham General Hospital. He had wanted to come on our first expedition but was prevented by busy work and domestic schedules. Despite being the oldest at

53 years, he became the most popular new recruit. He had endless energy, making collections of flowers and fossils, was involved in many of the experiments plus he was the expedition's doctor.

Other new additions included two final-year medical students, Nick Binns and Jonathan Evans (gratefully funded by the Arthur Thompson Trust), my younger brother Martin, John Taverner, general practitioner from Knowle near Birmingham and Kate Keohone, friend of the group. This made a total of 21 people, two groups of ten on exercise tests (10 on acetazolamide and 10 on placebo), eight of whom were on sleep studies. Ginette was excluded from the studies because she was fully acclimatised having already been in the Himalaya for five weeks.

With all these research questions in my mind, the departure day of 12 September saw me awake to a bright morning and the sound of the whole side wall of our house being knocked down. It was chaos, the air thick with dust. The wall, only one brick thick and starting to bulge, was being replaced. Barbara and I had arranged for it to be rebuilt while we were abroad. We completed the final packing in the dust-filled air then caught a taxi to the Medical School. Frank Davies and Dave Siviter (a climbing friend of Frank's) were finalising the baggage; all the metal boxes were packed, contents logged and weighed. We had 990 kg but were allowed only 670 kg on the plane. Regardless of excess baggage worries, the coach arrived and we loaded 51 boxes and rucksacks. If the bus could take them, we figured, so could the plane; that's what is called optimism.

At the Pakistan International Airways (PIA) desk at London Heathrow airport, we explained our weight problem, all 320 kg of it. Even though we described the medical importance of the expedition, they refused to accept any extra luggage. We had been in this situation several times before and swung our plan into action. A hurried phone call to PIA in London assured us of an uncertain extra amount. I offered a £500 inducement then used the Hawkesworth toe-trick under the scales. With Nev, Dave, Kate and others hanging around the scales, we 'lost' 150 kg. In spite of a widely swinging pointer, the weights were recorded to smiles and reassurances with a request for £1,012 (figure 4). We had saved £2,500. We paid with American Express travellers' cheques as my ulcer pain rapidly faded.

Barbara and I sat next to Pete Forster, who was his usual amusing self, relating stories of old BMRES trips, the Panadol Kids, the Prefects in Quito (consultants versus junior doctors) and the irascible Ted Olive. We were in store for more fun.

We stopped briefly at Dubai to collect home-bound Pakistani workers then flew to Karachi where we stayed overnight. All the baggage appeared and was put into the awaiting bus to take us to our hotel, The Inn. We arrived to discover that John Milles was missing. We had his rucksack but not him. After a worrying search of all our allocated rooms, the only remaining unchecked place was the airport. There, we found him fast asleep on some seats just outside the baggage hall, where he had laid undisturbed for over an hour. We bundled him into a taxi and returned to the hotel.

Over lunch Pete Forster went around the group checking the number of acetazolamide tablets each person had taken over the previous three days. Despite there being 13 medics on the trip, none had taken the correct amount – apart from Tim, who had taken six in one go, just before being questioned.

The following morning, we flew to Kathmandu. It was goodbye to Barbara, my wife of three months, who was flying to Delhi for a three-week tour of India, after which we would meet in Kathmandu.

The aging Boeing 707 trundled down the runway, tilting to port at it took off because all the passengers were on the left side wanting to see the Himalaya. After flying over Delhi and the Ganges, the eastern 8,000 m peaks came into view: Dhaulagiri, Annapurna I–IV and Manaslu. Chulu West, our planned climbing peak, was to the north of Annapurna but it was not distinguishable among the greater mountains.

Chris Brown from the British Council met us as we filed into the arrivals hall with our luggage. We held our breath as the customs officials checked all documents and requested that the boxes were opened (we had a few extra items). After explaining our medical research, they backed off, allowing us through.

Outside the busy terminal, we were collected by the tour company (ensuring that John Milles was with us) and departed for the Paradise Hotel. Nev and I drove off in a Land Rover to see Mike Cheney in order to finalise remaining details of the expedition. He was a small, stooped man who wore an enormous pair of colonial shorts and spoke with a residual posh English accent. His news about our plans was very disappointing. Having believed that Chulu West was our objective for the previous four months, we were told quite clearly that it was impossible. Base camp was at a modest 4,000 m and above it was snow and ice. There was no chance of getting everyone near the 5,000 m mark and the main peak was a difficult climb. Frustrated by the poor information we had received in Birmingham, we argued about the trip and how we had been misled. Eventually we agreed on climbing towards Himalchuli and setting a high camp at a little-known pass called Rupina La. We paid $900 for the new route and, irritatingly, had to hand over a further $300 for cancelling the trek to Chulu West.

Back at the hotel, Mike Cheney and Ang Ringee (our sirdar, or porter organiser) explained the change of plans to a bemused group. John Coote and Peter Dykes were supportive while Dave Siviter, our mountain guide from Wales, was not so sure. With the continuing rain, he argued, there would be snow down to 2,000 m and it could be up to a couple of metres deep. He was very pessimistic, while the rest of us were perhaps over-optimistic. Eventually we accepted our fate, for there was little choice. It was not a good start.

That night I lay in bed listening to the rain on the tin roof and dreamt of the monsoon. The first camp on our last trip to the Himalaya was a flooded pigsty. This time we were a week earlier. Would it be worse?

We had one more day in Kathmandu to prepare for the expedition. The medical equipment had been stored at the Sherpa Cooperative but needed checking. Everything was unpacked – generator, battery packs, blood-gas analyser, EEGs – then repacked to make loads of equal weights for the porters. Each pack was numbered and padlocked. By late afternoon the work was completed, allowing time for a wander around Kathmandu. Black clouds rose over the mountains to the north.

At our 7.30 pm meeting, we discussed everyone's worries about the next three weeks. We discussed David's comment about snow down to 2,000 m and two metres deep. Most were sceptical about his pessimism but we anxiously wondered if the monsoon was finished. Certainly, we had seen no mountains during the day and it had rained hard all night.

Next morning, after breakfast, a rather knackered lorry turned up at the hotel carrying our equipment, followed by two equally knackered buses. We climbed in and headed west out of Kathmandu along the Pokhara Road. Just as we thought all was well, a fan belt broke. Fortunately, another was discovered among a mass of spare parts and junk.

Jonathan amused us with his frolics on the roof. He had been thoroughly pissed the night before, and overindulged in hash. Eventually he fell off, thankfully when we were stationary. That briefly bought him to his senses. But after lunch we all were all off the roof with the arrival of rain.

By late afternoon we arrived at Gorkha (1,100 m), the main Gurkha village. In its central square, hundreds of people were gathered around our luggage, which had been dumped by the lorry. We pushed our way through the crowd, fearing it was being stolen. Thankfully, there was a ring of our porters and Sherpas protecting it. We unloaded our rucksacks plus remaining equipment off the buses and, watching closely for thieves, marched out of town away from the crowds and prying eyes. There were 114 porters. It felt like the old days of the Raj or the huge mountain siege expeditions of the 1960s. A pith helmet would have fitted the part.

Nepalese swing

The scale of the expedition was impressive. A long file of porters tramped along a wide track between paddy fields to our first camp in a school yard. It was already being prepared and at its centre was a large round arctic tent. John Simmons made many items for the army at his factories and had borrowed this one for the trip. As we approached, the rain started. A huge thunderstorm hovered over us, flooding the campsite. It was a quagmire and our tents leaked. It was a repeat of the first night's camp on the Thorong La expedition. Thankfully, we now had watertight metal boxes and we were not camped in a pigsty.

For the next three days it rained, torrentially at night and intermittently throughout the day. But there was no going back for we had a fixed schedule and the road bridge over the river that we had crossed into Gorkha had been washed away. As we proceeded onwards through sodden paddy fields, we could easily follow our long line of tottering porters thanks to the large red bivvy bags protecting their loads from the deluge. Frank had bought 100 from the UK for just such an eventuality. Others used cheap umbrellas bought in Kathmandu or Gorkha.

No one found it easy: we were always damp from rain and sweat, endured sore feet and had to contend with innumerable leeches. They leaned out from grass and bushes as we brushed past, grabbing hold of our smelly bodies then wriggling through tiny holes in shoes, shirts and trousers. Removing blood-soaked socks revealed their bloated bodies, up to an inch long, attached to our filthy feet. Mike Winterborn, a new member of the

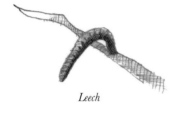

Leech

group, was horrified by the experience. He proclaimed in triumph that he had killed one. Pete Forster, in a foul mood, couldn't contain himself: "Single-handed, Mike?" he asked.

In order to avoid some of the worst night-time rain, we camped in school yards, trampled hard by a multitude of tiny feet, and slept in classrooms (figure 5). Children were awed to see huge westerners arrive in their tiny villages, along with our 100-strong entourage. Since it was the mountaineering route to Manaslu and Himalchuli, they imagined we were heroic climbers attempting yet another impossible route.

On one night, rather than be with snorers, I moved into the school storeroom, only to find Ang Ringee lying with a girl behind some boxes. I had not quite realised that the Sherpa sirdars were the matadors of the mountains, the roving lover boys of the valleys. They were wealthy, proud and in demand. Ang Ringee had a girl in every village. Not to be put off, I slithered into my bag. No noise could wake me after all the hard exercise.

Despite his attractiveness to the opposite sex, Ang Ringee was proving to be a poor leader. In particular, he was struggling to organise or control the porters. Baggage loads were distributed unevenly and a rebellious bunch hung about at the back requiring continuous coaxing from us. The worst were caught drinking rakshi (Nepalese beer) in village shops and were probably nursing hangovers. Yet the Drshuli Ghurka porters were amazing, carrying up to 120 kg. They used a short T-shaped stick for balance and again as a seat when there were no wayside stone rest stops. 50 kg was easy for them. Even the tiny Tamang cook boys, perhaps weighing 40 kg, would carry 35 kg.

To ensure that everyone kept moving, we had a rotation of sweepers at the back – Nick Binns, Ginette, Jonathan, myself and many others. From there we urged, cajoled and encouraged the porters carrying the bike, arctic tent and other heavy items. We stopped with them in wayside houses, as they glowered at the rain (figure 6). To show some leadership, I briefly carried the heaviest panier (the arctic tent plus extras). All were impressed as I stumbled into a school yard on our second night's camp in the small village of Khanchowk at 1,149 m.

John Simmons wanted to carry the 42 kg generator to the high camp. In Coventry, to support the generator, he had made a backpack with an added strap of leather for his forehead (figure 7). Every morning he was first off after breakfast to grind his way along the slippery paths, suffering as he went. He had an arthritic neck and swollen knees with smashed cartilages from his rugby days for Coventry's first fifteen. But he was big, strong and tough. Nevertheless, by the evenings he was exhausted while the porters, half his size, carried similar loads with ease.

Respiratory infections are a common problem on expeditions. Members bring germs from different places then cram together in enclosed spaces coughing and spluttering. This trip was one of those unfortunate experiences. Martin, my brother, was the culprit. He came with a bad cold and went on to infect many of us and subsequently Sherpas and porters. Perhaps because of their heavy loads and hard physical effort, they suffered most but one by one we all fell to its malign effects. Even the sirdar developed a chest infection. We passed around as many paracetamol as they needed, plus a few for their friends (figure 8).

One evening, in the midst of the hard wet slog, Ian couldn't find his rucksack. We searched everywhere but no bag. All he had to wear were the wet, sweaty clothes that he stood in. A Sherpa lent him a sleeping bag while we gathered together spare clothing, a pair of dry shoes, and even items such as underpants and a toothbrush. Next morning, as the loads were prepared for the porters, we checked every item but there was still no sign of his rucksack. There was loose talk of a porter carrying it off in the village – but who would want Ian's clothes, and rucksacks were normally strapped together in threes for carrying. Its loss remained a mystery.

Throughout these difficulties, we worked mornings and evenings on experiments. Blood-gas analyses, blood samples, overnight sleep studies, urine measurements – all lit by flickering electric lights powered by John's humming generator in the arctic tent. On the plus side, it was great to be finally underway and exercising. As we ascended, through Khanchowk and Bahakot (1,387 m) to Chitre (1,801 m), our mood improved, we relaxed, and experiments became easier with repeated practice. The Himalaya were starting to work their old magic.

From the rice paddies we passed into rhododendron forests, festooned with orchids, water and leeches. Then the vista opened above Chitre on a ridge. The camp was like an eyrie poised above the terraces. As rain threatened, we quickly assembled the tents to commence the evening's studies. A coordinated group of conscientious doctors and scientists all with the same goal of understanding more about the impact of altitude on bodies and minds. As we went to bed, a few stars appeared for the first time.

The morning confirmed our hopes for the weather. It was almost clear, providing our first mountain views. The high snows glistened in the dawn and we enjoyed views across to Annapurna. To the south, clouds rose in the warming air over the Himalayan foothills. The barometer readings were also rising and there were no threatening rain clouds. Maybe the monsoon was finished. The temperature rose as we enjoyed our breakfast views.

However, all was not well with the porters. The troublemakers at the back decided to strike. They wanted a pay rise, claiming that their loads were more than they normally carried. I doubted whether this was true but they were suffering with coughs and colds. I discussed the situation with Ang Ringee. He merely shrugged his shoulders and said he couldn't help. We tried to placate them by offering to treat their symptoms but that was rejected. We suggested splitting the loads and hiring more porters but they wouldn't have that because it meant less money each. In frustration, I located the heaviest load and started carrying it up the hill. Reluctantly the porters followed including their unpleasant-looking shop steward, Ocull. The weight was very heavy, perhaps 40 kg. I stopped as they caught up. I could not possibly compete with their extraordinary strength. But they respected my effort, stopping alongside me to sing, then helped adjust my pack. Annoying though they had been, I briefly felt great empathy with them. A common bond of great physical suffering. I managed another few hundred metres then passed the pack to Jonathan. Himalayan white-backed vultures soared overhead anticipating our demise.

Together we struggled to the lunch stop. Some of our team were impressed but others thought we were mad. I couldn't manage an afternoon haul. Only our generator carrier John had that sort of strength.

The evening camp was in a rubbish dump on top of a small hill at 2,746 m (Nyauli Kharka). Leeches abounded. They attacked us all and not just through our socks. I even got one on my forehead. And the altitude was starting to tell, for it was a cold evening. We made a fire in the centre of the camp while the porters made shacks of wood and branches. That evening there were no clouds or rain and the sky was clear (figure 9) so out came night-flying insects. We were bombarded with moths and mosquitoes that surrounded the village lights in a great buzzing halo as giant spiders spun webs. I was in bed early with a cold.

Giant spider

I awoke at 5.15 am to a glorious morning. All the peaks were clearly visible. We watched in wonder with uplifted spirits. As the earth rotated, the sun sequentially lit the main mountains of the Himalayan chain from Cho Oyu in the east to Annapurna in the west (figure 10). It was a display of great beauty. We ate breakfast as the superb panorama unfolded.

After breakfast, 14 porters, mostly the skinheads, were paid off with much grumbling. I half hoped that would be the end of our problems, but it was not.

We ascended the ridge in the cold morning air, many of us struggling under the effects of colds. Poor John Simmons was worn out and had a chest infection but refused to release the generator.

As we walked together, we discussed food. Although there was plenty available, it was of rather mixed quality. Lots of potatoes, rice and chapatis with tinned fruit for dessert but the beef and pork were tough. We had carried several chickens with us for the first few days but they had long since been eaten. Someone commented that they were starving and could eat a buffalo. In amusement, we asked Ang Ringee. No problem was his response. We were coming to the small village of Sumbre Kharka (2,895 m) for the night's camp. He would see what he could do. Others thought it was a good idea – so the hunt was on. Well, not really a hunt since they were tame but we did have to locate one. As the ridge broadened at the village, Ringee found a buffalo and came back with a price of $700 (which probably included $250 for his cut). We agreed.

With much bellowing, the poor creature's legs were hobbled and then its head was

Buffalo meat

forcefully tightened to the tree trunk with a rope (figure 11). Naively, I had expected it to be stunned, or shot, or even have its neck cut but it was not so. It was whacked to death with a long-handled hammer. We thought a single blow to the head would be sufficient but it shook off the first dozen strikes. With each wallop it staggered and bellowed with pain but not until the twentieth or more did it finally lie still. We were horrified. Several of us became vegetarian for the rest of the trip.

Despite the thoughts of the poor suffering animal, most of us tucked into buffalo steaks that night. Not quite as succulent as we had imagined but we ate heartily. The cooks spent several hours cutting the animal into manageable portions while we checked its liver for flukes. Sections of meat were hung out to dry overnight where they were beset by flies, beetles, and other blood-sucking, egg-laying insects.

Baseline studies are an important feature of any scientific endeavour. We had collected data in Birmingham and during the early ascent for parameters such as blood oxygen, sleep recordings and urine but there were others. Peter Dykes and Ian were studying food absorption and had developed very popular Yorkie Bar and lactose tests, the first for fat absorption and the second for sugar absorption. These needed a day to perform, so with the troublesome respiratory infections and the desire to avoid acute mountain sickness, we opted for a rest day.

The Yorkie Bar test commenced with a blood sample followed by rapid consumption of the eponymous chocolate bar. Subsequently, bloods were collected every half hour for four hours. Any delay in absorption would be reflected in slow increases in the blood levels of fat. Mysteriously, half-way through, the blood samples got muddled – some tubes had no names and some no numbers. We spent an anxious hour sorting out the mix up. It must have been the altitude.

That evening we had buffalo again. All but four of our 21 members by now had colds and varying degrees of bronchitis. Four people had bad diarrhoea but not the beef eaters as might be expected. Ironically, it was the four who had become vegetarian. In spite of the bluebottles and other meat infestations, the sun- and air-dried meat seemed remarkably uncontaminated. The generator hummed its tune into the night.

Over the next few days we needed to reach our high camp at 5,000 m but it proved difficult. The first day started well enough, with clear air and a rising barometric pressure. We explained to Ang Ringee that we needed to gain more altitude. He seemed to have no clear plan and we suspected he has not been on this route for a long time, if ever. Because some of the porters had been paid off, the remainder hassled for more money, particularly since there were now six loads of buffalo meat to be carried. Even the cooks were carrying some.

While there was considerable frustration in the group about the porters' speed it was not surprising that they had slowed since the average load had risen from 30 kg to 45 kg. I briefly tried a load but with the combination of altitude, a residual cold and the extra weight it was impossible. As the hours ticked by, progress slowed further. Then Neville got cross with Ringee, who came to me very upset. Diplomatically, I persuaded him to go for just one more hour. By luck rather than judgement, we stopped in a beautiful wooded glen at 3,645 m near Laprak. We had ascended nearly 760 m. The strongest of the porters were persuaded to go back and help their slower colleagues – for an extra fee, of course. As we gathered wood for the evening fire, we agreed the day had been good. The infections were settling, we had plenty of nourishing food, and the weather was cold and clear. The experiments hummed along, dinner was tasty, and a drink of Cadbury's hot chocolate before bed was unbeatable. I lay in bed wondering what Barbara was up to in the vastness of India. I hoped her trip was easier than ours.

The next morning was brilliantly clear with Bauda and Himalchuli towering over us (figure 12) at 6,672 m and 7,893 m, although, as usual, it clouded over by mid-morning. Martin and now Gron were feeling unwell, although it was not clear what was wrong with them. Peter Dykes thought they were both well enough to proceed so to help others carried their day bags. We climbed to 3,901 m by 11 am and by early afternoon were on a steep ridge at 4,130 m overlooking a lake. It seemed to be a good place to stop for the night, with the water looking invitingly cool 150 m below. The camp was struck, giving Jonathan, John Simmons and myself a chance to go for a swim; we were sweating after a fast descent. The lake was bitterly cold. Bravely, the other two swam while I climbed slowly back up in the thin air. I arrived to find the Sherpas seriously agitated. Apparently, there was a good god who lived in the lake who would be very upset with us for disturbing him. Bad things would happen. How right they were.

To prepare the camp, an area was cleared and levelled near the top of the slope for the arctic tent while the other tents were carefully secured to flattish surfaces (figure 13). Some camped slightly below the ridge to avoid any wind but this meant the sun set early and the temperature plummeted. The cook tents, also dug into the hill side, were below us, allowing the smell of cooking and buffalo to waft upwards. The juiciest portions had already been eaten while the tougher remaining meat needed prolonged boiling. From this they made momos (beef and flour dumplings) which were then fried. Despite their nice flavour, the altitude was reducing our appetites and after supper it was a relief to struggle into a warm sleeping bag and reflect on a challenging day.

That night the wind battered the tents on our mountain eyrie as I lay in bed wondering whether it would blow us off the slope. The metal boxes were scattered around the campsite, held down by only gravity and friction. I feared a strong gust would deposit them in the lake.

It was a further 900 m height gain to Rupina La. I anticipated we would be there by the following night.

We awoke to fabulous views of the mountains, including Rupina La, our destination for the day. Most of us were in high spirits but some had headaches. Martin was still poorly and Gron wanted to go home. He had psyched himself out. The same had happened to Ted Olive on the Thorong La, our first expedition. Gron was normally tough and resourceful. It was surprising how the hypoxia had undermined his determination so much. His pet theory of acute mountain sickness put it down to excessive exertion. So, in spite of being a strong fast walker, he would always proceed slowly and deliberately and was hardly ever out of breath. It hadn't helped on this occasion.

We had a medical conference to decide their fate. Martin was given a dose of acetazolamide and felt a little better within an hour. He had had a rough trip, suffering from a bad cold and chest infection, and needed to descend. Gron still wanted to go home. Tim generously decided to accompany them alongside Sherpa Ang Rita plus two porters to carry their luggage (figure 14). Within the hour they had set off for Barpak (1,950 m), the nearest town and at an altitude where they could recover. Upset by the turn of events, we talked through the consequences on the experiments of losing two members. The good lake god was taking his revenge.

After walking for an hour, it seemed that the route to Rupina La went upwards to the right while we were drifting down to the left following the Sherpas. It slowly dawned on us that we had been led the wrong way and were heading for a long descent. By 11 am we had gone down 600 m to the base of a large corrie well below Rupina La. There was a lot of grumbling and criticism of me and the organisation among my colleagues. I rushed ahead to find Ringee. On a small rise on the barren slope, I found him surrounded by 60 or so porters. They were determined to go home and Ringee could not persuade them otherwise.

Most expeditions seem to have a crisis point. A situation arises when the whole venture is on a knife-edge. This was it. How could the porters be persuaded to stay? And how could we climb the remaining 1,500 m to Rupina La? During the whole trip we had not ascended that far in a day and we were now at a higher altitude. We needed five days at 5,000 m to carry out the studies. The situation was critical.

The root cause of the strike was the lack of information supplied to the porters about the expedition. The Nepalese New Year celebrations started in a few days, making them determined to go home. We realised that there had been no error in the route – they had deliberately descended in order to leave. We discussed the possibility of more money but this had no effect. Rupina La was high above us in the low cloud and not remotely inviting. Dave Siviter said it would take four days. As the bickering continued, I took myself to one side and, lying in the warmth of the midday sun, closed my eyes and thought deeply. F***.

I tried to think rationally but at altitude decisions are not easy. But slowly my mind cleared. Rupina La was, after all, only 1,500 m above us. Merely the height of Ben Nevis, which can be ascended in three hours – or maybe six hours at altitude; only half a day's climbing. The Sherpas and cook boys were still loyal, there were 19 of us and we had carried very little so far. Perhaps, if we all took our own gear (at least the bare essentials) plus important medical equipment, the ascent would be possible. We could start very early in the morning and perhaps persuade some of the porters to join us, since not all were from the Kathmandu valley and had different New Year celebration days. The extra money was clearly swaying a few. This seemed like a plan but I first had to prove to the Dave Siviters of this world that the ascent was possible. I would reconnoitre the route that very afternoon with the fastest climbers – Jonathan for example.

Neville was in agreement so we gathered everyone together and brought in Ringee. We agreed to some extra money, an early start and full loads for everyone. After another hour of discussions, I left John Simmons to finish off the negotiations while Jonathan, John Milles and I departed for Rupina La carrying only chocolate bars. The route was not clear but after a long scramble over endless azalea bushes we found a good path ascending towards some big cliffs partly hidden in the mist. A Sherpa accompanied us and within two hours Rupina La was visible intermittently in swirling clouds. We ascended to within 200 m of the pass and there, set among an area of boulders, was a good campsite. Jubilant, we set off down. Cairns were constructed to identify unclear sections of the route then we ran to arrive back in camp 40 minutes later. Breathless and excited, we described our success to the gathered group.

The negotiations had gone reasonably well. We had 72 loads and Ang Ringee had retained 44 porters. Many were small, including several Tamang women (figure 15), but we had become very impressed with their strength and determination and knew they could carry full loads. They could descend after dropping off the important first loads then bring the remainder up the following day.

Over dinner there were endless discussions, to and fro, about whether we would succeed for several were hardened pessimists. At one point in the proceedings, Ang Ringee came in and said it was possible, but no one believed him anymore. Anyway, our plans were set, all we needed was reasonable weather. That night, Pete Forster came over to my tent to wish me a good night's sleep. I may have appeared calm to many but he could see the intense pressure I felt, and he was pleasantly very reassuring. I lay in bed thinking of the turmoil of the day and what lay in wait tomorrow. The success of the expedition depended on some good fortune. Bloody lake gods.

At 4.30 am I heard movements outside; Sherpas were starting to organise the ascent. I got up in the dark with no hint of the dawn but at least the sky was clear. Slowly the camp came to life and the sun rose. This led to a scramble to get the tents down, packed and tied together. I was tense, ready for the challenge, as were many others. The first porters left at 6 am while we milled around anticipating breakfast. The only talk was of the route ahead and its feasibility. I squeezed about 15 kg into my large rucksack, all my personal items, as did everyone else. Other loads were separated into essential experiments for the first day and those that could wait until later, such as the bike and the Yorkie Bars. But some heavy items were important, particularly the generator, the blood-gas analyser and the arctic tent for sleep studies.

As usual, I started at the back to ensure all the identified loads were on the move. I watched the tell-tale line of red plastic bags ascend the route. At the back were John Simmons and Dave, who both had bad chest infections. Mike Winterborn was also slow. After a couple of hours, two porters came running down the track having already dumped their loads at the top. I was impressed and delighted. The game was on. I stopped them and with a handful of rupees persuaded them to climb back up to the summit carrying Dave and John's bags. John could not possibly have carried a full load. Ten days of carrying the generator had completely worn him out. He was coughing continuously and in a poor state. He was the last person to complain but gratefully accepted help.

From the perspective of the day before, it had seemed an impossible goal. Now it was achievable. Gradually, we ascended and by 1 pm we reached the pass at an altitude of 4,846 m. It was a great relief. The weather had been kind, it was only misty, and all the correct equipment had been bought up. As the camp was slowly constructed, I walked up to the head of the pass to gaze at the east side of Bauda in relief. We had made it.

I descended with a great sense of happiness – that endorphin effect kicking in – but it was short-lived. The generator wouldn't start, which meant no experiments. It appeared as though the carburettors would not allow enough oxygen into the compression chambers. John Simmons was, as usual, responsible for the generator. He spent several hours experimenting with it and intermittently it would run perfectly but only with continuous care. It was essential that we had a stable electricity supply for the blood-gas analyser. It was a 1.5 kVa Honda generator. A similar machine had worked perfectly at previous high camps so we were at a loss to know what was wrong.

The campsite was on snow and ice in the middle of a large boulder field, with recent rock falls on one side. To avoid any danger from further avalanches, we camped in the middle, clearing smaller debris so that the tents could be pitched flat (figure 16). John Milles and I chose a large level slab of rock. Since it warmed up in the afternoon sun, we thought it might retain heat during the night. This would be better than pitching on ice. It took two breathless hours to secure our tent against strong winds in its precarious position.

That night we ate dinner crammed into the relative warmth of the arctic tent. John Simmons and I were very worried about the generator but most people were pretty upbeat. So far we had overcome all the difficulties thrown at us. Most of us were reasonably well, although a few had high-altitude headaches. With much to celebrate, Peter Dykes bought out a bottle of whisky. He had considered it an essential item. I didn't ask whether he had carried it up himself.

We ate by the light of head torches since we had no generator and I agreed to watch over the sleep subjects for the first few hours. A total of eight were being studied; four each night, half

Arctic tent

on acetazolamide and half on placebo in a blinded fashion. Each was allocated either a sleeping tablet (temazepam 20 mg) or placebo. Improved sleep was judged by how people felt and from studying sleep patterns on the continuous EEG recordings. The next few nights would be taken up with these measurements, and if all went well there was sufficient time to repeat the study on subjects who hadn't provided satisfactory results. On returning to my tent after midnight, I found that John had peed over his sack because in the dark he hadn't taken the top off his urine bottle.

I slept fitfully, still worrying about the studies, but the next morning proved to be clear and beautiful. After tea and breakfast had revived us, I worked on the generator with John Simmons. He still had bad bronchitis, expectorating bright red blood from time to time in great coughing fits, but most of us were well with little in the way of headaches. After an hour of futile effort, pulling the starting cord endlessly, the generator suddenly kicked into life. Remarkably, it then ran uneventfully for five hours – well into the afternoon. We managed to complete the blood-gas analyses and charge all the batteries for the sleep studies.

That afternoon Jonathan, Pete Forster and I climbed over the col to the glacier on the far side. It was great to be exercising at this altitude and feeling well. We watched and heard the avalanches crashing down off the east side of Bauda (figure 17). Huge seracs from a massive ice cliff plunged thousands of feet into the valley. It was an extraordinary place. We raced back over the col and down to the mess tent for afternoon tea.

The evening was a sombre affair. There was no light from the generator again and it was bitterly cold as we huddled in the big tent for an unappetising meal. It was not easy to eat at nearly 5,000 m. Talk turned to our most important experiment in the morning – the exercise test.

It was another beautiful clear start to the day, the sun's rays gradually moving onto the camp from the steep slopes above. As the sunlight touched the tents, ice on the inside melted, leaving trickles of water running downwards. Morning sun seemed to be a regular pattern for the early post-monsoon weather at this altitude. Then the heat of the day evaporated monsoon water on the lowlands which, rising on strong thermals, formed huge cumulus clouds that blocked out the sun by midday. The rising clouds cloaked our campsite, producing snow flurries and bitter winds. As the sun set, the sky cleared and a cold night followed.

John Coote was in charge of the exercise tests. In a sun-lit part of the camp, we set up the bike with the help of John Simmons. The experiment involved peddling at gradually increasing workloads (by applying a braking pressure to the wheel) until exhaustion. Results would be compared with sea-level measurements taken a few weeks earlier in Birmingham. Everyone was rather anxious about taking part since we knew it would be tough at altitude. How would each of us perform and what was the effect of acetazolamide? Our masculinity was on the line.

The Sherpas were fascinated, having heard a lot about the bike and watched it being carried every day by struggling porters. Not fully understanding the experiment, they had told us on several occasions that it was no use having a bike where we were going because there were no roads. When we finally put it together and they saw that there was only one wheel, they thought we were crazy (figure 18). John Coote dutifully worked hard all day and the next studying 17 of us. Through the gathering mist of the morning and afternoon snow flurries, he remained resolutely beside the bike testing us one after the other. My turn came and it was a real struggle. My performance was well behind some of the younger members such as Jonathan. John Coote did a great job and the results looked reliable. The old Griffith Pugh bike from the 1960s was still useful. We also tested Ginette and Ringee. Remarkably, her long-term acclimatisation allowed her to increase her heart rate much higher than everyone else – apart from Ringee. He performed like someone at sea level. We could see why Sherpas had so much strength.

At 2 pm on the second day, Martin and Tim appeared to enormous excitement and cheering. But there was no Gron; he had gone home. They had taken three days to come from Barpak. We were very happy to see them looking so well, albeit very tired.

Alongside the bike experiment, we needed to assess muscle mass. Peter Dykes had borrowed an ultrasound scanner that could measure the thickness of muscle between the skin and bone surfaces. The probe was positioned over the thigh and biceps and produced a scan on a small screen from which muscle mass could be derived (figure 19). It depended upon the generator, of course, so results were intermittent, but with persistence Peter measured everyone. To assess fat loss, we measured skin-fold thickness on predetermined sites around the body. As we were exposed to the elements during these measurements, there was much enthusiasm to perform them in the morning sun.

Other tests were going on in parallel, such as testing for proteinuria. Lysine was injected into a vein over a ten-minute period and urine samples were collected before and after the test, along with blood samples. While the lysine made everyone feel a little dizzy, the worst part was starving for four hours beforehand then drinking a litre of water to maintain a strong urine flow. In all, 14 subjects were tested over three days.

The second night we ate in the arctic tent with a sense of success but Ringee soon put paid to that. He told us all about the continuing problem with the porters and their festival. Our baggage could not be returned to Kathmandu in time for the plane home. We will see! We animatedly discussed his incompetence. I wondered what the morning would bring.

Unfortunately, it was cloudy. As the self-appointed official photographer, I had promised to take lots of photos of the experiments. The first pictures would be of the view down the pass to Himalchuli. I climbed past Martin who had also arisen early to catch the dawn. As I stood watching the rising morning clouds, Jonathan, Nev and Ginette come up from the camp carrying climbing gear. They were planning to climb the ridge and recce the nearest peak, Sampu (Rupina Kang). Climbing an unknown mountain in unpredictable weather seemed brave to me. But I looked on jealously and wished them luck.

Martin and I wandered back down for the Yorkie Bar tests and spent two hours trying to tease the generator into life. John Simmons was depressed about it and took its failure very personally. Maybe it was too new and hadn't been run in properly; maybe it just wasn't powerful enough; maybe the carburettors were badly set. Eventually, we just left it spluttering and, remarkably, after an hour of ticking over it sprang into life. I immediately felt much better. It hummed on for three hours then, as we were about half-way through the blood gas measurements, it unaccountably stopped – what a drag. The weather became dull, deteriorating into one of the worst days yet. Not the day to be climbing a mountain! I developed a headache which wasn't mountain sickness. I doubted whether I could suffer another frustrating trip like this one. It had not matched up to what I had hoped.

At 3.30 pm the climbers reappeared. Against the odds they had climbed the peak. Nev was back first and explained all about the climb, closely followed by Jonathan. Ginette was well behind, struggling down the ridge alone and then across the boulders. We gradually realised she couldn't see. In spite of it being cloudy all day, the ultraviolet light reflection had given her snow blindness. Several people scrambled up the slope to guide her the last 100 metres. Her eyes were bloodshot and painful. Their plan had been to recce the route but one thing led to another and they climbed to the top. She had realised early on that her sunglasses were in her tent, but believing they would not be out for long, it hadn't seemed worthwhile returning.

That evening there was a lot of discussion as to who might try next. Many had never climbed on snow and ice while others had experiments to finish. Dave was a registered mountain guide and came into his own. He would lead the second team. We had two ropes while Frank, Dave, Tim, Simon, John Simmons and myself had crampons and ice axes. That would make two ropes of three. A good day on the mountains would make up for some of the expedition's difficulties. I went to bed wearing my harness and climbing gear – everything except duvet jacket, boots and crampons.

Peeking out of the tent at 4 am, it looked very cold and forbidding. I struggled into boots and duvet jacket. John Milles wished me luck. First thing was to find some biscuits. Creeping quietly past Ringee's tent, I heard his girlfriend nagging – I almost felt sorry for him. I found a box of biscuits in the cook tent, together with three Yorkie Bars. The tests were complete so they wouldn't be missed. Then we were off. Up to the Rupina La col and onto the rocky ridge as the sun rose for a beautiful morning. We were in luck. We roped up. Frank, Dave and me on one rope with Simon, John and Tim on the other. It was exhilarating. The views were beautiful and the mountain beckoned. Frank was slow, as always at altitude, and this was as high as he had ever been. Reluctantly, he decided to turn back, which was probably for the best. He had taken an acetazolamide tablet the night before to help in the ascent but I was not sure that was wise.

After the ridge, we ascended a steep couloir covered in soft snow and onto a glacier. The footprints from our friends the day before were clearly visible, leading us on with growing confidence. The glacier led to a large bergschrund (crevasses where glaciers meet cliffs) with a small ice bridge at one end. David helped each of us across with a boot ice-axe belay onto the upper section of the glacier. Slowly we plodded up. John transferred to our rope because Simon couldn't tolerate his slow progress. He was indeed very slow but the least we could do was be patient considering all the effort he had put into running the generator. The next section was a steep snow and rock gully between two crumbling pillars, which required snow belays. From there it was a fine ridge to the summit. All five of us squeezed on and celebrated (figure 20). There were fine views of Bauda, Himalchuli and even Manaslu, an 8,000 m peak. I did a Yorkie Bar advertising photo for Peter Dykes, then we ate it.

But time was pressing. We needed to descend before the snow became soft and prone to avalanching. John felt wretched and tripped over his crampons as we started to descend. It was fortunate that he was roped. Would we make it down the dangerous couloir? The snow was like creamed rice – slushy and yielding. We went slowly back following our old footprints. Slower and slower – and poor John started coughing blood. We followed Tim and Simon down the final rocky ridge to Rupina La. I un-roped and whooped down the boulder field, being first into camp, much to Simon's fury. I felt like a hero – which made a change. The generator had not worked all day but who cared? I was too excited.

That evening I sat at the back of the arctic tent and talked animatedly to Pete Forster and Peter Dykes. I was euphoric from the climb while the Bergfuhrer (Dave) was delighted to have had his day of glory. This is what he had come for and he had clearly enjoyed himself. His old pessimism was gone. We shared some high-altitude rations that he had especially saved for the occasion. Hot, spicy European food. It finished a wonderful day in the mountains.

The last full day at the high camp loomed. I was not on acetazolamide so I took 500 mg to see if it would improve my exercise performance. It had not helped Frank, as he had hoped, but I wanted to try myself. I tested its effects after lunch. The three Johns and I went over the col to the glacier beneath Bauda. I was absolutely knackered and struggled to keep up. Was the acetazolamide affecting me adversely or was it tiredness from yesterday's climb? We mused that another expedition should assess whether acetazolamide was beneficial or not when prescribed acutely.

Back at camp, bags and equipment were being organised for the descent. The group was being split into two. Twelve would descend that afternoon to the lower base camp (where the porters had stayed), leaving four of us on final sleep studies with Pete Smith, John Coote, Peter Dykes and myself in a support role. There were a few other minor tasks to complete but to my surprise, and despite the generator problems, all experiments had been completed.

That night whisky and brandy bottles appeared from nowhere, hidden in peoples' bags for the past three weeks. Even Ringee found whisky for us. Happily, we got tipsy and solved the world's problems. We all agreed it had been a great expedition. Hypoxia and alcohol quickly erased the bad memories.

The descent the following day was in two phases, commencing with a walk to the porters' camp followed by a further descent to a sheep farm. Before the porters arrived, we rationalised the loads into manageable weights. There had been 72 loads coming up but less on descent because we had used the petrol, eaten lots of food, drunk the whisky and waste items could be burnt. We still needed to carry down full loads containing our personal gear. Some porters had arrived to help but the majority stayed at the lower base camp where we would meet them around lunchtime.

To my surprise, I was reluctant to leave. I had developed a peculiar attachment to that barren, inhospitable place. The human brain has remarkable ability to tolerate any situation. Maybe some Russian prisoners had even missed the Gulags! I hung around at the back of the group, supervising the camp, and tried to absorb abiding memories of a unique experience. Surely, none of us would ever return. The rubbish was burnt and we departed to the sound of light bulbs exploding in the fire. The arctic tent still contained 26 loads that would be brought down the following day. We were accompanied by six porters carrying blood samples, the generator and medical equipment. I trudged down the wet path in the mist.

Having completed the research component of the trip, I felt less responsibility for watching the back markers so I joined the front group led by Ringee. The route was far from clear. There were innumerable minor tracks through the pastures and small woods, all leading in different directions. Although we started together, we quickly split into several groups, going at different speeds. Remarkably, we arrived at a bridge from various directions and were together again. In single file, we walked further down but the temptation to get to the front was irresistible. I overtook a long line of our group by running down a scree slope to catch up with Nev, then piled on the pressure. In little time we lurched through the sheep farm beyond Kharka and selected a beautiful spot to camp. It had taken six hours to climb up but we were down in two and a quarter without really trying.

Over the next couple of hours, the team drifted in and we sat down to tea looking up at Bauda, Sampu (figure 21) and the mountains that had been ours for a few days. Rupina La looked very remote and insignificant. We were 1,400 m lower and felt so much better. Smiles came back to everyone. We ate well then slept soundly.

Day 22 – The race to Barpak.

The descent plan for the day was rather vague. Ringee had little idea of the route, as we had noted on the way up, but he assured us that the way down was easy and lunch would be at Barpak. The day started brightly, the generator whirred away happily at the reduced altitude, and breakfast in the slightly warmer air pleased us all. Appetites returned and after six helpings of porridge I was ready for the descent. We were hungry having lost weight from being at over 3,600 m for ten days. Grateful for the thicker air and not wishing to be burdened for the walk, I reduced the contents of my day sack to a minimum.

In the distance, shining in the sun on a promontory, Ringee pointed out Barpak, the town that Martin, Gron and Tim had descended to when they were ill. We guessed it was about eight miles due south and perhaps 1,500 m below us. The rough path contoured around a series of deep-sided wooded valleys to the east which were hidden from view, while the densely forested valley itself looked impenetrable. We thought that arriving by lunchtime was rather optimistic.

Having ensured that all luggage was packed, I followed John Coote and Ringee. We slowly overtook the back markers and some of the porters who had left early. At the head of the first side valley, a large waterfall tumbled across the path and plunged into the depths below. After two hours we found ourselves on the first promontory and again caught sight of Barpak. It seemed hardly any closer and we had already walked at least five miles. We started to realise that there would be no lunch that day, yet it was starting to be fun. I had been sweeper on the way up to Rupina La, why not a day at the front for a change? We caught up with Simon and briefly Ian but he had bad diarrhoea and stopped in a field to relieve himself. This was no time to wait for stragglers.

Walking with John Coote we came across Tim, Neville and Peter Dykes washing in a stream. They were convinced they were in the lead and gave chase as we passed without stopping. They shouted after us, not wanting to be left behind. There were numerous different parallel tracks through the woods. Many were boulder-strewn scree, which we jogged down to keep ahead. Paths criss-crossed from different directions so from time-to-time we came across others of our group on different routes. Jonathan then appeared from nowhere and stayed with us. John Coote complained that I was being competitive and irresponsible and we should wait for the others, but he couldn't keep up on one tricky descent. On another promontory, Barpak was again visible. We were perhaps half-way and it was already 2.30 pm. It was clearly impossible for everyone to get there by dusk. We had been on the move since 8 am already. Bloody Ringee clearly had no idea of the distance or how to get there.

The day developed into a race for the town. We could hear others on screes higher up the trail and pressed on at full speed, jogging where possible. By 5 pm Jonathan and I were still at the front. He had a slight limp from an earlier fall so, with a mile of easy path remaining, I ran ahead into Barpak's narrow streets. So much for arriving by lunchtime!

With Jonathan, we interrogated the English-speaking Gurkhas to find out why all the tea-houses were closed. Thankfully, at a well-constructed house in the centre of the village, a smart soldierly man welcomed us in for tea and biscuits. He was the Gurkha chief of the village and looked rather like Paul Newman. He explained that the following day was the most important holiday of the year so everywhere was closed in preparation. This presumably was why the porters had been so keen to go home the week before. We gratefully entered and climbed up the stairs to a small veranda overlooking the main street. An admiring crowd gathered below believing we had climbed Himalchuli.

As others came in over the following hours, we called down from our veranda, inviting them in. It became dark as our group arrived in dribs and drabs. By 8 pm it was pitch black yet porters were still appearing as we anxiously awaited the last of our bunch, Ian Chesner. We had dinner, drank beers and rakshi, and were excited from an invigorating day, but still no Ian. There were intense discussions about the chaos of the descent and Ringee's completely wrong information about the distance to Barpak. I was criticised for not waiting for everyone, but most of the debate was fuelled by beer and our anxiety about Ian. Had he fallen over one of the many precipices, become lost on a different trail, or been eaten by Abominable Snowmen? The suggestions were legion. He had not been seen by anyone since midday. However, we agreed that he had bad diarrhoea and that I might have been the last to see him alive. A few porters were still missing, so the likeliest scenario was that he was camping with them.

Late into the night, the festival started. Some managed to enjoy the fun but I was too tired. I returned to my sack on the balcony of the Gurkha house. I slept happily and soundly. It had been a great day.

The next morning was cold and sunny. Next to me lay Ginette and Tim still sleeping. Everyone was crammed onto the balcony in their sleeping bags. I quickly dressed in the cold morning air and walked around the town to meet with the first of the cook boys finally arriving from the descent. They had not seen Ian.

Over breakfast the remaining porters appeared with their loads but no Ian. A search party had been suggested the night before so the plan swung into action. Nev, Nick and I agreed to go back up the mountain with two Sherpas, Turky and Mingma, to where he had last been seen. Peter Dykes took charge of everyone else descending the valley. In short order, Sherpas and porters set off, pleased to be going down, while we contemplated a very long day. Still feeling the benefits of the thicker air, we had little difficulty walking back up for two and a half hours, shouting and whistling to attract Ian's attention. There were innumerable precipices that he could have fallen over and been knocked unconscious. Equally, there were many paths that headed directly down the valley rather than contouring to Barpak. When we arrived at his last sighting place, tired and somewhat worried, we turned around and within two hours were back in town.

Arriving at the Gurkha chief's house, we were given a written message from Peter Dykes saying that an Englishman had been spotted below in the valley and that it was probably Ian. Ringee had waited for us and was obviously delighted that we had returned safely. To help with our pursuit of the others, he arranged for three porters to carry our bags (20 rupees each) while other porters climbed back to the lower base-camp to bring down the remainder of the loads.

At 5 pm we departed, following the lead porter like the Pied Piper, down innumerable steps. There was no more contouring – it was straight down to the jungle. We jostled with small children running alongside. They were in awe of our size and whiteness. Expeditions through the town were rare, especially those with missing members. As we descended into the dusk, the temperature rose so by the time we reached a bridge at the valley bottom, 1,000 m lower, it was pitch black and hot. We stumbled on in the moonlight past dense jungle, waterfalls and fireflies. After 1.5 miles and at the end of a long bridge we unexpectedly came upon our camp. Ian was there. He explained what had happened:

"I stopped for squits many times and ended up in a hash field. Barpak was miles away but 600 m higher up and I had not seen anyone for several hours. I felt too weak to climb back up. I ate a couple of biscuits and laid down by a stream in the borrowed sleeping bag and smoked a reefer with tobacco and leaves from some dried plants. That deadened the hunger pangs. Next morning the decision was either climb to Barpak or contour round to find the group, but there was no direct path. Instead, I descended, crossing numerous steams and deep rivers through the jungle. After several hours, I met a woman who took me to her house and fed me on a goat curry. In gratitude, I gave her my umbrella. Her husband was an ex-Gurkha with his certificate on the wall. He agreed to help me down the valley and passed me over to another person after having paid him with my watch. The umbrella was then spotted by one of our members. Just then I heard English voices and we met up. It was only 24 hours but it seemed interminable. I imagined you were miles down the valley and would leave for Kathmandu without me." (See BMRES rule number 2, p8).

Ian had lost his rucksack, then himself. It was too much of a coincidence.

Losing Ian led to a heated discussion about the ethics of allowing people to walk alone on big expeditions. John Coote started an argument about people not taking enough responsibility for others, insisting that we should have walked in line. He accused me of being reckless. As leader, I should set a better example. Thankfully, Ian supported people taking their own decisions and in no way blamed me. After all, as I pointed out, we were all consenting adults. Neville bluntly told John not to be so f****** stupid. I was very grateful to be supported.

I slumped into bed at 11 pm. It had been a long day: sleep could not be denied.

We headed down the valley after re-crossing the bridge but soon stopped by the river for a testosterone test; to swim past a stopper wave in the fast-flowing current – great fun. Most people managed it. We were in holiday mode. After two hours we walked further down the river and did it all again. Oh, to be really clean after two weeks of accumulated dirt.

It was very hot and humid by the paddy fields and talk turned to work, relationships and booze. The camp was by a small village above the river with a rakshi shop. Tim bought up all their supplies and we tried to get hammered. John Milles chatted up Ginette and off they went for a swim together. Three weeks on an expedition does that. I fell asleep over dinner and sloped off to bed early. John blundered into the tent at some unholy hour.

Then it was our final day. Several of us were concerned about the 26 loads that we had left in the lower base camp in the arctic tent. Ringee had warned us that it might not arrive back in time for our plane to London. Generally, his predictions had been falsely optimistic. If he was true to form, we presumed we would never see any of it again. There were several items of very expensive medical equipment. It would be a disaster if they were stolen.

Personally, I had been rather preoccupied with how Barbara (with her friend Anne) was getting on in India. We had been married less than four months. Her well-being was of deep concern. My thoughts turned away from generators, lost people and experiments to our planned meeting in Kathmandu.

The day's walk was leisurely alongside the river. There was an alternative shorter hike over several ridges but the low-level route won the vote. It was a time for post-expedition relaxation and reflection, boosted by hot teas, bananas and red grapefruit from innumerable wayside shops. We chatted over a river-side lunch, all agreeing that the trek had been wonderful. Funny how the bad experiences had been forgotten so quickly, to be replaced by an overwhelming sense of contentment.

The walk ended alongside paddy fields of the gradually widening valley, with Gorkha a few miles distant. The campsite was beside the river, soothing us with its babbling noise. Across a suspension bridge was the road with a bus pick-up point for the morning.

Nepalese families from a small village wandered over to greet us and stare. Namaste! There was a bar with beer, where we became light-headed on alcohol, but there was more on offer – ganga (hashish). It was cheap and powerful, as some were to discover.

Relaxing in my tent, I heard a commotion in a neighbouring tent occupied by John Taverner and Pete Smith.

"Pete's copped it!" John shouted in alarm. I rushed outside to find him in great distress. Slurring his words, he repeated, "Pete's cop't it."

Inside their tent, I could see Pete lying in his sleeping bag, eyes wide open. I entered anxiously with Pete Forster. He was staring upwards and was immobile apart from shallow breaths taken in short gasps.

"I'm dead," he rasped in horror. "I'm dead." The smell of hash pervaded the tent.

Pete and I looked at each other and laughed. We shook him out of his dream-like state. His terror abated as he slowly came back to reality.

We crawled out of the tent dragging him with us and explained his hash overdose to others who had gathered outside in alarm. John Taverner was also well under the influence. We presumed that he had genuinely thought that Pete had died.

Pete Forster in his typically humorous manner wondered whether the term 'cop't it' was the typical description of death given by general practitioners (John Taverner), and whether a hash trance was in the current international list of medical descriptions of death. They both endured a lot of teasing.

We finished off the evening in a euphoric state. It was magical. Fireflies flickered around the campsite and the Milky Way shone in all its glory. In the distance, Bauda Himal was silhouetted along the Himalayan chain.

It was a short walk next morning to the buses parked on the tarmac road across the river. But there was a final flurry of experimentation. All personal acute mountain sickness questionnaires had to be handed in, which included filling in those that had been forgotten. Peter Dykes repeated the muscle thickness measurements plus weights and skin-fold thickness. There was an argument about the reliability of the scales because we could not believe the weight loss measurements.

The next stop was Kathmandu and the Paradise Hotel for a jolly good shower where, thankfully, Barbara had arrived safely from her Indian travels. Neville and Frank went to see Mike Cheney about the baggage. Much to their surprise, it was all waiting for them at his office. The porters were much quicker on their return journey. It had taken us five days to descend from the lower base camp while they did it in three. Mike explained that they were paid for each stage and not by the day or distance. They could probably have come down even faster. We were very grateful.

We left a tip comprising 15% of the total cost of the trek. It was to be distributed among all the Sherpas and porters but Ringee kept most of it. Mike Cheney said we should have distributed it to each person individually. Ringee was a scallywag.

The next day everyone apart from Barbara, myself and Ginette returned to London. Ginette planned to climb for a month while we had a week to explore the country. It was fond farewells following a great adventure but as we said goodbye Barbara keeled over from a gut infection acquired in Srinagar. Over the next few days she lay in bed recovering on a mixture of ciprofloxacin and codeine. A week later we returned to the UK having not left the Kathmandu valley.

Postscript:

Having a month off from the day job meant there was a lot of catching up but over the months our thoughts turned to the experiments and publications.

Alex and Ron Fletcher organised a research meeting the following year at the Medical School to focus everyone's thoughts on the experimental results. We showed that those on acetazolamide had better exercise performance, retained more muscle and fat, and felt better. These observations were subsequently published in The Lancet in 1986 and the Postgraduate Medical Journal. Other useful results included a better understanding of the mechanisms of proteinuria and intestinal absorption at altitude.

We described our observations to Chris Bonington. He took acetazolamide on his successful ascent of Mt Everest the following year and, aged 50, he became the oldest person to reach the summit.

Publications from the expedition:

1. Bradwell AR, Dykes PW, Coote JH. Effect of acetazolamide on exercise at altitude. Sports Medicine 1987; 4, 157–163
2. Bradwell AR, Dykes PW, Coote JH, Forster PJG, Milles JJ, Chesner I, Richardson NV. Effect of acetazolamide on exercise performances and muscle mass at high altitude. The Lancet 1986; 1(8488), 1001–1005.
3. Chesner IM, Small NA, Dykes PW. Intestinal absorption at high altitude. Postgraduate Medical Journal 1987; 63, 173–175.
4. Dykes PW, Richardson N, Milles J, Forster P, Coote JH, Bradwell AR; BMRES. Muscle, fat and body weight loss at altitude. Clinical Science 1985 69, suppl. 12, 69 29p.
5. Fletcher RF, Wright AD, Jones GT, Bradwell AR. The clinical assessment of acute mountain sickness. Quarterly Journal of Medicine 1985; 213, 91–100.
6. Winterborn MH, Bradwell AR, Chesner I, Jones GT. The origin of proteinuria at high altitude. Postgraduate Medical Journal 1987; 63, 179–181.

Fig 1. Top row left to right: *Frank Davies, John Taverner, Tim Harvey.* **Middle row:** *Jonathan Evans, Mike Winterborn, John Milles, Simon Morrissey, Pete Smith, Martin Bradwell, Kate Keohone, Pete Forster, Nick Binns, Neville Richardson, Ian Chesner, Jo Bradwell.* **Front row:** *John Coote, Peter Dykes, Ang Ringee and girlfriend, Dave Siviter, John Simmons.*

Fig 2. *Chris Bonington*

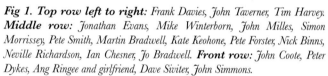
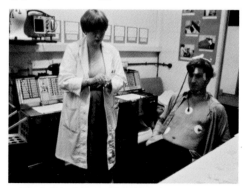

Fig 3. *John Milles with EEG leads in Farnborough*

Fig 4. *Thanks for the discount*

Fig 5. *A wet school yard*

Fig 6. *An early soaking*

Fig 7. *John Simmons; generator carrier*

Fig 8. *Say ahh! Peter Dykes with a patient*

Fig 9. *Evening camp under Bauda*

Fig 10. *Annapurna Himal*

Fig 11. *Buffalo meat*

Fig 12. *Sunrise on Himalchuli and Bauda*

Fig 13. *Camp above the lake god*

Fig 14. *Gron, Martin and Tim with Sherpas*

Fig 15. *Tamang porters*

Fig 16. *Camp at Rupina La*

Fig 17. *Avalanches off Bauda Himal*

Fig 18. *Ian, Pete F, Neville and Jonathan*

Fig 19. *Testing muscle mass*

Fig 20. *Sampu summit with Dave, John S, Simon and Tim*

Fig 21. *Sampu*

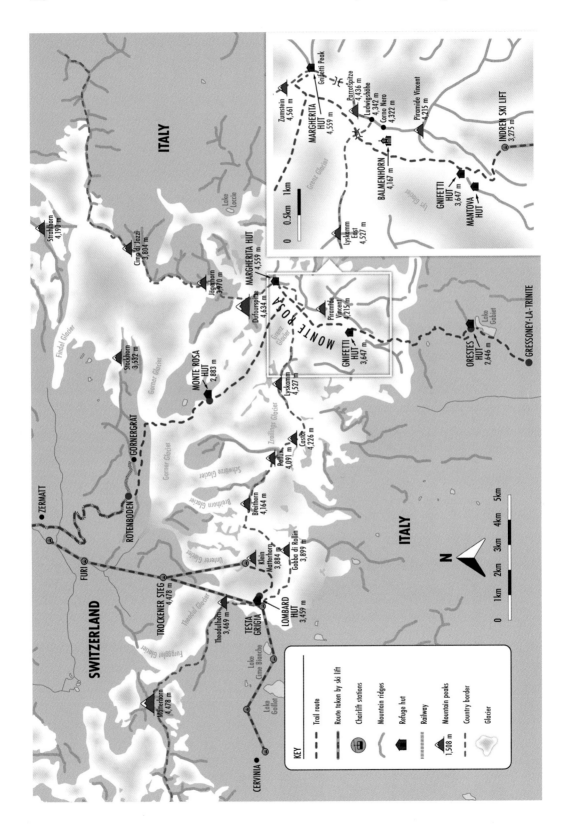

Alpine Interlude
Testa Grigia, Italy – March 1987

The Matterhorn and Testa Grigia with the Lombard Hut on the extreme left.

Down a crevasse

In the middle of the night, Phil awoke gasping for breath with bubbling in his lungs. Terrified, he felt he was drowning. It was acute mountain sickness with life-threatening pulmonary oedema.

Expedition members: Jo Bradwell, Patrick Cadigan, John Coote, Frank Davies, John Delamere, Norman Dorricott, Peter Dykes, Jonathan Evans, Ron Fletcher, Tim Harvey, Jörgen Jensen, Niels Lassen, Simon Meech, Phil Meridith, John Milles, John Potokar, Neville Richardson, John Simmons, Dave Siviter, Neil Stanley, Barbara Stone, John Tavener, Mike Winterborn, Alex Wright.

The results of the Rupina La experiments were intriguing. By increasing oxygen supply to the body, acetazolamide had prevented the normal loss of muscle seen at altitude, thereby improving exercise performance. Previously, we had shown that the drug improved kidney and brain function. The medication was giving body-wide benefits but we wondered if there might be harmful side effects. Brain blood flow was known to increase at altitude and increased further with acetazolamide. If altitude headaches were due to increased brain volume, they might be made worse if the drug was given acutely. We needed to find out.

At a hypoxia conference in Canada in 1985, I met the world's leading expert on brain blood flow, the redoubtable Professor Niels Lassen. He was head of radiology at the Bispebjerg Hospital in Copenhagen, Denmark, and had developed a technique that could measure brain blood flow using a radioactive isotope of xenon (xenon-133). In practice, the gas, dissolved in a salt solution, was injected into a vein. As it surged around the brain, it emitted gamma rays that were detected using a gamma camera (sodium iodide crystal detectors). Since the amount detected was proportional to the amount of blood in the brain, the actual blood flow could be calculated. (The radiation dose from xenon-133 was essentially harmless; it was a small dose breathed out seconds after being injected.)

Our keen interest in understanding cerebral oedema, combined with his interest in the technique, meant we teamed up to study brain blood flow at altitude. A major challenge was to obtain small gamma cameras. Those available in hospitals weighed 50 kg or more each and we would need several. Lightweight ones could be constructed but only for a high price. In the autumn of 1986, Niels persuaded a company in Denmark to make some especially for our study at a cost of £30,000. They comprised six separate detectors enclosed in a helmet. Each was a masterpiece of miniaturisation and together they provided a full view of the brain. Initial studies in Copenhagen were successful so the next step was to decide on a high-altitude location.

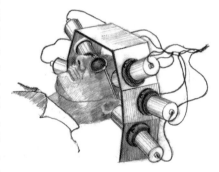

Minature gamma camera

After discussions of exotic places such as the Margherita Hut on top of Monte Rosa (4,559 m) and the Vallot Hut on Mont Blanc (4,200 m), we settled for the more modest altitude of the Lombard Hut at 3,475 m. This is a rustic mountain refuge/restaurant at Testa Grigia, poised at the very edge of a huge precipice on a high shoulder of the Matterhorn between Italy and Switzerland. From its windows there are unrivalled views of Mont Blanc, the Grand Combin and the Matterhorn.

The hut had two additional features that made it attractive. It was at the top of two of the world's best ski resorts – Zermatt and Cervinia – and it had a good restaurant. No other venues suited our purposes better. With the help of a translator in the Italian department at the University of Birmingham, we made a booking for the post-Easter fortnight of 1987 with Marcello Lombard, putting down a deposit of one million lira (£500). Two groups of 12 people would stay at the hut in sequential weeks to study brain blood flow with the new gamma camera.

The other challenge was to obtain enough xenon-133. Since the gas has a half-life of four days (its radioactive emissions reduce by 50% every four days), we needed a large supply if we were to study people over a two-week period. Furthermore, it was synthesised in a nuclear reactor at Amersham International, a UK company near London, so it would have to be taken across international borders. As there were international tensions because of the Cold War, a group of climbers carrying radioactive materials through several countries would be politically delicate, to say the least. If any certification were wrong or customs officers became difficult, there might be considerable publicity and governmental embarrassment, not to mention the risk that they would be sent to jail. Furthermore, impounding the xenon-133 for a day or two would reduce its activity, leaving insufficient for our studies.

Fortunately, Niels had colleagues in Switzerland who could have it delivered to a Geneva hospital. From there we could carry it by train to Zermatt, up a series of cable cars to the Klein Matterhorn at 3,884 m, then ski down to the Lombard Hut (front figure). Although this was possibly illegal, the hut was in a remote location a mere ten metres beyond the Swiss border. We could argue that it had hardly left the country. While three people were needed to carry the xenon-133, the rest of the group and the experimental equipment could travel through the Mont Blanc tunnel to Aosta and Cervinia. From there, rather primitive ski lifts could transport us plus equipment to the hut.

Over the following months we lined up 24 volunteers including ourselves. The fateful day arrived and the first week's minivan with 12 occupants departed from the Medical School.

Initially all went well. We arrived in Geneva on time to collect the xenon-133, which was supplied in several dozen 20-ml lead vials, making it safe to handle. Checking with a Geiger counter confirmed that trivial amounts of dangerous gamma rays were being emitted. Neville Richardson, Tim Harvey and I agreed to carry them to the hut.

We packed the vials into three rucksacks with additional lead lining to protect our backs and drove to the railway station in Geneva. They were heavy. Each weighted 30 kg, plus we had skies and ski boots for our ski descent. It would be strenuous even though it was only a couple of miles. The first challenge, however, was to be at the lower Zermatt ski lifts before they closed at 3.30 pm. We had to arrive at the Lombard Hut that evening to allow time for the gamma cameras and 131Xe to be checked before the experiments started the following morning.

Timing was tight. We had been delayed in our drive across France, while the Geneva hospital was slow to release the xenon-133. Anxiously, we checked train schedules to Zermatt and were reassured that we had an hour spare.

The train departed on the stroke of midday and travelled along the Rhone Valley to Visp. We changed to the Zermatt train, hauling our heavy bags as inconspicuously as possible across the platforms to avoid being asked what they might contain. In the mountains ahead, the sky looked threatening, with fresh snow on the valley sides. We tossed a few 'what ifs' into the conversation. What if the train were delayed? What if the winds were too strong for the lifts to operate? What if we couldn't carry the heavy rucksacks while skiing? Failure to arrive that evening might leave insufficient xenon-133 for the study.

As we approached Zermatt, the weather deteriorated. The Matterhorn was shrouded in ominous-looking clouds while all the upper ski lifts at Trockener Steg were hidden. It was snowing. From the train, we jumped into an electric taxi and sped to the lift station at the top end of the village. We quickly bought an afternoon ski pass and asked anxiously about the Kline Matterhorn lift. It was closed because of high winds from an incoming storm. It would not be re-opening that day.

"How about the drag lifts to Testa Grigia?" we fearfully enquired.

"Zey are open at ze moment," came back the reply.

The drag lifts were four T-bars in a row that ascended five kilometres over the ice plateau of the Theodul Glacier. They were less affected by high winds, allowing skiers to return to Italy over the Theodul or the Testa Grigia pass even in bad weather. Reassured, we caught the cable car to Furi then changed to the Trockener Steg lift. The snowstorm increased as we ascended. It was just 4 pm so we had 30 minutes before closure of the top ski lifts. As the lift stopped, we jumped out, tightened our boots and rapidly donned skies, goggles and gloves, staggering with our heavy loads to the T-bar drag lifts. Tim started to ski but the weight of the lead vials was too much. He promptly fell over and had difficulty getting up, rather like a tortoise on its back. Neville and I struggled to ski but by bending a long way forward we could balance just enough to stay upright.

As we turned the corner, we could see that the long line of T-bars leading up into the storm were not moving and had no skiers on them. Heavy-hearted we went to the control hut to question the occupant.

"Sorry, zey are clozed for ze night," he smiled back at us.

We explained we had to get to Testa Grigia that evening because of important medical research with many people depending upon us.

"Sorry, zey are clozed for ze night," he replied firmly. There was no doubt he meant it.

We had discussed the possibility of skiing up. It would take 4–5 hours to climb from 2,939 m to 3,459 m over the snow-covered glacier. Neville had ski touring bindings, allowing him to step upwards as he ascended, and could probably get to the hut. Mine were regular downhill boots and skies so I would have to walk, carrying the skies on my shoulders. Since there were several feet of fresh snow it would be impossible. Also, the storm was intensifying and night approaching. Tim declared it was ridiculous to go up. He was going to stay in a hotel and with that he carefully skied off down the piste towards the lower cable car, leaving Neville and I wondering what to do.

Although Neville could possibly make the ascent, going alone would be reckless. If only I had ski mountaineering gear! Then we realised there was one possibility. The snow under the T-bars would be compacted by the weight of skiers and might support a walker. I shouldered my skies, tightened up the rucksack and walked to the start. The guardian had gone home so there was no one to object. Indeed, there was no one anywhere. The glacier was totally deserted. All skiing had ceased for the night, there were no lifts moving and no ski patrols to warn us of dangerous areas.

I was fit and strong, as was Neville. This could be a great challenge, I thought. This could be a story that would be told for years to come: 'How we climbed up the side of the Matterhorn, at night, in a storm, to deliver essential medical supplies.' We harked back to the time we had completed a 3½-day trek in the Himalayas during an 18-hour overnight hike (Chapter 1). Admittedly, that was 10 years ago but that trip was over 50 km in length whereas this was a mere 5 km.

We ascended into the growling storm for the next two hours. Fresh snow on the lift track thickened to 12 inches but the base remained hard. I gasped and panted with the effort, hardly able to speak. Neville skinned up alongside, struggling with his heavy load in the thin air. By 7 pm it was pitch black, the blizzard reducing visibility to a few yards. We passed onto the second ski-lift track then started on the third as the wind and snow subsided to reveal a starlit night. It was bitterly cold but finally the elements were in our favour. On the third section, the snow was too deep so we drifted to the right, away from the lifts towards the Matterhorn and its precipices. There was sufficient starlight to judge our whereabouts and distant lights flickered at the Theodul pass. The mighty shape of the Matterhorn blocked out all to our right.

Suddenly there was danger. High winds had blown all snow off the ridge on which we were climbing, revealing hard black ice underneath. Inadvertently we had climbed off the snow cover into a crevasse zone. I fell backwards as my ski boots lost all grip, fortunately sliding into soft snow. Realising our error, we tracked back to the ski lift and pressed on. Gradually the shape of buildings could be seen, then a bobbing head torch. We heard shouts of delight and willing hands clutched rucksacks and skies. Exhausted beyond measure, we reached the hut, its embracing warmth, and the excited glow of welcoming friends. It was 8.45 pm. We had been struggling up the glacier for nearly five hours.

"Where's Tim?" someone asked.

"We thought he was with you," we joked, and explained how the huge weight of his rucksack had put him on his back like an overturned tortoise.

"We knew you would make it," claimed Niels. "That's what we expect of the British. We will try the xenon-133 immediately so everything will be ready for the morning."

From the outside, the hut is an inconspicuous wood and metal construction tied to the cliff edge. Its balcony on the Italian side is suspended over an abyss that plunges 500 m to a ski area. The freezing toilet has the highest free drop in the Southern Alps. But inside, the hut is a haven of hospitality and noisy life. We found our group were in the middle of a wine-washed meal, Italian style. Everyone was merry. What a contrast from our five hours of hell.

The experiment had been set up in one of the bunk rooms. With his Danish senior lecturer, Jörgen, Niels set to work. Or rather Jörgen did. A man of Niels's stature needed a sidekick and Jörgen was the chosen one. He was charming, knowledgeable, and an expert with the apparatus. He immediately fitted in with the group. Within an hour, a participant was lying down, his head strapped inside the crystal helmet and he was injected with our precious cargo. It worked perfectly.

Throughout the following day, all 12 of us had our brains scanned. Four of us had mild headaches and loss of appetite from acute mountain sickness. After each person was tested, they were free to indulge and by mid-afternoon most of us were skiing the slopes above Zermatt on fresh snow from the night's storm. It was bliss.

The other experiment concerned the sedative, temazepam. On Rupina La, at nearly 5,000 m, we had shown that acetazolamide was helpful for sleep but we had only studied six people on temazepam. We needed more participants. Furthermore, the 10 mg dose we had chosen previously had little effect, so we proposed trying 20 mg. Tony Nicholson's sleep laboratory at Farnborough was again used for baseline studies.

At Testa Grigia we had enough equipment to study four sleepers at a time. On alternate nights for two weeks, individuals were wired into EEG electrodes and given temazepam or placebo. Brain waves were studied by Barbara Stone, a senior officer in the RAF, and Pete Smith of 'Pete's cop'd it' fame from Rupina La.

As before, we had many electrodes on our scalps, two near our eyes to check for eye movements and one below the chin to check for muscle movement. Placing the electrodes involved shaving a small area of hair from the scalp and carefully cementing the contacts in place. The electrodes were protected by a soft hat so

EEG electrodes

that turning in the night was painless and the electrodes were not rubbed off. We looked rather like Frankenstein's monster when we were fully wired up. Placing and removing the electrodes was time-consuming so they were left in place during the day. A ski hat was used to prevent them from becoming unstuck while skiing. This produced considerable amusement at lunch times and coffee breaks. The weather was warm, the sun out and we were hot, so naturally we removed our hats. Onlookers were curious and then felt sorry for the weirdoes who had electrodes on their heads.

Since we were in Italy (the first ten metres of the ledge was Italian), none of the hut staff spoke much English but they did speak a little French. Alongside our hut there were Italian and Swiss customs posts manned by several officials. Naturally, during the week the customs officers came into the hut for refreshments. It was a close-knit community living at the edge of survival. During stilted conversations, we asked them about their jobs. Hundreds of skiers went over the high pass every day and no passports were ever checked. With the rather slow intertwined communications in English, French, German and Italian, they explained that they were looking for drug smugglers, for which the penalties were extreme. We imagined that xenon-133 was not particularly addictive, and could hardly be called a drug, but had they known it was radioactive…

To diffuse the subject, the conversation was rapidly changed to human rights. Women had only recently been granted the vote in Switzerland, 60 years after Britain and most of the civilised world. They were teased about their slow progress. Their defence was that women came from all over the world to marry Swiss men.

The xenon-133 saline solutions were not completely benign. After his dose, Patrick developed rigors (intense shivering) and lay in his bunk hardly able to talk. The duty doctor was called – Ron Fletcher, our sagacious senior physician. He took a quick look and said, "I think I'll come back when he's a little better." A perceptive view from an old-style physician who didn't know what to do.

One night we were battered by a snowstorm. The hut shook, the wind howled and pounded the windows, building up huge snow drifts. The rooms were bitterly cold and the toilets froze. Chairs on the veranda were blown down the precipice towards Cervinia. Next morning, we skied in fresh, creamy, untracked snow.

At the end of the first week a few people returned home, including Niels and Jörgen. Others stayed in Zermatt to ski without the impediment of experiments and weird scalp electrodes. The xenon-133 studies were complete. On the afternoon of 4 April, the second group arrived, including Jonathan, John Coote, John Simmons and Phil Meridith for sleep studies.

After an uneventful night and day, the early hours provided unexpected drama. At 2 am, Phil suddenly awoke with bubbling sounds in his lungs and a feeling he was drowning. He realised that he had pulmonary oedema caused by acute mountain sickness. Fluid on his lungs was asphyxiating him.

How did he know? Because he had developed the same symptoms on the Thorong La in the Himalayas several years earlier. As on this occasion, he had awoken in the middle of the night gasping for breath and with a terrible headache. It had been impossible to descend immediately but at dawn he was evacuated to Muktinath then Jomsom. There he was given frusemide (a strong diuretic) and made a full recovery, even completing the rest of the Annapurna circuit without difficulty.

The symptoms he was now suffering were the same. He was also confused and unable to help himself. As bad luck would have it, all the qualified doctors from the first week had descended to ski from Zermatt. That left Jonathan, a fifth-year medical student, as the only person in the hut with any clinical experience. He stepped up to the mark. The obvious symptoms were confirmed to give a diagnosis of severe pulmonary oedema. The treatment: oxygen and descent.

One of our metal equipment boxes contained life-saving oxygen (brought along for just such an emergency) but the padlock keys were in Zermatt with Mike Winterborn. Fortunately, John Simmons was on hand. He had a Swiss army knife which included a saw in its armamentarium. Over the next half-hour he cut off the aluminium clasps that held the padlocks. In the fourth and final box was an oxygen cylinder and mask. To everyone's great relief, Phil was connected to the oxygen supply and felt better within minutes.

However, descent was the only guarantee of recovery. The warden of the hut had awoken with all the kafuffle and, seeing our plight, he contacted the Testa Grigia cable car manager to explain the emergency. Despite it being the middle of the night, within minutes a piste-levelling machine arrived with two drivers. They took Phil the 100 metres up to the cable car station, started its motors and accompanied him down the 1,700 m to Cervinia – none of which Phil remembered. At the bottom he was taken to the Crystal Hotel. A local doctor appeared and gave him frusemide.

For the next two days, Phil spent his time walking around Cervinia and had a succession of grateful visitors. There was only cold running water at Testa Grigia so his hot water bath became a very enticing place for the great unwashed up in the hut. By the final day, he was fully recovered.

Phil had always wanted to come on one of our main expeditions but he realised it was too risky. Perhaps interesting from a medical research viewpoint, but ethics committees would never allow it. Nevertheless, because of his climbing passion, he later trekked to high altitude many times and developed pulmonary oedema on three occasions, twice while on the Mont Blanc range and once on Mt Kenya. Taking acetazolamide seemed beneficial.

Phil's escape from the jaws of death was not the only adventure that week. Neville Richardson also stared death in the face on this trip, as described in this account published in Reader's Digest:

Upside Down in a Crevasse

He swung from his skis like a carcass in a slaughterhouse. Would he hang there till he died?

Neville Richardson felt exhilarated by the Alpine air, the sheer physical joy of outdoor exercise. The Liverpool University lecturer was 37, fit, strong and had come to Zermatt with friends to Testa Grigia. Now, at 9 am on 8 April 1987, he was ascending Monte Rosa, Switzerland's highest mountain. So ominous was the weather that one companion, Patrick Cadigan, a cardiologist, had decided to stay in the Bétampf Hut, half-way up Monte Rosa, where the trio spent the night. But Neville Richardson's other friend, hospital consultant John Delamere, joined 'Nev' in a spirited bid for the 15,200-foot summit. They set out on skis to begin with; rock-climbing would come later. At 12,000 feet, as they skied onto the Grenz Glacier, the wind rose and there were flurries of snow. But the Grenz, covered by new snow, looked inviting. They pressed on.

9.30 am. Richardson, 200 yards behind Delamere, suddenly felt his skis sink beneath him. In seconds, terrified, he found himself plummeting head first down a crevasse. It varied in width from about five to seven feet. He could hear his skis, six feet long, clattering against the jagged sides as he fell. Richardson dropped 70 feet, then stopped with a violent jolt. Both skis had jammed across a bottleneck. His ski-poles shot from his hands and vanished into the crevasse's depths. Had he been doing downhill skiing, his red plastic boots would have been fixed to his skis with heel and toe clips that opened automatically in an emergency. He would have fallen straight out of them and gone the way of his poles. But, because he was ski-mountaineering, the skis were fastened to his ankles with straps, and to the toes of his boots by clips which needed to be released manually. The straps and clips had saved his life. For the moment.

Suspended from skis, swinging upside-down like a carcass in a slaughterhouse, Richardson flailed around with his arms, frightened, disorientated, and cursing his stupidity. 'Crossing a glacier unroped after new snowfall! You asked for this!'

He could hardly move his head. His rucksack, weighing 16 pounds, had swung down against the back of his neck. Peering upwards with difficulty he could see a tiny circle of daylight – the hole he had made in the snow as he fell. He also saw in alarm that his skis, almost parallel with each other, some 12 inches apart, were bent like bows, pulled down by his 12-and-a-half-stone weight. The skis, four inches wide and of man-made fibre with steel edges, were immensely strong. But they could bend further and slip from the ledges – merely two inches wide – that supported them, letting him continue his headlong plunge. Below, Richardson glimpsed the crevasse gaping open to seeming infinity. Then he saw the blood. Large crimson blobs welled from a deep cut on his forehead, staining the ice.

I'll hang here until I die, he thought.

9.35 am. On the glacier John Delamere stopped and waited for his friend to catch up with him. Worried by the worsening storm, he was about to suggest that they abandon the trip and rejoin Patrick Cadigan. To Delamere's surprise there was no sign of Richardson. The swirling snow was obliterating even Delamere's own ski-tracks. Nev must have gone down already because of the weather, he thought. Delamere turned his skis for the Bétampf Hut.

Deep within the eerie, green–blue twilight of the crevasse, Richardson felt the cold begin to numb his body and his mind.

"John!" he shouted frantically. His voice was muffled by the vast gleaming cliffs of ice.

Somehow he had to get himself upright. I must pull myself up and unclip my boots, he reasoned. He tried to reach them but the rucksack dragged him down. The sack contained means of survival: food, an ice axe, crampons, pitons and a first-aid kit. It had to be put in a safe place. He noticed a ledge ten inches wide at waist level. Swinging the sack off his shoulders and curling and twisting his body upwards, he squashed the sack on to the icy perch. An experienced climber, he considered his main strength to be in his legs. This movement was torture for his abdominal muscles.

Once more painfully bending from the waist, he wrapped both arms around his left ski and hung under it like a sloth. As he stretched out a hand to unstrap his left ankle and unclip the boot – disaster. His shoulder knocked the rucksack off its ledge. In despair he heard the sack and its precious contents plummet downwards. The crevasse was so deep there was no distant, final crash. The rattling simply grew fainter and fainter.

9.38 am. Richardson managed to free both of his ankles and boots. As his legs swung below him, thrashing in space, he felt the ski supporting him tilt and wobble. Would he now be able to haul himself up safely? Anxiously, with infinite care, he got his right knee on to the ski. He extended his left leg sideways, found a purchase on the ice wall with his foot and slowly, hardly daring to breathe, raised himself to a kneeling, then crouching, position on the ski. It sagged in the middle so perilously that he shuffled over to his left, to the tiny ledge where the tail-ends of both skis rested. There, standing on the tail-ends, the ledge beneath then taking most his weight, he was upright at last. His back against the crevasse wall, he stood trembling with fright, shattered, drained of all energy, fearful of overbalancing and following his rucksack's fate.

Delamere, arriving at the Bétampf Hut, was worried to find Cadigan alone. A blizzard raged outside. Visibility was nil. Searching for Richardson was pointless. But around 10 am the storm eased. Visibility rose to 20 yards. Delamere set off on skis up the mountain, hoping to find his friend.

The crevasse creaked and groaned threateningly. It seemed a living thing. Richardson was convinced the sides were about to crush him to death by closing together – an illusion created by snow collecting round the rim of the hole 70 feet above, making it smaller.

He shouted: "Help!" but knew in his heart that no one could hear him.

Richardson remembered his emergency radio, a tiny transmitter–receiver worn around his neck. Of the type used for locating avalanche victims, it sent out a continuous distress signal. It was set to transmit. But even supposing Delamere had switched his radio to receive, its range was a mere 20 yards. Richardson dismissed the radio as useless. Scaling the glass-like walls in rubber-soled boots was out of the question. For a wild moment he considered going down the crevasse to retrieve his ice axe and pitons. With them, he would have a fighting chance. Reason prevailed, however. They might be hundreds of feet below. Bloody silly idea, he told himself.

10.10am. He had to do something. Placing his left foot on the tail-end of his right ski, and bracing his right boot against the opposite wall, Richardson stooped, picked up the left ski and propped it at chest level across the abyss, the ends resting on small creases in the ice. It reminded him of a ladder rung. A brilliant thought clicked. Use the skis one after the other to create a 'ladder'! As he climbed on to his first narrow 'rung' he felt it twitch like a springboard. He caught a sickening glimpse of the void yawning below. But the ski held.

Again and again he repeated the manoeuvre, jamming one ski across the crevasse at chest height and climbing onto it with the other ski in his hand, progressively clambering higher and higher, never knowing if the next step would be into eternity. He relied on grooves, holes, pockets – any recess he could find in the ice. When there wasn't one, he wielded the end of a ski as a pick to dig out a niche.

Richardson spurred himself on relentlessly. Don't stop. Keep your weight off the centres of the skis as much as possible. Stand on the ends. The skis were slippery with snow and the cold had robbed his hands of all feeling. One ski sprang out of his grasp. For a terrible split second he watched it start to fall. But his other hand quickly batted the ski against his leg and pinned it there. He fumbled another ski when lifting it overhead. It slipped and clattered on to the ski below. He just managed to catch it.

In his jacket pocket he had found a two-yard length of all-purpose nylon tape with a karabiner safety clip at one end. Each time he positioned the ski on which to climb next, he tied one end of the pink tape around the ski and clipped the other end to a loop on his climbing harness. As an aid it was purely psychological. He realised that if he fell he would drag the ski with him. But he felt tied to a solid object. Only 12 feet now to the surface of the glacier. Here the crevasse tapered to a chimney the width of a manhole – too narrow for laddering with skis. In desperation Richardson pondered this unexpected hazard. Tentatively he stabbed a ski-tip at the chimney wall. To his joy he found it was not ice but hard-frozen snow. By thrusting his back against the chimney wall, he would be able to kick footholds in the opposite wall and propel himself upwards.

You will need the skis to get back to the hut, he reminded himself. Lob them up on to the glacier. In his exhausted state they felt as heavy as cabers. Moments later Richardson kicked, writhed and clawed his way to the surface. It was 11 am. He had been inside the crevasse for the most harrowing 90 minutes of his life. Reaction set in. Collapsing on to the snow, he began to shiver uncontrollably. He could not believe he had escaped. As Richardson skied shakily down the mountain, he met two Austrian climbers who gave him gloves and escorted him to the Bétampf Hut. Patrick Cadigan, awaiting news and expecting the worst, was amazed when the hut door burst open and Richardson appeared, covered in snow and blood. He had cuts in head and hands, a dislocated finger and bruised knees, but no serious injury.

Later, John Delamere returned from his search to find Richardson drinking hot chocolate.

Neville Richardson, who lectures in physical chemistry, has recently won a grant to research the behaviour of metals and semi-conductors for the electronics industry. He still skis and climbs mountains. "I'm incredibly lucky to be alive," he says. "One day I'll go back to Monte Rosa – not to find the same crevasse; that would be impossible. But it will remind me that a miracle happened."

– By Anthony Greenbank: Reader's Digest, November 1988

A day after Phil's episode of pulmonary oedema, I visited him in Cervinia. His story of acute mountain sickness and the night-time rescue was extraordinary. "Quite some drama," I sympathised, "and most unfortunate, but Neville has been down a crevasse."

I described the accident and his remarkable escape. "Typical of that bastard to upstage me," he lamented.

Postscript:

Neville's rucksack was found by a Norwegian climber 10 years later. Crushed and torn, it had been spat out from the end of the glacier. His mother's address was inside. Imagine her horror as she opened the letter from the climber describing where it had been discovered and what might have happened to her son. Not wishing to worry her, Neville had never told her about his fall.

Fig 1. *Lombard hut at Testa Grigia*

Fig 2. *Ski lifts at Testa Grigia*

Fig 3. *Matterhorn from the Lombard hut*

Fig 4. *Lombard hut view to Cervinia*

Fig 5. *Testa Grigia or 'Grey Head', ice-cap*

Fig 6. *Lombard hut in a blizzard*

Fig 7. *Lombard hut dining room with John Simmons*

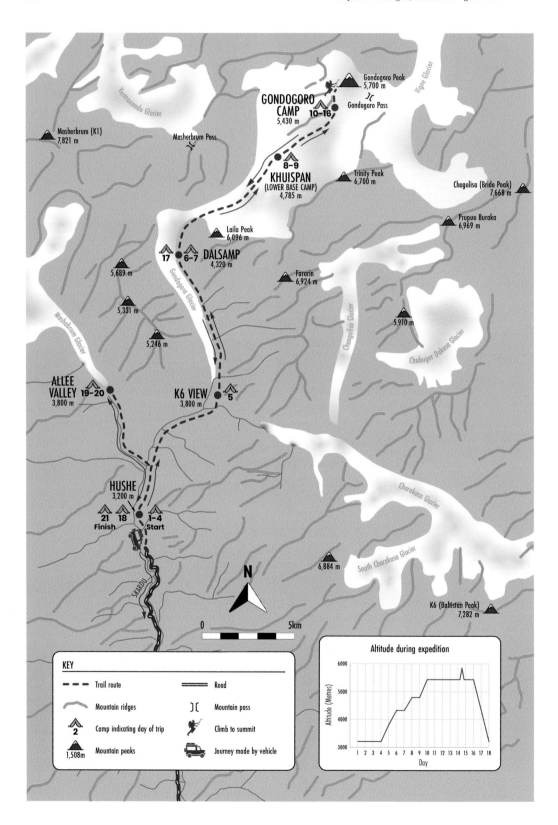

Chapter 5
Gondogoro, Karakoram – June 1987

Laila Peak (6,096 m)

Radioactivity

Within a few minutes of the radioactive injection, Tim collapsed,
became semi-conscious and was barely able to speak.

Summary: Twenty-five of us camped for a week at 5,430 m close to Gondogoro peak in north-east Baltistan. There we made the first accurate measurements of cerebral blood flow in acute mountain sickness using the radioactive xenon technique. We also undertook a trial of acetazolamide in the treatment of acute mountain sickness plus further studies on sleep, carbon dioxide inhalation and proteinuria.

Expedition members: Richard Boyce (cameraman), Jo Bradwell (leader), Ian Chesner, John Coote, John Delamere, Norman Dorricott, Peter Dykes, Jonathan Evans, Pete Forster, Ginette Harrison, Tim Harvey, Jörgen Jensen (Denmark), Simon Meech (medical student), John Milles, John Potokar, Marcus Raichle (USA), Neville Richardson, John Simmons, Dave Siviter, Pete Smith (RAF), Neil Stanley (RAF), Barbara Stone (RAF), Geoff Tsang, Mike Winterborn, Alex Wright (deputy leader) (figure 1).

I gazed past our 'little village' in the snow at 5,400 m, to the vast jumble of mountains, rock spires and glaciers, and out towards magnificent Laila Peak, glowing pink in the sunset. Hidden behind us but impinging on our conscious minds were Chogolisa, Broad Peak, the Gasherbrum and mighty K2 itself. Recent problems melted away, leaving me calm and contented. Over the past two weeks we had been prodded and poked, bled, developed gut rot, nausea, headaches, had our brains tested, been poisoned with different gases and irradiated. It had been a challenging expedition, counterbalanced by extraordinary mountains, rivers and people. Now we only had to survive the journey down the fearsome Karakoram highway.

After our successes at Rupina La, we had set our sights on the Karakoram as our next expedition target. The mountain range is an extension of the Himalaya across the Indus River into northern Pakistan. One always thinks of the Himalaya as the greatest mountain range but the Karakoram contains the world's second highest peak, K2, and the greatest concentration of peaks over 8,000 m.

Following a visit in the summer of 1986, John Delamere's future wife, Helen, thought the region would suit us. It had good tourist infrastructure, potential for a base camp above 5,000 m and her suggested trekking agency, Karakoram Experience Ltd, had extensive knowledge of the region. Since ours was a big group with complex research projects, its managing director, Glen Rowling, offered to be our guide (accompanied by his girlfriend Sue). We would need every bit of help if we were to transport radioactive xenon-133 into Pakistan and up a mountain.

As always, timing for the best weather was important. Being so far west, the Karakoram doesn't have monsoons but they are further north and thus colder than the Nepalese Himalaya. The best time for trekking is therefore in the relative warmth of July, which usefully coincided with university holidays.

We had two major projects in mind – sleep studies and cerebral blood flow measurement in acute mountain sickness – both of which were continuations of studies started three months earlier in the Alps. The cerebral blood flow study would reveal whether mountain sickness headaches were due to increased blood flow in the brain. The plan was to ascend at a moderate rate to 5,400 m and, as each individual became ill, we would measure their cerebral blood flow. An hour later, after swallowing six tablets of acetazolamide (1.5 g), each person would be retested. We anticipated that people's susceptibility to mountain sickness would vary with altitude, allowing experiments to be carried out on different days. If several people became ill simultaneously, we would stop for a day to test them all. Any who reached top camp without symptoms would also be studied before and after acetazolamide. We had spoken to several people who had developed severe headaches after taking the medication when fully acclimatised and wanted to know if this was associated with increased cerebral blood flow.

Important results from the Rupina La expedition resulting in a Lancet paper had given the Society a high profile for fundraising. This encouraged the pharmaceutical company Wyeth to give us £70,000 for the sleep studies. A successful grant application to the Wellcome Trust provided a further £14,000 for the cerebral blood flow measurements, which was largely to pay for the xenon-133. The gas (dissolved in a saline solution) was extremely expensive because of its short (5 days) half-life. We were planning 40 tests over a three-week period but Amersham International Ltd had to manufacture nearly 1,000 doses to allow for its rapid decay. It would take nearly two weeks to produce and test before we even started to use it. The heavily discounted price was £20,000. Although we couldn't afford it, we decided to worry about the bill when we returned home. Fatefully, it was scheduled to travel with us on the plane as unaccompanied baggage.

Our eve of departure planning was interrupted by a live interview for the BBC radio programme Women's Hour. The producers thought that a woman's perception of sleep studies at 5,000 m would make good listening. Barbara Stone was interviewed, with me as a token male. Nervously rehearsing our 15 minutes of fame, we awaited our turn in the BBC studios at Pebble Mill in Birmingham. During the live broadcast, I gave a general account of our expedition while they focused on Barbara's feelings about going to high altitude with a bunch of testosterone-driven climbers. I spoke too fast and Barbara became nervous, so we struggled to fill the time. It was not a satisfying experience.

But the following interview was intriguing, for we met the Queen of Nagaland. She was a typical white English woman in her 40s, living in England, except she was a queen. Her grandmother had visited a remote part of eastern India called Nagaland early in the 20th century where she successfully defended native rights against the British Raj. As a result, she become a local celebrity and was adopted as their sovereign. After living there for many years, she was eventually deported for racial incitement. Although never allowed back, her descendants inherited the crown. By 1986 there were no contentious issues with the government so her grand-daughter, as reigning queen, was allowed to visit – to great acclaim. Our story of climbing mountains to test sleep was nowhere near as exciting.

We rushed back to the Medical School to finalise storage of the equipment – a blood-gas analyser, centrifuges, syringes, needles, plus two generators; a dozen boxes in total. Because we had experienced endless problems with a Honda 1.5 kVa generator on Rupina La, we switched to a 2 kVa model made by Haverhill, which had carburettors especially modified for altitude. One was tested in the hypoxia chamber at RAF Farnborough and worked perfectly.

In the evening before departure, we adjourned to Henry Wong's, a nearby Chinese restaurant as others arrived – Jörgen from Copenhagen with two more boxes containing the precious gamma cameras, Tim with boxes of inflatable bags and gas bottles, and a special delivery box of radioactive dextran from the USA.

Next afternoon, we left the Medical School for London Heathrow airport to catch a Pakistan International Airlines (PIA) flight to Islamabad. At the departure desk, we met Marcus Raichle from the USA who would help with the cerebral blood flow studies. He had replaced Niels Lassen who was unable to join us because of work commitments. Although unfamiliar with our brain-scanning equipment, Marcus was a professor of neurology and a world expert on cerebral blood flow. He seemed very pleasant and we all thought he would fit in well. I also met for the first time our filmmaker, Richard Boyce, a friend of Norman Dorricott. We had made a film on the first expedition but it had not turned out well, largely because the cameraman had been unfit and developed acute mountain sickness. Richard seemed fit enough and was a professional cameraman at ITV. Furthermore, he had brought with him a television quality Panasonic video camera. It did seem as though all the ingredients were in place for the production of a good film.

We were guided to a first-class ticket desk which had been especially opened for us even though we were travelling pig class. We were nearly 300 kg over our allowance of 780 kg, but with a combination of our boot under the weighing scales trick and passing some medical boxes directly onto luggage trolleys, we registered 100 kg underweight. It was our lucky day.

There were smiles all around, we shook hands and were delighted with our good fortune. There were final departure photos of the group then onto the plane where we all sat together, animated and excited. I sat between John Coote and Ian Chesner. We talked about the challenges of the Karakoram, the numerous experiments and, inevitably, whether the xenon-133 was really in the baggage hold below us. We had export licences, import agreements, invoices and university letterheads but that was not the same as actually having it in our hands. I fretted, reflecting on my experience carrying a rucksack full of xenon-133 up the Matterhorn three months earlier (see Alpine Interlude).

The plane stopped at Paris for four hours and then flew to Islamabad, arriving at 6 am. We were four hours jet-lagged and had hardly slept. Beyond customs we met Ginette. She had been climbing in the Himalaya for months; she was fit, tanned and acclimatised. Alongside her was Mr Shariff, the Amersham representative in Pakistan. Regrettably, he was one of those people who instilled instant mistrust. With a shifty look, he haltingly explained that the radioactive xenon-133 would clear customs shortly. What a relief! Everything was going smoothly. We walked outside, blinking in the bright sunlight, our noses assailed by the tropical smells from millions of people living in poverty. It was also very hot, with 46°C forecast.

We piled into a decorated multi-coloured bus with our bags and boxes, and raced along narrow, crowded streets, horn blasting, to the Sherazade Hotel in Rawalpindi (the neighbouring city to Islamabad). The hotel was modest, lacking air-conditioning. We were hot, tired and irritated as we hung around the reception area waiting for room keys that had been mislaid by the receptionist. I was allocated to a six-bed dormitory that included Marcus, providing an opportunity to become acquainted.

After breakfast, many slept but I anxiously awaited Mr Shariff's news. He appeared, but without the xenon.

"Well, where is it? I demanded.

"I don't know," he nervously smiled back, evading the truth. "Pakistan is not the same as England."

We had suspected from his body language at the airport that something might be up. After an hour of questioning, we realised that we had a huge problem. The xenon had not been on our plane after all. Our interrogation suggested that Amersham had phoned customs officials in Islamabad a few days earlier to ensure it would be released upon our arrival. However, they were told that it would take three days to be cleared, so they had sent it to Karachi, 700 miles away.

In hushed tones, Mr Shariff explained that he had something special in his briefcase. Checking around and seeing no watchful eyes, he cautiously opened it to expose a hoard of used, low-denomination rupee notes. Little had the Amersham staff in the UK realised that bribes were needed. Unfortunately, he explained sadly, there was no one to bribe, as the relevant customs officers were in Karachi. Highly irritated, we told him to find our xenon.

But there were additional uses for the money. Because we were on a British research expedition with no official government recognition, we had to deal with Mr Munirujeen. Glen Rowley described him as an awkward, officious, petty-minded, puffed-up nobody who, unfortunately, held power over who could or could not go trekking. We went as a gang to appear important, filing solemnly into the great man's office, me directly in front of him. He gave me a dressing-down for not sending him our previous research papers (I had never been asked to), for not informing him of our trip (it had been planned for a year) and for leaving litter everywhere (we had not yet been on the trek). It was hard to say nothing so I tried flattering him. He was unmoved.

Our expedition was balanced on a knife-edge. I felt like a condemned man trying to negotiate with a firing squad. All our hopes and expectations rested with that self-important tyrant. After another 30 minutes of earnest grovelling (and the gift of a bulging envelope), he gave us another reprimand and permission to proceed, providing we sent him a full report. There was a final tirade on rubbish disposal and instructions not to photograph women or soldiers. We were dismissed into the scorching heat.

It was time for lunch and perhaps some sleep, but no, Mr Shariff reappeared. He had been in contact with the ministry responsible for radioactive materials, which confirmed that our precious xenon was in Karachi. We would have to make a special 'deal' or it would not be released for three days. We found it impossible to know the truth. Shit. Changing the import licence to Islamabad was possible but we would need authority from Amersham in the UK and it was Sunday. Nothing could happen until Monday morning, when we were all booked on a 6 am flight to Skardu in the Karakoram. Shit, shit, shit…

After lengthy discussions, Alex and Dave agreed to wait for the xenon in Islamabad while it was flown from Karachi. We wondered whether Neville or Pete Forster might be more forceful negotiators. However, Alex could be very determined and stubborn when pushed and would never get angry under pressure. We would see. The rest of the expedition would proceed to Skardu since flights, accommodation and transport were booked and paid for. As leader, it was felt that I should go with the main group to ensure that everything was ready for when the xenon-133 eventually arrived. There was £50,000 worth of experiments resting on the xenon-133. Under Mr Shariff's guidance, I typed out three medical product release forms using an ancient typewriter from the days of Empire. Would these papers really be sufficient to extract our all-important radioactive element from the jaws of Pakistan's intransigent bureaucracy?

I returned to the hotel for a brief respite from the 47°C heat, lying under the bedroom fans to snatch precious moments of sleep. Then it was dinner time. Six of us went to the Holiday Inn for a superb Pakistani curry. After lengthy discussions about life, the universe and xenon-133, we were in bed by midnight. It was only the second day but it seemed like a week since we had left Birmingham.

Moments later, the 2.45 am alarm sounded. Jet-lagged and tired, we filled out our daily mountain sickness and sleep questionnaires in all their tedious detail, gathered our bags and piled into two buses for the journey back to the airport. In the quiet of the night, the drivers raced each other, tearing along the roads in parallel, one then the other inching ahead. Red traffic lights were ignored as we rushed past, each bus desperately trying to overtake the other. As the road narrowed, our bus backed off, only to try overtaking again immediately afterwards. It was no surprise to learn that death rates in Pakistan were 50 times those in the UK.

Flights to Skardu are never guaranteed. Afternoon clouds and storms in the Karakoram preclude late departures; ours was at 6 am. We had a few anxious moments at the weigh-in but all bags were cleared as our boot trick performed its usual magic, despite intense security. A Boeing 737 could take a little extra we presumed. We looked back past the ticket desk at Alex and Dave to wish them luck. We had taken most of their personal luggage so they could fill their rucksacks with the xenon-containing lead pots. We hoped to see them the following day.

As the Boeing 737 climbed steeply, we all watched in wonder as Nanga Parbat, K2, then Broad Peak came into view. Nanga Parbat was nearest, exposing its great Rupal face, followed by the Diamir flank as we banked. It seemed close enough to touch. To the north, the massive pyramid of K2 stood out above its neighbours. Then we descended among cathedral spires of snow-covered peaks, remote and awesome in their majesty. The deep cut of the Indus Valley and Skardu beckoned us into a remote and beautiful landscape.

The gear was slowly cleared through the small customs post, after which we signed the entry book for Baltistan, a semi-autonomous region. Jeeps then ferried us to the headquarters of Baltistan Tours in Skardu, our tour operator for the next three weeks. I clung onto the back of one jeep as it raced along dusty roads. A tyre burst under me and we slithered to a standstill. An everyday event, it appeared. It was rapidly changed and we pressed on to a stone enclosure containing some stone hovels. Above the entrance a large banner declared 'Baltistan Tours Ltd', beyond which tents were being erected (figure 2). We had booked rooms at the modern K2 hotel but it was closed as winter snows had collapsed its roof.

From inside a rundown shed appeared Iqbal, a short, black-bearded, handsome man with piercing eyes and strong legs. He was second-in-command of the operation and our sirdar for the expedition. Other swarthy characters appeared from another building grandly entitled HEAD OFFICE. Beyond a low stone-walled enclosure, a scruffy crowd gathered, watching and waiting (figure 3). Keen eyes and itchy fingers. Iqbal said they were harmless.

The day in Skardu (2,400 m) had been set aside for cerebral blood flow measurements but we had no xenon. In the evening we received a phone call from Alex. Mr Shariff had been in contact with customs officers in Karachi who promised its immediate release, but by nightfall it was still in Karachi. As on earlier expeditions, baseline studies were proving difficult to collect.

However, Mike did manage to measure blood gases and collect urine samples after injections of radioactively labelled dextran molecules (complex and bulky polysaccharides). At Rupina La, we had shown that altitude proteinuria (excess protein in urine) was due to kidney leakage through the glomerular basement membrane, rather than failure of reabsorption by renal tubules. The question was, why? One possible mechanism was loss of the basement membrane's negative charge. A recent test for this had been developed in the USA based upon injection of positively and negatively charged dextran molecules. One was labelled with radioactive carbon (^{14}C) and the other with radioactive hydrogen (tritium or ^3H). In the experiment, the two radiolabelled dextran molecules were injected intravenously and blood and urine samples were collected over two hours. The samples were then saved for measurements in Birmingham.

The ^{14}C dextran had been flown from the USA to London a few days before we departed, courtesy of Marcus Raichle. I had spent some time persuading the customs officers at Heathrow to part with it but they had struggled to find the product name on their list of medical substances. They had found CO_2 and CS_2, but no C14. Worried about the importation of an illegal substance, they phoned Amersham International for more information. They pointed out it was written ^{14}C and not C14, but the amount, 250 Ci (curies), was enough for a nuclear reactor. Very alarmed, Amersham phoned me. I explained that it was actually 250 µCi (micro-curies), one millionth of the quantity. It arrived in Birmingham in the nick of time – the night before our departure.

As we undertook this and other highly sophisticated studies, we marvelled at how modern science was being intermingled with ancient landscapes and culture, hardly touched by half a millennium of progress. Below our campsite flowed the broad sweep of the Indus and beyond it rose the majestic snow-capped Karakoram mountains. However, there was one sign of modernity in that remote town – cricket. The Skardu warriors took on BMRES. We were beaten by 130 runs to 97 but since a few of us had played on the Baltistan side we claimed a partial victory.

Bed that night was courtesy of Baltistan Tours – sleep where you like! Individuals were strewn over the compound in tents, on ground sheets, and on the veranda, scattered between our equipment. No one minded, not even the sophisticated Marcus and Barbara. We thought how well she was coping; snatched from the reassuring comforts of Middle England to this poverty. Aged 40, she had perhaps come for 'her last taste of adventure' – a final fling before being subsumed by the trappings of suburban conformity in the Home Counties. First night a PIA flight in pig-class, second night in a bunk room with five blokes, and the third night on the floor of a Baltistan hovel with 23 blokes: the shock might have deranged lesser people. Furthermore, the snorers had yet to be identified and isolated. Ian received three thumps and Tim two thumps before the night was over, but despite everything it was our first decent night's sleep.

The following day, our fourth, we drove to Hushe, a remote village up a side valley of the Indus River gorge. The dawn saw clear blue skies, the surrounding 6,000 m Karakoram peaks glowing pink in the early sun's rays. After breakfast we had our last chance to contact Alex by phone. We spent an anxious hour at the K2 hotel desperately trying to reach him but to no avail. The chance of the xenon or our friends arriving any time soon looked remote.

Our open-topped jeeps arrived for the 70-mile journey. We clambered on board, our cameraman Richard at the ready. The unfolding drama of the landscape would make a great start to any film. Behind our racing vehicles, a plume of dust rose high in the air while alongside roared the Indus, a huge thundering, tumbling river in a desert of sand and rock with jagged snow-capped peaks. It was a remarkable experience. Yet even in that extreme climate, we saw oases of bright green. As side streams entered the river, there were intricate terraces of apricot and mulberry trees, cornfields and vegetable plots. We stopped at one for tea to let the jeep engines cool. Richard filmed a passing convoy of camouflaged army lorries heading for the Kashmir front in their war with

India. Then we were off again.

We passed over the Indus on one superb British-built suspension bridge, guarded by a soldier. He refused to be a photographed, but one on the next bridge was more obliging (figure 4). We reflected on Mr Munirujeen's warning not to photograph the military or women. Lunch was at a filthy squat of a house where we eagerly ate locally produced eggs and meat. Then we pressed on through the Surje Valley, dust devils springing up across the river's wide flood plains in the afternoon heat. A brigade of soldiers paraded past in full ceremonial regalia, further reminders of the Raj era.

By evening, as we approached Khapalu we noticed petrol on the floor. Our equipment included a 50-gallon container of petrol for the generators. We had smelt fuel for some time and now found the cause; the drum was leaking. Quickly stopping, we emptied out all baggage to expose the drum. It had three holes in it, one at the end and two on opposite sides, so tipping the container in any one direction failed to stop the flow. We had no other containers – what could possibly be done? The answer was soap. The driver hammered a bar of it into a paste then pressed it on the holes, immediately sealing them. Such ingenuity was remarkable. The drum was repositioned vertically and we were off again.

As night arrived, we caught up with the other jeeps, the road steepened and we turned north. High above us shone Masherbrum (7,821 m) in the evening light, ethereal above lesser peaks. As we ascended, the road twisted and turned above a deep river canyon raging with glacial melt water. We grew nervous as our jeep slithered on the road, bald tyres desperately trying to grip its surface, rock worn smooth by grit from innumerable wheels. Worried about the drop, I jogged alongside the vehicle with Jonathan.

At 9.30 pm, in the pitch black, we reached Hushe (3,200 m). Dozens of adults and children came out to visit us, shouting as they milled around the jeeps. It was the home of Ibrahim, Javed, the cook team and many of our porters.

At our camp in a school yard, we reflected in wonder about our amazing journey, then about Alex, Dave and the wretched xenon. I went to bed for a restless, worried sleep. When would they arrive with or without their precious cargo? Any longer than three days would endanger the study. Over two half-lives of the xenon had ticked by. It was 12 days since manufacture; 1,000 doses were now reduced to 200.

Back in Islamabad, Alex and Dave were struggling to track down the xenon, as Alex recorded in his diary: *'Islamabad, Tuesday, 30 June. We went to the fortress of the British Embassy for eight o'clock this morning. Inside were queues of people looking for settlement in the UK. We finally met an official who would write a letter to allow the xenon to be flown from Karachi. We were promised it for the afternoon. We returned to the hotel waiting for the Amersham rep, Mr Shariff. At 2.30 pm he phoned to say that he was at a government office trying to get a transfer permit but it would take at least two days. At 5 pm he phoned again to explain that he was going to Karachi immediately to bring it back tomorrow. Progress at last.*

Then, Mr Fayad from Baltistan Tours appeared at the hotel saying it was impossible to get a flight to Skardu before 13 August – in six weeks. Since he had already cancelled two of our bookings (anticipating daily that we might be leaving for Skardu), the airline didn't trust him anymore. We decided to go to the head offices in Islamabad first thing in the morning to sort it out. Mr Safdar Shah (Fayad's boss) knew the chief so he agreed to come with us. At 11 pm we had a phone call from Mr Shariff in Karachi saying that the xenon was released and he would definitely bring it on the 4 pm flight on Wednesday. Hurrah!'

Wednesday 1 May dawned brightly in Hushe. By 6 am we were all up, awed by the surrounding mountains shining in the clear air. After breakfast we moved camp from the school to a site below the village. The population trooped after us, hordes of children demanding 'pen sahib' or 'sweet sahib'. A flat pasture lay beside a tiny stream so we settled among piles of cattle dung, breathing heavily in the thin air. I bagged a tent with Peter Dykes, believing he was a non-snorer. Realising it was pitched close to the stream that could enlarge with a rainstorm or snow melt, I moved it to higher ground, although I failed to persuade others to do the same.

After a conference in the large mess tent, we decided to have a rest day and undertake experiments the following morning. It had been a tough trip so most wanted time to relax and enjoy the mountains. Neville and I fancied ascending to the snout of a glacier that was visible some miles away. It was a superb walk, first alongside the river and then across a plain covered in poplar trees to a huge menacing ice wall. A stream poured out of a large blue cave in the middle. We attempted to enter but the stream had cut a deep trench that was painfully cold to wade through. Despite several attempts, we gave up and returned to camp by 6.30 pm after a long hike. Others had been rock climbing or walked up side valleys.

That evening it was cold as we all assembled for another conference in the mess tent. Rather surprisingly, some people already had mild mountain sickness. A few others had diarrhoea, in particular my tent mate Peter Dykes. He was in and out of the tent all night. I lay in bed listening to him and distant guns. They were firing on Indian troops in the military zone 15 miles to the east.

Alex's diary: *'Islamabad, Wednesday, 1 July. Up to the PIA head office in Rawalpindi by 7.30 am. No information about the flight to Skardu tomorrow but this morning's was cancelled because of bad weather. Waited in the hotel: 44°C and humid, but saved by the fan. Phoned the British Embassy who said no permission was needed to transport the xenon. Perhaps writing a letter of explanation was too much hard work.*

Mr Fayad came with the tickets for the flight. He merely smiled when we asked how he had obtained them. Then a phone call from Karachi. It was Mr Shariff saying the 'cargo' would be on its way at 5 pm but there would be a lot of additional expenses – naturally – that's how things worked. At 7 pm a taxi arrived containing Mr Shariff and the precious xenon in 18 kg of lead pots. What a relief. We arranged a wake-up call for 4 am. There was no message from the others.'

Hushe; Thursday 2 July. Despite the lack of xenon, we had to start the acetazolamide trial because Norman, Richard, Neil and Pete Smith had mountain sickness. Out came the generators, blood-gas machine, centrifuges, syringes, needles and tubes. The four were entered into the trial – 1.5 g of acetazolamide or placebo. Other studies such as xylose absorption, muscle strength and capillary fragility were started. I sat alone by the river contemplating the problems. I could see the all-important cerebral blood flow studies slipping from our grasp. We desperately needed the xenon.

In the afternoon I drove down the valley with John Milles and Peter Dykes to try to find our missing friends. I feared that we had made the wrong decision by leaving them in Islamabad. We had tried so hard to make the cerebral blood flow studies work but it looked like it was going to be a very expensive failure.

By the evening it was obvious that 1.5 g of acetazolamide had improved those with mountain sickness. Neil and Norman were both dramatically better while the two on placebo, Pete and Richard, were still poorly. At least one of our projects was working. Yet, despite the problems, most people were enjoying the expedition. The food was good, the porters were excellent and we were in a beautiful location.

Our evening conference was all about whether to wait for Alex and Dave or go higher. We could barely afford to wait any longer. We were resigned to the loss of the cerebral blood flow experiment but we had to press on so that the acetazolamide trial could continue. After endless deliberations, we agreed to wait one last day.

That evening the porters had a party with the ritual slaying of a goat, Muslim style, amid great revelry. My tent mate Peter Dykes woke me yet again, this time with gory details of the poor animal's fate. Then he was in and out during the night tending the mountain sickness victims. He was the doctor for the rest of us and tended his flock very diligently. I vowed to move into a tent with Neville at the first opportunity. I had too much on my plate to be woken up every hour.

Alex's diary: *Thursday 2 July. 'Awoke to the alarm at 4 am. There followed a hairy drive to the airport sitting in the back seat of a taxi alongside a box designated 'Special Medicines'. How special they were.*

My heart nearly stopped at the airport as I saw a line of police with special metal detectors. Remarkably, the lead pots were not identified. Maybe the machines were not switched on. The airport was on high alert but extensive security checks and the X-ray machines all failed to detect 18 kg of lead with its radioactive liquid in my rucksack. I couldn't bear thinking about the consequences if they had been found. The only item of interest was the ophthalmoscope because of its batteries. Then by mistake we were ushered onto a plane going to Karachi. Thankfully, we realised before it was too late. Finally, we were seated on a Fokker 27 bound for Skardu. It was half empty; so much for needing to book six weeks in advance. It accelerated down the runway and climbed, revealing marvellous views of Nanga Parbat.

At Skardu we waited in vain for our guide Iqbal and transport to Hushe. After many hours a four-wheel-drive Toyota appeared, filled with sacks of grain to give it traction on slippery roads. Thankfully, the temperature was lower due to the altitude. I cut my hand on the box containing the xenon. There was blood everywhere.

We set off at 1.30 pm for Hushe. After 30 minutes there was a loud hiss as the back offside tyre deflated. They rushed to put on the spare but there was none. By chance a Toyota jeep passed containing a previous student of Mr Iqbal's and they had the correct tyre. One of the men from our car was left by the roadside with the punctured tyre to hitch a lift back to Skardu. 15 minutes later, as we were going along there was another hissing noise as the new tyre deflated. We just made it to a small tea house before it flattened completely. Two hours passed and at 5.30 pm an uncle of Mr Iqbal passed in his Toyota and he had a spare tyre which we swopped. Off again with a push start. 30 minutes later there was a sinister sound from the engine compartment. The alternator was broken and leaking oil. The next hazard was the bridge crossing a deep river gorge. We were obliged to walk in case it collapsed. Shortly afterwards on the edge of a precipitous cliff there was a broken-down vehicle blocking our passage, then the headlights failed. It was completely dark and impossible to proceed since the alternator was not charging the battery. We unloaded everything including the isotopes allowing our car to crawl past with a few inches to spare above a 30 m vertical drop. The road was only made of rubble and angled sharply towards the cliff edge.

Iqbal fiddled under the bonnet, solved the electrical short and the lights came on. We drove on till 9.30 pm and found a rest house. Iqbal was worried about robbers so they advised us to keep the door locked. As the lock was on the outside we were locked in all night. Finally, to bed worrying about our slow progress and wondering how far up the mountain the others had gone. Why had we not started from Skardu earlier? Because Mr Iqbal, as a magistrate, had been dispensing justice all morning.'

Hushe; Friday 3 July: we were all awake by 5.30 am for an early breakfast and experiments. The trial placebo subjects Richard and Pete were no better so they were given acetazolamide at a dose of 250 mg twice daily. This did seem rather odd as the treatment group received 1.5 g as a single dose, but that was the protocol. Blood gases were measured and samples were centrifuged.

Suddenly, at 9.30 am there was shouting from the village and down strode our missing friends with Iqbal and a porter carrying the xenon. They arrived to cheering and a very warm welcome. Then we realised we hadn't filmed his arrival. Richard was poorly and resting on his bed, but we dragged him out with his camera. Alex and co. retraced their route 200 metres and, to further cheering, repeated their entry into camp.

Alex told his remarkable story. Even that very morning they had difficulties. The Toyota refused to start because of a flat battery. Out came a local tractor to provide a pull-start using Dave's climbing rope. He was most unhappy in case it broke. Alex was particularly pleased to be reunited with his personal items. He had not changed clothes for seven days.

Finally, and after so much effort and worry, we could start the cerebral blood flow tests. Six subjects were tested, several twice, once before and once after 1.5 g of acetazolamide (or placebo).

I walked along the river very relieved. After supper and final tests, it was time for bed and a decent sleep. It had been a very tough start to the expedition but the hard part, climbing to 5,400 m, still lay ahead.

Ascent to Dalsamp Lakes

Next morning, we were itching to leave. We now had 5–6 days in which to make top camp. During the ascent, we anticipated that a few people per day might develop mountain sickness and be entered into the drug trial. Cerebral blood flow would be tested and then retested after taking the tablets. The whole procedure took several hours. Ascent time was only a few hours per day so we would have the afternoons and evenings to make the measurements.

We performed two cerebral blood flow tests after breakfast and the camp was slowly packed up. A group of 90 porters arrived from the village dressed in rags with flip-flops or worn-out rubber boots on their feet. Iqbal negotiated load size, payments and distances with them. The weight of each bag was carefully assessed and porters allocated to different-sized packages. It was £5 per load of 25 kg per day, while the generator carriers received £10 per day since their loads weighed 35 kg. After a couple of hours of haggling, the porters gathered their loads and moved off at a robust pace. We were all on the road by 11 am.

As we walked along the gently ascending path on a wide river flood-plain, the cold of early morning gradually gave way to the heat of midday. The sun rose in a clear sky and the air was still. At lunch we hid under fir and willow trees admiring the superb mountains. The afternoon was even hotter. Many of us were sunburnt. It was hard to keep cool.

Another two-hour walk and we were at our camp by 2.30 pm, to be rewarded with a superb view of K6 and other 6,000 m peaks (figure 5). Our altitude was 3,800 m. Above us, a huge rock face was warm in the western sun, a fine waterfall tumbling 500 m down its vertical face. In England, it would have untold numbers of climbers on it. Here, it was one of a thousand similar peaks and ignored.

After a quick bite to eat, Nev and I scrambled along a vigorous river cutting onto a moraine of the K6 glacier. We boulder hopped and scree ran till we reached the snout – a great amphitheatre of ice constantly on the move. It was like a lunar landscape, yet above the glacier was a beautiful clump of trees, bright green in their spring foliage. We ran back down to the camp feeling very energetic, but arrived to a mutiny. Peter Dykes and John Coote were the ringleaders. They were not happy with the proposed 4.30 am start, demanding 6.30 am instead. In my absence a calm debate had evolved into a hot-tempered rebellion. Peter, in particular, was feeling the strain. He had been suffering from diarrhoea for several days, had several experiments to supervise and was the group's doctor. This entailed keeping an eye on any member becoming ill and treating a long line of villagers that formed outside his tent every evening. Nonetheless, the following day was over a tricky glacier and we were two days behind schedule because of the late arrival of the xenon. We eventually compromised on 5.30 am.

While many were struggling with the altitude and diarrhoea, others were starving, eating double portions at dinner as they awaited tasty-looking blancmanges. They had been placed beside the river to set but as the afternoon sun melted mountain ice, the stream rose, carrying away our eagerly anticipated desserts. Alex was mortified.

Perhaps surprisingly, we had seen no other westerners since we had been at Skardu but that night two groups appeared. One consisted of some rather miserable men, but the other tents were occupied by three 'game' girls (as John Milles described them). They were soon chatted up and came over for drinks. Gin and whiskies came out for their benefit.

It was a clear evening sky with a beautiful sunset. Then the Milky Way appeared, brilliant in the thin air. We slept under the stars to enjoy its beauty.

Edelweiss

Despite the mutiny, everyone was up by 5.30 am and ready for a good trek. We planned to ascend to 4,320 m over 6–8 hours. It started with tent calls of 'milik tea sahib' from Javed and the usual 24-hour urine collections supervised by Norman and John Delamere. Anticipating another scorching day, we ate and packed quickly, allowing individuals to depart as soon as they were ready.

The path led up past the snout of the Gondogoro Glacier then onto its lateral moraine. Alpine flowers abounded, filling meadows with bright colours that were a sharp contrast to the grey rubble off the glacier.

After lunch the route steepened, forcing us to scramble alongside a series of deep pools in the ice. One slip and it was into the freezing water. Iqbal had attached fixed ropes to help but it was a miracle that no one fell in. In places, we splashed through glacial water, with black ice cliffs rearing up above us like a moonscape, and small rock avalanches cascading down as the ice melted in the sun. Then we were onto a white section of the glacier with wide crevasses (figure 6). Some trick of air and water flow caused it to shudder, like the breathing of a huge beast of the deep. A short scramble followed, leading to spring meadows with alpine flowers and brisk rivulets tinkling through the grass – our 4,320 m camp at Dalsamp (figures 7–9). John Milles and others swam in the glacial water – it must have been their public-school upbringing. I looked on with Pete Forster scowling at their privileged ability to suffer.

The porters slowly arrived and set up our tents, which we eagerly scrambled to occupy for an afternoon doze. But first we went skiing. Opposite the camp was a steep ramp of snow avalanche debris. With Neville and Jonathan, we slowly carried skis up the 100-metre slope. It was desperately hard work at that altitude. We skied down to great cheers, particularly from the porters who had never seen skis before. Jonathan, not to be outdone, went back and did it again. He was a bundle of energy, little affected by the altitude.

Our rock athletes tackled a huge boulder. Ginette, John Potokar and Jonathan just managed to climb up its vertical face. Much to the amusement of the watching crowd, a Balti porter in tatty clothes and sawn-off wellies climbed it with ease. We clapped our approval.

As we were enjoying ourselves, Mike, Barbara, Jörgen and Marcus struggled in, exhausted, gaunt and with a degree of mountain sickness. Some people, including Neil and Pete Smith, had done remarkably well after acetazolamide but others, such as Richard, were bent and lethargic. Pete Forster and several others were suffering from gut rot, which was thought to be due to Giardia, a parasite infection, caught from drinking contaminated water. They were treated with Flagyl (metronidazole) and Lomotil (diphenoxylate and atropine).

The long day was finally over. The sun set abruptly and it started to freeze. We gathered in the mess tent for curry and hot potatoes, wondering which of the cooks was causing the bowel infections. We were too tired for a post-dinner conference, so it was an early bedtime. By 8 pm the camp was quiet.

It is strange how a combination of exercise and altitude demands so much sleep. It was the second night in a row that I had 11 hours, plus an hour in the warmth of the afternoon sun. No wonder mountain monks revel in their high holy places, tucked away from the world.

Many were very quiet at breakfast, but as the sun warmed the camp, moods improved; it was a rest day with few experiments. And beyond our little encampment the views were superb – Trinity Peak, Masherbrum and a host of other 6,000 m mountains.

David Siviter, our climbing guide, had a chance to show off his skills. Ice axes, crampons and ropes were located and soon he was teaching the novices ice-climbing techniques and how to arrest a fall. There was also the film to consider. We had fallen into the same trap as on previous trips. Richard, our cameraman, didn't understand the experiments and had developed mountain sickness. He was clearly physically fit and strong at sea level but once altitude-related illness developed, he became lethargic and demotivated. Feeling perfectly well, John Milles took charge, marching Richard around the camp to great effect, filming as they went.

The warm sunny day turned into a beautiful evening and all too quickly the dinner gong rang. The expedition was settling into a pattern of walking, experiments and a rest day. The generators were working well, there were no xenon worries and those developing acute mountain sickness made good recoveries when given big doses of acetazolamide. For a change, everything was going to plan.

Lower base camp

By the time I awoke, the campsite was partly cleared and breakfast was being served. Those with acute mountain sickness seem to have improved overnight, thanks to either acetazolamide or acclimatisation. The stream that had been quite a river the previous evening had shrunk to a trickle, starved of water by the hard overnight frost.

Ice hoodoo

After breakfast, Richard, accompanied by his newly appointed director, John, rushed around trying to construct a film. First the porters were filmed streaming out of the camp, then the urine collections were lined up on a small ridge above the camp with spectacular views of Masherbrum (figure 10).

All day we walked up the moraine, often on the top of a ridge of rocks and ice (figure 11). Initially, a thin coating of soil covered flat areas, on which grew scattered yellow and blue alpine flowers. But as we ascended, the glacier became more evident, with cliffs of black ice and rubble. This forced us to walk on a central ridge of large boulders with occasional ice 'hoodoos' (rocks poised on pinnacles of ice, their shadows protecting the underlying ice from melting) (figure 12). Melt water, trickling down ice faces, sparkled in the hot sun, accompanied by the occasional rumble of rock fall. It was difficult to know where to walk – on unstable rocks, on ice pinnacles sharp enough to cut skin or on wet snow that easily collapsed.

We plodded slowly upwards in increasing melt water from the rising sun. Trickles became streams then rivers, cascading over the ice. I watched Jonathan then Ginette jump a five-foot torrent but I was too tired and was carrying a heavy sack. I just waded through up to my knees; good old trainers.

Lower base camp at Khuispan (4,785 m) was perched on a rubble bank in the middle of the moraine. As we arrived, some tents were already pitched, with Neville guarding one for us to share. We watched on as slower members trudged in; 400 m altitude gain was taking its toll. Ian struggled in and asked how I felt, before vomiting over the rubble. Pete Forster watched on feeling miserable.

'I feel well,' I replied.

'You have a pact with the devil, you bastard,' was his retort.

The main focus of experiments were the sleep studies. Individuals were studied in the arctic tent, which was pitched on a small area of flat ground cleared of rocks and turf. Behind it, porters constructed rock walls facing the sun both to shield it from wind and to re-radiate the sun's heat from the day.

It was soon clear that Pete Forster, Ian and Marcus were not well. Low blood oxygen levels confirmed the clinical impression of mountain sickness. Pete Forster's diary described his feelings as he became ill and entered the acetazolamide trial:

*'Started the walk with Neville and John Delamere but gradually dropped behind with a developing headache. Reached lower base camp by midday but exhausted with headache worsening. Snow clouds were gathering so helped erect the tents but suddenly debilitated by acute mountain sickness. Felt extreme weakness and lay across a rock unable to move, very irritable with a posterior headache. Attempted to sleep but unsuccessfully. By 2.30 pm all the party was in with Ian very poorly and Marcus suffering from weakness and nausea. I am inducted into the medical tests. I need to enter the drug trial but that is four hours away. Before that there are four venous blood samples, three capillary stabs, three radioactive injections (^{14}C and ^{3}H dextrans, plus xenon-133). Scalp electrodes are fitted for sleep studies while Tim tries the CO_2 rebreathing experiment. By the time the medication arrives, I am slightly better; after another hour, I am much improved. Headache and irritability are down and my appetite is recovering. Then, a further brain scan and capillary oxygen measurements. The response indicators suggest I am on acetazolamide. **This is not a trial for the ill**. To bed and asleep by 8 pm.'*

Ian was worryingly poorly; as others were unwell and we needed to do more sleep studies, we agreed to stay at Khuispan for another day. I turned in at 9 pm with two subjects still being investigated. The generator whined into the night, running perfectly. They finished at 11 pm. It was a very impressive effort by Jörgen and his team.

We were woken by the 4.30 am Muslim call to prayers. Of the three who had entered the drug trial, Pete and Marcus were feeling much better, mirrored in improved blood-gas results; we presumed they were on acetazolamide. Ian's condition, however, was worse. He felt awful and was oedematous. We broke the code and found he was indeed on placebo, so he was given 1.5 g of acetazolamide. Alex, Barbara and Jörgen had deteriorated overnight, providing three more victims for study. After breakfast, they were entered into the study and by lunchtime they were on acetazolamide or placebo.

While the main experiments were being conducted, other aspects of altitude physiology were being investigated. Tim had a particularly interesting study – breathing carbon dioxide (CO_2) (figure 13). It had been known for a century that CO_2 stimulated breathing. As was poetically described by Miescher-Rüsch in 1885: "Over the oxygen supply of the body, carbon dioxide spreads its protective wings; especially as it cares for the brain." For 50 years, CO_2 had been promoted as a treatment for hypoxia, even for climbing to high altitude. But its use gradually lapsed, perhaps through lack of accurate measurement techniques. Now was our chance to reassess its application with our fancy instruments.

Tim added CO_2 to air-filled Douglas bags (500-litre transparent plastic bags) to produce a 3% mixture, 80-fold higher than normal air concentrations (0.04%). On inhaling the combination, our breathing rates increased, leading to a striking rise in blood oxygen levels and a prompt relief of headache and nausea. Using radioactive xenon, Jörgen showed a 20–40% increase in cerebral blood flow. The improvement was attributed to the dilating effect of higher blood CO_2 concentrations on cerebral blood vessels, thereby increasing oxygen delivery to the brain. It was equivalent to descending thousands of feet. We were all very excited about this dramatic result. Tim had produced a rare popular experiment. We persuaded him to make up more CO_2 mixtures then sat alongside him sniffing the gases.

Meanwhile, Neville, Glen and Ibrahim checked out the route to Gondogoro Peak, visible against a backdrop of larger mountains. They had departed shortly after the 4.30 am call to prayer. We expected them back by midday but well before that Neville skied in, arriving 1½ hours ahead of Glen. They had been at the top by 9.30 am and found a great campsite at 5,400 m, around 250 m below the summit. As this was considerably higher than we had camped on previous trips, it should prove useful for our experiments.

We had a 2 pm conference to decide the best plan for the next few days. John Coote wanted to conduct more sleep studies at Khuispan, so eight subjects plus the three RAF supervisors would remain behind while the rest of us would ascend. We would need 40 porters for each day's loads but the other 50 could go home, returning for our final descent. Javed elected to stay at Khuispan while Ibrahim would ascend with the first group. For an hour we debated which experiment and associated equipment took priority until Ibrahim recommended sending most of it to the top camp that afternoon.

The ascent group located their equipment and put it outside their tents for the morning. Climbing boots, crampons, ice axes, skis, ski boots and high-altitude clothing. We worked until dark on experiments and then re-allocated ourselves among tents so as not to disturb the sleep subjects in the early morning.

Six days at top camp (5,430 m)

At 3.30 am, the alarm sounded alongside porters' voices. Using torches, they were vying for the lightest loads under the watchful eye of Iqbal. It was a crisp, bitterly cold dawn with intermittent snow. There was much moaning as we gathered our belongings. Many were not happy and asked if they could be spared packing duties so as to start the climb early. Marcus, Mike, Richard and Peter Dykes were particularly miserable, with Peter quite puffy-faced. It seemed wrong that they should not do their share of the packing but we let them go ahead. Alex was also poorly with a bad headache so we put him on acetazolamide but he didn't enter the trial; we hadn't time to test his cerebral blood flow.

As the team and porters departed, I watched over the last of the packing with Ginette, wondering if we could catch them up. She was very fit and completely acclimatised and I still felt well. Iqbal haggled with five porters over the weight and price for carrying the two generators. It was their way of extracting extra pay. Mammutt was the strongest and agreed to carry one on his own. In the confusion we sent up the skis and forgot Jörgen's gamma camera.

Ginette and I jogged down the small boulder slope from the camp onto the moraine rubble. Beyond it, a mile-long line of people stretched out over the steepening glacier. Ginette slowly got ahead by taking a direct line up the ridge while I traversed diagonally up a snow slope and onto a col where Glen and Sue were resting. There was no time to talk, indeed no breath for talking. I overhauled Ginette, a few porters struggling with their heavy loads, then Pete Forster, who was ascending slowly with Ian. Next to be overhauled were Marcus and Jörgen, puffing and panting as we climbed above 5,000 m. The leaders were 400 yards ahead, up a steepening slope. There was no slowing now. I passed Norman then Geoff. He was up for the race. I climbed abreast of the porter carrying my rucksack and rummaged in it for sunglasses but to no avail. Geoff had overtaken me but I gradually caught up, sweating profusely despite the freezing temperatures and falling snow. He stopped, gasping over his ice axe and I was passed.

On and up. Who was left? Richard came into sight, going well despite his recent mountain sickness. Acetazolamide must have done the trick. I overhauled him, much to his annoyance, leaving only the 25 leading porters ahead. They were climbing in two parallel rows, using long white sticks splayed out like oars of a galley, and singing. Carrying 25 kg apiece, they moved remarkably quickly. As I passed them, they acclaimed me as a leader and very strong, and we exchanged mutual flattery. I briefly led the group, feeling profound empathy with their huge physical effort, their culture and their camaraderie, only to drop back to climb in their midst. Time passed quickly: the depot from the previous day came into sight and we arrived to a joyous celebration. The porters cheered then sang the Pakistan national anthem followed by God Save the Queen. It was a very emotional occasion. I had gained their respect, but to show who was the strongest, Mammutt, the generator carrier, danced in the snow with a generator on his back, all 35 kg of it. It was an amazing achievement, especially since he sank a foot or more into the snow with every step. I had taken 1 hour 55 minutes. Could Jonathan beat that when he came up tomorrow, I wondered?

Richard came in shortly afterwards and managed to film some of the celebrations. As others drifted in, afternoon clouds blocked the sun and it began to snow heavily. It was most unpleasant, particularly for those feeling ill. We had to forget the chat and erect the tents. This meant digging through two feet of snow to the hard pack below. Those feeling well dug hard while the ill members looked on. It was exhausting: a few shovel-fulls, stop for 20 breaths, then start again. Ginette and Barbara worked particularly hard.

First, we dug in the cook tent then the large mess tent but we only had two shovels. Out came 'dead men' (wide aluminium snow anchors), pot lids, frying pans and bowls. Those suffering from mountain sickness retreated to the cook tent, exhausted from their climb. Two hot chocolates later, we started to dig out protective holes for our own tents. With Norman, we carefully cut large blocks of snow to put upwind of our tent which we had placed close to the mess tent to minimise walking distance. Others were also digging in and gradually, despite the blizzard, the camp took shape. The last of the porters arrived and dropped their loads. Then, to shouts and singing, all the porters headed back to Hushe. They would be back to rescue us in six days.

By midday, after what had seemed like a lifetime, all the tents were erected just as the weather cleared to reveal a fabulous view of the surrounding mountains: Trinity Peak, Laila Peak, Masherbrum and a host of others. We were on top of the world. It made all our hardships worthwhile.

However, not everyone was happy. Poor oedematous Peter Dykes, suffering badly from the altitude, burst into tears. With Pete Forster, we tried to soothe him, yet he was in complete denial of his illness. He was a tough sod and at 59 the oldest in the group. We discussed starting him on the trial but we had left the cerebral blood flow equipment at base camp. We couldn't even be bothered to run the generators. The altitude had finally done for us. So instead, we blew up our air beds and dozed in the sun. Ginette was the only one with any energy and built a snowman.

The setting sun glowed yellow on Masherbrum then faded to rose pink on the surrounding peaks. It was time for dinner then bed. Norman shared his whisky with me. It tasted great. We talked briefly but who knows what about. We had six days at this height so there was plenty of time for chat.

It was a very cold first night. I lay in bed wondering about who would become ill next. There were four people remaining (excluding those on sleep studies) who had yet to develop mountain sickness – Ginette, Geoff, Dave and me. I was more worried about the cold. My old 40-Winks sleeping bag was inadequate despite salopettes and duvet jacket; just getting in it with all my bulging clothes on was a struggle. And the tent was too small. I was on a spare blow-up mattress that took up over half the tent. Norman had a smaller airbed but a better-sized sleeping bag, a great puff ball of goose down; a proper four-seasons affair. My 40-Winks, made of artificial fibre, would have to be retired.

I awoke to some irritating shouting outside at 7 am only to realise it was Jonathan. He had made the ascent from Khuispan in just 1½ hours, beating my time by 30 minutes. He poked his nose into the tent to gloat. As an encore he climbed a further 250 m to the top of Gondoro Peak with Ginette. Ah well, I thought, he is 20 years younger.

Norman and I lay in the warmth of our bags unwilling to stir for another hour. As the sun hit, ice that had condensed inside the tent from our breath started to melt and drip on us.

Norman was up first, benefiting from acetazolamide, while I had a mild headache. As I struggled out of the tent, others arrived from the lower camp. Most were well but Neil needed help and was very miserable. A tough RAF type perhaps, but now quite out of his comfort zone.

All equipment had now arrived from Khuispan so we needed to start experiments. But motivation was difficult in the warm morning sunshine. Pete Forster had devised a bleeding experiment – literally (figure 16). A polythene suction tube was attached to the lower lip for a minute, after which the number of petechiae (small capillary bleeds) were counted. A report had suggested it related to acute mountain sickness but Pete's results showed no association. I found breakfast quite inedible and was content to lie on an airbed enjoying the sun's heat.

Three people were started on the trial, the maximum number the cerebral blood flow instruments could cope with. A generator was fired up, allowing Mike to use the blood-gas analyser, with Ginette and Ian taking bloods. It was a relief that it worked after the freezing night. Some of the results might need 'modifying' or 'interpreted' in light of the challenging setting in which they were generated. Then Jörgen's equipment was up and running, ready for afternoon tests. First was the poorly Peter Dykes, who had been on placebo. The generator droned on, hunting in the thin air. 'Make sure the bloody thing is refuelled in time,' I muttered to John Simmons. Just as Pete was given xenon, the wretched machine stopped. I was getting agitated with the whole process. We had to be quicker. By now it was 2.30 pm and we had to finish before sundown because the gamma camera detectors would freeze (figure 17).

I noticed David Siviter sitting back and not helping with the experiments. I grumbled at him to be more helpful. Then it was my turn for a xenon injection and the gamma camera helmet. Geoff failed to place the detectors properly. Richard and John Milles wanted to film it being put on again but I refused. It was all right for them, they were on acetazolamide. By now I was in a foul mood, with a bad headache. The helmet was repositioned but still squeezed my temples. The Venflon injection needle in my arm hurt. After 15 minutes, which seemed an age, it was over. I swallowed six capsules of some or other medication, questioning what the hell I was taking because I was feeling so bad.

An hour later, while lying in the tent filling out the acute mountain sickness questionnaire, my knees started tingling. And, for the first time all day, I felt hungry. The penny finally dropped. I had developed acute mountain sickness that had been relieved by acetazolamide and my oxygen levels were rising.

I took a few photos of the sunset but developed a bad headache then become nauseous. The headache worsened – a real throbber. Dinner was called but I felt too ill. A second cerebral blood flow test at $2\frac{1}{2}$ hours showed increased flow while my blood oxygen levels had risen significantly. I lay in my bag and missed supper, my head throbbing even on codeine. Why was I responding badly to acetazolamide when others had improved quickly? Was I more sensitive for some reason? Was it an unusual side effect or was it because I was partially acclimatised? Perhaps the dose was too big? If so, Ginette could be much worse. Several people poked their head into the tent to see if I was OK. At 8 pm Norman came in and offered his whisky. I went to sleep apprehensively but had a good night's rest and was better by the morning, a sure sign that acetazolamide was working.

Only three people didn't develop mountain sickness – Geoff, Dave and Ginette. The protocol was that they too should receive acetazolamide with cerebral blood flow assessment, despite having no symptoms. The first two were given 1.5 g and both developed mild headaches. Ginette was last. As she only weighed 55 kg, we reduced the dose to 1.25 g. Within 30 minutes, her cerebral blood flow had increased hugely and she developed a bad headache. Over the following hour, it worsened progressively, she became nauseous and very frightened. Initial treatment with paracetamol and brandy, our panacea, had no effect. It was unclear what was happening but thankfully she showed no signs of cerebral oedema. Tim tried oxygen, but it didn't help. Should she have dexamethasone? With no clear diagnosis and showing a slight improvement, she was left to tough it out overnight. By the morning she had recovered. Acetazolamide was not as benign as we had thought.

Pete Forster kept us amused through Ginette's drama. He wondered who should be eaten first if we were stuck at top camp for weeks. Each defended their position. Jörgen, a Danish special, would be tasty. Dave was the fattest. Alex would be too old and tough, but he might have a tender liver since he didn't drink alcohol.

The expedition finally developed some sort of routine. Bitterly cold mornings, then warmth as the sun touched the tents. Struggling for breath while dressing for breakfast served outside in the sun or inside sheltering from snow showers. Several hours of experiments, while concentrating hard to ensure they were being conducted properly. Clinical assessments, blood samples, keeping the generators going, then basking in the afternoon sun if conditions allowed it. Dinner and bed (figures 14–15).

By day 3, most experiments were complete, which was fortunate because there was a blizzard. We had to dig out the tents several times. Everyone joined in, even those such as Peter Dykes and Ginette who had been ill. We dug out the tents again and again, and when it finally ceased it was time for bed.

Emergency descent

We awoke on the fourth day to bright skies and a foot and a half of fresh snow. We stood around our half-buried tents blinking in the bright sun. Most were feeling good from a combination of acclimatisation and large doses of acetazolamide. However, Glen Rowling's girlfriend, Sue, who was not part of our experiments, wasn't well. She had coped easily on the ascent, being young and fit, but had stayed in bed all the previous day. Now she had alarming symptoms, including loss of peripheral vision and tingling down her right arm. Examination by our professor of neurology, Marcus Raichle, indicated that her eyes were normal but her right hand was not moving properly.

Hypoxic brains work slowly, even those expertly trained. Marcus suggested aspirin as it would reduce the risk from blood clots and ease any mountain sickness or migraine headache, but she had none of those features. A befuddle of doctors, however, did agree that any person with apparent brain problems at 5,400 m needed dexamethasone; 8 mg for two days was duly prescribed. It was also agreed that she should descend immediately under medical supervision.

Although there were 17 doctors in the group, most were involved in experiments or still recovering from illness. Jonathan had plenty of surplus energy but he was a sleep subject. That left one person – me – although Pete Forster wondered what use an immunologist would be if she deteriorated. Even so, I was volunteered to go down. A night at Dalsamp Lakes was very attractive as it was 1,100 m lower. With 15 minutes to prepare, I grabbed my rucksack, sleeping bag and gloves but little else and bade farewell.

Glen, Sue and Ibrahim had already left and were 200 metres ahead. I followed with Mammutt the generator porter on my heels carrying my bag. He was strong enough to carry Sue if needed. By carefully treading in their deep footsteps, we soon caught up. Sue was desperately slow. I moved in front to try to make the steps firmer. She was not wearing gaiters, so her feet were wet and very cold, raising the risk of frostbite. On the first rocky ridge near Khuispan, we replaced her socks with dry ones, warming her feet in Glen's armpits, then pressed on.

After the brief rest, Sue felt a little better. Thank goodness she wasn't going to have a stroke. However, she became slower and slower as the afternoon turned to early evening. The final climb up a moraine slope involved a rest after every step. Beside Dalsamp lake, Mammutt and Ibrahim had set up our tents. She was put to bed while we chatted till dusk, benefiting from the thicker air. Supper was merely cheese, a few biscuits and water. Preoccupied with the rescue, we had brought little food and no hot beverages and had barely drunk anything all day. I went to bed hungry, only to awake two hours later with a terrible thirst. I went out for a long drink at the stream. It was snowing fitfully, the wind tugging at the tent. It would be much worse at top camp.

At dawn, I was awakened by Mammutt for breakfast. He had climbed back to Khuispan in the dark to search for food. Glen had assured us that a stash of it had been deposited for the return journey but little could be found under the fresh snow. His total journey had taken four hours. Breakfast was a little cheese, noodle soup and black tea. Thankfully, Sue was up and feeling much better.

I bade farewell to Sue and Glen then, with Mammutt and Rosa Ali, started the long slog back up the glacier. It took three hours to reach Khuispan, where we found Kraft cheese slices and a piece of a sausage but nothing else under the snow. Maybe the supplies would appear when it melted in late summer. After our snacks, we lay about in the warm sun until it was too late to climb further. The porters were superb, taking care of my every need– plying me with warm drinks, sacrificing their food and preparing the tent. In the evening Mammutt made a smoky fire of dead twigs to warm our hands as we watched Laila Peak, rose pink in the setting sun. As they had little English, there was no conversation yet there was an unspoken bond between us. I had huge respect for their kindness, their knowledge of that remote, beautiful mountain landscape and their complex relationship with visitors from unknowable foreign lands. I wandered over to nearby cliffs in the dusk to gaze on the lonely campsite in that astonishingly beautiful and remote setting. We could have been the last people on Earth, clinging to life when all else had disappeared. Two tents in a wilderness of beauty. Spirituality suffused my consciousness. No wonder religious fervour pervaded romantic loneliness. I felt a great surge of warmth for nature, the porters, humankind and life. I went to bed calm and content.

At first light, under a perfectly clear sky, Mammutt appeared with a cup of black tea. Sleeping in all but my duvet jacket, I dressed quickly and ate the remnants of our food. The tent was quickly packed and we were off. I carried nothing. Mammutt and Rosa Ali ascended quickly, despite their heavy rucksacks. But I was not to be beaten that easily, passing them as they paused in a snowdrift. There was no stopping now – the sun was rising and I was going for top camp. For the first hour the frozen snow barely took a boot print but it softened as the sun rose. I arrived just as the camp was stirring. Jonathan rushed over and asked my time. I had taken 1 hour 27 minutes, beating him by three minutes. But as he pointed out, I had had four extra days acclimatising. Nevertheless, not bad on a few pieces of Kraft cheese.

While I was away, Mike had carried on with his urine studies using the radioactive dextrans. Tim was the fourth to be injected. However, within a few minutes he collapsed, became semi-conscious and was barely able to speak. Panic. Sixteen doctors, ten opinions, no diagnosis, no blood pressure apparatus and a broken thermometer. It was probably not acute mountain sickness but when in doubt give steroids: prescription – 8 mg of dexamethasone intravenously and lie him in the sun. He slowly came around, coughing and shivering. After a two-hour nap he was restored, albeit a little wobbly. We discovered later that anaphylactoid (anaphylaxis-like) reactions are an uncommon but usually harmless side effect of dextran injections.

One of the expedition treats was climbing the nearby Gondogoro Peak. A summit of 5,700 m, more than 1,000 m higher than Mont Blanc, would be a major challenge in most mountain ranges, but we were already camped at 5,430 m so most were keen to become 'Himalayan mountaineers'. This was going to be a mass assault. Fresh snow from the blizzard, 25 cm of it, was no barrier to our intrepid explorers. John Delamere led while Ginette and Jonathan stamped out a trail for everyone else to follow. The vista opened up, and Masherbrum (7,821 m), Gasherbrum I (8,068 m) and Chogolisa (7,668 m) came into view, the latter peak infamous as the last resting place of the great Hermann Buhl, solo conqueror of Nanga Parbat in 1953. To the south, adding to the mountain panorama, Laila Peak spiked out from a sea of clouds. BMRES packed the small summit for a photo poised on a dangerously overhanging cornice. Only the inexperienced Jörgen and Alex resisted the peer pressure to make the ascent. A day later, Pete Forster made a solo ascent but on the steep descent fell headlong. Gripping his ice-axe in naked hands he pressed the pick with all his strength into the hard snow. It worked. Only the week before, David Siviter had shown him how to use it. It saved his life but skinned his knuckles. Always wear gloves when carrying an ice-axe.

Everyone was relieved that the experiments were finishing: last urine samples, last blood samples, last clinical questionnaires. Norman set fire to our clinical waste – urine bottles, syringes, medical swabs together with the rest of the rubbish. Maybe there was more hidden under recent snow that would be buried in the glacier perhaps to emerge in 20–30 years' time.

I gazed past our 'little village' in the snow, to the vast jumble of peaks, rock spires and glaciers, and beyond towards magnificent Laila Peak, glowing pink in the sunset (figure 18). Hidden behind Gondogoro but impinging on our conscious minds were the huge peaks of Chogolisa, Broad Peak, the Gasherbrums and mighty K2 itself. Residual stress melted away leaving me calm and contented. Over the past two weeks we had been prodded and poked, bled, developed gut rot, nausea and headaches, had our brains tested, been poisoned with different gases and irradiated. It had been a challenging expedition, counterbalanced by extraordinary mountains, rivers and people. Now we just had to survive the journey home.

Descent

We were up at 5 am in the freezing dawn to collect our gear and squeeze it into our packs. We would need dozens of porters. Over breakfast we discussed their reliability and whether they would come up as planned to our desolate, frozen camp. They didn't let us down. Murmurs on the wind grew to singing then shouting as 65 porters emerged from the mist. It was a most memorable vision; the mass approach in six columns, sticks out sideways, as if rowing uphill (figure 19). There was multiple hand shaking, congratulations and embraces worthy of long-lost brothers. We were saved.

Bags, boxes, food and tents were sorted out with much shouting and milling about as Javed and Ibrahim assessed box weights and porter loads. Our little 'village' was cleared of all rubbish; latrine and fire pits were filled in even though all traces of us would disappear in the next snowstorm.

Nev, John Milles and I remained at the cleared camp as everyone disappeared across the glacier into the mist. We waited and waited in eager anticipation, controlling our urge to descend. We would easily be first down – we had skis. Tighten boots, check bindings, goggles and gloves, then down the gentle slope on soft snow following the multitude of footprints. It was an easy descent; within minutes we were gliding past porters and Sherpas who had never seen the like before. They cheered as we floated past, weaving and coasting among them. Beyond a rock band, we skied down a narrowing snow thread to the lower base camp. It was 30 minutes for

us, two to three hours for the others. Surely, we gloated, few can claim to have skied the Karakoram.

The remnants of our lower camp were cleared, high-altitude clothes changed for shorts and fleeces then it was down the glacier onto the moraine. We bade farewell to Ginette and John Delamere who planned an assault on nearby Trinity Peak.

The return to Dalsamp lakes took another three hours, compared with six when I had accompanied Sue. In the warm midday sun, the camp was a riot of colour, a meadowland of forget-me-nots, wild rhubarb and gentian, such a contrast to the black and white of high camp. But we were still at 4,200 m, so with the setting sun it cooled abruptly, with sleet soon followed by snow. Porters, without tents or ground sheets, huddled under overhanging rock faces, their camps for the night.

The second day of descent took us to Hushe. It was another early start on a freezing morning, the lakes having built up an inch of ice overnight. How could the porters tolerate such temperatures?

Descent and the rising sun led to a hot summer's day as we passed K6 view camp to the relative civilisation of Hushe. Relaxed after a successful expedition, we enjoyed the mystical, beautiful walk: huge mountains, pristine rivers, glistening glaciers and alpine meadows full of flowers. But thoughts turned to home and what awaited. When could the studies be analysed? What about families and children? Would work colleagues resent our month's holiday?

We passed our porters praying together on the roadside, a mullah leading the flock. In Hushe, the village elders welcomed us, relieved that all was well. Nev, Dave and I were invited to Javed's house in the centre of the huddled buildings for tea and biscuits and introductions to his family. As most porters were from the village, our payments were important for the finances of many families and would make a big difference to the local economy. 150 rupees per porter (£5) per day, 500 rupees for the main cooks and 1200 rupees to Javed per day. Plus a tip of $500.

Holiday outings

The research part of the expedition was over but we weren't due back in England for another seven days. Four were for the return journey, which left three for adventures. While we had all got on well together, enough was enough so we split into several groups.

Ginette and John Delamere made a sporting attempt at Trinity Peak. This was the 6,700 m mountain on the south-west side of our top camp. Unfortunately, fresh snow from the storm prevented them reaching the summit. On steeper sections 'it flowed like rice', they reported, with a huge risk of avalanches.

Six attempted the walk to Skardu – Neville, Pete, Tim, Geoff, Ian and John Simmons; 25 km to Khapalu then 95 km of dusty roads to Skardu. Midday heat, blistered feet and sunburnt skin were the main difficulties, and only Ian, Neville and Geoff completed the journey on foot.

Many recovered in Hushe or explored the Indus valley at Khapalu. The highlight was crossing the river on a zak. These primitive rafts are based on trapping inflated cattle skins (plus a few tyre inner tubes) in a cage of wooden branches. Two men with simple poles paddled as the stream swept them down river to the opposite side.

John Milles and I returned to the calm of the mountains with two porters and a cook boy. A side valley off the Hushe river led up the Allee Valley to the extensive Masherbrum Glacier. Eleven kilometres long and a kilometre wide, it carved its way through mountains, pine forests and alpine meadows to terminate in a ten-metre high wall of ice and boulders. But, like all the glaciers, it had retreated many miles over the past century, leaving a wide fertile plain. Arriving in the late afternoon and dozy from the warm summer sun, we stopped for tea then decided to camp at its very tip. The sun set and a cold adiabatic wind rushed down from Masherbrum. Tucked in as we were below the ice wall, we felt quite secure. We assumed that boulders around the campsite had been deposited as the ice retreated. Not a bit. In the calm of the night, groans and creaks from millions of tons of moving ice kept us awake. Small rock falls rattled down the face, occasional boulders bouncing past the tents. In the morning, we moved the camp ten metres downhill.

On the second day we climbed onto the glacier. There were many huge ice hoodoos supporting room-sized boulders marching in a line along the middle of the glacier. Beyond the ice, bountiful summer meadows led up to Masherbrum and other peaks. We had never seen such fairy-tale beauty. Wondering if some of the alpine flowers were rare, we collected a box full of different specimens then wandered back for a second night under the snout.

On the third day, we ambled back to Hushe, reluctant to leave that beautiful landscape and rejoin civilisation. Next day was the drive to Skardu and the fancy lakeside K2 hotel. Although the roof had collapsed from winter snows, it had been partly repaired since we had last been in the town. It seemed like heaven compared with our accommodation over the past three weeks and an extraordinary contrast to the poverty of Skardu. Spectacular views of the surrounding mountains greeted the eye. We arrived in time for an international cricket match: Skardu town 126, BMRES 46 – another defeat. We had a few final measurements – fat-fold thickness and weights. Ian had lost the most – 10 kg in three weeks.

Back to civilisation

From Skardu it was a 22-hour, 650 km road trip or one hour by plane. The problem was that we only had eight tickets for a flight in two days' time (due to some overbooking cock-up). If cancelled, which was commonplace, we would miss the flight to London.

Glen and Sue, who had re-joined us, tried to sell us the overland journey – the Karakoram Highway, often referred to as the eighth wonder of the world. It was reputed to be spectacular but it took two days and had a lethal reputation. It had been opened only eight years earlier after 20 years in construction at a cost of more than 1,000 lives, with continuing fatalities annually from avalanches. Death on the highway or death in a small plane. Most preferred the flight but we negotiated among ourselves to suit everyone. I chose the road (figure 20).

Over the following two days the over-landers journeyed beside the Indus to Islamabad through the north-west frontier. It was the most extraordinary road journey any of us had experienced. The Indus River carves a stupendous ravine between Nanga Parbat (8,126 m) to the south and Rakaposhi (7,788 m) to the north. The narrow asphalt road is hacked into unstable cliff faces, sometimes beside the river and at other times high above. There are no villages for they would be swept away in rock falls triggered by the sporadic huge earthquakes.

The 5-hour journey on the first day started beside the river's upper course on a one-lane road with passing places. We passed Rakaposhi and turned north to the Hunza Valley to arrive by mid-afternoon at the old colonial-styled town of Gilgit and the Park Hotel. It conjured up thoughts of British Empire days, the Great Game between Britain and Russia in Victorian times and the novel Kim by Rudyard Kipling.

The next day we departed at dawn with 500 km of the journey remaining. The minivan was rather crowded so I elected to travel in a jeep with our luggage. I was quite content not to talk for the 17-hour journey for I felt slightly nauseous and preferred to be alone. Well, not quite alone, because there was a driver, but he spoke not a word of English.

The wide, aged-scarred mountain plateau was completely dry with no hint of habitation or greenery, even beside the river. The sun came up and the temperature soared. It was too hot to eat and at rest stops we hid in the shade clutching cold drinks. By 11 am it was a furnace. Then we entered the deep narrow canyon that skirted the west side of Nanga Parbat. High above, white glaciers glistened above forests of pine trees but we were in the rocky desert of the Indus gorge on a narrow, twisting road that rose up to 300 m above the river. Intermittently, there were small walls protecting vehicles from tumbling over the edge. Disconcertingly, crashed vehicles littered the bottom of the precipice. The Indus, swelled by the melting summer snows, swaggered its way through the crumbling mountains, roaring as it went. At one point it collided with house-sized boulders, creating a great thundering arc – an extraordinary display of nature's power. In 2010, a huge avalanche blocked the river for several months, creating a 22 km lake that submerged many villages and flooded more when it burst.

The afternoon came and went and we pressed on into the night. The drivers only stopped briefly as their concentration was dimmed by heat and the strain of watching the road. Suddenly, the jeep braked hard, shaking me out of drowsiness. The driver was struggling to concentrate, his eyes half closed. I watched with growing anxiety as his steering became more erratic. We had no common language; talking to keep him awake was not an option. As we veered towards the open precipice, I grabbed the wheel, forcing the jeep back towards the cliff face where the driver braked hard and stopped. He had fallen asleep. Using signs and grunts, I persuaded him to let me drive. He immediately fell asleep as I cautiously drove for the next two hours to the city of Askole at the end of the great canyon. The river had fallen 1,800 m since leaving Skardu, a similar drop to the Colorado River through the Grand Canyon.

The minibus group had its own difficulties; a bald tyre was changed, a speeding ticket of 15 rupees was paid (around 50p), there were army stops and projectile vomiting stops with barely time for sufferers to exit the crowded van. They arrived into the furnace of the Rawalpindi Hotel at 9 pm to meet me and those who had arrived on the plane in the morning. As Pete Forster wryly noted as the exhausted occupants tumbled out: 'Marcus was white knuckled, Neil grey, Richard was vomiting and Mike was still bald. Flying had been the correct choice.' The drivers received 200 rupees (£8) each for the 17-hour day.

The plane journey had also been a spectacular though less scary journey. They stayed in the K2 hotel for the first day, acquiring a salmonella infection; John Simmons, Neville, then Pete developed diarrhoea. Next day at 8.30 am under a cloudless sky, all eight piled into a Fokker Friendship for a sphincter-gripping flight. It started with tight circling over the Skardu valley to gain height, providing magnificent views of Nanga Parbat.

The final day of our four-week adventure had arrived. We had a few more hours as tourists. I re-visited Flashman's Hotel in Rawalpindi on the Great Trunk Road, which I had stayed at 10 years earlier on a World Health Organisation travelling fellowship. Built in the days of the Raj, it had catered for lords and officers, hosting the biggest decision-makers of the sub-continent. It was unchanged. Others bought rugs and carved stoneware with little regard to their weight.

Mr Shariff, the Amersham representative, turned up and was impressed with our achievements. Mr Munirujeen, the petty official, didn't get a visit. Then it was final packing. I was considerably overweight because of the plants we had collected in the Allee Valley but was confident that we could argue our way out of excess baggage charges.

There was a final group meal at the Holiday Inn then it was off to the airport for 11 pm. A large sign at the terminal entrance warned that exporting plants from the country without a licence was illegal. Concern turned to panic when police started opening every metal box. Security, for some reason, was extremely tight. Maybe they had wind of our radioactive xenon imports. John Milles and I retrieved the two boxes containing the plants and hastily dumped them in some bushes.

As the boxes were weighed, our worries returned. Between us, 365 kg of 'presents' had been added, since they were pre-weighed in the hotel. Metal boxes were re-opened and people guiltily extracted gifts that had been hidden among the equipment. I was guilty too. No one was prepared to dump rugs or stoneware. We donned big boots, several layers of clothes (in spite of the heat and humidity in the airport) and hand-carried as much as we dared. With a combination of the boot trick and bypassing the weighing machine we were down to 65 kg at a price of $700. It could have been much worse.

Evolving salmonella infections acquired at the K2 hotel added to our woes. Poor Pete Smith vomited in the middle of the line and his trousers filled with diarrhoea. Bloody curries. Then, unexpectedly, we were landed with an airport tax of 250 rupees ($15) per person ($375 in total). It was fortunate that we had retained some group cash as individuals had spent all their own on gifts. We departed an hour late, squeezed into economy class with big boots, duvet jackets, fleeces and other clothing. To make matters worse the food was foul and there was no alcohol.

On the journey home we had an unscheduled stop for fuel at Istanbul because the plane was overweight (was that our fault?), then to Paris and London by 12.30 pm for another clash with customs. Thankfully, we had no illegal plant imports but rugs had been deliberately under-priced with falsely low sales invoices. Barbara was heavily fined for deception. It was a relief to be on the bus to Birmingham after 20 hours of misery.

Postscript

It was three weeks before we all recovered from gut infections, with many needing ciprofloxacin (a potent antibiotic). Stool cultures identified *Salmonella skarduii* or some such name.

There was also trouble with Amersham over the price of the xenon. They claimed it had cost £100,000 to produce but out of goodwill had only charged £20,000. It was impossible to pay such a huge amount. After a lot of fuss, we agreed on £3,000. Also, there was no good quality film, so it was never produced.

From a research point of view, the expedition was very successful. Tim rapidly dispatched his CO_2 breathing experiment to *The Lancet*. They loved it, publishing it shortly after submission. The xenon cerebral blood flow study took rather longer but was accepted by a top US publication, the *Journal of Applied Physiology*. We showed that cerebral blood flow increased at altitude, increased further on acetazolamide but was not related to acute mountain sickness or headaches. It has since become the Society's most cited article.

The following year we presented the results at the biennial Hypoxia Symposium in Banff, Canada. Due to an adverse pound sterling/Canadian dollar exchange rate, we couldn't afford accommodation at the Banff Springs Hotel in addition to flights and conference fees. To save money we slept below our posters in the lecture room, putting our day clothes in a conveniently located wardrobe. 'Defending our posters', we explained to patrolling night porters who obligingly did not report us to hotel management (figure 21).

Publications from the expedition:

1. Bradwell AR, Winterborn MH, Wright AD, Forster PJG, Dykes PW. Acetazolamide treatment of acute mountain sickness. Clinical Science 1988; 74 (suppl. 18): 62.

2. Forster PJG. Microvascular fragility at high altitude. British Medical Journal 1988; (296): 1004-5.

3. Harvey TC, Winterborn MH, Lassen NA, Raichle ME, Jensen JB, Richardson NV, Bradwell AR. Effect of carbon dioxide in acute mountain sickness: A rediscovery. The Lancet 1988; 8612(332): 639-641.

4. Jensen JB, Wright AD, Lassen NA, Harvey TC, Winterborn MH, Raichle ME, Bradwell AR. Cerebral blood flow in acute mountain sickness. Journal of Applied Physiology 1990; 69: 430-433.

5. Nicholson AN, Smith PA, Stone BM, Bradwell AR, Coote JH. Altitude insomnia: studies during an expedition to the Himalayas. Sleep 1988; 11: 354-361.

6. Winterborn MH, Bradwell AR and BMRES. Mechanisms of high-altitude proteinuria. Clinical Science 1990; 78 (suppl 22): 19-20.

Fig 1. Back row, left to right: *John Simmons, Neil Stanley, Pete Forster, John Milles, Marcus Raichle, Pete Smith, John Potokar, Ian Chesner, Alex Wright, Neville Richardson. Middle row: Richard Boyce, John Delamere, Norman Dorricott, Jonathan Evans, Tim Harvey, Peter Dykes.* **Front row:** *Jörgen Jensen, Barbara Stone, John Coote, Sirdar Iqbal, Dave Siviter, Ginette Harrison, Geoff Tsang, Mike Winterborn. (Photographer Jo Bradwell)*

Fig 2. *Camp at Baltistan Tours in Skardu*

Fig 3. *Child in Skardu*

Fig 4. *Bridge over the Indus*

Fig 5. *K6 and surrounding peaks*

Fig 6. Gondogoro Glacier

Fig 7. Alex Wright at Dalsamp camp

Fig 8. Peter Dykes and John Potokar at Dalsamp camp

Fig 9. Dalsamp camp

Fig 10. Masherbrum from Dalsamp camp

Fig 11. Porters with generator and ice boxes

Fig 12. Jonathan Evans on an ice/ rock hoodoo.

Fig 13. Tim's CO$_2$ experiment with Mike Winterborn

Fig 14. *Alex Wright at top camp*

Fig 15. *Norman Dorricott at top camp*

Fig 16. *Pete Forster with capillary leakage suction tube*

Fig 17. *Cerebral blood flow with Jörgen Jensen and Alex*

Fig 18. *Laila peak (6,069 m)*

Fig 19. *Porters arriving at top camp*

Fig 20. *Along the Indus River to Askole*

Fig 21. *John Milles defending his poster in Banff*

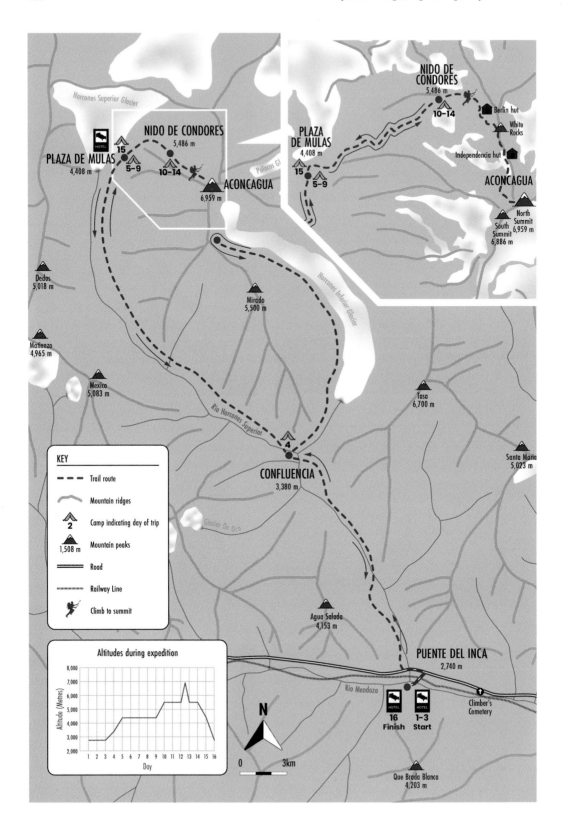

Horcones Superior Glacier

NIDO DE
CONDORES
5,486 m

PLAZA DE MULAS
4,408 m

15
5-9
10-14

ACONCAGUA
6,959 m

NIDO DE
CONDORES
5,486 m

Berlin hut

White
Rocks

PLAZA
DE MULAS
4,408 m

15
5-9

10-14

Independencia hut

ACONCAGUA

North
Summit
6,959 m

South
Summit
6,886 m

Polacos Gl

Horcones Inferior Glacier

Dedos
5,018 m

Matienzo
4,965 m

Mexico
5,083 m

Rio Horcones Superior

Mirado
5,500 m

Tasa
6,700 m

Santa Maria
5,023 m

4

CONFLUENCIA
3,380 m

Glacier De Oro

KEY

- - - -   Trail route

⌒⌒   Mountain ridges

⌂ **2**   Camp indicating day of trip

▲ 1,508 m   Mountain peaks

══   Road

·······   Railway Line

Climb to summit

Agua Salada
4,153 m

PUENTE DEL INCA
2,740 m

Rio Mendoza

Climber's
Cemetery

16
Finish

1-3
Start

Altitudes during expedition

8,000
7,000
6,000
5,000
4,000
3,000
2,000

Altitude (Metres)

1 2 3 4 5 6 7 8 9 10 11 12 13 14 15 16
Day

N

0   3km

Que Brada Blanca
4,203 m

Chapter 6
Aconcagua, Argentina – January 1990

Science or the summit

*"There are only three real sports: bullfighting, car racing and mountain climbing.
All the others are mere games."*

– Ernest Hemingway

Summary: Top camp on the 1987 Karakoram expedition had been near Gondogoro Peak, allowing most of us to reach the summit. Why not an even bigger mountain? We chose Aconcagua (6,962 m), the highest summit Malloryaltitude physiology at 5,486 m and a drug trial of methazolamide versus dexamethasone. Seven of us subsequently climbed the mountain.

Expedition members: Steve Boyer, Jo Bradwell (leader), John Delamere, Matthew Dugas (medical student), Jonathan Evans, Richard Filer (medical student), Pete Forster, Nick Gompertz (medical student), Ginette Harrison, Gron Jones, Chris Imray, Ian MacLennan, John Milles, John Potokar, John Simmons, Bjorn Sperling, Martin Wildman (medical student), Mike Winterborn, Alex Wright (deputy leader).

A particular attraction of the Karakoram had been Gondogoro Peak, a mountain that we could all climb. Emboldened, we wanted to try something bigger. This would be difficult in the Himalayas because the snow line is around 5,000 m. However, it is much higher on many peaks in the Andes. Not necessarily in Ecuador, where we had been before, but in the rain shadow of more southerly mountains. Even Aconcagua, at 6,962 m, has snow-free routes in the summer. It is the highest peak in the southern hemisphere and indeed the highest mountain outside the Himalaya/Karakoram ranges. Long warm days melt the snow on its west face, providing an easy path to the summit. En route is the Nido de Condores campsite at 5,486 m, where we could perform experiments. The optimal time of year is from late January to early February, the southern hemisphere summer.

Another reason for attempting Aconcagua was that a keen climber had joined the group – Chris Imray. He was a trainee surgeon who had recently come to Birmingham. He loved the mountains and had spent six months in Kathmandu as a student. Having heard about BMRES, he was curious about its activities. By chance, I was giving a lecture on the recent Karakoram expedition at the university students' union the day after we met, so I invited him along. Over a pre-lecture beer, we discussed mountains, expeditions and experiments and became instant friends. He later claimed that I said he was a 'thinking surgeon, which was a rarity', but he took it as flattery rather than insult. Over the subsequent months, Chris, Ginette, John Delamere and others promoted the idea of climbing Aconcagua.

Another enthusiastic newcomer was my head of department, Ian MacLennan. A brawny Scot with height to match (nearly 6 ft 4 in), he was a strong climber and hill walker. We had competed several times on long distance walks, culminating in a 67-mile epic from Birmingham to Clun near the Welsh border. He was tough, formidably competitive and was keen to cut his sporran on Aconcagua. Affectionately known as 'Big Mac', or 'Mad Mac' when irritating, he fitted into the group perfectly.

Finally, as usual, there were the medical students. We set an essay entitled 'How does the bar-headed goose fly over Everest?', and acquired three students, courtesy of the Arthur Thompson Trust. We normally limited their numbers to two but on this occasion they agreed to split the grant money three ways.

Having decided the location, we could plan the experiments. In the Karakoram, we had shown that acetazolamide could be used to treat acute mountain sickness. Since methazolamide was faster acting (chapter 3), we wondered whether it would produce quicker relief of mountain sickness symptoms when given acutely. We also wondered about the effect of dexamethasone. A recent study by a Swiss group (led by Oswald Oltz and Peter Bartsch) had shown that it was useful for treating people who developed high-altitude cerebral oedema. Comparison of the two on Aconcagua would make a good study. As usual, we would need all the usual paraphernalia such as blood-gas analyser and generators.

Also, we wished to follow up on Tim Harvey's experiments on cerebral blood flow and carbon dioxide (CO_2) inhalation. His Lancet paper (chapter 5) study needed to be repeated with different gas mixtures. Needless to say, we could neither afford the cost nor imagine the administrative nightmare of taking radioactive xenon to Argentina for cerebral blood flow measurements. Instead, Niels Lassen suggested that we use the much simpler transcranial Doppler method. The technique was to direct a pulsed sound wave (using an ultrasound source) at the middle cerebral artery in the skull. From the reflected signal, a scanner could detect the rate of blood flow. To accompany the instrument, Niels promised us an enterprising young doctor, Bjorn Sperling, who could make the recordings. We enthusiastically agreed.

In the year-long build up to the expedition, we approached several travel companies to organise all the logistics on the mountain. We settled on Exodus Travel since they were helpful, competitively priced and had a good reputation.

On the night before we departed, I had a pre-departure soireé with Barbara at the Copthorne Hotel in the centre of Birmingham (once labelled an architectural carbuncle by Prince Charles). My daughter Annie was five months old and my son Edward was four years old. She was going to have a hard time while I had fun. A lone soprano serenaded us exquisitely with Andrew Lloyd-Webber's, 'Don't cry for me Argentina'. Barbara responded with tears, fearful of Aconcagua's lethal reputation. It had claimed more than 100 lives.

We departed from the Medical School for London Heathrow by coach at 2.30 pm on Friday 12 January. We were seen off by wives, partners and children, plus a film crew from Central Television. Although we were newsworthy, the Medical School Dean, Sandy McNeish, showed little interest. He didn't approve, as we hauled all our medical equipment and climbing gear into the entrance hall of the Medical School, including some 'borrowed' items such as centrifuges. At Heathrow we met up with Jonathan Evans and Pete Forster.

Our usual worries about excess baggage (390 kg) were unfounded. With the help of staff from Exodus, we and our baggage (which was not even weighed) were waved through and by 10.30 pm we were aboard our 10-hour Varig flight to Rio de Janeiro. We changed planes and by the following evening were ensconced at Hotel Crillon in Buenos Aires. It seemed we were having an unusual run of good luck.

Shortly after arrival, Stephen Boyer (Peter Dykes's stepson-in-law) arrived from Albuquerque, followed by Gron Jones from San Francisco, and our good luck started to run out. His rucksack was lost. He had taken six flights from the Berkeley University in California (via Paraguay), where he had been attending a particle physics conference, but his bag had failed to keep up. Then we hit another snag. The special cargo of gas cylinders for the blood-gas analyser was stuck in customs. Apparently, we had not filled out the correct forms, which could lead to a heavy fine. Furthermore, since it was now Sunday, they might not be released until Wednesday. We started to fear a repeat of the xenon fiasco in Pakistan.

But we did enjoy Buenos Aires: Parisian-style buildings (it is known as the Paris of the South), beautiful flower-lined avenues and splendid, tanned, curvaceous women. To add to its delights, we had the first of many steak meals washed down with liberal amounts of tasty Argentine Malbec.

Our tight schedule meant that we had to entrust Exodus Travel to sort out the gas canisters and Gron's bag. Accompanied by Diego (a guide from the company Trekking Argentina), we departed at 6 am the following morning, by bus, for the long journey to the Andes – 1,077 km. It was hard to believe that beyond the spectacularly flat Pampas lurked a huge mountain range. We passed through an empty vastness of grassy plains, encountering only an occasional farm. We didn't spot any people, but we did see cattle, horses and exotic wildlife from huge birds of prey to tiny humming birds and a myriad of butterflies. We reached Hotel Internacional in Mendoza, at 1 am, to a spectacular thunderstorm. Innumerable placards proclaimed that Las Malvinas (the Falkland Islands) belonged to Argentina. It had been eight years since the war with Britain, but Latino sensitivities remained raw.

Early next morning we were on the search for liquid nitrogen for storing the blood samples. Fortunately, bull's semen was in huge demand in Argentina and was stored in liquid nitrogen, so there was a ready supply in Mendoza. We also needed climbing permits. We trooped off to a rather derelict sports arena to pay our $60 fees. The authorities had just imposed it, yet another tax on tourists. We also needed to find Gron some high-altitude equipment in case his rucksack failed to materialise.

At 6 pm we departed for the four-hour bus journey south to Puente del Inca, the road-head for Aconcagua. The modern-looking but unreliable bus – all flash and no substance – broke down twice on the way but at least we had spectacular mountains to admire as we fretted about our progress. There was ample evidence of government control over the population, including several police check posts and an army barracks. Gradually it cooled as we climbed to 2,740 m at Puente del Inca where a fine stone and wood hotel, the Hosteria, welcomed us. We were met there by four Argentinians who would look after us for the next two weeks: Marie-Sue, Sebastian, Rueben and Alfredo. A meal of beef steaks followed. We had eaten beef at every meal, beef sausages and black pudding for breakfast, beef cutlets for lunch and every part of their anatomy for dinner. They were obsessed with it.

Next morning was a chance to sightsee. The name of the settlement, Puente del Inca (Inca bridge), comes from a natural rock arch over Las Cuevas River and coincides with some sulphurous hot springs (figure 1). Alongside them were dilapidated thermal baths, which were probably at their best 80 years earlier. Their main use now was for staining pottery. The sulphurous water was diverted over trays of clay pottery, imparting a bilious yellow colour. It was hard to imagine who would buy them.

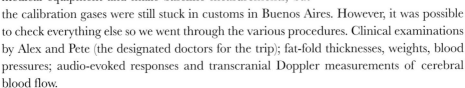

The remote settlement now comprised an army camp, a station (for the weekly goods train), a telegraph post and the hotel. A few half-wrecked sheds acted as cargo depots for exports to Chile. A mile away was a cemetery for those who had died on Aconcagua. The largest headstone marked the resting place of a British surgeon: 'In Memory of Edward J Cotton. MD. FRCS 1862 – 1908, RIP'. It was a chilling reminder of its dangers.

We had planned one day at Puente del Inca to check the medical equipment and make baseline measurements, but the calibration gases were still stuck in customs in Buenos Aires. However, it was possible to check everything else so we went through the various procedures. Clinical examinations by Alex and Pete (the designated doctors for the trip); fat-fold thicknesses, weights, blood pressures; audio-evoked responses and transcranial Doppler measurements of cerebral blood flow.

The electricity supply came from the hotel because poor John Simmons was still struggling with the generators that we would be so dependent upon for the next fortnight. For some reason they were proving truculent, but by midday two were working. The third had been dropped in transit, crushing one end. It looked a sorry mess and needed to be stripped down.

However, the good news was that Gron's rucksack and the gases should arrive the following afternoon. The authorities were prepared to release them on payment of a $700 'fine' and they would be sent overland to Puente del Inca. To pass the spare day, many of us climbed a small peak called Penitentia to the south of the hotel. At a yellow rock band, 800 m above the hotel, it was possible to see the top of Aconcagua about 30 miles away. It looked huge. Our descent was accompanied by strong winds and snow flurries – not good omens. As Alfredo, one of our Argentinian guides, gloomily pointed out, that meant heavy snow falls on Aconcagua.

The next day was cloudless. John Simmons stripped the generator and found that the fuel lines were full of rust debris, presumably dislodged during its tumble. It was all sorted out and started perfectly. Hopefully, we would not have generator problems at top camp, but it was always a worry having experienced major problems in the past. With the guides, I was introduced to a muleteer who would provide transport. We could hire as many mules as we needed since they were hanging about waiting for tourists.

One of our concerns was the students, particularly Nick and Matthew. Although intelligent and very pleasant, they were quite inexperienced in the mountains and certainly ill-equipped for an ascent of Aconcagua. Perhaps our selection criteria should be changed from an academic question on bar-headed geese to a test of endurance on one of our big summer walks (chapter 8). At least we could advise them not to climb, whereas Mike was more of a problem. He was unfit, overweight and very stubborn. He could easily put himself and others at risk. To add to our concerns, the gases and Gron's bag still hadn't arrived. Apparently, they were in Mendoza.

The evening meal was, as ever, beef steak lubricated with Mendoza wine costing 70 US cents a bottle. Pleasant though the restaurant was, the hotel had no beds for the night. We had made reservations for only two nights and now it was the third. Instead, they offered us a dilapidated store room. We managed as best we could on air beds scattered around the floor. Above us, a broken corrugated roof clattered in the wind. Softies such as John Milles and Pete slept in the hotel.

I lay in my bag worrying about the expedition. We had already been delayed by one day and had a tight schedule with many experiments. If the gases failed to arrive, most of them would be compromised. Then there was the issue of climbing Aconcagua; Ginette, John Delamere and Chris were obsessed with it. Their conversations were all about the conditions high up; weather, snow, ice, wind speed and mountain sickness. Their drive to climb was paramount, greater than their involvement with research. While we had a fair balance of researchers and climbers, I could imagine that performing research on a pure climbing group would be impossible. But first we had to have those calibration gases. If any further delay reduced the chances of climbing Aconcagua, there would be a mutiny.

Medical boxes and gas cylinder

Early next morning, already the seventh day of the expedition, to our collective relief the gases finally arrived, together with Gron's bag. Finally, we could move upwards. We had a maximum of ten days to perform the experiments, leaving four days to tackle the mountain and return to Puente del Inca.

But the immediate problem was getting to our base camp at Plaza de Mulas over the next two days. It was 30 km away at an altitude of 4,408 m. We had reserved sufficient mules and donkeys but, annoyingly, because of our one-day delay they had been rented by an American group. We were now short. Diego and Sebastian said there was no choice but for us to carry some of our personal equipment. Since the animals were so much quicker than us, they could make two journeys to our one so everything would be set up for when we arrived. If everyone carried 10 kg that would save nearly 200 kg, which was five donkey loads. The 10 kg would have to include food for two days since there would be minimal cooking on the way.

Carrying packs, it was a six- to eight-hour hot dusty hike to a half-way camp at Confluencia. From the hotel, we crossed the Mendoza River, then turned north along a dusty track to gain our first view of Aconcagua (figure 2). We entered the Parque Provincial Aconcagua and, accompanied by Pete, Ian and John Delamere, we pushed ourselves hard in the afternoon heat. Above us bands of tinted rocks formed brightly coloured paintings on the barren mountain sides.

After 15 kilometres, a powerful river of glacial melt water from the south side of Aconcagua blocked our path. Suspended over the torrent was a pulley hanging from two steel wires. Ginette was first across; we thought the lightest person should go first and why not the only woman? Precariously suspended over our doom, we were winched across one by one. Ian was the heaviest (102 kg). The wire drooped dangerously under his weight to just above the water and near the end he fell in. No bones were broken and the entire sequence was captured on video. It would make good viewing later (figure 3). He dried out quickly in the hot sun.

Confluencia marked the merging of rivers from the north and south sides of Aconcagua. Sebastian, our guide, had carefully explained that we should meet there, but in our enthusiasm we had overshot, only realising when we met climbers descending from the mountain's great southern glaciers. We retraced our steps 3 km to near Ian's pulley bridge and welcoming tea and biscuits.

That night we slept out on the dusty ground looking up at the Southern Cross. It was cold and the streams froze. We were already at 3,380 m.

The second day was another hot slog, eight hours around the west side of the mountain to Plaza de Mulas (4,408 m). The route took us up a deep glacial valley with huge screes plunging down from Aconcagua. At the north end was the hanging glacier of Horcones Superior. We were constantly crossing small streams in the glacial moraine. In the distance loomed a steep zig-zag track. As we started its ascent, our mules came past us, being driven hard by their masters. A dead mule lay beside the path. We drank muddy water from a stream and put iodine in it.

A blue and white Argentine flag appeared as we crested the rise, then tents and more tents. Plaza de Mulas is the main base camp for the mountain and the second largest mountain encampment after Everest. On the far side our green arctic tent was being erected, with a blue mess tent and a few smaller ones surrounding it. We join the huddled masses – a dump of litter, noise and dogs. So much for 'getting away from it all' (figure 4). Aconcagua loomed above us, the summit hidden behind its lower slopes.

Another batch of mules arrived around 5 pm carrying our remaining tents. We set to, clearing rocks and smaller rubble, unpacking boxes and bags, only to develop headaches in the process. We had ascended 1,000 m and it hurt.

Three hours later, John Potokar struggled in, a presage for the future. Even Martin with his broken foot (fractured before we left Birmingham) was not much slower, while the students plus Mike and Steve took up the rear after 11 hours of walking. Other people converged on the area. Knackered climbers descending from Nido de Condores and others up from Confluencia. Many were from the USA and Europe. One group of English were planning to ascend over the next two days, spending their first night at the Berlin Hut followed by a summit attempt. Independencia Hut, a little higher, contained two bodies, somewhat off-putting for sleeping. They had been awaiting retrieval by the army for two weeks, but mountain conditions had been too severe.

That night we feasted on steak and wine beautifully cooked by the delectable Marie-Sue (figure 5). She had been a beauty queen in Buenos Aires. It was very good.

The first sounds of the dawn were our cooks preparing breakfast and climbers clanking their equipment. Frost clung to the inside of the tents until the sun touched it. What would the day bring? Our first research day. Would the generators or the blood-gas machine play up? Would we have a subject for entry into the trial? We were still at a relatively modest altitude but the most susceptible people might have a touch of sickness.

I lay in bed waiting for a supine blood pressure recording and then it was time to get up for a quick breakfast and to work. The clear sky and little wind reassured us as John built up the three generators from their separate halves and they all hummed happily. Pete and Alex sat outside their tent questioning then assessing us one by one for any hints of acute mountain sickness. John Delamere, Ian and Ginette started collecting ear lobe blood samples but it was premature. Mike couldn't start the blood-gas machine. The electrodes had frozen. They were changed and the whole tedious process of calibration was restarted. Mike stubbornly pressed on for hours. His doggedness was ideal for the job; he refused to give up despite the tedium of endless fiddling with the instrument's controls. As we worked, groups of climbers from the neighbouring tents came over to investigate, curious about our studies and perhaps fearful of the mountain, their own vulnerability and the two bodies in the Independencia Hut.

In the course of the clinical examinations, Martin was diagnosed with significant altitude sickness. He felt unwell with a bad headache and was slightly ataxic (unsteady on his feet). He was entered into the methazolamide/dexamethasone trial, randomly allocated to one pill or the other. Bjorn measured his cerebral blood flow and we awaited the blood gases, and waited, and waited. With no blood-gas results available, the drug trial and the gas experiments would have to be aborted. In my exasperation, I wandered alone over to the glacier with its remarkable ice penitentes, to brood over the potential disaster looming over our expedition, my hypoxic brain searching for solace from the responsibilities. An hour later, John Milles and Pete came over with the best news I could imagine. The blood-gas machine was working.

The instrument had been relocated to the arctic tent where the sun's warmth seemed to help. Eventually, by 6 pm, carefully corralled in its box, it gave meaningful results. Martin was duly tested, breathing in a mixture of 5% CO_2 and 95% O_2 from two large Douglas bags that we had filled from the gas bottles. Recordings were taken periodically of the blood flow through his brain while Mike, Ginette and John took blood samples from his ear which were slowly analysed. It was nearly midnight before they were finished.

A particularly interesting experiment, brought along by Pete, involved a pressure chamber called the Gamow bag. It was a one-man plastic sausage for treating severe acute mountain sickness. A long-haired hippy called Igor Gamow had demonstrated it at a hypoxia conference in Banff (figure 6). We were particularly impressed by the knowledge that he was the son of physicist George Gamow, who was famous for being an early advocate of the Big Bang theory of the origins of the universe and quantum tunnelling (whatever that is). The chamber was inflated with air using a foot pump to above ambient pressure while a small aperture allowed continuous replenishment of air. John Potokar, who had particularly low O_2 levels, was put in after supper while we watched him through the plastic side-window. After 30 minutes in the bag, he felt considerably better, and his O_2 levels were increased.

Over dinner we discussed further ascent the following day. We assumed that most people would rapidly acclimatise at Plaza de Mulas but to provoke mountain sickness we would need to go higher. The proposed top camp was at Nido de Condores (nest of condors) with a height gain of 1,100 m to 5,486 m. Alfredo explained that the mules could make two journeys in a day with 50 kg or so each so three would be sufficient. Six people wanted to ascend with them and perhaps carry some gear. Chris and Ian were particularly keen to accompany them but, thankfully, my responsibilities were at base camp. Many others had experiments to complete and there could yet be more illness at our current height.

It snowed a little in the evening but by midnight it was clear and cold.

In the morning, some were not so brave or not so well. Ian, who had been raring to go, had facial and peripheral oedema, and was considered unfit for the ascent by our doctors, Alex and Pete. He was not happy, but the toughest Scotsman in the group had to abide by the recommendation of the medical team. By the time breakfast was over, the ascent party was down to three, Chris, Jonathan and Richard. Along with Alfredo, they departed at 10 am carrying 10 kg each, followed by the mules 30 minutes later. We watched the small dust plume marking their ascent up the zig-zag scree slope towards Aconcagua.

For most of us it was a day to acclimatise and explore the area. Many walked to the penitentes. John Milles and I encouraged Steve Boyer and Gron to go high up on this strange and beautiful glacier in order to film its beautiful architecture (figures 7 and 8). At its lower tip, water rushed out of an icy cavern.

The generators and blood-gas analyser worked well and Pete put three subjects into the Gamow bag – Ian, Alex and Matt. It was inflated to twice atmospheric pressure for 30 minutes and blood gases were measured. It was a very satisfactory little experiment.

Rock on ice penitentes

As the afternoon wore on, we watched our advanced climbing team descend, moving slowly among other climbers coming off the mountain. They were knackered. But they had done well; $4\frac{1}{2}$ hours up and 2 hours down with a camp established at Nido De Condores. We were all ready for the big push in the morning.

At our regular evening conference, Martin suggested a change of plan. If, he suggested, all of us went up together, then too many might be ill at the same time for proper assessment. It might be better to split the party into two, with half waiting until the following day. Those running studies would ascend on the first day with potential subjects while others remained below. This did not please everyone. Ian was desperate to be in the ascent party, but was not performing any experiments so he was selected to stay down. Others, who required more acclimatisation, such as Nick, Matthew, John Potakar, Alex and Gron, would also stay down, as would the film crew of John Milles and Stephen.

Alfredo assured us that we would not have to carry any of our own equipment. Three mules would be enough. Unfortunately, he was too optimistic. Having packed and weighed everything, he realised it was too much for them. Tediously, we repacked so that we each carried 10–15 kg of personal items while those with climbing gear such as ice axes and crampons had even heavier loads. There was much grumbling but I could not conjure up more mules. John Simmons, to show he was the toughest, bravely added one of the oxygen cylinders to his rucksack. I didn't. By the time we were all packed and ready for an early start, sleep beckoned.

That night the wind rose, buffeting the tents and making sleep difficult. We had drunken noisy neighbours and some of us were suffering from gut infections requiring urgent dashes to the loo tent.

At first light, I finished packing my bag and quietly ate breakfast, looking up with trepidation at the ascent and nervously down at my bulging bag. The freezing wind outside and the racing clouds did not look at all inviting and there was a sprinkling of snow high up. As people came into the mess tent for breakfast, it was apparent that all was not well with the group. Poor Alex was outside his tent holding his head, Bjorn looked very pale, Matthew stayed in his tent and Nick looked ill and said he felt sick. All had bad headaches, a clear indication of mountain sickness. We had thought everyone was acclimatising well, but many had deteriorated overnight. We collectively agreed to remain at Plaza de Mulas for another day. The alpinists voiced their dissent, their chances of summiting in jeopardy.

The four sick people entered the trial, starting with the worst. The slow tedium of the gas trial (20 minutes of 100% O_2 followed by 20 minutes of 95% O_2 plus 5% CO_2) was followed by the drug trial with cerebral blood flow measurements and several blood samples. The gas machine ran well all day as we pressed on till 9 pm. Pete managed to study eight subjects in the Gamow bag; 30 minutes of hyperbaric pressure produced 20% increases in blood oxygen saturations, but within 15 minutes of coming out of the bag, they were back to their original low levels.

Chris and Alfredo made a second ascent to Nido De Condores to check on the tents, which remained intact despite the winds. This prompted Ian to make a solo attempt and not to be out-done I went up myself to see how I was performing. I was pleased to find I was quicker and Ian had some facial oedema back in camp. I was teased for rising to the bait of competition. He was my boss at work, but not here in Argentina.

That evening, it came to our notice that it was Pete's 41st birthday. Over dinner, Sebastian, Ronaldo and Marie-Sue came in singing 'Happy Birthday' in Spanish, led by a beaming John Milles who had primed them. Bottles of sparkling cider, Mendoza Malbec and whisky were the inevitable outcome of an amusing and happy evening. The generators hummed as the blood-gas team worked on, missing the fun. It was all right for some.

We couldn't leave the ill people without medical care at Plaza de Mulas, so we agreed to stay for a fourth day. Thankfully, no-one else became sick. A few were still oedematous but definitely improving. It gave us a chance to explore or go up to the next camp, particularly since the sun was out.

Across the valley a large building was under construction with helicopters flying to and fro, so we investigated. Climbing up a steep path to over 4,500 m we came to a cable car station alongside a large steel and stone building in an early stage of construction (figure 9). There we met the manager of the site and a major-general from the Argentine army who spoke good English. He explained they were building a ski resort – and proudly announced that it would be the highest in the world (figure 10).

This was most intriguing. We thought of our poorly team with mountain sickness and wondered how many skiing days in a week's holiday would be achieved at this height, or, indeed, how many deaths! We had a long discussion about the problems and they agreed our medical advice might be helpful and they would visit our camp that evening.

Many carried gear up to the next camp, including John Simmons, Pete and even Mike, while Jonathan and Chris climbed to the Berlin Hut at 5,930 m, only 1,000 m below the summit. The big push for acclimatisation by the mountaineers was being taken very seriously.

As the evening came, the hotel manager appeared and Doppler and Gamow bag were demonstrated for his benefit (figure 11). It was an early bedtime. Tomorrow all of us were definitely going up.

It was day 13, we were half-way through the expedition and, finally, there was nothing stopping us from ascending. However, we had lost three days. A summit attempt on Aconcagua was starting to look difficult. We would need at least two days testing people, which left only two for the mountain. We could only hope that the weather was in our favour. Many climbers waited a week or even two at Plaza de Mulas but still failed because of bad weather. We would need to be very lucky.

The sun rose, the ice on the tents melted and it was calm. Before breakfast we had the army tent down in our haste to start but there were problems brewing. Ian asked me for a quiet word. Since an operation some years earlier, he had suffered from the occasional ear infection requiring antibiotics and now he feared a recurrence. Fortunately, he had no temperature so altitude pressure changes could account for his symptoms but it seemed sensible for him to remain at Plaza del Mulas for two days. If it worsened, he would need to descend to Puente del Inca. His chances of climbing Aconcagua were poor.

An American walked into the camp claiming he had pulmonary oedema from being overnight at Nido de Condores. His diagnosis was correct. He was short of breath, cyanosed (blue lips) and had fluid in both lungs. It was a repeat of a similar illness 20 years earlier when in the Himalayas. Knowing his susceptibility, he had taken acetazolamide for the previous seven days and had ascended slowly. In the night, he had become breathless. Recognising the symptoms, he had descended immediately. We gave him oxygen and nifedipine. Two hours later he still had some pulmonary oedema and was advised to descend. He was the perfect subject for our film, willingly describing his symptoms and his subsequent descent on a mule.

The first mules departed with our baggage and one carrying Marie -Sue so she could prepare food for our arrival (figures 12 and 13). We followed in twos and threes accompanied by Alfredo. I stayed back with Chris and Jonathan to ensure that all the camp was cleared, then helped Rueben and the cooks reload the mules for a return journey to top camp. When all the bags were tied on, there was still space for our three rucksacks. This was most welcome; the ascent would be much easier carrying only a small day-sack.

We left a miserable-looking Ian in the camp and started the long grind up the steep, dusty, cinder-covered track, often slipping backwards on rounded lava grit. It zig-zagged upwards and out of sight (figure 14). The sun beat down, only made tolerant by a cold breeze from glaciers high up the mountain. The western buttresses of Aconcagua rose above us but the summit remained hidden. The half-way point was marked by a small wooden monument tethered to the ground by wires. The first of our mules passed us on their way down, as did exhausted summiteers, one group of six all dressed in blue ski outfits complete with ski poles. Finally, we cleared the face for a brief rest on the flatter ground of El Manso. Suddenly, we heard shouts as two huge boulders bounded towards us from the high cliffs. One passed within ten metres of us then ploughed through El Manso, miraculously missing all the tents. A second boulder was thankfully not so close and lost momentum on the steep scree.

Up ahead our team mates, carrying 10-15 kg each, struggled with their loads, climbing towards another col above a snow field. Just beyond it the green arctic tent was visible. We skirted around the snow field to be met by a welcoming Marie-Sue with hot soup and a cheese sandwich. We were at 5,486 m, the highest camp of any BMRES expedition. Surrounding us in some ancient crater was a moonscape of volcanic debris (figures 15 and 16).

Eroded lava flow

Inside the arctic tent was a scene of disarray. Gron was lying in the middle fast asleep with others in different states of exhaustion. After a rest we had the tiring job of erecting the tents. Everyone had to erect their own. Several people noticed that I had not carried my rucksack while they had made two journeys carrying gear. They were justifiably upset. I explained how it had happened and apologised. It had been an error of leadership.

As the afternoon turned to evening, many developed headaches and felt unwell. Those individuals already on medication seemed to be generally better than others. There would be more sickness in the morning. Slowly. the second arctic tent was erected. Other tents were aligned north-eastwards so we could watch the sun set over the Pacific Ocean from the warmth of our sleeping bags. Panting in the thin air, with periodic breathing and a headache, I lay in bed worrying about the research and the mountain. Did we have time for both? Which one would lose out? So far, we had entered only five people into the trial over four days. Every study would take longer at Nido de Condores. The complexity of the tests meant it would take three days to test everyone then we needed two days to get down. That left no time for climbing.

Alfredo suggested that we could gain one day extra by delaying the bus journey back to Buenos Aires from the morning to the night. Not enough time exclaimed the climbers; not enough time exclaimed the experimenters. Who would lose out? Certainly, the mountain's lure was infectious. More and more wanted to try. The trail leading upwards to the White Rocks looked so simple, so straightforward. The temptation of the mountain was hard to resist. Only if the weather worsened and more became ill could we complete the studies. Only then would the climbers accept the summit was impossible.

I couldn't make out whether my growing headache was mountain sickness or the responsibility for failure. We had either taken on too much research or too much mountain. Single-minded climbers such as Ginette and Mac found it easy to focus on their goal. Those leading complex experiments demanded they came first. My hypoxic brain couldn't disentangle the two. Research first or mountain first? We had a maximum of four full days at our high camp. We needed at least two for the tests, and two for Aconcagua if the weather was good. Not enough unless we were incredibly lucky. I slept badly.

The wind rattled the tents overnight. Woe betide those who needed a pee – it was bitterly cold outside. Those taking methazolamide on the drug trial may have felt better but diuresis meant they had to get up more. I slept in my thermal underwear, trousers and duvet jacket and still felt cold. My old 40-Winks sleeping bag, made from manufactured fibre and used since the first expedition, was now 13 years old. Some of the youngsters in their modern goose-down bags were perfectly warm and comfortable. I vowed to invest in a new bag for any future expedition. By the morning, ice covered the inside of the tent, a thin layer of snow covered the outside and our bags were wet from dripping ice, a familiar experience.

The camp stirred late, the sun hidden by the huge cliffs around Aconcagua. Who was ill today? Lethargy and headache kept many in their tents until the sun appeared. Our slow movements and rapid breathing on the slightest exertion testified to the low oxygen levels – 50% of sea-level values.

We were expecting Alex and Pete to make a quick medical round but it was Alex alone. Pete was suffering from mountain sickness. He had awoken in the night with a blinding occipital headache and felt disoriented and nauseous. In contrast, Alex, on methazolamide, felt better than at the lower camp of Plaza de Mulas. It was Pete's turn for the trial. Stephen was another victim. John Simmons was also not well, with swollen legs half-way up his calves. He had put on 3 kg of oedema fluid but stoically resisted any treatment. Nick Gompertz was unwell even though on methazolamide and Matthew Douglas had an infected tonsil. To their relief they were allowed to descend (figure 17). They were not heartbroken to be going down while we were not overly impressed with their endeavours.

Pete and Stephen entered the trial in late morning. Pete was first. It meant a couple of hours lying down with a mouthpiece as the different gases were piped in (figure 18), while an electrode was used to measure auditory-evoked potentials and the brain blood flow sensor was pressed against his skull. John and Ginette extracted blood from his ear. Then he entered the drug trial. By late afternoon the medication's identity became clear, as he experienced tingling in his heels, improving oxygen levels and falling pH. He was on methazolamide.

While many were busy, others had time to explore the area, and wonder about Aconcagua's huge northwest face and the path that zig-zagged up and out of sight. Who was coming down? What was the weather like at the top? Would we need to stop on the mountain overnight or could it be climbed in a single day? Where were the Berlin Hut and the White Rocks? We quizzed climbers as they came past. Were there really dead bodies in the Independencia Hut? Talk about the severity of the climb and reports from exhausted climbers dominated all conversations.

An Australian physicist from Melbourne came to our tents worried about his blurred vision. Examination by Alex revealed bilateral retinal haemorrhages and floaters in one eye. A Canadian from the adjacent camp also developed a large retinal haemorrhage with central vision blindness and was duly dispatched to a lower camp. If in doubt go down was always the advice. But on the positive side Ian breezed into the camp from Plaza de Mulas. He felt much better on methazolamide then proceeded to walk up to White Rocks, 600 m higher, to show us how well he felt.

By late afternoon, we had only entered two more in the trial – now on seven, we would be lucky to reach ten. I wondered who would be struck down next. Would it be me? John Simmons seemed a probability but he was tough and likely to resist. Even if people were in denial, Pete and Alex were skilled enough clinically to find them. And it was obvious that, once on medication, individuals' health rebounded and they were even able to ascend, as Ian had demonstrated.

On the second day at Nido de Condores only two more entered the trial. John Simmons was first. He had a terrible night's sleep. As he noted in his diary: 'I tried to sleep in the arctic tent, but could not get my head comfortable. I noticed periodic breathing along with a headache. I seemed to need to take sudden deep breaths.' He was slow and rather confused, having difficulty even getting out of his tent. The second was John Potokar, who had a severe headache and nausea. He had not acclimatised well at Plaza de Mulas and, despite being a fit climber, had lagged behind many others while ascending.

We prepared to enter them into the trial but the generator wouldn't start despite all our best efforts. Just fiddling with the carburettors with gloves off froze fingers and warmed tempers. John discovered an on/off switch had broken but by the time it was fixed it was too late for blood-gas tests. Because of the generator failure, our new subjects were spared the gas mixtures and entered the drug trial in the evening. It seemed that the trial would end early through lack of subjects and equipment failure. The climbers must have been relieved.

The final experiment of the trip was one devised by Chris (figure 19). He had been awarded a prestigious Porritt Fellowship by the Royal College of Surgeons to study fat absorption. It was unclear whether altitude weight loss was due to reduced fat absorption or reduced food intake. The experiment started at breakfast when Chris fed us a Marathon bar, a cup of muesli and radiolabelled fatty acids. For a few minutes each hour for the following eight hours, we blew bubbles into two small jars of blue liquid that contained a complex salt solution (figure 20). Expired CO_2 slowly changed the liquids from blue to clear and they were stored for later analysis. Since his experiment lasted most of the day, that meant no food until at least 6 pm.

The day ended in spectacular fashion with a great sunset. We walked over to the ridge facing the dusk to marvel at its beautiful colours and Jonathan's acrobatics on lava pinnacles silhouetted against the twilight (figure 21).

Did the weather bode well for the climb? Was it difficult or just a hard, non-technical slog? Whatever the challenges, seven people had died on Aconcagua since the New Year, and it wasn't even the end of January. The next morning was the day the climbers had so keenly awaited. A delayed start from Puente del Inca, prolonged experiments and illness had squeezed the climb to a maximum of two days.

Aconcagua

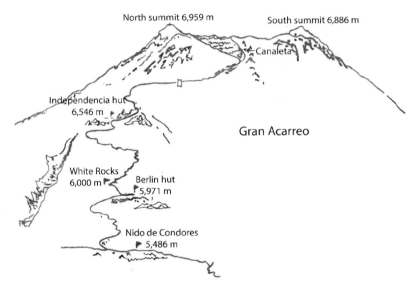

There were 14 climbers, plus Alfredo, our guide. Individuals' abilities, ambitions and climbing speed were matched to ensure that no one would be alone. Steve had not been well for a couple of days and wanted to go down; Gron would join him after first ascending to White Rocks at 6,000 m.

Six of us – Chris, Ginette, John Delamere, Jonathan, Bjorn and me – thought we could reach the summit in one day even though it was almost 1,500 m above Nido de Condores (5,486 m to 6,965 m). I thought a lightweight ascent was preferable to carrying a tent, cooking equipment and food. A few pills of acetazolamide might also provide a boost as the air thinned to 40% at the top. Although its use in the Karakoram had given us headaches when we were fully acclimatised, I popped 750 mg and hoped for the best.

We were desperate for an early start but last-minute clinical assessments and blood samples delayed us until 10 am. There followed a frantic change of clothes into high-altitude gear. Ginette, Jonathan and John were off first at 10.30 am, while Chris and I, delayed by experiments, plodded behind 30 minutes later. Bjorn was delayed for even longer, but we didn't wait. Although it was a clear calm day there were 'sun-dogs' from atmospheric snow crystals and grey clouds to the north-west. Because of the sun's warmth, I chose to climb in shorts and trainers as high as possible.

The steep but easy path of lava rubble zig-zagged upwards to north-facing cliffs and past the Berlin Hut at 5,971 m (figure 22). Within an hour we were at White Rocks, an outcrop of soft limestone, where it became noticeably colder. We followed the very obvious path, the only problem being the massive effort of breathing at such a height.

Those preferring a two-day assault with an overnight stop at White Rocks had a more leisurely start. Pete Forster, John Milles and Martin were off by 1 pm, while John Simmons with Alfredo, Richard, Ian, Mike and John Potokar (who was still suffering from mountain sickness) departed a little later.

Laden with overnight tents, food, cooking and climbing equipment, they took three hours to reach White Rocks. Alfredo obligingly helped erect the tents and made coffee as each person arrived. Mike arrived two hours later having outpaced John Potokar who was just too ill. He hadn't shaken off his altitude headache so he turned back at the Berlin Hut. Despite his huge pack, Mike had no tent; he intended sleeping in a bivvy bag.

As we passed Independencia Hut, with its two frozen climbers, I struggled to keep up with Chris. Whether it was lack of food or water, age, 750 mg of acetazolamide or maybe just the altitude, I felt lethargic and gradually dropped back. As the afternoon gave way to the early evening, I struggled up the long scree slope known as the Canaleta. Every step was an effort. I was in a tormented world of desperate breathing, aching legs, thirst and the cold. Looking back, I saw Bjorn who was slowly catching up. After an age, the slope eased off, the Canaleta was over and rock pinnacles appeared on the right. I sat panting, waiting for Bjorn. He was going surprisingly well. I figured that if I tucked in behind him I would speed up, but it was too much effort.

Going ever more slowly, I climbed above the rock pillars to perhaps 50 m below the summit ridge but feared that the actual summit was still a long way off. Worryingly, I had yet to see the others return. Maybe they had taken a different route down? My pace slowed to a crawl. The weather was good; it was clear with little wind. But it was nearly 5 pm and nightfall was getting ever closer. It was very cold. I had no more clothes to wear, no food and little water. It was no place to be with such low reserves. I would probably not survive a night out. I had a young family and a loving wife. Why lose everything for a few hours on a mountain? Feeling very disappointed after such a huge effort, I turned around and stumbled down the Canaleta tasting the bitter bile of defeat.

At 7.30 pm John Simmons, at his overnight camp, watched me come over the ridge above White Rocks, walking slowly and completely swathed in clothes including a duvet jacket, balaclava and ski goggles. He came over to congratulate me. He had to ask twice before I convinced him that I had failed. The others had not yet been seen, so turning around was the right decision. I would have been near the summit overnight. After a cup of tea, I laboured on downwards to Nido de Condores and a place to lie down. I rationalised that the leader's mountain job was not always to climb to the summit but to ensure that others do.

An hour later, John saw four people coming down from White Rocks. Chris raised his arm aloft in triumph. They had made it. Jonathan was first to the top and waited an hour for the other three. There was tea and congratulations all round. But what about Bjorn, alone at nearly 7,000 m, and inexperienced? He was on the summit ridge when they had descended past him at 6 pm. As dusk approached and the wind increased, there was still no sign of Bjorn. There was an intense discussion about the foolishness of leaving him near the top. We had repeatedly stated that no one should climb alone – it was just too dangerous. We had invited him on the trip and then abandoned him in a terribly dangerous place. It reminded John Simmons of climbing the volcanoes on Ecuador when no one took responsibility for others (chapter 2). It had happened again on a much more dangerous mountain.

Pete suggested looking for him, but where to look in the dark? Maybe Bjorn had gone on down and missed the tents? They could only wait as the wind turned gale force and bitterly cold. Conditions higher up would only be worse. John Simmons went outside the tent into the rising wind. Mike lay nearby, sheltering behind a rock in his bivvy bag. He had been offered a place in a tent but, being his usual stubborn self, had refused. John climbed to the ridge and looked up the mountain towards Independencia. There, in the gloom, a lone figure could be seen slowly descending. The clothes and huge fur hood of his goose down duvet jacket made him immediately recognisable. It was Bjorn.

He had made it to the top – just. John led him inside the tent and gave him drinks. He was so relieved to be out of the gale. He had done remarkably well, particularly since he had had a throbbing headache most of the day with the risk of severe mountain sickness. But it was now too late for him to descend to Nido de Condores.

Overnight the wind increased further. Individuals were up repeatedly to check guy ropes as the blast roared around the tents. Cruel bitter winds tore at their flimsy covering and poor Mike in his bivvy bag, hiding behind a rock. They feared the tents would rip open in the tremendous battering and be blown away. Sleep was impossible with roaring wind, four crammed together in a shaking tent, and individuals going out for a wee.

The next day was the last chance for the group to reach the summit. John Simmons wrote in his diary:

'The gale force wind was little better at dawn. Alfredo's advice was to 'get the hell out of here'. We had been weakened by no sleep and the altitude. The situation looked hopeless. We all descended but after ten minutes Ian and I, then Mike changed our minds. We wondered if the path higher up might be in the lee of the great cliffs. By 10 am the wind had reduced slightly so we climbed back to the White Rocks campsite where we met Marty an American climber. He had just descended from a col with his partner Sally, where he had camped overnight. Severe winds had blown away his tent leaving only the hoop-poles. 'Only fools wishing for frostbite would try for the summit today,' he stated. Ian and I turned once more to descend.

Yet, the wind had slackened a little. We could probably get up to Independencia since it was close. Wearing all our gear and taking plenty of water, we set off for the short climb. In 1½ hours we reached the hut, passing two Canadians who had turned back because of the wind, but it was continuing to abate. Above a small ridge the path traversed upwards to the dreaded Canaleta.

Full of indecision, but finding the route possible we slowly continued, other climbers just visible ahead. I was now very determined to not give up. Ian struggled behind me up that horrible scree slope. Then to some rocks that seemed near the summit.

Is this where Jo had to give up, 50 m from the top? Then I realised that I was approaching some rocks and snow on a ridge and there was no slope ahead. I was on the ridge between the north and south peaks. To one side was a drop of thousands of metres down the great south face (figure 23). It was difficult to absorb for a few seconds and I could imagine that if one's concentration was affected by hypoxia, they might well step straight over the edge. Now it was time to turn to the last hurdle. I scrambled slowly upwards keeping a close eye on Ian behind.

He shouted up, 'Do you think we can make it?' I replied, 'Of course Ian, nothing can stop us now.'

Much lower down Ian had said we should turn around at 6 pm. It was now nearly 5.30 pm, but if it had taken another two hours we wouldn't have turned back. Who would have thought that after the gale of the previous night we could have got this far? With our goal in sight, I had renewed energy and set off up the last hurdle of red and white rocks. Within 15 minutes I was on the top of the world. Certainly, for a moment I may have been higher than anyone else on earth at nearly 7,000 m. About ten minutes later Ian arrived and we congratulated ourselves and each other. I turned around through 360o and it was quite obvious that nothing was higher anywhere. We had climbed it! We probably didn't stay more than 20 minutes.

We left about 6 pm. On the way down we passed three Italians going up incredibly slowly. We descended very quickly. Ian was often waiting for me. I think he was hungry! It had been a beautiful day after the terrible night. Remarkably, by 8 pm we were back at the tent. We struggled to pack it and then it was down and within ¾ hour we were at Nido de Condores. As I approached the campsite Chris came striding up to me with a water bottle of tea and took my rucksack the last few yards. He congratulated me and I reminded him of the meetings back in Birmingham when I had told him, "I really want to climb this mountain."

Jo came out to congratulate me but many others had already descended. Mike Winterborn had made a brave solo attempt but became exhausted on the Canaleta and turned back.'

Descent

By the time all the climbers had returned, the camp at Nido de Condores was partially deserted. I preferred to wait for their news in that alien volcanic landscape rather than descend. The harsh beauty of the mountains was more compelling than rushing back to civilisation.

Seven mules arrived after breakfast, and equipment was packed and loaded, followed by a final clear up. The rubbish and clinical waste were set on fire but stupidly someone had dumped full butane gas canisters, which whizzed off in all directions. We followed the animals down, leaving only Rueben to guard the remaining equipment for a second mule carriage. We were soon past El Manso, then down the scree to the Plaza de Mulas where others were waiting for news of the climb. Sebastian and Marie-Sue, who looked more beautiful by the day, cooked garlic-flavoured steaks that were consumed with a plentiful supply of Mendoza red wine. It was a happy, drunken evening. We were all safe with no accidents or injuries.

Our last day on the mountain was the long walk to Puente del Inca. Carrying modest packs, we completed the 30 km walk in 10 to 12 hours. As on the ascent, it was hot and dusty but a wind from Aconcagua pushed us downwards so we arrived at the hotel by early evening.

We heard John and Pete's story of how they had left Nido de Condores and descended directly to Confluencia, then spent a day hiking to Aconcagua's great south face and its huge glaciers. They met an Austrian expedition with a film crew preparing to record a solo ascent by Thomas Bubendorfer (who failed). He was a flashy 27-year-old extrovert who was making his name by solo climbing the world's great ice faces.

At the Hosteria Hotel, we washed and scrubbed ourselves clean after two weeks without showers, followed by the inevitable steaks and wine. It was a very happy evening (figure 24), all of us sitting together on one big table. I gave everyone imaginary awards for their contributions, followed by Pete Forster's views of the expedition in his inimitable amusing way. Light-headed on Malbec, we loaded the coach and by midnight were bound for Buenos Aires and our next adventure.

Postscript

Mountains or medicine? Fun or research? Too big a mountain or too many experiments? We were caught in the middle. An enjoyable expedition with seven summiting Aconcagua, but the research largely failed. Many experiments were not completed because of difficulties with the blood-gas analyser and low recruitment to the methazolamide/dexamethasone trial. We had been too ambitious.

Publications from the expedition:
1. Bradwell AR, Wright AD, Winterborn M and Imray C. Acetazolamide and High-altitude Diseases. International Journal of Sports Medicine 1992; 13: S63-S64.
2. Forster PJG, Bradwell AR, Winterborn MJ, Delamere JP, Harrison G and BMRES. Alleviation of hypoxia at high altitude; A comparison between oxygen, oxygen and carbon dioxide inhalation and hyperbaric compression. Clinical Science 1990; 79(suppl. 23): 1.
3. Imray CHE, Billingham M, Milles JJ, Wright AD, Filer R, Bradwell AR and Neoptolemos JP. Lipid digestion absorption and metabolism in severely hypoxic subjects. Gut 1990; 31: 10: A1196-1197.
4. Sperling B, Lassen N, Harvey T, Bartsch P, Bradwell AR and BMRES. Middle cerebral artery blood velocity during CO_2 inhalation at altitude. Clinical Science 1990; 78(suppl 22); 24.

Photos by John Milles, Jo Bradwell and Pete Forster.

Fig 1. *Puente del Inca*

Fig 2. *Aconcagua from the park entrance*

Fig 3. *Ian in the drink at Confluencia*

Fig 4. *Plaza de Mulas*

Fig 5. *Marie-Sue, Jonathan and Mike*

Fig 6. *Igor Gamow (centre) with his bag*

Fig 7. *Jonathan and Steve*

Fig 8. *Penitentes*

Fig 9. *Hotel under construction*

Fig 10. *The General with his secretary*

Fig 11. *John Potokar with the Gamow bag (PF)*

Fig 12. *John Milles loading mules (PF)*

Fig 13. *Mules ascending to Nido de Condores*

Fig 14. *The route to Nido de Condores*

Fig 15. *Camp at Nido de Condores*

Fig 16. *Looking south from Nido de Condores.*

Fig 17. *Dinner in the arctic tent: Alex, Matthew and Martin.*

Fig 18. *Bjorn testing cerebral blood flow with Jonathan*

Fig 19. *A quiet moment for Chris*

Fig 20. *Gron blowing into bottles*

Fig 21. *Lava pinnacles in the sunset.*

Fig 22. *Towards the summit from Nido de Condores*

Fig 23. *South face of Aconcagua from the summit*

Fig 24. *Expedition over. Pete and John Delamere.*

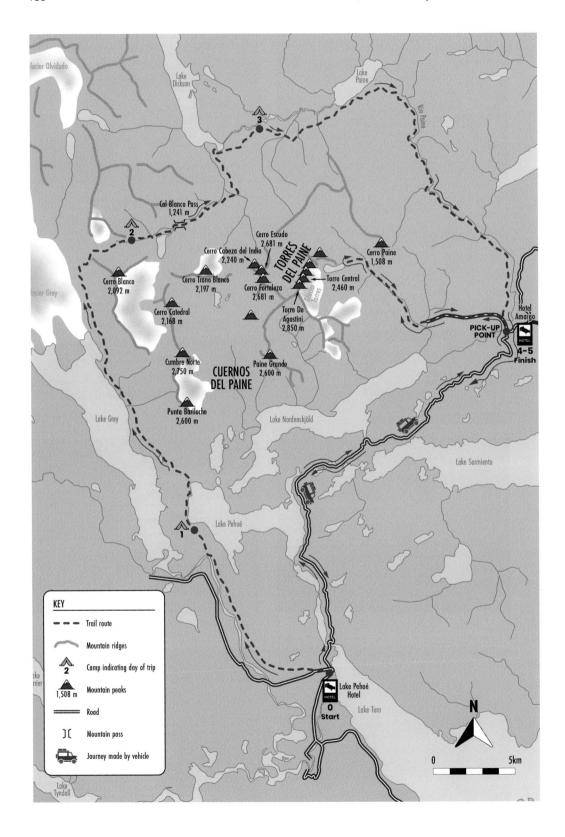

KEY

– – – Trail route

  Mountain ridges

2 Camp indicating day of trip

1,508 m Mountain peaks

  Road

] [Mountain pass

  Journey made by vehicle

Torres del Paine

After relatively short expeditions, individuals or groups go their own way. Some return home, others climb mountains and a number take to the hills. On this occasion, Pete Forster, John Simmons, Ian MacLennan, Mike, Chris and I teamed up to attempt the tour of the Torres del Paine in Patagonia. In books on great walks of the world it consistently rates in the top 10. It proved to be an unforgettable experience.

On the long bus journey from Aconcagua to Buenos Aires, Pete pointed out its merits: beautiful mountains, huge glaciers, an unspoilt wilderness, a path that encircled the whole National Park and, at its centre, three huge granite spires. Our main concern was whether we had enough time. The guidebook indicated the circuit, some 120 kilometres, would take seven days, the total time we had remaining before our return flights to the UK. Patagonia is 1,500 miles to the south of Buenos Aires, and from the airport at Rio Gallegos in Argentina to the National Park in Chile it is a further 8–10 hours by car. Since it would take one to two days to get there and the same time to return, that left only three to four days for the seven-day walk. The guidebook emphasised that its severity should not be underestimated. Although we were lean and fit from Aconcagua, we couldn't afford to hang about.

As we drove across the Pampas, we discussed our plans with Diego, our tour guide. There were regular flights to Rio Gallegos which he could investigate as soon as the bus arrived in Buenos Aires. He thought it would be impossible to arrange ground transport into Chile, so we would have to take our chances on arrival.

As soon as we were back at the Hotel Crillon in Buenos Aires, we checked at a travel agent. By good fortune, a flight was available the next morning at a cost of only US$30 per person. We reserved six seats to return six days later, on the night before our departure to the UK. The travel agent assured us that it was likely we would find suitable transport into Chile but the circuit walk was unfeasible in the time we had available: "Tourists normally spend two weeks in the Park and even then, because of the usual foul weather, they often fail to complete the route. In the summer, rainstorms may last for several days and snow can occur on any day of the year," she helpfully observed.

We departed early next morning leaving Alex to organise the return of all the equipment to the UK. We later discovered that he had spent most of the morning in the Varig Airline offices trying to get replacement baggage tickets for the excess luggage. I had thrown them away up at Puente del Inca while clearing up. The usual problem of being overweight (180 kg) was eventually solved by giving US$100 to Diego and US$200 to the check-in man. "A hundred dollars to one man are worth more than a thousand dollars to a big company," he wisely noted, accepting the bribe.

At 1.30 pm, our plane landed at Rio Gallegos, a hot dusty town where we quickly located the airport tourist office. In a flood of incomprehensible Spanish, a young woman pointed to the terminal exit. Outside sat a row of beaten-up Mercedes cars and two old Mercedes vans. The first van driver didn't understand a word we said but the second, a fit youthful fellow lazing nearby named Ricardo, had a smattering of English. We asked if we could employ him for six days before explaining what we had in mind. He was interested and suggested a rate of US$150 per day per person. It is my natural inclination to haggle so while the others turned away in embarrassment I set to work. I explained our plans; it was only two days' work, one there and one back, so he could have four days' holiday in the middle, fully paid. Within the hour the van was secured at US$110 per head and we piled in feeling slightly guilty about the hard bargain I had struck.

The journey started well enough on tarmacked roads but within a few miles they deteriorated to stones and dirt. A dust plume chased the van as we bucked and shuddered deep into Patagonia. On the vast windswept steppes, there was no hint of the ice-capped Andes that we eagerly anticipated.

We stopped briefly for refreshments at a tea house/post office. It was a white bungalow with a corrugated iron roof. Inside we were greeted by white tablecloths and napkins, upon which we had tea from a china teapot and biscuits on china plates. An oak dresser was adorned with cups, saucers, Toby jugs and other bric-a-brac from the Welsh valleys. In 1865, 153 Welsh colonists had landed to the north and their house style and traditions had spread to southern Patagonia. Our hosts spoke in fluent Spanish with no hint of a Welsh accent. It was most peculiar.

The road passed through Rio Turbio, the scruffiest coal-mining town imaginable, near the Argentine/Chilean border. Coal dust blackened the outsides of all buildings and presumably the insides of all lungs. A brief stop for refreshments at a squalid café in the town centre confirmed our impression of this grim settlement. Shortly afterwards, we ascended to the green foot-hills of the Andes. A lonely graffiti-daubed customs post marked the border. Inside, the obligatory photograph of El Presidente and maps of Las Malvinas adorned the walls. The islands were occupied and claimed by the British in 1774, 50 years before Argentina was even a nation and 100 years before General Juan Manuel de Rosas brutally conquered the Araucanian Indians of Patagonia. Regardless of battles with the British eight years earlier, we were allowed through without comment and entered a different world: clean, organised and with beautiful scenery.

We crossed the remaining part of the narrow Patagonian peninsula on tarmac roads to deep fjords and the small town of Puerto Natales. It was reminiscent of a Norwegian village, with low colourful houses squared up to resist the westerly winds. Worn hills, like the western highlands of Scotland, loomed over the town, with snow patches clinging to their upper slopes, while the open ocean was hidden beyond numerous peninsulas. These trapped the huge fresh water outflow from the southern Patagonian ice cap so the sea was barely salty (figure 25). Black-necked swans paddled in pristine waters.

We needed a plan for the next four days. The journey had taken longer than hoped so it was now late evening. Ricardo could take us to the Torres del Paine next morning and drop us at the start of the walk but we needed four days' food since none would be available in the National Park. The small shops stocked everything we needed but were closed till the morning.

For the night, we selected a fine wooden hotel by the sea and dined on fresh salmon and tasty Chilean wine. Food was uppermost in our thoughts, for we were still suffering from altitude starvation. What would be our forthcoming requirements? The total walk was 120 kilometres so we would need to consume perhaps 5,000 calories per day. A few basics such as porridge, bread, butter and sardines were the only items we could agree upon. All other food and luxuries such as chocolate, to satisfy individual tastes, would have to be carried personally. The weight of the communal provisions had to be shared alongside other loads such as tents, sleeping bags, carry-mats, cooking stove and fuel.

Next morning, as the first food shop opened, we purchased our necessities. The weight seemed huge. In another shop, John bought a new pair of leather boots made by a local cobbler. It was a triumph of hope over experience. They were hard, knobbly and unyielding but he was not to be dissuaded – after all, the walk was only for four days. Meanwhile, Ricardo ominously bought three new tyres for the next part of the journey. We thought the drive across the peninsula had been bad enough. He reassured us, explaining they were half the price and of higher quality than in Argentina.

It was a 150-kilometre, two-hour drive on the customary dirt roads. As we headed north, the three Torres del Paine rose in the distance. Alongside them stood the remarkable Cuernos del Paine, with their black slate tops upon pink granite shining in the unspoilt paradise of summits, forests and lakes (figure 26). Condors soared overhead, flamingos dipped their heads in turquoise lakes while llama-like guanacos and nandos (South American ostriches) grazed beside the road. We were hooked.

The lunch stop was at the Pehoé Lake Hotel to gorge on our last proper meal before buying permits at the park entrance. The ranger explained that since we were only in the park for five days, we could not attempt the circuit. We fobbed him off by agreeing to walk only part way round.

By 4 pm we were loaded up for our circuit attempt. We shared the weight of the communal goods equally so Mike, being the smallest, carried relatively more compared with his size. His rucksack did look inordinately large. His short legs would have to move fast.

We set off at a brisk pace, leaning forward under heavy rucksacks into the strong wind. Stunted trees, bent in the opposite direction, testified to the persistent westerly gales. After nearly four hours we reached a relatively sheltered spot near Lake Pehoé with magnificent

views of Cuernos del Paine (figure 27). It was not freezing but a
warm meal was needed. Needless to say, the cooker refused to light
in the wind and we ate cold food. For warmth we illegally lit a
small campfire, dug deep into the turf and heated oxtail soup. Mike
hobbled in an hour after everyone else, looking only slightly larger
than his rucksack. He already had bad blisters having insisted on
wearing leather boots. A half kilogram tin of Dubbin bulged from
the back of his sack, but all the Dubbin in the world would not have

softened his boots. John Simmons's new Chilean footwear were also causing problems.

We had patiently waited for Mike to arrive before eating (largely because he carried
the bread and butter). Then we tucked in. Although we had estimated that we would
need 5,000 calories per day, the weight and volume had seemed so huge that we had
cut back. However, we had not taken into account the high-altitude weight loss suffered
on Aconcagua. We had all shed many kilograms and now that we were at sea level
our bodies craved food. We gazed up at the magnificent Paine Grande and went to
bed hungry.

In the morning, Ian made porridge and the tasty outcome guaranteed his breakfast
job for the next few days. Unfortunately, it had to be rationed even though we needed
more. Still peckish, we loaded up our rucksacks, leaving Mike with the light items such as
bread and porridge. Even though the rest of us took the heavy things, such as the cooking
utensils and tents, his bag was still the heaviest. Close inspection revealed a full-sized
Filofax weighing two kilograms, a second pair of boots, numerous items of clothing and
several large chocolate bars, in addition to his much-loved tin of Dubbin. Frustratingly,
he was also slow getting ready in the mornings. We marched off, leaving him cooking
toast on the wood fire and covering his blisters from a huge roll of medical tape. Feeling
guilty, I went back to help him pack and encourage him along. John hobbled ahead in his
new boots.

The wind moderated and the sun shone as Mike and I walked past Lago Pehoé
towards Lago Grey. The path ascended into a primeval forest of huge oaks and wild flower
pastures, flaunting an untouched world. Occasionally, we caught glimpses of Lago Grey,
its northern end dominated by Glacier Grey (figure 28). It is a huge outflow glacier from
the Southern Patagonian Ice Field. As we climbed higher, the whole glacier gradually
appeared, iridescent in the summer sun and bright blue sky. Blinking from its brightness
and beauty, we climbed until it was a few hundred feet below us, with the forest touching its
sides (figure 29). Shards of aquamarine ice, the size of skyscrapers, crashed down creating
mini-bergs that floated into the milky green lake. In the distance, the ice cap shimmered
in the heat. We descended towards the ice wall. There we met the others who had waited
patiently for two hours. We lay in the warm grass, surrounded by summer flowers in the
forest, and admired the rare beauty. But we had to speed up. I hung some of Mike's gear
around my sack then walked ahead with the others, leaving him alone to the mercy of
wolves and bears.

The next section of the walk followed the glacier for several miles. Unexpectedly,
we came across evidence of human activity, such as tree felling. It heralded a camp for

Operation Raleigh, one of John Blashford-Snell's Outward Bound projects. English gap-year students were improving the path as a summer scheme. We spoke to them briefly but had to press on to complete our day's schedule as we still had many miles to go. Thankfully cooled by a breeze from the ice cap, we marched at high speed to below Col Blanco where we set up a camp fire in the forest. It was sunset before John limped in, his blisters even worse.

We were very hungry after the long day. We looked at the meagre rations that had to last three more days and realised they were nowhere near sufficient. Each of us had special treats such as chocolate or nuts but these were not intended to be our main sustenance. And there was no sign of Mike who was carrying the bread. He had not been seen since lunch. We cooked our evening meal, but still no Mike. Annoyingly, he also carried the box of porridge. Our empty stomachs gnawed at us but there was little for breakfast apart from the porridge. Our diaries became obsessed with food. Pete's evening entry read: *'In exchange for blister plasters, I obtain a beef and dumpling meal from John – delicious; supplemented by Oxo, tea and cocoa. John and Ian have an unfortunate concoction of soup and pasta.'*

The light faded and the trees loomed darker in the blackness. It would be impossible to walk without a light. Strange animal noises in the forest encouraged us to keep a bright fire going throughout the night. It would also act as a beacon for Mike. We were anxious for him, and concerns he might be lost dominated our conversations. We agreed that he would never keep up so someone would have to go back for the communal food. I was volunteered. We went to bed hungry and I dreamt of food.

At first light, around 5 am, I quietly left to find Mike (or his remains). I was worried that he might have drifted off the path in the dark for it would have been impossible to find him in the wilderness. I also wondered how I was going to extract the precious porridge. On the other hand, it was a pure delight to jog back down the path without a rucksack. The sun rose in the cool of the morning while the ice cap sparkled in the distance.

After an hour, there with still no sign of Mike. When I came upon the Operation Raleigh camp. It was alive with activity so I started my enquiries. They would know at what time he had passed the previous night.

"Have you seen a short, slightly balding man with a huge rucksack and a tin of Dubbin?" was my starting tack. "He may have struggled through here last night trying to catch up with his friends."

"A charming man called Michael with a harmonica is staying with us, if that is who you mean," replied an attractive girl.

Just then, Mike emerged from a tent in the middle of the camp. Smiling, enthusiastic and with harmonica at the ready, he came over for a chat. I was relieved, but only briefly. He had not the slightest remorse, had no intention of trying to find us, and was proposing to serenade the girls over breakfast.

Not wishing to ruin his chances of marriage, I gently guided him to one side and explained that I had walked back over 10 miles to find him (exaggerating somewhat to make my point). "We were worried, and what about the communal food you are carrying?" I tried to lay the emphasis on our concerns for his wellbeing rather than the porridge but my hunger and irritation got the better of me. "Please give me some of the food," I rasped.

He realised that his possession of the all-important victuals gave him considerable leverage. Would he use this to force us all to wait at our campsite while he caught up? But there were other matters on his mind. He looked repeatedly across at the girls who were waiting in eager anticipation for another romantic tune.

Making an enormous effort to control my growing exasperation, and rumbling stomach, I conceded that we might wait at our campsite. I also demanded some of the porridge, since it wasn't all his. I agreed that he should keep one sixth of it and we would leave him some sausages, coffee and sugar.

He thought he might stay with Operation Raleigh for the morning. A good meal with wine the previous night had emboldened his ardour to fantastical delusions. He was in no hurry whatsoever.

From his tent he handed over the all-important porridge and some bread (the rest probably having been shared with the girls the previous night). Thanking him through gritted teeth, I emphasised that we had a flight back to the UK in four days' time that would not wait. I suggested he might find it easier to retrace his steps.

I strode back tired and hungry but delighted with the successful negotiations. By 9.30 am I was at the camp where we ate porridge cooked over a wood fire. John had already set off towards the mountain pass, so after a quick bite I shouldered my pack. We rose through the forest into low scrub then scree, with magnificent views of Lago Grey and the distant ice-capped summits. Racing each other, it took just an hour to reach Col Blanco (1,241 m) where we met John. The weather was perfect: blue skies, a cooling breeze and stunning views (figure 30). We had been warned repeatedly of the awful weather and rampaging storms, even in summer. But on this occasion Patagonia was warm, calm and extraordinarily beautiful.

From the col, the long descent to the north was on scree past a small lake with the Los Perros glacier falling into it. We briefly stopped. We then followed a grass and scrub track before re-entering the forest where the trail disintegrated into a quagmire. After two hours following orange waymarks, we stopped for another brew with bread and cheese supplements. We were amazed at how well the bread had kept (although we had already eaten most of it).

After an hour spent watching two avalanches crash down from a high glacier and discussing Mike's location, we picked ourselves up and trekked off, still downhill, sometimes over moraine banks and at other times in forest. We were all feeling lean and fit and walked briskly together, stopping for the occasional drink of icy stream water. We passed another Operation Raleigh camp, where students were making a bridge over a small river that rushed with melt water. The afternoon heat was intense but thankfully we were largely protected from the sun by tree cover. The river we were following was getting bigger by the minute and there were some impressive waterfalls. We were making for Lago Dickson and at about 5 pm we could see it.

John started to limp then dropped back to re-plaster his sore feet while we continued to a beautiful flower meadow, alongside a clear broad river. It was idyllic. There was shade from trees with level ground for the campsite. A dome tent was already pitched and, despite the heat and humidity, a hiker was resting inside. We sat down, tired and happy – but not for long. We found ourselves besieged by swarms of voracious mosquitoes, large horse flies and tiny midges, and they hurt. Our paradise was transformed to hell. As fast as possible we put on leggings, thick socks and cagoules to cover all parts of our bodies. It was not enough, so we put up the tents. But the insects were everywhere and still biting. We now realised why our neighbour was in his tent. Hiding for the same reason, we debated possible tactics to counter the external horror. It would be impossible to cook outside, or inside and we needed food.

After some discussion we agreed to move away from the meadows and into a drier area, perhaps on rocks. We rapidly de-camped and, fighting our tiny assailants, marched in a high-speed convoy away from the beautiful Lago Dickson and down river. We climbed a small hill off the path through prickly shrubs, but gained no reprieve from the insects. Then John spotted that the river further down had some wide shingle beds and suggested we camp there. He reasoned that the glacial river might be too cold for insect growth. We agreed. After another hard half-hour, through prickly shrubs, we finally arrived at a mercifully insect-free area. We rapidly lit a fire, soothed our feet in the cool water and cooked supper. Tesco lasagne and soup prepared by Ian made our night, and there were still no insects. Behind us soared the rose-tinted peaks of Cuerno Escudo and Cuerno Paine Medio, with the main ice cap to the north.

Around our driftwood fire, the chat turned inevitably to Mike. Was he still serenading the girls? Had he gone back or was he coming over the col? Would he be fast enough to catch the plane home? We thought that he was probably a day behind. Pete was on great form and we had many good laughs but we were still hungry. Most of the communal food was gone. We had personal food which we kept hidden from each other, unwilling to share it, but it was rapidly being depleted. The calorie usage was huge for we were walking and climbing 30 to 40 kilometres a day with heavy packs.

There was no need for tents in the warm evening, so we lay down by the cool stream in our bivvy bags hoping there would be no overnight flood. As dusk descended, marauding mosquitoes smelt us so we zipped up tight to keep them out. I killed the few that had entered my cocoon. Through the thin Gore-Tex covering, I listened to the whining hordes outside with their mini chainsaws.

Hoping the others wouldn't overhear, I quietly opened my last small white chocolate bar. It tasted magnificent. I slowly savoured each creamy piece until, alas, it was finished. A few small flakes had fallen to the side. I licked them from the bag and then searched around my feet for any peanuts or currants that might have fallen from previous night-time snacks. I went to sleep thinking of breakfast.

Thankfully, the night was dry and we awoke to the smell of Ian's magnificent porridge. Hunger is the best cook; we relished its taste as we scratched our numerous insect bites.

Because we had walked several miles fleeing mosquitoes the previous evening, we reckoned we could complete the circuit on that third day. It was around 30 kilometres to a park exit at Amarga; there was little climbing and we were lean, very fit and carrying less since the food had mostly gone. At 9 am we left our pristine camp and set off in single file towards Lago Paine. John kept up for a while through the scrub and thorn bushes but after reaching the path he dropped back as we moved into top gear. With blisters like his how could he race?

Soon we were competing, with the lead changing repeatedly. The route skirted the central mountains that rose above us, many with fresh coverings of snow. Occasional orange waymarks guided us through bogs and the low scrub. As the path undulated over spurs from magnificent big peaks, we saw distant clouds rolling down the ice cap towards us. We sweated up slopes in the growing heat of the morning and jogged down the far sides. A strengthening wind pushed at our backs, guiding us to the park exit, with rain flurries adding extra incentives. The beautiful Rio Paine rushed beside us.

Lunch saw off the last vestiges of food: a few morsels of cake, the odd square of chocolate, and breadcrumbs from the bottom of the packs. Hunger pushed us onward. Far behind us, John quizzed a walker on our whereabouts, who retorted that he had seen four crazy Brits chasing each other along the track.

Forest and shrub gave way to grass and then to fenced meadows around a large estancia – the first signs of habitation for three days. We asked how far we had left to go, only to discover that it was still four to five hours down the valley to Amarga, then another eight kilometres to a restaurant. The path stretched into the distance down the valley.

Ian was in the lead up one of the ascents and by the time we reached the top he was well ahead. He was running! He looked back guiltily. We realised that we all might end up running the last 15 kilometres as the yearning to win increased. As he crested then descended the next rise, we ran in pursuit, hidden from his view. A crazy contest, but we could not allow Ian the satisfaction of an easy victory.

Stunning views of the granite Torres del Paine, their glaciers glinting in the sun, were cast aside for the race. On the next ridge Ian turned around and realised he had lost ground and his game had been spotted. He hated losing, but so did we. We played cat and mouse over the next four ridges to within a mile of the end. Finally, I could no longer stand the irritation of Ian still being in the lead. To the amusement and ridicule of Chris and Pete, I ran after him to the exit gate at Guardia Laguna Amarga which I assumed was the finishing line. There I found him sprawled on his back in a privet hedge, completely knackered but muttering, "I won, I won." Indeed, he had. Soon after, the others arrived, and lying exhausted on the grass, we roared hysterically with laughter. Amazingly, a walk that should have taken us seven days had been completed in three.

But, of far greater importance, there was food. A rickety plank on a narrow suspension bridge took us over the ice-cold Rio Paine to a youth hostel just beyond the park entrance. Inside were fellow hikers and a small shop that sold food, although it was due to close in a few minutes. They had little on offer except a few tins of salmon. We bought the remaining stock and savoured its exquisite taste (normally I don't like cold salmon).

We chatted to two young English women who had spent five weeks walking and climbing in Chile. They had spent six days on our circuit and, like us, had run out of food. They were lively, pretty and their exploits very impressive. As Pete noted, "One had breasts of creamy white skin, tantalisingly revealed whenever she bent forward over the stove." In his defence, it was nearly a month since we had left home.

An hour later, John limped in to our cheers and Ian's arms raised in triumph. We gave him our remaining salmon. As dusk descended, we prepared ourselves for the last eight kilometres along the road to a hotel. Then I had a thought – why not ask Ricardo to collect us? In rudimentary Spanish we explained our predicament to the hostel receptionist and by some miracle of Patagonian communication he was located fishing nearby (no mobile phones in those days). Perhaps a suspicious-looking Argentinian, hanging about in a Chilean national park, was of importance to the police. Whatever. Within the hour his smiling face appeared at the door and we were saved. Well, at least the five of us were since Mike was nowhere to be seen.

Ricardo had located and booked the Hotel Serrano, near the Cornos del Paine, so we were doubly grateful for the deliverance. We bade farewell to our two female friends. From nowhere Pete conjured up a bar of chocolate for 'Miss Creamy White' and off we sped. Ricardo asked what had happened to Mike. Pete joked that we were so hungry that we had eaten him. Unaccustomed to English humour, he was not sure whether or not to believe us. Pete could be the funniest guy ever.

The hotel was a haven. After rapidly washing off three days of grime we re-dressed in our least dirty clothes and headed for supper. Since it was too late for the main dining room, we ate next to the kitchen on cold ham, guanaco burgers and rice with lashings of beer and red wine. Pete ordered a fourth bottle followed by large whiskies. We were well-fed and well-oiled.

In the haziness of hangovers next morning, we slowly considered our plans. We now had a day spare: should we fully complete the circuit to where we entered the park or visit the central area? What could be better than going to the heart of the park and see the actual Torres del Paine up close? We might also find Mike.

After breakfast Ricardo drove us back to Amarga where Mike might have stayed the night. He hadn't, so leaving John behind because of his blisters, we retraced our steps from the previous day: past the estancia, across Rio Paine and up towards the Torres. Imagine, barely 100 years earlier all this country had been empty so settlers had bought huge land holdings including those magnificent mountains, and the same distance from the equator as Birmingham

We ascended through vegetation reminiscent of Japanese gardens with strange yellow bonsai-like trees and narrow streams. Finally, we climbed over a boulder field and looked across to the ice-clad Torres del Paine beyond a freezing lake. The breath-taking pinnacles of rock had been climbed first by a team that included Sir Chris Bonington (Central Tower, 1962). It was too late to climb across the glacier to their bases but the views were extraordinary (figure 31).

But dream time and holidays were now over. It was time for home. We grudgingly turned around and descended towards the lower slopes of the mountains and a forced march to the hotel. The heat beat down upon the arid landscape, dusty in the summer sun, with thousands of small thorn bushes dominating the sloping ground. Curiously, in their midst was one brightly coloured bush of a similar size to the rest but with what looked like a decorated blanket thrown over it. The anomaly was so visually striking we remarked on its appearance. Then it moved. At a distance of several hundred metres it was hard to discern but a one-humped camel came to mind. As we approached, it took on the appearance of a human – a cross between John the Baptist and Lawrence of Arabia. It was a large rucksack with a tin of Dubbin on the back of a small man studying a map. It was Mike! "Would you like a piece of Cadbury's fruit and nut chocolate?" he proffered.

By an extraordinary chance we had found him in the middle of the wilderness. He had strayed off the path for some hours and had drifted towards the Torres del Paine where he had become lost. We had saved him from being benighted and missing his flight home. We shared out his load and frog-marched him back to the Laguna Amarga Hostel. Ricardo was much relieved that we had found him as it would have done his reputation no good to have a client eaten.

Friends reunited, we had another boisterous, wine-fuelled evening, but this time with full service. Oswaldo, an impeccably dressed waiter in black and white (reminiscent of Manuel in Fawlty Towers), attended to our every need. He fed us extra guanaco burgers in spite of fierce protestations from the diminutive, sour-faced Spanish hotel manager who tried to dampen our raucous behaviour. 'Rosa Kleb' as Pete called her. "Her husband probably committed suicide," he wise-cracked.

The piercing sarcasm finally turned on Mike and how his selfish actions caused so much concern to the rest of us. He was oblivious. I went to bed with my face sore from laughing.

The next morning, we left Serrano to return over the 550 kilometres of bumpy rubble roads to Rio Gallegos. We were hung-over and hot. The eight-hour journey was tedious and uneventful until just 200 metres from the tarmacked roads of the town, when we came close to disaster. The front wheel tyre blew-out. We were travelling at 70 kilometres per hour when it happened so by the time we stopped in a deep ditch, the rim of the wheel was 12-sided. Ricardo did well but was shaken up and very disappointed. The damage would be the end of his profit. At the airport we paid him off and much to his delight compensated him for the ruined wheel. It worked out at US$150 per head, the original asking price.

We flew the 3½ hours back to Buenos Aires where we met the others in the Hotel Crillon for our final night of the expedition. We looked very scrawny (figure 32). The high altitude had inhibited our appetites for three weeks and we had starved around the Torres del Paine while exercising hard. Ian had lost 17 kg, down from 102 kg to 85 kg.

The Torres del Paine circuit had been the walk of a lifetime. Some of the group had sat on the beaches of Santiago but most had gone home. Chance had taken six of us to one of the most beautiful and unspoiled mountain regions in the world. On a thankfully routine flight back to London the following day, our minds buzzed with all the memories.

Photographs courtesy of Pete Forster.

Fig 25. *Glacier near Puerto Natales*

Fig 26. *Torres del Paine*

Fig 27. *Cuernos del Paine*

Fig 28. *Glacier Grey*

Fig 29. *Glacier Grey*

Fig 30. *Col Blanco. Left to right: Jo, Ian, John and Chris*

Fig 31. *Torres del Paine*

Fig 32. *Pete and Jo after the walk*

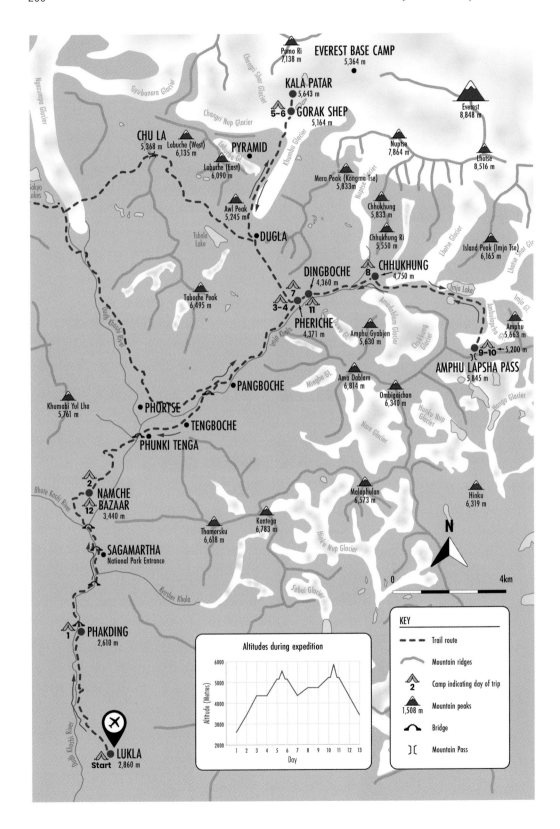

EVEREST BASE CAMP
5,364 m

Pumo Ri
7,138 m

KALA PATAR
5,643 m

5-6 GORAK SHEP
5,164 m

Everest
8,848 m

CHU LA
5,368 m

Lobuche (West)
6,135 m

PYRAMID

Nuptse
7,864 m

Lhotse
8,516 m

Lobuche (East)
6,090 m

Mera Peak (Kongma Tse)
5,833m

Awl Peak
5,245 m

Chhukhung
5,833 m

DUGLA

Tshola
Lake

Chhukhung Ri
5,550 m

Island Peak (Imja Tse)
6,165 m

DINGBOCHE
4,360 m

7

8 CHHUKHUNG
4,750 m

Taboche Peak
6,495 m

3-4

11

Imja Lake

PHERICHE
4,371 m

Amphu Gyabjen
5,630 m

Amphu
5,663 m

9-10   5,200 m

AMPHU LAPSHA PASS
5,845 m

Khumabi Yul Lha
5,761 m

PANGBOCHE

PHORTSE

Ama Dablam
6,814 m

Ombigaichan
6,340 m

TENGBOCHE

PHUNKI TENGA

Malaphulan
6,573 m

Hinku
6,319 m

2

NAMCHE
BAZAAR

12

3,440 m

Thamersku
6,618 m

Kantega
6,783 m

N

SAGAMARTHA
National Park Entrance

0   4km

1 PHAKDING
2,610 m

Altitudes during expedition

KEY

- - - - Trail route

Mountain ridges

2 Camp indicating day of trip

1,508 m Mountain peaks

Bridge

)(Mountain Pass

LUKLA
Start   2,860 m

Chapter 7
Everest – April 1993

Everest, Nuptse Ridge and Lhotse

Female hormones

"Why do you want to climb Mount Everest?" asked a reporter from the New York Times.
"Because it's there," replied George Herbert Leigh Mallory.
"Sometimes science is the excuse for exploration. I think it is rarely the reason." (18 March 1923).

Summary: The climbing success on Aconcagua left us dreaming of Everest. Not to climb it but to reach Base Camp and perhaps attempt a small neighbouring peak. Progesterone had been noted to improve breathing at altitude so we compared it with acetazolamide in preventing acute mountain sickness. A fast ascent rate used to provoke illness for the clinical trial took its toll. We subsequently split up into three groups to explore the Everest region.

Expedition members: Maggie Beazley, Steve Boyer, Jo Bradwell (leader), Patrick Cadigan (deputy medical officer), Ian Chesner, Martin Cooper, John Delamere, Peter Dykes, Jim Evans (student), Pete Forster (medical officer), Tim Harvey, Ron Haydock, Helen Hoar (student), Chris Imray, Brian Johnson, Ian MacLennan, Graham Mead, John Milles, Simon Morrissey, Seamus Mulholland (student), Neville Richardson, John Simmons, Bill Unertl, Alex Wright (deputy leader and medical officer) (figure 1).

Aconcagua had been tough. We endured days of suffering from high-altitude illnesses and the huge physical effort of climbing the mountain. The high camps had been difficult and I had failed to reach the summit.

There had been the additional responsibility of leadership and trying to balance the conflicting demands of too many experiments, all the while suffering from oxygen starvation. On returning home, there was no warm afterglow of a fancy paper in *The Lancet*.

I was also busy at work and had a young family to consider. Lying in my inadequate sleeping bag in the top camp at Nido de Condores (5,486 m), I vowed not to go on another expedition any time soon. Although this was partly tempered by the subsequent wonderful walk around the Torres del Paine, on returning to England I still felt the same.

As the months went by, I held my resolve; others could go on a future expedition but not me. But one year turned to two and the itch resurfaced. That unfathomable atavistic urge for adventure. Perhaps the routine of work, the unlimited demands of three young children, or the desire for something different gradually transformed the satisfaction of domesticity to a yearning for excitement. Not a re-boot, not an escape from the daily grind, but the possibility of another thrilling escapade with mates. It was time to feed the mountain *rat*. However, to drag me out of self-imposed retirement, it would have to be somewhere special. No one fancied another barren volcano, so our thoughts returned to the Himalayas.

Inevitably, discussions touched on Everest. I had read Chris Bonington's book *The Everest Years* plus earlier heroic stories by John Hunt, Eric Shipton and Wilfrid Noyce. Everest was tempting. In the spring of 1992, it was suggested that we should trek to Everest Base Camp and then go climbing. There are innumerable peaks and passes in the area with easily enough variety for any of us, whatever our skill level. We could split into small groups after the research to satisfy our individual wishes. But importantly, Gorak Shep, near Everest Base Camp, would provide a great location for high-altitude studies. I was persuaded – Everest it was.

The allure of the world's highest mountain enticed Neville Richardson, Peter Dykes and Simon Morrissey out of retirement. They had missed the previous one or two trips but were keen to see Everest. We soon had 20 participants including friends such as Patrick Cadigan, Ron Haydock and Bill Unertl. Quite sufficient numbers for the expedition but this didn't take into account any students. Although there was no obligation, the trips had become part of medical student folk law, an exciting perk and good for their CVs. Professor Owen Wade, head of the Arthur Thompson Trust, indicated they would cover the costs of two students providing we made the selection.

For the first three expeditions, students had approached us: Norman Waterhouse on the first expedition, David Lort on the second and David Parker plus Tim Harlow on the third. While they had all been excellent companions, we thought that for the fourth expedition (Rupina La), rather than the students select us, we would choose them. Following an announcement in the students' magazine, *BUMS* (Birmingham University Medical Students), we interviewed around a dozen and selected two – Nick Binns and Jonathan Evans. We based our choice on their friendliness, physical fitness and exam results. We couldn't take any who might fail the course. The trip was a reward for good performance, not an escape from poor results.

A slightly different tack had been tried for the Karakoram expedition. By selecting popular students, we thought we might also find those who were the best company. At the interviews we asked each of them which of the applicants they thought would be the most suitable companion for an expedition. Simon Meech joined us but our other selection had some dodgy exam grades so wasn't allowed to come.

Since we were interested in altitude science, we wondered whether the brightest students might contribute to our studies. For the sixth expedition, we therefore selected students who wrote the best essay on the interesting altitude question of 'How does the bar-headed goose fly over Mt Everest?'

Bar-headed goose

Each spring these birds migrate over the Himalayas from the plains of India to breed on the high Tibetan plateau, taking them to heights of over 7,000 m within a few hours. Such ascent rates would kill humans but the birds have physiological adaptations allowing them to carry out this extraordinary feat. Of the eight students who wrote essays, we selected three we thought could withstand the physical rigours of a month-long Himalayan trip.

At interview, it was apparent that other students were keen to come but didn't want to write a challenging essay. They felt they couldn't win against the swots. This resonated with us who as students would have failed a similar selection process. Essay writing favoured introverted academic types rather than easy-going extroverts. Primarily we wanted people interested in mountains, who preferably had climbing experience, were outgoing and easily passed their exams.

For the Everest trip we therefore proposed a different selection method. Each winter and summer for many years, my secretary, Margaret Richards, had organised big walks (chapter 17), so why not invite the keenest students to join us? We would have a chance to meet them socially and any who were still keen after a weekend of suffering were the sort we wanted. Two years before the Everest trip we had a walk in the Cairngorms (chapter 17). It was a mere 30 miles with 12,000 ft of ascent over the four 4,000 ft summits: Cairn Toul (4,236 ft), Ben Macdui (4,295 ft), Braeriach (4,252 ft), Cairn Gorm (4,081 ft) plus Beinn Mheadhoin (3,878 ft). A 4 am start after an overnight bus journey from the Medical School was tough enough, but the 16-hour walk proved too arduous for many. Neville and I reached the end at 7.30 pm to be greeted by several of the group but none had climbed all the peaks. Worryingly, some were still missing, including the three students. By 10 pm, we had eaten dinner and dusk was approaching but there was still no sign of the students. Eventually we found them back along the trail, but they resolutely refused help fearing rejection if they didn't finish. The last, Helen Hoar, came in at 11.30 pm, in the dark. We were most impressed. Jim Evans and Seamus Mulholland were the other two. We invited all three to Everest.

The research side of the expedition was centred around a drug trial. Steroids in the form of dexamethasone had proven use for preventing and treating mountain sickness. The reasons for its effectiveness were unclear but progesterone (a related steroid hormone involved in pregnancy) stimulates breathing, a feature we thought might increase oxygen levels at altitude. Since it had a different mode of action from acetazolamide, the two

Progesterone capsules

drugs might even have an additive effect. To test progesterone, we divided our team of 24 into four treatment groups of six people who took either placebo or acetazolamide (250 mg twice daily), medroxyprogesterone (30 mg twice daily) or both. Concerned that the drugs might impair exercise performance, we planned to assess everyone using the exercise bike that we had used at Rupina La. As news of our project leaked out, it led to considerable amusement, even producing local newspaper headlines of 'Sex change doctors tackle killer mountain' and 'Everest by hormones'.

The other study concerned the mechanism of mountain sickness. Its severe form, high-altitude cerebral oedema, is associated with raised intra-cerebral pressure, but whether this occurred in early mountain sickness was unknown. Measuring intracranial pressure normally involves a lumbar puncture (putting a needle in the lower spine) but we felt this was unacceptable on a field expedition (although others had done it). Alex came up with a clever alternative. Dr Robert Marchbanks from the National Ear, Nose and Throat Hospital in London had shown that intracerebral pressure was transmitted onto the eardrums (tympanic membrane), enabling it to be measured with a simple gadget (tympanometer) that he had designed. At a meeting he liked the project, even lending us his equipment.

Funding for the expedition came from a variety of sources. The Wellcome Trust once again supported the research while Alex Wright organised a hepatitis A immunisation trial, with Smith, Kline & Co. donating the £14,000 investigators' fee to BMRES. The Arthur Thomson Trust paid for three students while the balance of costs came from personal donations.

As always, we used a trekking organisation to run the logistics. On this occasion we chose the company run by Doug Scott (specialist trekking co-operative, Cumbria, CA4 0EL). He was the most accomplished climber of his generation and the first British person to reach the summit of Everest (via the south-west face with Dougal Haston in 1975). John Delamere had met him at one of his numerous lectures and invited him to give a presentation in the Great Hall at the University of Birmingham. This holds 600 people, and by charging a modest amount we reckoned we could raise £1,000 or so towards our expedition costs. We agreed to his fee of £400 and filled the hall. At a subsequent meeting at his house in Hesket Newmarket in Cumbria, he agreed to organise our trip with his girlfriend, Sharu, as our trek leader. Reputed to be an Indian princess, she spoke several languages and had accompanied Doug on many of his climbs.

Although the best time to visit Nepal is in the autumn with brilliant clear days and cold, star-lit nights, we thought a spring trip would make a pleasant alternative. In April the temperature is higher and the monsoon hasn't started. By chance, it was the 40th anniversary of the first ascent of Mt Everest, of which more later.

As the expedition date approached, Mike Winterborn, a staunch member for the past four expeditions, became ill with leukaemia and couldn't come. Fortunately, Graham

Mead, a research colleague, stepped in to keep the membership at 24 for the trial.

To Kathmandu

Departure date was Saturday 3 April, with a flight to Dhaka and then Kathmandu. We had the usual last-minute panic as experiments were finalised then the traditional send off from the Medical School (figure 1). We bade farewell to spouses and partners and I shouted, 'see you in Kathmandu in a month' to Barbara as the bus sped off to London Heathrow airport. En route, Helen Hoar, one of our new students, unwrapped a beautiful Easter cake of black and white chocolate in the shape of Mt Everest, Nuptse and Lhotse. We hungrily devoured her masterpiece.

There were no excess weight problems at the check-in desk, the medical equipment passed through without comment and we were soon on a 9-hour overnight flight to Bangladesh. Not renowned for its mountains (average height above sea level is 10 m) or its wealth (127th in the world), it nevertheless made an indelible impression. As we arrived jet-lagged and bleary-eyed in the crowded Dhaka airport terminal, the departure board indicated an immediate flight to Kathmandu, with seats to spare. During an intense discussion as to whether there was room for everyone, we were greeted by Chris's father, Sir Colin Imray, the British High Commissioner for Bangladesh. (He had been knighted for his remarkable success in famine relief after the 1991 cyclone, which killed 140,000 people.)

All thoughts of the early Kathmandu flight evaporated. Our baggage was collected by Sir Colin's staff as we were guided through the VIP lounge and into the car park. There purred his green Bentley, parading its Union Flag (figure 2). I sat in the front seat, Sir Colin driving, with Chris and Patrick in the back. If this was what being leader of an expedition meant, bring it on. A bus brought the others, plus baggage, through the crowded streets to the High Commission enclosure, past smart Ghurkha sentries into a haven of calm.

Welcomed gracefully by Sir Colin and Lady Shirley (figure 3), we were fed, watered and swam in their pool. Lunch comprised cold beef and prawns, Stilton cheese in cucumber sandwiches, all washed down with a zappy white Burgundy. Enjoyed under the shade of tropical trees, it was delicious enough to satisfy the most epicurean of palates. I mused at the contrast between us, the people outside the compound, and our camping over the next two weeks on the flanks of Mt Everest.

Our time in paradise was short; three hours later we were back at the airport. We had fretted about being late for the flight, but we were escorted to the VIP lounge as our bags were cleared through customs by embassy staff. Within minutes we were on the plane, exclusively occupying the first five rows. We later discovered that 24 people had been bumped off the flight for us. Sir Colin had a lot of power.

It was a one-hour evening flight from Dhaka to Kathmandu and its new airport. Anxieties surfaced as we arrived since we had forwarded three generators, gas canisters for the blood-gas machine and loads of climbing equipment. Six years earlier there had been great difficulties with customs officials over radioactive xenon imports; we didn't want a repeat experience. Sometimes 'fines' had to be paid for improper documentation. Suspecting that the system remained imperfect, we had a wodge of rupees at the ready.

In the arrivals hall we met Sharu, her sister Divia and Gelzen, our *sirdar*. Welcoming garlands of flowers were draped around our necks. Our luggage was loaded onto a bus, which departed for the hotel with most of the group, leaving Neville, Pete, Simon and myself to extract the forwarded equipment. In a large metal cage next to the customs bureau we could see our gear. Our rigorously prepared documents were inspected, but for some inexplicable reason they were wrong. As the office was shortly to close for the night we were in a dilemma. We needed the equipment immediately for an early morning start. But we had a plan – boldness.

Some years earlier, while on a WHO project to Pakistan, I had been faced with a similar situation. Returning through Egypt, I had deposited an attractive hand-made rug at a huge bonded warehouse in Cairo to avoid import duty, levied at 100% of its value. A few days later, immediately prior to my return to the UK, I went to reclaim the rug, only to be told that it was closed for a few days because of a strike. This meant I would lose it as the flight was departing shortly

By the open entrance door stood two soldiers, at attention, with rifles at their sides. I explained that I had a flight to catch in an hour and wanted my rug. They did not move nor seem to understand, so I palmed some Egyptian notes while shaking hands with one of them and showed my blue WHO diplomatic passport. Avoiding eye contact, I stepped through the doorway and located my precious rug. Holding it tightly, I walked out past the guards, down the steps and into the airport terminal. At the time I was amazed that such boldness had been successful. Could the same tactic work here?

We asked if we could check our list of equipment against items in the cage. They opened the gate and indeed everything was present and correct. Knowing this, we started carrying the generators out into the customs hall. With much shouting, two customs officials grabbed the handles. It developed into a tug-of-war. Other staff bolted the gate and guards started fingering their rifles. Realising that we had lost the argument, we beat a hasty retreat to a taxi and disappeared into the turmoil of Kathmandu. I kicked myself for not having offered some rupees. Battle would have to recommence in the morning.

Our elegant hotel, the Narayani, was quiet and sophisticated, with attractive wooden furnishings in tropical hardwoods and a beautiful rear flower garden. It was a sanctuary of peace from the noisy, smoky filth of Kathmandu and its innumerable cars and tuk-tuks. In the 16 years since our first visit, the city had been transformed from a quiet medieval backwater to a heavily polluted metropolis.

At our 7 pm group logistics meeting, we described our failure to extract the equipment from customs. A more subtle approach based on financial 'compensation' was agreed for the following morning. Other items required were trekking permits, plane tickets to Lukla and liquid nitrogen for storing blood and urine samples. The day finished with a fine meal at the hotel.

Next morning, we cleared space in a couple of the bedrooms and by 7 am we were all busy with tympanometry in the expert hands of Alex, Chris and Simon or the bike test with Patrick and Tim. Over a brief coffee by the pool to discuss tactics, we departed for our 10 am meeting with the customs officers. Sharu believed it was basically a question of paying a sufficient amount to the appropriate people and being patient.

On our best behaviour, we were introduced to the chief customs officer. With due grovelling, we acknowledged that a large 'fine' was necessary for the incorrect documentation. With smiles all round, we signed their numerous forms and then waited; had lunch and waited some more. It transpired that 20,000 rupee (~£300) was needed for the officials plus a little extra for the younger staff to carry the equipment from the cage to our bus. Other forms were completed and inducements paid. A dozen willing hands put the loads onto trolleys, with 2,000 rupee tips for each of the inside and outside porters, policeman, armed guards and customs security men. We were back at the Narayani by 3 pm feeling surprisingly pleased with ourselves despite having parted with £400.

Mac and Bill were equally successful with their quest. They had filled the Dewar flask with liquid nitrogen acquired from a veterinary centre that stored bulls' sperm. The exercise tests were completed, the tympanometry measurements had gone well, which left only the blood-gas analysis as the remaining uncertainty. Now that we had the gas canisters, John Delamere and his team could set up the instrument while we had a few hours down-time in Kathmandu.

Durbar Square and Tamil are always fascinating, with their colourful roadside stalls, exotic Buddhist and Hindu temples, and primitive back streets bustling with noise. We soaked up Kathmandu. It had been eight years since our last visit, and I had forgotten its beautiful, primitive mysteries. Then there are the 'deals'. Two girls followed Neville and myself for two hours trying to sell bracelets. They started at $20 each, slowly fell to $5 until Neville negotiated three for $5. We were probably done.

We were back at the hotel for our daily 7 pm debriefing. The three generators worked well but the blood-gas analyser wouldn't calibrate and the hotel's electricity failed several times during their attempts. It was time to give up, so a bunch of us went to KC's restaurant for sizzling steaks accompanied by wine and Pete's sizzling wit, much at John Milles's expense. Poor John Delamere had a memorable incident. He inhaled a piece of steak and started choking. Seeing his plight, Simon grabbed him from behind squeezed him hard from behind – a classic Heimlich manoeuvre. Out-shot the meat. Lucky there was a surgeon with us.

Into the mountains

We were up by 5 am to organise the loads for our two flights to Lukla. Each twin engine Otter carried 16 people plus luggage. Breakfast was forbidden, not because of possible air sickness in a small bouncing aircraft, not because of the fear-inducing flight, but because fasting blood samples had to be taken after we landed.

I was in the second group, waiting anxiously at the hotel for our dilapidated bus to return from dropping off the first group. It was late. Had it broken down? Had the driver gone to sleep? Had it crashed? The tension mounted. With 30 minutes remaining to the scheduled departure time, which included a 15-minute drive through busy traffic, the bus returned. How could we possibly make it in time?

We raced through the city crowds, horn blaring and pedestrians running for safety. On arrival, with tourists pressing on all sides, we were hassled to the departure gate by Sharu. There was a rudimentary weight check and a ticket inspection; beyond the desk we could see a forlorn-looking Simon, dumped off the first flight because of overloading. The airway's authorities had little control over tourists' bribes for extra baggage. There was also huge pressure to clear backlogs of passengers after bad weather. We scrambled on to an ancient jam-packed Yeti Airlines plane. The engines roared, the bumpy airstrip flashed below us, then calm descended as we rose above the smog. Our eyes feasted on a Himalayan panorama: Langtang Himal, Gauri Shankar, Cho Oyu and, in the distance, Everest itself, towering above the clouds.

For 30 minutes the plane bumped in the turbulence of rising thermals over high windy ridges, until the tiny airstrip at Lukla (2,840 m) appeared above a cliff. Currently known as the Tenzing–Hillary airport, it is perched on a high ledge over the deep Dudh Koshi river valley, which drains the Everest region. With repeated plane crashes, it is rated as the most dangerous airport in the world. Just 460 m long and 20 m wide, the runway has an uphill gradient of 12% and ends in a rock wall. Fear swept the plane as we dived down 1,000 m from the last high ridge to the tiny rubble airstrip. We banged down hard then raced steeply upwards towards the rocks with the engines screaming in reverse. In the last few seconds, we turned sideways and stopped. Smashed planes on either side testified to the perils.

There were shouts of 'out, out, out', as we cleared the air-strip for the next plane to land. Above the end wall, dozens of people moved towards us desperate to leave. Within minutes our plane was reloaded and roared off, dropping sharply into the deep valley as the runway ended, before slowly easing upwards into the clouds (figure 4).

We scrambled up the embankment to where our friends from the earlier flight had gathered. In a sun-drenched pasture, the blood team, led by Peter Dykes and Graham, were collecting venous samples and separating the serum. A generator hummed as tea and biscuits were served, followed by a welcoming cooked breakfast.

Shortly afterwards, Sharu arrived with the remaining luggage. We counted everything, only to find that three blue drums of equipment were missing. A quick search revealed they had been mixed up with others from a Spanish expedition and were being carried off up the path. I raced after their porters and, gasping with breath, managed to retrieve them. In the pell-mell of arriving and all the churning tourists and porters, it was easy to lose track of our 45 boxes and bags. We identified each bag but to our consternation one was missing. Instead we had a rucksack belonging to someone called Sally Rose. Some unfortunate trekker must have lost it. We looked around the airport area but no one was looking for a rucksack.

The blood sampling was finished, and the equipment was loaded onto yaks and dzos (a hybrid of yaks and domestic cattle) while porters carried more bulky items. The blood-gas team of John Simmons, John Delamere and Ian Chesner departed first, with their yaks, to set up their equipment at our night's stop. Others departed in small groups while I waited with Pete and John Milles to make sure Sally Rose didn't appear. After half an hour we gave up, handed her bag to one of our porters and followed the others up the broad track. We thought she might be further up the trial.

The walk commenced with a steep climb up innumerable steps then a short descent to Phakding at 2,610 m, 200 metres lower than Lukla airport. It was a four-hour walk past well-built stone houses (figure 5), vibrant spring flowers, alpine forests and unpolluted air. It ended after a long suspension bridge over the Dudh Koshi where our campsite was being organised on a grass pasture in front of a tea-shop (figure 6). When all the animals and porters had arrived, the bag-count showed Ron's was missing. Feeling responsible, I apologised for its absence fearing that the nearest place to find high-altitude clothes would be back in Kathmandu. He took one look at Sally Rose's bag and grabbed it, saying that his stuff was inside. Sally Rose was his daughter-in-law. What a clot. We had so nearly left it at Lukla airport. We labelled all the rucksacks with BMRES, in bold letters, plus the owners' names to prevent losses over the following days.

We had three-man tents for two people and two large rectangular tents, placed end-on for dining and experiments. Soon the generator was whirring with successful tympanometry underway at one end and the blood-gas team struggling at the other. First the pH measurements were not stable then the blood oxygen results looked odd. The reference electrode was changed and after another hour of fiddling – success! The team rattled through 24 sets of blood gases in an hour. It had to be a record.

After supper, discussions turned to our route over the next few days. To ensure that the drug trial was successful, we had to provoke mountain sickness by ascending quickly. We had originally planned to be at Namche Bazaar (3,440 m) on the first night, so we were already behind schedule, but we had to stay at the Sherpa capital – the Sherpas had friends and relatives living there. To retrieve the situation, we wanted to bypass Tengboche (3,860 m) and camp at Pheriche (4,371 m) on the third night – an ascent of 930 m. That would leave a climb of 800 m to Gorak Shep (5,164 m), a little below Everest Base Camp, for the final day. That should provoke a fair bit of illness, I thought with relief as I went to bed. So far so good!

After a good night's sleep, we set off at 7.15 am prompt for the short sharp ascent to Namche Bazaar. Our smartly dressed *sirdar*, Gelzen, led from the front, with us trailing behind in small groups. We jostled past countless porters and yaks. The animals carried 100 kg but, remarkably, some porters carried up to 140 kg (figure 7). These heavy lifters of the Nepalese community were part of an army of ants ferrying loads across the lower foothills of the Himalaya. With no roads, and yaks more expensive, humans were the main lorries of the Sherpa community, meeting the demands of innumerable expeditions.

The ascent from Phakding to Namche Bazaar is barely five miles and 800 m of ascent but it should be savoured. Dramatic peaks such as Kangtega (6,783 m) and Thamserku (6,623 m) tower over the route, while the Dudh Koshi roars alongside the path. It is reminiscent of high Swiss valleys, except for the roadside tourist bazaars and *mani* walls with their prayer wheels.

After two miles, the entrance gate to Sagarmatha National Park blocked the route. The park was set up in 1979 to protect the Everest region and is now a UNESCO World Heritage Site. We met at the park entrance to pay our 650 rupees per person fee. Then, led by Mac, we followed the trail past flowering

Rhododendron

rhododendron and magnolia trees, criss-crossing the river as we spread out in a long line, positions depending on some combination of fitness and one of the drugs we were taking – placebo, progesterone, acetazolamide or both active compounds. Slowed by the thin air, it was a tough climb to Namche Bazaar. On the final stretch, Everest came into view for the first time. Just topping the Nuptse wall, its dark triangular summit and its snowy plume seemed awesomely high (front figure). By 11 am the leaders were ensconced in a Sherpa guest house, drinking tea as others dribbled in. The porters didn't start arriving until 4 pm, making us realise that it would have been impossible to have made Namche Bazaar on the previous day. The camp was set up in a yak pen near the village centre (figure 8).

Namche Bazaar is the Sherpa capital and famous for being the starting place for Everest expeditions. At an altitude of 3,440 m, it is above the mountain sickness threshold, so most trekking groups pause for a couple of nights in order to acclimatise and enjoy its bazaars. It had a south-facing amphitheatre of stone buildings and crop terraces that had not yet been planted. There were tempting souvenir stalls and bookshops but most of us were quite content to drink tea and enjoy the busy scene. Above us was Khumjung village, the Japanese-built Everest View Hotel and the Syangboche airstrip. It used to take direct flights from Kathmandu but the dangers of staying overnight at the hotel were too much even with piped oxygen on demand. There had been several deaths from cerebral oedema before flights were cancelled.

The successful ascent of 1953, exactly 40 years earlier, had passed this way and surviving members were back for a reunion (figure 9) – Lord Hunt, Sir Edmund Hillary, Tenzing Norgay, George Band, Michael Westmacott and others. We chatted with Chris Bonington, who was sporting the latest and best Berghaus climbing gear.

The experiments were conducted on the top floor of a house overlooking the tents. During the afternoon we obtained good data sets for the blood gases, tympanography and clinical examinations. Even at the relatively modest height of Namche, there was a large spread of oxygen results due to the different medications.

Some members were struggling, though. Poor Patrick had a bad dose of gut rot, John Simmons had a chest infection and Tim seemed exhausted from the physical effort. Only Martin seemed to be genuinely affected by the altitude. Even at Phakding he had developed a bad headache. It had recurred since arriving in Namche Bazaar and he had mild ataxia (incoordination). He would struggle the following day if we climbed another 800 m.

Over supper we argued with Gelzen and Sharu over the logistics of ascending to Pheriche. Although only 14 miles, it was a long day at high altitude for the porters. Could we possibly hire more or maybe yaks? Could the porters start very early to take into account their ascent rates? What was the extra cost for compressing a two-day ascent into one? Eventually, they agreed to our wishes provided they could locate sufficient yaks and extra porters to help our ill members, Tim, Patrick and Martin. Important heavy items such as the blood-gas analyser and a generator would be sent early to ensure they arrived with us. It was early to bed for an early start.

The push to Pheriche

At 5.15 am we heard the cries of the 'tea sahib' and the sound of tent zips. Beyond the tents were our yaks: 29 in total, including new ones brought down from the yak farm at Khumjung. The great beasts were tethered in two lines beyond the tents.

We ate breakfast in the gloom of the cold, cloudy dawn, all well clothed in duvet jackets and thick trousers. Most of us had slept well but not everyone. While Tim felt a little better, Patrick looked and felt awful, suffering from diarrhoea and vomiting overnight. Martin had mountain sickness – a bad headache, facial oedema and lethargy. We broke his drug trial code, which showed he was on placebo. He was given 500 mg of acetazolamide in the hope that it would get him to Pheriche.

By 7.15 am, the tents were down, bags packed, porters loaded and we were on our way to the police station to have our trekking permits stamped. Since Peter Dykes had lost his, there was a protracted discussion about passports and the validity of our group. Yet another fine was paid, and we moved on.

Ascending through the town, I looked back eastward to Parcharmo and the Tashi Lapcha pass (5,755 m), the return route to Kathmandu for some of us. It looked very high. Ahead were clear views of Everest above the Nuptse wall.

Shortly after the start we passed Tim, Patrick and Martin sitting by a wall with their accompanying porters. Patrick looked particularly rough. We were doubtful he would get to Tengboche, never mind Pheriche.

The trail crossed the Dudh Koshi at Phunkhi, where we admired the water-driven prayer wheels, before climbing a steep path through azalea scrub to reach Tengboche monastery (3,867 m) (figure 10). It was being repaired after being partly gutted by fire in 1989. Inside the dark grandeur of the impressive building were innumerable Buddhist artefacts dimly lit by rancid smelling candles. It was made famous by climbers from the early Everest expeditions, who recounted stories of the monks blessing their attempts. Beyond were

Ama Dablan

fabulous views of Ama Dablam.

I felt good. I had started slowly to check that all the equipment was on the move but walked steadily past the yaks, porters and poorly members to catch up with the leading group. I reasoned that I must be on the combination of acetazolamide and progesterone.

We halted at a tea house in Pangboche with Ama Dablam towering over us (fig 11) but the top of Everest was ominously hidden in high clouds that drifted our way. Six milk teas later we were ready for the final push to Pheriche. In spite of the cold air and the hidden sun, it was shorts and trainers for the hard slog in the thinning air. We were each locked into thoughts of who would next get altitude sickness and what they were taking. We had 800 m of ascent for the day, far faster than the recommended rate of 300 m per day. It would surely stretch out the group based on their medications.

Beyond Ama Dablam, with Lhotse and the huge wall of Nuptse in front, the path split. We followed the wider path, assuming it would go to Everest Base Camp. We followed it along the main river valley, only to end up in Dingboche, with a ridge between us and Pheriche. Nearly everyone had followed us. We had a very demanding ascent followed by a steep descent to Pheriche.

In deteriorating weather, Pheriche looked dismal, a few primitive buildings including a couple of cold draughty stone-built tea houses and a tiny hospital (figure 12). We gathered in the bitterly cold Himalayan Guest House as the sweat from the brisk walk chilled us further. Despite rapidly dressing, hot lemon teas and huddling over a meagre wood-fire, we shivered as we waited for our rucksacks to arrive. Accommodation was a freezing dormitory or camping. I settled for a tent to avoid snorers.

At the Himalayan Rescue Association hospital, we met Dr Rebecca Tunstall. She was in her 30s, had initially been a nurse then, after studying medicine, she had trained as a general practitioner. But she didn't like the NHS working conditions so had come to Nepal. Her first posting had been at the high-altitude rescue post in Manang (on the Annapurna circuit) where she had met Jonathan Evans (a member of previous BMRES expeditions) and knew Ginette from her climbing reputation. A fellow resident doctor at the hospital was an Australian who despised the Brits. It was his 20th wedding anniversary and his daughter's 18th birthday. We could not understand why anyone would want to spend six months in such a desolate place. Interestingly, they had a Gamow bag and a small metal compression chamber but oxygen was rarely used as it was too expensive.

As the afternoon turned to evening the slowest members arrived, including Patrick, having made a truly heroic effort. Several had bad headaches, including Ian Chesner and Brian, but Martin had improved on acetazolamide. Helen was very quiet and Graham seemed dazed. Many had blue lips and ears from cyanosis. Peter Dykes, Ron and John Simmons had taken it very slowly and arrived after 6.30 pm, while Sharu and Divia arrived after dark. Porters, yaks and their herders drifted in over many hours and tents were finally pitched, allowing us to lie in our sleeping bags trying to get warm.

In contrast to us, the well-acclimatised cooks and cook boys were in surprisingly good form, easily producing a hot tasty meal which the healthy people ate in the mess tent.

We reflected on a long day amid spectacular mountain scenery. There was no need for an early start since Gorak Shep was only five miles away.

Recovery at Pheriche

That night it froze hard. A gusty wind carrying snow rattled the tents. Getting out for a wee was a grim experience. It was pitch black, bitterly cold and we were surrounded by invisible yaks, their dangerous presence betrayed only by tinkling bells. I had a slight headache but feared for those who were feeling poorly. Dawn exposed the snow-covered valley; a cold, penetrating wind blew and thin clouds whisked past a pale sun. Sure enough, the fast ascent to Pheriche had taken its toll. Mountain sickness had struck.

Pete did a rapid survey of his flock, checking to ensure no one had pulmonary or cerebral oedema before commencing his clinic on the patio of the guesthouse. It was an impressive effort since he felt unwell himself. The four suffering most were Helen, Graham, Seamus and Patrick. It was clear that we could not go higher with so many struggling.

The only person who didn't visit the surgery was Tim. Pete persisted in his enquiries and realised that he needed a home visit for he was still in bed. It was immediately apparent that he was far from well. He had a Lake Louise score of six (above three is considered positive for mountain sickness, with a maximum score of 15) although he had no headache, a cardinal symptom. However, he felt exhausted and was short of breath with tightness in his chest. In medical speak, he had a fast irregular pulse, modest hypotension (100/90) and basal crepitations (lung fluid). Patrick, our cardiologist, performed an electrocardiogram, which showed a very fast abnormal heart pattern (atrial flutter with variable block) – a serious matter. Fortunately, we had the necessary medication – digoxin (0.5 mg), frusemide (40 mg) and aspirin (300 mg). Pete Forster noted in his diary: *"It will take a big effort not to harden my heart against Tim Harvey. Fifteen years ago, Jo noted atrial fibrillation on an Alpine peak with several subsequent episodes of fast arrhythmias and advice to have cardiac investigations. There was no notification of this on his medical health form sent out by Alex. He seems to think that hypoxia- induced tachyarrhythmia is not relevant!"*

Tim lay in a tea house bunk while we monitored his response to treatment. By the afternoon his pulse had slowed and he felt well enough to get up for a huge diuresis. Frusemide was working. However, it was too late to descend. He wanted to remain at Pheriche until we returned from Base Camp, although he accepted the wisdom of descending to Namche Bazaar. Perhaps he could be accompanied by Patrick who was still feeling rough from gut rot. He vowed not to come on another BMRES expedition. We all felt that from time to time.

For others, there were experiments to run. The tympanometer was set up in a treatment room of the Himalayan Rescue Centre; alongside, the blood-gas analyser team coaxed their instrument into producing results, having kept it warm overnight with hot water bottles. After a gallant effort, satisfactory results were produced, revealing that many had very low blood oxygen levels, particularly Tim and Ian Chesner.

During the afternoon, the weather deteriorated with intermittent snow. It was like a Scottish glen in winter. The upper end, towards Everest, was covered in dense clouds with no hint of the huge mountains. A steady trickle of trekkers descended from Base Camp, where conditions were worse, commenting that Pheriche was a haven of spring weather with its green fields and inviting tea houses. Although there was more snow up the valley, they said the trail was well marked and it was only a morning's walk. Sharu was also reassuring, having been to both the south and north sides of Everest with Doug Scott.

By late afternoon Tim was much improved, with a slower heart rate and improved breathing, while others had benefited from acetazolamide. We ended a tough day with a tasty supper rounded out with Cadbury's Bournvita, banana fritters and cake for Seamus's 25th birthday.

I sloped off early to be alone in my tent to contemplate the suffering of my friends and what conditions might be like the following day. Would the ascent to Gorak Shep be difficult? Would we all make it?

Everest and Gorak Shep (5,164 m)

The morning arrived with a bright cloudless sky and a layer of fresh snow covering the grim valley in dazzling beauty. Even Pheriche looked attractive. It was time for Everest.

A quick health check showed that Tim felt stronger and had a steady pulse. Despite protestations, the medical team decided that he should descend. It would be stupid for him to ascend to Gorak Shep and we couldn't leave him alone in Pheriche. Patrick had thought to accompany him but antibiotics for his gut infection and acetazolamide for mountain sickness had worked their magic. Tim would be helped down by a Sherpa, together with a yak and herder to carry his bags. He described his experience in *The Lancet:*

Om Mani Padme Hum

Thyangboche *Monastery (3,867m) Nepal.*
The Sherpas and Tibetan yak drivers encourage
their weary beasts with soft whistles and sweet
whispers, repeating over and over again the sacred
Buddhist incantation "Om Mani Padme Hum".
We are three days out of **Kathmandu** *(1,400*
m), just four days from sea level at **Dhaka** *and*

Om Mani Padme Hum

by the evening we will be at Pheriche (4,267 m). To the north lies the huge face of **Nuptse**
concealing all but the tip of **Everest** *itself. The rate of ascent is highly dangerous – 900*
m a day – but we are a medical expedition studying acute mountain sickness and in true
scientific tradition we need to acquire the disease ourselves in order to know it.

Pheriche *– a grim little hamlet of a dozen or so stone and turf dwellings, ten miles*
from base camp. Two people died here last week of mountain sickness. A bitter cold wind
howls down the valley from the Khumbu glacier bringing flurries of snow. It was here in
1975 that Dr Peter Hackett spent several weeks assessing trekkers' mountain sickness. In
a classic paper he showed those who climbed faster than 300m/day had the highest rate
of mountain sickness (The Lancet 1976; ii:1149-55). The accompanying editorial was
alluringly entitled "See Nuptse and Die".

We do our experiments and huddle into sleeping bags, cold, breathless and exhausted.
The pace has proved savage for animals and men alike. Six porters have failed to arrive and
a mighty yak has dropped dead.

3 am. Awake dyspnoeic and very frightened. Angor animi (feeling of impending
death)? There is a severe weight on my chest – like a dead yak – and a pigeon fluttering
within. Half-asleep, tired and hypoxic, I struggle unsuccessfully with self-diagnosis. The
next day the other 15 physicians (and three professors) join in the diagnostic debate, giving
at least 30 different options. An ECG resolves the problem; atrial flutter of 160/min with
2:1 a-v block, a touch of angina, and some left ventricular failure. Not real mountain
sickness. Disappointed, the doctors soon lose interest. The expedition leader decides to press
on upwards to further suffering at Kala Pattar (5,643 m) whilst I, with a Sherpa and three
yaks for company, slowly and ignominiously retreat towards Thyangboche.

We reach a ridge. The clouds part and the sun lights up a massive mountain. "Look
sir," calls my Sherpa, excitedly "See – Nuptse!" (figure 13). I turn away, fearful and
tachycardic. "Om Mani Padme Hum," murmurs Nawang Sangay Sherpa to himself with
each footfall. "See Nuptse and die," I respond as I stagger after him.

"Did you have a good holiday?" asks the Medical Director on my return.

After the usual breakfast of porridge, eggs and chapattis, we started leaving at 7 am,
the slow ones first with a few of us hanging back to allow the higher camp to be set up.
It was a flat open valley for over three miles, gently climbing to the tip of the Khumbu
Glacier outflow at Dughla (4,620 m). We ascended onto its moraine slope, slipping on
soft patches of snow and mud that covered hard ice (figure 14).

A tea house at Lobuche (4,930 m) was our next stop, followed by a short walk to the
Pyramid research station. It is owned by an Italian high-altitude research group and

was available for research studies. It shone in the bright sunlight, its shape reflecting the beautiful triangular shape of Pumori (7,161 m) to the north (figure 15). The mountain was named by George Mallory using Sherpa words, *'pumo'* meaning young girl or daughter and *'ri'*, mountain.

A little further on we again met Chris Bonington, the walking Berghaus advertisement. With a cheery greeting, he told us we had three hours to go but only 300 m of ascent. Another trekker was a middle-aged English woman who was keen to tell us about her father who had led the 1953 expedition; she was John Hunt's daughter.

Alongside the Khumbu Glacier moraine lies Gorak Shep (5,164 m), a tiny hamlet with a primitive guest house. It was crammed with trekkers hiding from the chill wind. On offer were potatoes, cheese and popcorn amply supplemented with warm teas. When our mess tent was put up, our cooks welcomed us with more hot tea and biscuits. Most of us were too tired or 'knocked off' to appreciate the spectacular west face of Nuptse hiding Everest and the base of the mighty Khumbu ice fall that rose beyond the stone buildings.

Above Gorak Shep, Kala Patthar offers views of Everest from 5,643 m. In shorts and trainers, I followed Chris, Graham and Jim Evans up the slanting ridge. Everest emerged from behind the face of Nuptse as a rhomboid black slag heap, stark and dramatic (figure 16). Below us, 30–40 tents were huddled among the seracs at Everest Base Camp. We watched as the sun set on Everest, then a freezing wind blew down the Western Cwm. We descended rapidly, desperately trying to warm up, but even with vigorous exercise it was impossible. I found my tent and as quickly as possible, struggling for oxygen, put on thermals, trousers, duvet jacket and Berghaus fleece, only to lie in my sleeping bag shivering.

Most had enjoyed the day's walk but those with mountain sickness at Pheriche had struggled. Helen lay pale and exhausted on a stone wall, lips the colour of her mauve jacket. She was tough. The advice is always to descend with mountain sickness but she had been put on acetazolamide and climbed another 800 m through sheer determination. She was emotional and anxious but rather than descend immediately she wanted to stay overnight. Pete examined her but there were no signs of cerebral or pulmonary oedema so she was put to bed in the relative warmth of her duvet jacket and sleeping bag. But Pete was more worried about the three students than the old lags of BMRES such as Tim who had to take their chances. Seamus lay exhausted in bed and even Neville was struggling. Normally one of the toughest and the last to complain, he had moderate mountain sickness with facial oedema and a severe headache.

Ian Chesner was poorly too. He wrote in his diary: *"Found tent and blew up my lilo – felt like the top of my head would come off. Shivering in my bag with duvet jacket feeling awful. Head better if I kept still. Turned up for supper but only had some onion soup – wasn't certain it would stay down – then back to bed. One of the worst nights I've ever had, cold, shivering and headache seemed to keep me awake most of the night."*

The morning exposed a desolate scene. Fresh snow coated the tents, campsite and peaks, serried ranks of covered rocks ascending upwards testifying to the overnight snowfall. The campsite stirred. No fast movements in the thin air, many individuals walking slowly with blue lips and holding their heads. It was not a day for Easter eggs despite being Easter Sunday. After breakfast, picked at by many because of altitude nausea, it was clear that Pete, Ian, Seamus, Nev and Alex were in need of treatment. A few were surprisingly well, including John Delamere, Chris and Jim, while those who had already been treated, such as Patrick, Graham and Martin, had made good recoveries.

We erected the experimental tent, the sun came up over the peaks and we set to work, starting with the ill ones. With Graham helping, I tested everyone on the bike at 75% maximum heart rate (figure 17). There was a huge variation in exercise ability, presumably due to mountain sickness. Poor Ian Chesner could only manage a pathetic 0.75 kg workload and felt nauseous.

For the poorly ones, it was a miserable day of lethargy and nausea while they were slowly tested. They spent much of their time in their sleeping bags, eating little. Those on placebo were prescribed 500 mg of acetazolamide, which worked over 3–4 hours – dramatically so for Neville.

In the evening I sat with Neville in the stone tea house as local children played beside the peat- and dung-fuelled fire. Water dripped through holes in the roof tiles and ran down the walls to form a dank puddle in the middle of the room. Rotting food contaminated the stone floor. We huddled by the fire, bending low to avoid the smoke-filled ceiling. What a hell-hole to be brought up in.

Descent

With an unexpected suddenness, the research was over. It seemed extraordinary that we had only been on the mountain for five days yet the research was complete. Now we had two weeks for climbing and trekking without the encumbrance of experiments. On most previous expeditions we had all descended together from mountain tops before going our separate ways. This time we were saying our farewells right at the summit of our climb.

We broke the drug trial code contained in an envelope. Five of the six who had become ill were on placebo – a good result. I was on acetazolamide alone although as I had felt so well I had presumed that I had been on both active drugs. Acetazolamide was provided for Steve who was on placebo and Mac who was on progesterone.

Before descending we had to find each person's climbing equipment in several blue barrels. This proved surprisingly difficult. Hypoxic brains made decision making slow and this, combined with the intimidating prospects of climbing high on remote routes, worried the novices. It was a distinctly difficult morning, with the less experienced members wondering if they had taken on too much.

Post-expedition adventures

Group 1: Patrick, John Delamere, Graham, John Simmons, John Milles, Alex, Sharu and Divia.

Their initial plan was to visit Gokyo Lakes via Cho La but fresh snow blocked the pass. Instead, they descended to Phortse, via Pheriche, before turning north into the Dudh Koshi valley. Deep snow impeded their ascent for a day. At Gokyo Lakes, the weather cleared allowing them to traverse west into the Bhote Koshi Valley and back to Namche Bazaar. Although the valley was closed to tourists, Sharu persuaded the army to let them through. It was not open to regular tourists until 2002. Eric Shipton had ascended the valley in 1952 in his failed attempt to climb Cho Oyu (8,153 m).

Group 2: Jim, Seamus, Helen, Ian Chesner, Peter Dykes, Ron, Maggie, Steve and Brian.

Tachi Lapcha pass and Rolwaling Valley. This was considered a soft option compared with group 3's route to Makalu Base Camp but that was far from reality. It is a high, uncompromising pass with dangerous rock falls and heavily crevassed glaciers.

The route started innocently enough going west from Namche Bazaar to the small settlement of Thame (3,800 m), which used to be a trading post with Tibet via the Khumbu La (5,716 m). The path then narrowed and rose up steep moraine slopes avoiding the southern glacier from Tengi Ragi Tau (6,940 m). It snowed a little each afternoon but the clear sunny mornings tempted them upwards. They stayed at the precarious campsite of Tashi Phuk, 30 metres from the top of the Tashi Labtsa pass (5,755 m). It is sheltered from rock fall and avalanches by a slightly overhanging rock wall. Their high camp allowed an attempt on Parcharmo (6,273 m) from its southern side. This is regarded as a mere 'trekking peak' but it is dangerous as Joe Simpson (of *Touching the Void* fame) had discovered. In 1991, he fell from near the top and broke his left ankle, an experience he described in *This Game of Ghosts*.

Six of them attempted the peak, starting at 3.30 am, but bitterly cold winds, lack of experience and poorly equipped Sherpas prevented them reaching its summit. The Nepali tradition of wishing to please their clients, despite the dangers, had raised expectations above reality. There was a rapid retreat from fierce winds to the relative safety of the pass.

There followed a difficult descent onto the Drolambao Glacier, needing several abseils and traversing of big crevasses in a blizzard. Below the last rope pitch, camp was made at 5,500 m, surrounded by huge mountains in a continuing snowstorm. The porters were grossly under-dressed, with rubber boots and thin clothing; few had gloves. They shivered uncontrollably waiting to abseil and huddled together at night to fight the cold. Our chaps had all the correct high-altitude clothing but were still cold at night despite wearing everything and being cocooned in four seasons sleeping bags.

The following two days brightened up, with the sun producing intense snow-reflected glare. At one point, Ian found seven porters prostrate on the ground, their eyes closed in pain from snow blindness. They hadn't been given sunglasses. Fortunately, they rapidly responded to anaesthetic and steroid eye drops.

In the afternoons the weather deteriorated to thunderstorms while the sun's heat led to snow and rock falls, with the occasional sound of large avalanches. Several stone shoots had to be negotiated as crashing sounds were heard high up. Few rocks reached the path but the psychological effect was huge, speeding everyone quickly onward. On one steep snow-slope, two legs were sticking out of the snow vertically with an upturned wicker basket nearby. A porter on a previous expedition had died but the *sirdar* said, "It's ok, he is not one of ours". Peter tried to cover him with snow.

They descended to the Trakarding Glacier and past the frozen Tsho Rolpa Lake (4,534 m) before finally feeling safe. Once past the village of Na, the route became pleasant, with potato fields and rhododendrons finally giving way to alpine forests. They were the first over the pass that year.

Group 3: Nev, Bill, Martin, Pete Forster, Chris, Ian MacLennan, Ian Chesner, Simon and Jo.

Amphu Lapcha Pass to Makalu Base Camp. This option was for the tough guys. As one guide book commented: 'The survival rate among the inexperienced does not make nice reading.'

As our group prepared to leave Gorak Shep, Simon unexpectedly decided to go home. He was in the middle of buying a property near Glasgow called Bog Hall and wanted to return urgently to sign the various papers. Group three was down to eight members.

Nev took charge but as he was still a little knocked off from mountain sickness, organising the climbing equipment took ages. This left time to visit Everest Base Camp, so I set off before lunch accompanied by Chris, Graham, Jim and Mac. Despite the very obvious path, we got lost on the glacier and instead followed the Pumori Base Camp trail. Realising our error, we tried again but it started snowing so we returned to Gorak Shep having failed to reach our goal by a few hundred yards. But we did see the Khumbu ice fall. It looked massive, rearing up into the clouds that covered the upper part of the Western Cwm.

By the time we arrived back in camp everyone else had descended. The threatening weather spurred us on to Pheriche. Below Lobuche we met up with group 1, who had camped for the night before their planned ascent to the Gokyo Lakes via the Cho La. We continued on to Pheriche in further snow flurries. The hamlet looked bleak. What a miserable place. We huddled in the café where we had stayed on the ascent and drank tea. Other members came in over the next couple of hours, covered in snow and very cold.

We discussed the prospects for the next two weeks. Ian Chesner still felt ill with mountain sickness and decided he would take the easier path over the Tashi Lapcha pass with group 2, so we were down to seven. Mountain sickness had put him off ascending too high again. What a difference the drugs had made to those who were taking them.

Next morning the weather was still lousy with low cloud and a thin layer of snow on the tents. The Tashi Lapcha group departed as we waited for the wind to moderate, but eventually it had to be faced. After lunch our intrepid party left the limited delights of our Pheriche tea house into a snowstorm for a four-hour ascent into a bleak wilderness. Past the *mani* stone walls of Dingboche (4,410 m) to Bibre and then the village of Chukhung (4,750 m). It was not steep but the ascent into the wind and snow was enough to keep us miserable. By the time we had reached the desolate village, Pete had had enough. Having suffered from mountain sickness for several days he didn't want to suffer any more. We were down to six.

The snow continued overnight and into the following morning before the sun appeared. After re-checking all the climbing gear and refuelling on a porridge breakfast, we left the last lonely house with its boiled potatoes and Cadbury's drinking chocolate for the southern moraine of the Lhotse Glacier. The trail split before Lake Imja Tsho (5,010 m), going north to Island Peak (named by Eric Shipton) and south to the Amphu Lapchu Glacier with its infamous pass. On route we bumped into two climbers from the 1953 Everest expedition, George Band (who made the first ascent of Kangchenjunga in 1955 with Joe Brown) and Michael Westmacott (past President of the Alpine Club).

They were off to climb Island Peak. We talked about Everest and the impact it had on their lives.

As we climbed onto the Amphu Lapcha Glacier in the midday sun, there were superb views of Baruntse (7,168 m), with its massive glacial summit, Nuptse and Lhotse (figure 19) and, to the south, the Amphu Lapcha pass itself (figure 20). While setting up camp on a nearby moraine, we chatted to a couple of American climbers from Yosemite who were waiting to cross. They were concerned about a group of climbers at the top of the pass. It was difficult to be sure of exactly what was happening because of the distance, but it appeared as though individuals were abseiling 30–40 m and then being belayed to one side. Shortly after, we saw several large objects tumbling 200 m from the top. Not large enough to be bodies, they stopped just before a large crevasse.

Very slowly the first person climbed down the face towards us at the base of the glacier. She was English, from London. She was part of a trekking group that had tried to climb Mera Peak (6,461 m) to the south but had struggled badly in the repeated snow falls. Exhausted and very cold she explained the difficulties of the pass. There was half a metre of fresh snow above a treacherous cornice followed by a tricky ice wall that needed an abseil. One porter was severely ill with acute mountain sickness and unable to walk so he was currently being lowered down. Several bags had become detached from ropes and fallen down the face, as we had seen. They had several guides and many porters but most had little climbing experience and were frightened of descending.

Ang Tsring, our *sirdar*, and two other Sherpas went across the glacier to investigate. As dusk came, we saw their flickering head torches ascend a little way before returning. Other lights flickered higher up as more people tried to descend. Ang Tsring returned in the dark. It was not good news. There were still 30 people at the top of the pass and the porter who had descended was semi-conscious. Some of their team had set up camp a little way above us in order to help the group descend in the morning.

Our cooks fed us hot food and drinks as we huddled up for the night wondering whether we had taken on too much. The recommendation was to climb the pass in the early morning but that hardly seemed possible. We would have to wait until the descending group were all down safely. It was a bitterly cold night with all the porters huddling together under blankets in the mess tent.

At first light they started coming down. We looked up with growing anxiety about their slow progress and the degree of exhaustion they were suffering. Overnight the porter with mountain sickness died.

The sunny morning allowed us to lie on airbeds in the warmth, soaking in stunning views of Lhotse rising massively above Island Peak (6,189 m) (figure 21). Even so, we became more and more agitated. If we were to reach Makalu Base Camp we could ill afford to lose any more time. Clearly, there was no possibility of going over the pass that day. The other issue was equipment. Although their porters had crampons, ice axes and thick high-altitude suits, they were struggling. In contrast, some of ours only wore short rubber boots which could not take crampons and their jackets were thin and hardly windproof. Even if they managed the pass, the glaciers beyond would be difficult as they were in a dangerous condition with unusually large amounts of snow.

All day we lay beside the glacier looking up at the chaos unfolding before us; intermittent shouting, long periods with no movements, then tediously slow descents. It was 4 pm before the last person was down. We discussed various options and all agree it would be impossible to proceed and still be in Kathmandu in time for the plane home. We would have to abandon the route and climb something simpler. Nevertheless, Chris, Mac and Martin wanted a crack at the pass in the morning so we agreed to stay another night. The Sherpas re-erected the tents as we donned all our clothes for another cold evening in the mess tent and an early night.

Next morning, unwilling to wait around watching our chaps climb, Neville, Bill and I put on crampons and marched down the new snow to the valley below with our porters. Turning around we watched Chris, Mac and Martin slowly ascend to the col before stopping under the overhanging cornice.

Seeing no movement for half an hour we continued in beautiful weather past Island Peak and Lhotse to Chhukhung village. Ang Tsring collected a flask full of tea and climbed back to the Amphu Lapcha pass to await the climbers while we lunched on boiled potatoes then continued our walk down in perfect weather to Dingboche and camped in a field.

In late afternoon, the others arrived with tales of their climb. At the top there was a 10 ft ice traverse followed by a 6 ft overhanging cornice. It would have been impossible to get the porters and Sherpas over it – especially in wellies. We were depressed with failure, our dream over. Chris was inconsolable.

Next day was the long walk to Namche Bazaar. Although bitterly disappointed, we relaxed with easy walking in hot sun and ample oxygen (figure 21). At Phunki Tenga, by the water-driven prayer wheels in the Dudh Koshi, we met Peter Hackett breezing up to Base Camp. Looking fit, tanned and younger than when we last met him, we talked of Everest, acetazolamide and our experiments with progesterone. He was planning a month on Mt McKinley to study acetazolamide with brain scanners. He certainly was tough.

That evening we camped in Namche Bazaar with our brains a little clearer, and ruminated on the reasons for our failure. Clearly, the risk to the porters on the pass was too great; with porters and Sherpas, we had somehow accumulated 18 people in our group, many inexperienced. Chris was most upset, laying all the blame on poor organisation by Doug Scott and his team. Behind his back we joked that the progesterone had feminised him. He was starting to make lists and wanted to rush back to Kathmandu for a handbag. Not a joke we would have dared make in front of him, or indeed in the 'Me Too' political climate. Progesterone had also put Patrick on the turn, fancying the male yaks with their beautiful eyelashes.

Gradually a plan emerged. Nev, Bill and Chris decided to walk back to Kathmandu on the traditional route from Everest via Jiri. Mac, Martin and I still wanted to traverse to the east. Since the upper route had proved impossible, we could take the lower route via Surke, Phedi and Tumlingtar to Hille where a bus would be waiting. It was a shame to waste the opportunity. The route was first recorded by HW 'Bill' Tilman and Charles Houston in 1950 while walking to Everest. Nepal had been banned to foreigners until then, so it was arguably the first Himalayan trek ever undertaken.

For ten days we traversed the foothills of the Himalayas while seeing few western visitors. Nevertheless, it was busy with Nepalese porters as it is the main eastern trade route to Namche Bazaar. They were the strongest and tallest we had met, many carrying over 120 kg for long periods.

We traversed three passes, the highest being Salpa La at 3,349 m, before descending to the Arun river valley and Hille. We stayed in remote *gompas* with chanting nuns and in tiny houses, their bedrooms vacated for their important western visitors, or camped beside rushing streams to drown out the noise of yapping dogs. Ang Tsring and his mates always wanted to stay in the centre of the villages to chat up the girls, while we wanted to sleep in the countryside away from canine infestations.

As we descended to Tumlingtar, we were hit by a huge hailstorm. It came from the north with the noise of an express train. The first sign of it was a black curtain of cloud descending from mountains to the north, like something from a science fiction film. Then it engulfed us. Hailstones two inches across smashed into thatched roofs, trees and vehicles. We fled for cover in a steel-roofed barn and within minutes there was several inches of ice everywhere. Trekkers we sheltered with, said that Shipton La from Makalu was blocked with three feet of snow. We could never have crossed to Makalu Base Camp over the Amphu Lapchu pass.

Our hired bus at Hille had been planned for 20 people not just us three, but it rapidly filled with trekkers turned back at the Shipton La. We allowed them to stay, on the condition that no one smoked. During the long drive overnight to Kathmandu, the bus driver fell asleep, hitting a stationary lorry in the middle of the road. The bus was impounded by police until 9 am and the payment of a 7,000 rupee bond. In the heat of the following day we rode on the bus's top to keep cool, as our crazy driver raced down hills and overtook on blind bends. We were back at the Narayani Hotel in Kathmandu after 12 days away. By a marvellous coincidence, Barbara arrived five minutes later. We had a five-day walk planned near Annapurna.

Group 4. Tim and Simon.

Tim's descent, elegantly recorded in *The Lancet* as Om Mani Padme Hum, took him to Namche Bazaar then Lukla airport. Bad weather had held up flights for Kathmandu for several days, leading to hundreds of agitated trekkers hanging around the village. In marched Simon, desperate to get home to buy Bog Hall. Flashing a gold credit card, he demanded a flight, eventually chartering a small plane. Tim, together with tourists who helped Simon with the costs, flew to Kathmandu where Simon found an early flight to London.

Postscript

The expedition was one of the best. Despite press criticisms of too many trekkers and widely scattered rubbish on the Everest trail, we found it uncrowded, unpolluted and beautiful. The sheer scale of the mountains, the industry and warmth of its people, and its climbing history made it an unforgettable and wonderful trip. The painful ascent rate that decimated the group, changed into warm memories of happy companionship.

The drug trial showed, once again, that acetazolamide was better than placebo. There was little difference between those on acetazolamide, medroxyprogesterone, or both drugs because of the limited numbers in each group. We could not determine which of the drugs was better, or if the combination made any difference.

The tympanic membrane study found no increase in fluid pressure in the brain with mild or moderate symptoms of acute mountain sickness. While increased pressure is present in high-altitude cerebral oedema, it was not a feature of early disease.

References

1. Bradwell AR. A tough trip to Everest. *Queen's Medical Magazine* 1994; Spring: 21–24.
2. Bradwell AR, Wright AD, Imray C, Fletcher R; BMRES. Progesterone in acute mountain sickness. *The 9th International Hypoxia symposium* 1995. Published in: *Hypoxia and the Brain.* Eds. Sutton, Houston and Coates. Queen City Printers Inc.
3. Harvey T. Om Mani Padme Hum. *The Lancet* 1993; 342, 363.
4. Wright AD, Imray CHE, Morrissey MSC, Marchbanks RJ, Bradwell, AR. Intracranial pressure at high altitude and acute mountain sickness. *Clinical Science* 1995; 89, 201–204.
5. Wright AD, Winterborn MH, Forster PJG, Delamere J, Harrison GL, Bradwell AR. Carbonic anhydrase inhibition in the immediate therapy of acute mountain sickness. *Journal of Wilderness Medicine* 1994; 5: 49–55.

(JM) - Photographs by John Milles

Fig 1: left to right Back row: *Brian Johnson, Helen Hoar, Jim Evans, Steve Boyer, John Milles, Ron Haydock, Jo Bradwell, Peter Dykes, Ian MacLennan.*
Middle row: *Graham Mead, Bill Unertl, Ian Chesner, Neville Richardson, Alex Wright, Maggie Beazley*
Front row: *John Delamere, Patrick Cadigan, Tim Harvey, Seamus Mulholland, Martin Cooper, Chris Imray, Mike Winterborn and John Simmons*

Fig 2. *Chris and the High Commission Bentley*

Fig 3. *Chris, Sir Colin and Lady Shirley Imray*

Fig 4. *Lukla airport*

Fig 5. *Modern Sherpa house*

Fig 7. A modest load (JM)

Fig 6. Camp at Phakding (JM)

Fig 8. Camp at Namche Bazaar (JM)

Fig 9. Welcome

Fig 11. Ama Dablam from Pangboche. Pete and Neville.

Fig 10. Tengboche monastery

Fig 12. Pheriche (JM)

Fig 13. See Nuptse and die

Fig 14. *Up to Gorak Shep (JM)*

Fig 15. *The Big One (JM)*

Fig 16. *The Pyramid and Pumori (JM)*

Fig 17. *Bike test at Gorak Shep (JM)*

Fig 18. *Approaching Nuptse and Lhotse*

Fig 19. *Amphu Lapsha Pass*

Fig 20. *Island Peak under Lhotse*

Fig 21. *Mountains, mountains, mountains!*

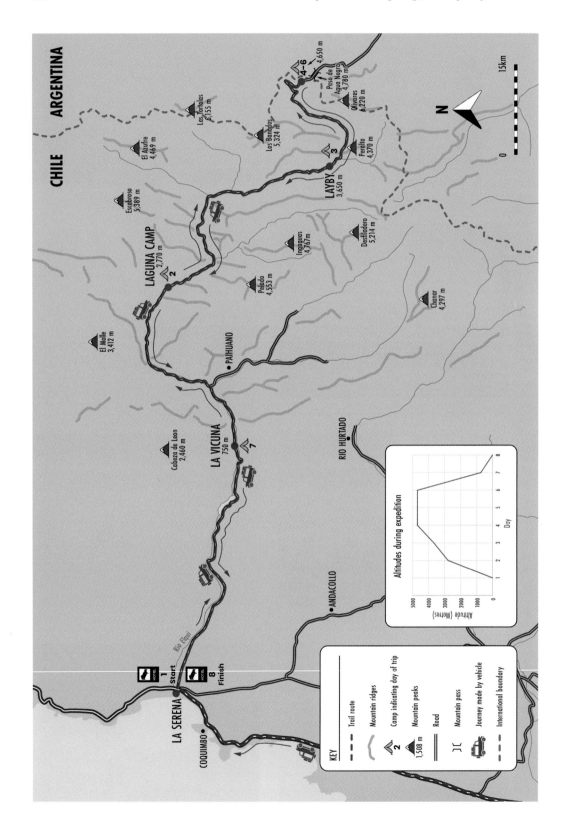

Chapter 8
El Paso de Agua Negro, Chile
– January 1997

El Paso de Agua Negro

Black Water Pass

"The mountains are caHnd I must go."

– John Muir

Summary: The high desert pass of El Paso de Agua Negra, connecting Chile with Argentina, provided easy road access to 4,650 m where we camped beside a small glacier. We re-checked the effect of progesterone on acute mountain sickness and studied oxygen supply to the brain using near-infrared spectroscopy while breathing a variety of gas mixtures.

Expedition members: Maggie Beazley (Medical officer), Steve Brearey (student), Ian Chesner, Tim Clarke, Dick Clayton, Pete Forster, Dan Hale, Peter Hillenbrand, Helen Hoar, Chris Imray, Brian Johnson, Barry Joseph-Lester, Andrew MacLennan, Ian MacLennan, John Milles, Damian Mole (student), Jon Morgan, John Simmons, Sarah Walsh, Alex Wright (leader) (figure 1).

It may seem from previous chapters that our yearning to suffer on mountains is ridiculously high, even approaching that of serious mountaineers, but that is only part of the story. There are other factors driving our desire for pain-free expeditions, such as being with mates and the pleasure of travel to new countries. However, much of the drive for our repeated episodes of suffering is medical science. Not necessarily from an altruistic perspective but from an interest in unsolved medical problems. The same intellectual challenge that drives children to explore their emerging world compels us to understand the mysteries of high-altitude diseases.

Understanding of acute mountain sickness had massively increased since our first expedition 20 years earlier. Dozens of articles described all its features, from mild headaches and nausea to post-mortem findings in those who died from high-altitude pulmonary or cerebral oedema. We liked to think that our group had made some modest contributions, captured in articles in The Lancet and other august journals, but there was more to discover. In particular, two key aspects remained a challenge − identifying those who might be susceptible to mountain sickness and improving medication.

Susceptibility to mountain sickness is partly genetically based and partly due to acclimatisation rates. 'Going too high, too fast' is a major provocative factor and certainly what we practise when we want to demonstrate drug effects − such as on Everest. Yet there is a huge spread of individual responses, particularly in the effects of altitude on the brain.

Chris Imray is a vascular surgeon who, when operating on carotid arteries, uses a gadget called a niroscope to monitor the effect of clamping blood vessels on brain oxygenation. The technique involves shining near-infrared light through the skull and measuring the reflected light. Its wavelength can be used to assess the amounts of oxygenated haemoglobin in the brain and hence the oxygen supply. Since the reflection can be measured continuously, changes in oxygen supply can be monitored second by second.

The second aspect of mountain sickness needing further work was management with drugs. Acetazolamide was effective but the role of progesterone was not resolved by our studies on Everest. We decided to try it again but with a simpler trial design − a direct comparison of progesterone with placebo.

These two studies were our focus. On a previous trip to the Andes (chapter 6; Aconcagua), we had struggled to carry out experiments while climbing. This could be avoided by driving to a high-altitude hut. But where to? We had been impressed with the infrastructure in Chile when we visited Patagonia in 1990. It was sophisticated, westernised and safe but there are no high huts. However, there is an Andean road pass at 4,780 m connecting Chile with Argentina − El Paso de Agua Negro, the Black Water Pass. It is 300 miles north of Santiago and connects La Serena on the Pacific coast to the town of San José de Jáchal in Argentina. The road is made of gravel and sand, but it is well maintained to cope with lorries from the numerous mines and it is open in summer. Hot dry days in the high Atacama Desert should make it easier to perform our experiments. We could readily ascend from sea level to our study altitude in three days. Afterwards, individuals could have a mountaineering holiday or do whatever they wanted. Black Water Pass it was.

We approached the company Karakoram Experience to make the necessary travel arrangements and they, in turn, suggested we use a local agent, ACE Travel, for all our ground requirements in Chile.

Starting a month before departure, we performed baseline measurements on cerebral oxygenation using the niroscope. Medroxyprogesterone (30 mg per day) was purchased from a local chemist, while placebo tablets were made using lactose. Our 20 members were then randomised to placebo or active drug. With successful applications for funding to the Arthur Thompson Trust for two students (Damian Mole and Steve Brearey) and sponsorship from the Mount Everest Foundation, we were ready.

As the final few days approached in early January, I had to withdraw from the expedition. I had plans to take the family to Grenoble in France for a six-month sabbatical starting a few days after returning from Chile. Details such as where we would stay and schooling for three children had not been finalised. It would have been quite unfair to leave this to Barbara. I handed the reins of leadership to Alex with an assurance that I would find my replacement to maintain study numbers for the progesterone/placebo trial. I phoned an old friend, Barry Joseph-Lester, with the opening line, 'Do you fancy a trip to Chile? Everything is funded, but I do need to know in 24 hours otherwise I must find someone else.'

He phoned back the following morning. He had persuaded his partners in an architecture practice that it was a unique opportunity and too good to miss. The following day I handed him my trial tables together with four injections for his travels – hepatitis A, hepatitis B, typhoid and tetanus.

I was both saddened not to go but six months in the Alps would not be so bad.

From the diaries of Alex Wright, John Simmons and Ian Chesner

Sunday 12 January: departure day from the Medical School. Tim Harvey and Jo were there to see us off. It certainly will be a different trip without them – is this a new era or the beginning of the end of major BMRES expeditions? 'These weighty questions have no answer,' Ian mused.

We milled around the entrance to the Medical School weighing rucksacks and equipment boxes; 460 kg was our free allowance on the plane and an extra 100 kg had been paid for in advance. Alex wrote down the weights from the scales: 660 kg in total. Not low enough. Small heavy items were crammed into hand luggage, big boots donned, extra sweaters worn and weights re-checked. Still 80 kg excess. It would have to be negotiated at the departure desk.

It was a 2-hour drive to London Heathrow and an Aerolíneas Argentina check-in desk, where we met Pete Forster, Dan Hale, Sarah Walsh and Tim Clarke. Underlying worries about the medical equipment and excess weight troubled our excited conversations.

'Have we enough time to negotiate the excess baggage, or just pay up and have done with it?' we mused.

The security staff searched every box as we laboriously explained their contents and answered their questions.

"Why don't the pill bottles in your medicine box have any personal names?"

"Why doesn't the blood-gas analyser have any gases?"

"Why are you taking generators and do they contain petrol?"

We had purchased two 1.5 kW Honda generators which John Simmons had recently tested at his factory in Coventry, leaving a smidgen of petrol in the tanks. Damian and John emptied out a few more drops but it was not good enough for the security staff. We even put a naked flame inside to prove there was no danger. Despite convincing one official, the manager, George, refused our entreaties. "Someone can stay until tomorrow to accompany them as cargo, but they are not allowed on this flight," he insisted.

We could not afford to lose a day by splitting the group. Reluctantly, we took them to his office to collect on our return. The only saving grace was that the excess baggage was now within our weight limit. With minutes to departure, we rushed through security checks and onto the plane. We slumped into our narrow seats only to hear that the departure was delayed. Was that our fault we wondered?

As the packed Jumbo climbed to 39,000 ft for the 13½-hour flight to Buenos Aires, we speculated whether Jo would have got the generators on board – relaxed conversations helped along by tasty Argentine Malbec.

Although it was a long flight, Buenos Aires is only three hours behind London time and it was high summer. A balmy 20°C welcomed us as we descended from the plane to the asphalt. How pleasant after England's cold wet winter! But too hot for the heavy boots, sweaters and duvet jackets that we were wearing to minimise weight.

We transited rapidly through the airport to a Boeing 737 for the 2-hour flight to Santiago. Soon we were looking down on the vast Pampas where we could follow the road we had taken by bus seven years earlier. In a cloudless sky there were spectacular views of the Andes, Aconcagua, and maybe even Puente del Inca.

We arrived at 11.30 am and waited anxiously at the baggage carrousel wondering what might be missing or damaged. But we needn't have worried. Everything arrived. Customs officers showed little interest; our equipment list was stamped and we ambled through to find a smiling Christian from the ACE Travel Agency waiting for us in the arrival hall.

The only airport hitch was the failure of Christian to release our O_2 and CO_2 cylinders from customs even though all the documents had been faxed through the previous week. We hastily wrote a description of them on a BMRES letterhead which produced an equally rapid release note from customs. But the cylinders themselves would not be available until after 4 pm. The officials were having a siesta in another office.

Two buses took us down-town past European-style buildings and through streets with a bustling city atmosphere to the attractive Victorian-style hotel Diego de Almagio (the name of the first Spanish conquistador to reach Chile). Behind the Victorian façade was a modern hotel with a swimming pool.

Leaving John Simmons and Damian to find a 1.5 kW generator, others enjoyed the warmth of the summer sun, a quick dip in the pool and walking the attractive squares of Santiago.

That evening we had a reception at the hotel hosted by Christian and his assistants Louis, Marco and the beautiful Natasha, our French/Chilean cook for the expedition. It started with a pisco sour, Chile's national drink, which contains an aromatic fruit brandy

made from distilled muscatel grapes with added
lemon juice. Sour and strong, there was no rush for
seconds. There followed a slide show of our proposed
route to El Paso de Agua Negro at 4,780 m. It all
seemed well organised and simple. We would drive up
the coast for a day, ascend over three days to the pass,
and spend three days on experiments, leaving two
days for the descent. We would be back in nine days
for post-expedition adventures.

The route was so easy but we reminded each other
that it was the fastest ascent rate we had ever made;

Pisco Sour

sea level to nearly 5,000 m in just three days. All previous expeditions had started with a
few days acclimatising at much higher altitude than Santiago, such as Quito when we
went to Chimborazo or Kathmandu in Nepal. It might be tough.

After the meeting we had a short walk to an Austrian-style restaurant serving beautiful
steaks and Chilean wines. We were all happy.

With mild hangovers, counter-balanced by three hours jet-lag in our favour, we
were up and ready for action by 7.30 am. A huge display of Chilean meats and fruits
welcomed us for breakfast. Shortly after and working in teams, we loaded three minivans
with our equipment and were off by 9 am. It was a 7-hour journey north up the Pan-
American Highway to our first-night stop at La Serena so there was little time to hang
about. Almost immediately Ian Chesner was stopped by the police for going through a
red traffic light. Nervously, he produced the van documents and his driving licence. The
policeman said he would have a judgement in ten days – it all sounded very serious – but
his face broke into a broad smile as we waved us on with only a warning.

We drove north on a tarmacked road through fertile valleys dotted with vineyards
beyond which were clear views of the Andes. As the route approached the coast, we saw
banks of clouds covering the deep-blue Pacific Ocean and wonderful sandy beaches.
Entering the coast town of Los Vilos, described in the guide books as a working man's
holiday resort, we were again stopped by the police, this time for failing to observe the
police patrol signal.

In the town we were directed to a fine restaurant overlooking the bay for lunch where
we ate delicious sea bass and fish stews. As our guides ate their meals at siesta speed,
there was time for a swim among the Pacific breakers rolling in from Australia. Lounging
on a hot beach in the summer sun made the water most enticing but it was surprisingly
cold – and dangerous. Dick Clayton, who was a weak swimmer, was caught in a rip-tide
and nearly drowned. Watching from the beach, Sarah suddenly spotted him bobbing
in deep water and struggling to stay afloat. With Brian's help, they swam out to hold
his head up and guide him back to shallow water coughing and spluttering. He seemed
more embarrassed than grateful for the deliverance.

The afternoon drive was through irrigated fields of tomatoes, onions and potatoes
but the desert climate was always apparent from the prickly pear cactus hedges marking
many field boundaries. After three hours, we reached the port of Coquimbo and shortly

after the seaside resort of La Serena, our stop for the night. A large cathedral marked its importance as the second city to be established in Chile by the Conquistadors in 1554, three years after Santiago. One mile inland we came to our stop for the night, the Hotel Cristobal Inn, a rather exclusive establishment with a fine pool, gardens and views over the sea.

The plan was to have a quick meal before baseline measurements for the experiments. Unfortunately, there was insufficient time to measure everyone so lots were drawn as to whom would be assessed that evening. They could leave in the morning to set up the next camp while the remainder completed their tests. We were provided with a function room on the ground floor where everyone set about their tasks: blood-gas analysis (Ian Chesner and team), generator (John Simmons), cerebral oxygen measurements and CO_2 inhalation with various gas mixtures (Chris with the help of four anaesthetists, Sarah, Tim, Dan and Jon).

As had unfortunately occurred on previous trips, the blood-gas analyser was temperamental and failed after only five measurements. A repeat of the tribulations on Everest. A phone call to the UK would be needed in the morning.

Those not running experiments wandered into the carnival-like atmosphere in front of the cathedral. A meal at a modest-looking restaurant, rather like the front room of a house, provided more than enough for everyone. There was all manner of meats on two enormous platters, beef, pork, chicken, sausage, black pudding, kidneys and plaited small intestine, together with chips and salad followed by more and yet more until everyone was stuffed. All for £10 a head. Damian negotiated a 'doggy bag' but enough was enough.

On returning to the town square at midnight, we found a large crowd being entertained by a band of musicians playing mandolins and guitars. Beside them were a man and woman performing dramatic street theatre that required little Spanish to understand the theme of married life – a sort of Punch and Judy show. We mixed with the happy throng, taking flash photos of the show. Spotting Ian with his camera, the main actor stopped mid-performance and mocked him in front of the crowd of 200 or so. Finding it impossible to refuse requests to dance, Ian entered the ring, the baying onlookers willing him to perform. Damian was dragged in to help translate. Being well-fed and a well-oiled, Ian entered into the spirit of the show with dancing and ribald foolery. It was a thoroughly enjoyable evening.

Over the next three days we drove eastwards to El Paso de Agua Negro – a straightforward journey of no more than 100 miles up highway 40. Easy in theory, perhaps, but in practice we would quickly enter the zone of acute mountain sickness. Novices on the expedition were worried if they would be stricken, while experienced members wondered who would 'tough it out'.

The first group in two minivans left after breakfast while the remainder set to work. A phone call to the technical manager in the UK, David Verghese, sorted out the blood-gas analyser. He suggested one of the printed circuit boards might be loose. Re-adjusting it in its slot brought the instrument to life, allowing a good set of results. Along with other tests, the second group was finished by midday.

The route followed the Rio Elqui valley, which cuts a deep chasm into the colourful volcanic screes spewed out by ancient volcanoes. Bountiful sun, warmth and water are ideal growing conditions for muscatel grapes and its distillate pisco. Scattered among the terraced vineyards were numerous small distilleries, making it the main area producing the drink.

A last fill-up for the minivans at La Vicuna was followed by a long gentle drive up the dusty, dry valley. To our surprise, we had to leave our passports at a border customs office that regulated the movement of people going to Argentina. The two countries were still unable to settle their political differences from lingering annoyance at Chilean support for Britain over the Falkland Islands war.

We gently ascended over another 20 miles along the rubble road to arrive at Laguna camp alongside the river, where the advanced partly had set up all the tents. We were at 2,770 m (figure 2). Not high enough to cause any problems but nevertheless we were a little breathless on exertion.

We hunkered down for the night, stuffed on barbecued pork and beef with cold beans and hot potatoes followed by fresh fruit, liberally washed down with Chilean wine. It was cooked most efficiently and served by Natasha, still wearing the shortest of shorts. Christian and his three assistants were really the most helpful group we had come across on expeditions (figure 3). We were warm, satisfied and in a beautiful mountain environment. That night many slept in the open to admire the dramatically bright Milky Way.

As on the previous day at the hotel, each morning of the ascent involved the same set of tests. With repetition, the teams were getting more efficient and results poured out of the various instruments. Interestingly, the O_2 concentrations appeared to be separating into two groups – those above 58 mmHg and those below. Was this the effect of the progesterone we wondered?

We departed across a wooden river bridge and past a near-empty reservoir. Above us, huge colourful screes of reds, oranges, greens and yellows covered the mountains with distant views to the occasional glacial peak. Despite being barren, dry and dusty, the rocky landscape was stunningly beautiful (figure 4).

The road twisted and turned through the canyon. We saw few cars but passed many lorries full of minerals from numerous high-altitude mines. A couple of hours driving in low gears found us at our camp at 3,650 m on a layby beside a stream. There was time for a scramble up the steep mountains but poor Stephen fell running down scree and cut his arm on the sharp rocks. It was stitched up by the expert hands of Maggie and Peter Hillenbrand.

Now the altitude was starting to show. By the evening, Maggie and Dick had lost their appetite and others had mild headaches. Another 1,000 m of ascent tomorrow would be difficult. Although it was cold, it was another night to sleep in the open watching the Southern Cross. By morning the bags had a coating of frost.

The final day of the ascent started as the sun rose and thawed the frozen ground. Our routine continued with breakfast followed by experiments. The cerebral oxygenation experiments worked well, particularly in the warmth of the arctic tent. The generator hummed perfectly but frustratingly the blood-gas analyser failed completely.

We set off for high camp at 2 pm. The drive was only 35 km up to El Paso de Agua Negro – the border pass. It was a struggle in the thin air for the three loaded minibuses which required pushing on two occasions and worryingly we were running low on petrol. We halted a few hundred metres before the pass while one minibus recced the top (front figure), but it was far too windy. We retraced our route a few hundred metres to below a field of large ice pinnacles (penitentes) at 4,650 m which emerged from rubble covering a small glacier (figure 5). In the completely barren landscape, it could provide all the fresh water we would need for the next three days.

Penitentes

The camp was slowly constructed as we struggled with low oxygen levels. Tents were erected and experiments sorted out for the morning. But there was still time to admire the stark, barren mountains, some topped with glacial snow. John Simmons worked hard to level a surface for the arctic tent. Unfortunately, a trickle of melt water from the glacier increased to a small stream in the intense sun and threatened to flood all the flat area that he had worked so hard to prepare. A minor trench to channel the flow elsewhere ended up as a major civil engineering project as more and more people were recruited to stem the tide of water. Eventually ice axes were bought into play until we were all exhausted. But rescue was at hand. The sun set and the water froze solid. We were spared further effort till the morning.

In the afternoon we assisted an Argentine family whose car would only move a few of yards at a time because of the altitude. It was obvious that the adults were suffering from mountain sickness, having driven directly from sea level. We gave them acetazolamide but both vomited their tables. Despite Maggie and Pete Forster suggesting descent, they insisted on proceeding because the pass was so close. After a couple of hours of tinkering with the engine, John Simmons checked the air filter. Inside were several slices of onion. Apparently, it was a local superstition that it would prevent high-altitude sickness. Once this was removed the engine fired a little better. Pete Forster volunteered to steer their car up to the pass while it was towed by a passing four-wheeled truck.

That evening many were ill. Dick Clayton was the worst but Steve, Chris and Sarah Walsh were all feeling rough with Maggie and Alex being only a little better. Most people were off their food and it was bitterly cold.

As we arose next morning in temperatures well below freezing, it was apparent that the altitude had laid waste to the group. As well as the people suffering on the previous evening, even John Simmons, who was normally pretty robust, had swollen ankles and a puffy face. Poor Dick was the worst – he had a severe headache, puffy face and felt miserable. He would have to be treated, but first we needed to test him: cerebral oxygenations, blood-gas analysis (which was still a challenge – wretched instrument), peripheral oxygen saturations and clinical questionnaires. Only afterwards could we offer him acetazolamide. The whole day was taken up with experiments. Everyone worked hard despite the freezing air and altitude headaches (figure 6).

Dick failed to recover on acetazolamide so he was given 12 mg of dexamethasone intravenously. Within a couple of hours, he was miraculously better and then manic and impossibly talkative. Quite a drug!

Pete Forster at top camp by Barry

A particular worry was our return drive since there was little petrol remaining in the vans. Pete Forster volunteered to descend to the last petrol station that we had stopped at in La Vicuña. With Christian, he loaded the one van that was quarter-full with spare petrol from the generator and gathered together all potential petrol containers. But it was not quite that simple. The engine was too cold to start. John topped up the oil, put boiling water in the radiator and tried to start it by rolling down the hill. As the morning warmed up, it coughed into stuttering life and eventually all cylinders worked. He reversed back to the camp and collected all the cans for the long journey down.

On the second morning, many felt better as we acclimatised. Pete sensibly spent the night in La Vicuña – lucky him – and returned in the morning with plenty of fuel and Chilean Malbec wine. Overnight at lower altitudes had made him feel better, even well enough to bring out the Gamow bag and study ten subjects. Each was tested at an increased pressure equivalent to an altitude reduction of 700 m which produced good peripheral oxygen saturation responses. By 3 pm we had completed our studies.

From then on it was holiday so the talk turned to the coming week. The mountaineering group wanted to tackle a nearby 6,000 m peak. To check out the area, Jon Morgan set off at 2 pm to traverse the long ridge above us (figure 7). He arrived back at 8 pm absolutely exhausted and required oxygen for two hours. And this was our most experienced and fittest mountaineer... Others, such as John Simmons, Ian and Bryan, found climbing equally tough. No one was able to climb much above the camp without being shattered. We were just not acclimatised.

Our final dinner at high camp was followed by a presentation of experimental results and we broke the randomisation code. Initial results suggested there was no difference between progesterone and placebo. Some people, such as Barry, who was on placebo, seemed remarkably unaffected by the altitude. From his pocket, he pulled out his secret – Polo mints. They had kept him well for the past few days. What with onions for cars and Polos for altitude headaches, we would have to reconsider our medical management of acute mountain sickness.

Restlessness, headaches and shortage of breath kept many awake on the final night. We arose early and had breakfast in the bitter cold as the sun rose. But even then, freezing fingers slowed the packing of equipment and tents. Then the minibus engines wouldn't start in the cold. They would have to be pushed downhill. Two started after a few minutes but the third was completely lifeless. With a tow-rope from the leading van, Mac pulled the lifeless vehicle while Ian drove the rear van. It took over an hour in the warming sun and many kilometres of descent before it kicked into life.

Just as all our problems seemed over, we had a puncture. Dan tried his best to undo the wheel nuts but we needed our engineer, John Simmons. He was much stronger and understood the power of leverage. But the nuts were stubborn. He managed to twist them all a little but then the spanner bent. 'What more could you expect from a Hyundai minivan,' he complained. A bigger spanner was found in another vehicle. Within a few seconds, John had removed the nut but it had broken from its bolt. Two more came off in a similar manner. With only three left he tried undoing them the opposite way and guess what – it worked. He finished the job but the van had only three wheel-nuts remaining. Careful driving would be needed down the bumpy road and the 300-mile drive to Santiago.

The customs post delayed us 1½ hours but all passports were retrieved without any problems and by 5.30 pm we were at La Vicuña. With all the breakdowns and equipment falling off roof racks, it had taken seven hours from the freezing pass. Now it was a treat to be among trees and vineyards again. We found a campsite with a swimming pool and enjoyed relaxing in the warmth of the evening with a fine barbeque to match, marvelling at the contrast from the previous three nights.

The only problem overnight was the incessant barking of dogs. It became apparent the next morning that the dogs may have heard thieves since our trainers and swimming trunks, left to dry outside the tents, had vanished. Peter Hillenbrand went to the local police station and found that other campers had missing shoes. A trail of socks led to a gypsy camp nearby which was raided to recover our stolen items.

The expedition was now starting to fragment. Damian and Dan departed on the 10 am bus to the Atacama Desert in the north. The climbers, Ian and Andrew MacLennan, Chris, John Simmons and Jon, arranged to ascend a 6,000 m peak (by agreement with a gold mining company near the pass). Pete Forster had seen enough of the high road and decided to stay in La Vicuña and wait for the climbers to return. Everyone else departed at midday to enjoyed the 60 km ride through the vineyards to La Serena.

The final day was taken up with the long drive to hotel Diego de Almagio in Santiago. A burst tyre somewhere above the gold mine had put paid to the climbers' 6,000 m peak ambitions. As if especially coordinated, all three vans arrived within 10 minutes of each other.

The final evening together was at a restaurant near the hotel and happened to coincide with Pete Forster's birthday. After a marvellous mixed grill/steak/salad, wine and a specially made almond cake with candles, we sang happy birthday. It was quite a contrast to the quiet day alone he had planned in La Vicuña and the days of hardship at high altitude.

Post-expedition exploration

Short and sweet, the expedition was over in ten days. The previous trip to Mt Everest had also taken ten days, but then we were perched at Everest Base Camp with the world at our feet. This time it was a hotel in Santiago at sea level. The group split into three. One group flew south to Punta Arenas and walked in the Torres del Paine National Park, having been intrigued by our heroic walk seven years earlier. They repeated our trip in a very respectable 4½ days (compared with our 3 days). But the weather was unkind to them, with rain most days and visibility generally poor.

The climbers attempted a 6,000 m volcano in the mountain district to the south but failed to reach its summit and then river-rafted. Damian and Dan explored the Atacama Desert with its volcanoes, geysers and remote oases.

Return home

Everyone was back in Santiago by 31 January. There were the final preparations for returning such as gas cylinders to empty and dispatch to the UK by freight. We took the generator to a machine-hire business who paid us 211,000 pesos – just over $500. Natasha and Christian accompanied us to the airport where the baggage was accepted without any fuss. Then it was home via Buenos Aires and London Heathrow. As we flew back over the high Andes, we wondered about Chile, and how the great mountain barrier makes the Chileans see themselves as almost living on an island: the Pacific Ocean to the west and south, the Atacama Desert in the north and the great Andean barrier to the east. A beautiful country and lovely people.

Postscript

The benefit of progesterone on symptoms of mountain sickness was borderline. Those in the treatment group felt only marginally better than those on placebo. Peripheral oxygen saturations were slightly higher but the cerebral regional oxygen saturations were similar. Its relatively weak effect on breathing and the side effects of female hormones meant it would not be a useful mountain sickness therapy. It would never displace acetazolamide.

Publications

1. Imray CHE, Barnett NJ, Walsh S, Clarke T, Morgan J, Hale D, Hoar H, Mole D, Chesner I, Wright AD. Near-infrared spectroscopy in the assessment of cerebral oxygenation at high altitude. Wilderness and Environmental Medicine 1998; 9, 198–203.
2. Wright AD, Beazley MF, Bradwell AR, Chesner IM, Clayton RN, Forster PJG, Hillenbrand P, Imray CHE. Medroxyprogesterone at high altitude. The effects on blood gases, cerebral regional oxygenation and acute mountain sickness. Wilderness and Environmental Medicine 2004; 15: 25–31.

Photographs by John Milles

Fig 1. Back row left to right: *Louis, Peter Hillenbrand, Tim Clarke, Maggie Beazley, Sarah Walsh, Chris Imray, Steve Brearey, Helen Hoare, Jon Morgan, Brian Johnson, Damian Mole, Andrew MacLennan, Pete Forster, Alex Wright, Dick Clayton, Dan Hale, Ian MacLennan, John Simmons, Ian Chesner. Front row: Christian, Natasha, Marco, Barry Joseph-Lester.*

Fig 2. *Evening at Laguna camp. Barry, Dick, Chris, Steve, Helen, Andrew, Damian, Tim and Maggie*

Fig 3. *Natasha, Christian, Louis and Marco*

Fig 4. *Up to top camp*

Fig 5. *Top camp below the penitentes*

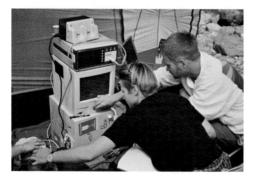

Fig 6. *Sarah and Chris measuring cerebral blood flow*

Fig 7.
Top camp

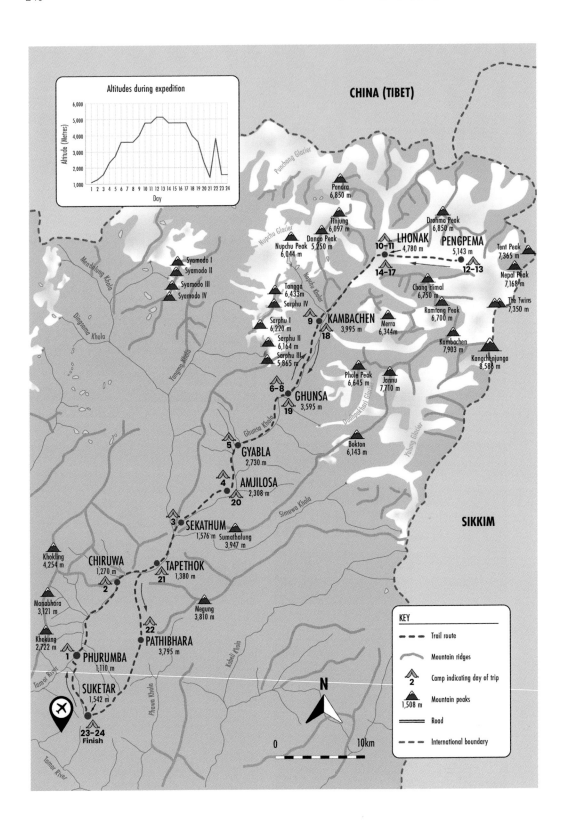

Altitudes during expedition

CHINA (TIBET)

Punchong Glacier

Pandra
6,850 m

Tinjung
6,097 m

Drohma Peak
6,850 m

Nupchu Glacier

Dango Peak 5,250 m
Nupchu Peak
6,044 m

LHONAK
4,780 m
10-11

PENGPEMA
5,143 m

Tent Peak
7,365 m

14-17

12-13

Nepal Peak
7,168 m

Syamodo I
Syamodo II
Syamodo III
Syamodo IV

Chang Himal
6,750 m

Mendelung Khola

Tangga
6,433m
Sarphu IV

Ramtang Peak
6,700 m

The Twins
7,350 m

Dingpang Khola

Sarphu I
6,220 m

9

KAMBACHEN
3,995 m

Merra
6,344m

Kambachen
7,903 m

Kangchenjunga
8,586 m

Yangma Khola

Sarphu II
6,164 m

18

Sarphu III
5,865 m

Phole Peak
6,645 m

Jannu
7,710 m

6-8

GHUNSA
3,595 m

19

Dudhpokhari Glacier

Yalung Glacier

5

GYABLA
2,730 m

Bokton
6,143 m

4

AMJILOSA
2,308 m

20

3

SEKATHUM
1,576 m

Simuwa Khola

Sumathalung
3,947 m

SIKKIM

Khokling
4,254 m

CHIRUWA
1,270 m

TAPETHOK
1,380 m

21

2

Manabhara
3,121 m

Megung
3,810 m

22

Khokung
2,722 m

PATHIBHARA
3,795 m

Kabeli Khola

1

PHURUMBA
1,110 m

N

Tamor River

SUKETAR
1,542 m

Phawa Khola

23-24
Finish

KEY

- - - Trail route

⌒ Mountain ridges

⌂ 2   Camp indicating day of trip

▲ 1,508 m   Mountain peaks

═ Road

- - - International boundary

0   10km

Chapter 9
Kangchenjunga, Nepal – October 1999

Kanchenjunga from Pengpema

Killer storm

That Alpine witchery still onward lures,
Upwards, still upwards, till the fatal list
Grows longer of the early mourned and missed.

Frances Ridley Havergal, 1881

Summary: The technique of near-infrared spectroscopy offered a rich seam of potential studies on tissue oxygenation at altitude. This became the scientific focus of the next trip – but where to? We debated the Tasker, Jrhaps the most beautiful mountains in the world. The Himalaya won. After a 10-day trek to eastern Nepal, we set up a high camp looking towards Kanchenjunga the third highest peak in the world. But disaster struck. A huge storm enveloped the region, forcing us to flee for our lives.

Expedition members: Maggie Beazley (medical officer), Jo Bradwell (leader), Colin Chan, Tim Clarke, Jim Evans, Pete Forster, Peter Hillenbrand (deputy medical officer), Helen Hoar, Chris Imray, Brian Johnson, Tom Lupton (medical student), Robert Major (medical student), John Milles, Damian Mole, Lee Romer (PhD student), Belinda Simmons, Dan Simmons, John Simmons (engineer), Sarah Clarke (née Walsh), Alex Wright (deputy leader).

During the night of 18 October 1999, cyclonic winds blowing at 125 mph slammed into the coastline of the East Indian state of Orissa. Tens of thousands of people had been evacuated from coastal areas all the way to West Bengal. Buildings, trees and power lines in the port of Gopalpur were damaged, and road and rail transport brought to a standstill. Many lives were lost. After making landfall, the cyclone weakened before heading in a northerly direction towards the Great Himalaya and Kanchenjunga, where an intrepid group of British doctors and medical scientists were trying to conduct high-altitude studies. We fled for our lives. We were lucky, escaping unscathed. Tragically, on Dhauligiri, 200 miles to the west, an avalanche took the life of our dear friend and BMRES member, Ginette Harrison.

Eighteen months earlier, in the summer of 1998, we were chatting at our monthly meeting about a future expedition; the adventure rat was gnawing again. It was over a year since Chile, a road trip to the desolate Agua Negro – a camp in a dry wilderness. What we really craved was a long trek among some beautiful mountains when we could all get to know each other. Perhaps it was time to go back to the Himalaya? It had been six years since Everest which, although exciting, had seen us only briefly all together as a cohesive team. Once the experiments had been completed by the tenth day, we had separated into small groups to climb or trek. The last time we had stayed together throughout an expedition had been in 1984, at Rupina La – 14 years earlier.

In consultation with Doug Scott and his wife Sharu, we agreed on Kanchenjunga, the third highest peak in the world (8,586 m). The name translates as 'the five treasures of the snow' in the local dialect, referring to its five summits. Doug knew the mountain well since, on 16 May 1979, he had made the third ever ascent of Kanchenjunga and the first without bottled oxygen. He had been accompanied by Peter Boardman and Joe Tasker, who died on the north side of Everest three years later. Our very own Ginette Harrison had become the first woman to reach the summit on 18 May 1998; until then, it had been the only 'eight-thousander' that had not seen a female ascent. Indeed, it seemed to be a very British mountain, for it was first climbed by Joe Brown and George Band in 1955. Like all climbers, they stopped short of the sacred summit as an oath to the *Chogyal* (ancient kings of Sikkim) that the top would remain inviolate.

In our case we planned to stop short of base camp. On the north side of the mountain, across the huge Kanchenjunga Glacier, lies the flat yak pasture of Pengpema at 5,000 m. Doug thought it might be a good place for our research. Because of his personal knowledge of the area, we agreed to use his company, Specialist Trekking Ltd, to arrange our trip.

At 4.30 am, Friday 1 October, we congregated on the front steps of the Medical School waiting for our bus to Heathrow Airport. Our early start would give us 3½ hours at the Gulf Air ticket gate. We hoped that would be long enough for us to hassle our excess baggage onto the flight to Bahrain. But we needn't have worried – it was accepted without any questions. Our only problem was that we were missing our three friends from Norfolk: Pete Forster and the honeymooners Sarah Walsh and Tim Clarke. We thought it was a little enthusiastic for young lovers to join the great unwashed for a 23-day trek, but each to their own.

As we waited with mounting anxiety, an Exodus trek bound for the Himalaya filed past us. To our disbelief, their leader argued vigorously that acute mountain sickness was due only to dehydration. Minutes before the gate closed, our missing three appeared. Why was it so difficult to get 20 doctors in the same place at the same time? We clambered aboard wearing big boots plus thick high-altitude clothes to save weight, and by 10.30 pm we were airborne.

Bahrain had the unusual time difference from London of 5¾ hours, perhaps wishing to distinguish itself from old imperial masters. Nevertheless, we arrived punctually at 1 am, local time. We had booked through to Kathmandu but, because of some administrative cock-up, we were ordered off the plane – apart from Alex and Belinda who for unknown reasons were allowed to stay. In the busy terminal, I desperately tried to validate the tickets for an onward flight. Fortunately, there was one an hour later which was largely empty since most passengers had caught the first flight.

We flew on, happy enough, but after landing in Kathmandu and counting the baggage we discovered that two essential boxes of medical equipment were missing and probably still in Bahrain. Gloomily we went to the hotel. We were met by Captain Tek, head of the Sherpa Cooperative, and our *sirdar* for the expedition, Sherpa Mahesh. They seemed very professional, and reassured us that everything possible was being done to locate our lost luggage. With little more to do, we adjourned to the eighth floor of the hotel for dinner and beers.

Jet lag and a heavy night meant a slow start next morning. Other late risers included Sarah and Tim, who feared being mocked for appearing too early after the first night of their honeymoon. Getting up late meant a tight schedule for the day since we were flying towards Kanchenjunga the next morning. We checked into the more upmarket Narayani Hotel. Maggie, Sarah and Tim retrieved calibration gases for the analysers from customs (with the assistance of £200), and we checked our equipment. It was bad news – some of our delicate equipment had been damaged in transit. Furthermore, although two of our missing boxes had been located in Bahrain, it would take at least two days for them to arrive in Kathmandu. They would then have to be sent onwards by helicopter or up the mountain trail. Despite these problems, we had no choice but to proceed with our trekking schedule since the planes were booked. We organised the luggage into personal items for the plane and the remainder which would travel by bus to our first campsite. That night we went to KC's restaurant to drown our sorrows.

I had a poor night's sleep gnawing on the problems – a leader's tribulations. Had we ordered enough petrol for the generators? Would the generators play up as they had in the past? Would the missing equipment turn up? Would we need to fork out $10,000 to fly it to a high camp by helicopter? Was the monsoon finished? Would the porters be awkward? Suddenly the 4.30 am alarm sounded; we had early morning flights.

I was first up for breakfast, followed by others nursing hangovers and Tim and Sarah, who had unwisely chosen mutton the night before. It was a quick pack-up and onto the bus for Tribhuvan Airport, where we found the usual chaos. The Lonely Planet Guide got it just right:

Fun and Games at Kathmandu's Domestic Airport

Getting hold of a ticket and a confirmed seat is just the start of the game of roulette that is domestic aviation in Nepal. On the day of departure, you will arrive at a domestic terminal in Kathmandu to be greeted by a scene of absolute chaos, as hundreds of trekkers, porters and guides struggle to get mountains of luggage through the disorganised check-in procedures. Somehow, you must negotiate this melee and find the check-in desk for your flight. Often, there is no check-in desk for your flight, until somebody decides to open one at the last minute.

Once you succeed in checking in your luggage (you must stow any sharp objects and place trekking poles inside your hold bag) and pay the departure tax at the bank counter in the terminal, the real fun and games begin. The flight number on your ticket is unlikely to bear any relation to the flight number on your boarding pass. Passengers are assigned to flights in a flurry of activity just before the airport opens. Or maybe they put all the names in a hat and a tame macaque picks one out at random – who knows? The number of flights and the destinations served are permanently in flux as airstrips open and close with the changing weather.

More fun awaits in the departure lounge, which has a shop selling tea and biscuits and not much else. Departure announcements are almost non-existent and the digital flight noticeboard has a permanent syntax error, so you must rely on a combination of luck and diligence to make it onto your plane. The prevailing wisdom is to hover by the departure gate and surge forward whenever an official from your airline comes to the door. It is a rare day when a flight leaves on time, but somehow, amazingly, most passengers make it onto the right aircraft.

Once on board, you will be given a boiled sweet and a bung of cotton wool to jam in your ears to dim the noise of the engines, then it's off into the great blue yonder. With any luck you should reach your destination a little shaken, but certainly stirred by what has to be one of the most surreal, maddening, exhilarating experiences in Nepal.

Hundreds of people milled around inside the terminal, all of whom seemed to be ahead of us in the queue for the few planes available. With 20 minutes to departure, Captain Tek somehow guided us past the noisy throng and through security. Eleven of us crammed onto a Royal Nepalese Airlines twin turboprop, with every passenger carrying huge bags. It was hard to imagine how it could possibly take off with the excess weight, never mind land without the undercarriage collapsing. The airline had a very poor safety record.

Low clouds threatened, with the nearby mountains ominously hidden. But without ceremony, we noisily accelerated upwards. Suddenly we broke through the cloud cover, providing spectacular views of Manaslu, Everest and Makalu and, in the distance, Kanchenjunga itself. After 50 minutes, we descended to the grassy airstrip at Suketar (1,542 m), where a wobbly landing was followed by spontaneous clapping at our safe deliverance (figure 1). The engine stopped and we disembarked into the magical calm and beauty of the mountains.

Lined up to greet us at the tiny airport's arrivals hut were the senior members of our Nepalese team: Mahesh; head guide Leeda Sherpa; second guide Ang Tsring (who had accompanied us on Everest); chief cook Keepa Sherpa; and Pemba and Lakpanarabu, two of Ang Tsring's sons. We were in good hands. A long table laid out for lunch awaited us in the fresh air while we marvelled at the fabulous distant mountains and the surrounding tropical forests.

It was a relaxed wait for the others, who flew in at 11.30 am. All present and correct – so far so good. Meanwhile, the bus carrying our porters had driven from Kathmandu to Taplejung and would meet us at the road head as we descended to the Tamor Khola, the river that drains the north and west sides of Kanchenjunga. We left the second group to finish their meals while we were led off by Mahesh for our 3-hour march through the paddy field terraces and bamboo thickets of Bunkulung, Gadidanda and other villages. The day's stop was at a small wooden schoolhouse perched on a hillside above Phurumba (figure 2). Thankfully, our ever-attendant Sherpas had erected our tents, for the monsoon was still in evidence. By 4 pm it was pouring.

This was our first research day. We needed to establish baseline data for comparison with results higher up the mountain when we became hypoxic. While some tests were rather tedious, the wobble-board was good fun. Brian, who had an interest in rehabilitation, reasoned that since ataxia (poor gait) was a feature of mountain sickness, a delicate balancing test would be a sensitive indicator of early disability. The experiment involved standing on a flat circular board that was balanced on a sphere resting on a horizontal metal base-plate. As subjects lost their balance, the edges of the board touched the base-plate, completing an electrical circuit. Each contact was recorded over a three-minute period. Naturally, it became highly competitive.

In contrast, the paced auditory serial-addition test (PASAT) of cognitive function was no fun at all. From an audiotape, numbers were continuously read out at progressively faster speeds. Participants listened to two new numbers while having to remember and add together the previous two numbers, with calculations recorded by a colleague. As the tape got faster, it became increasingly difficult.

It rained intermittently through the evening but by morning skies were clearing, providing views across low clouds to the foothills. Below roared the Tamor Khola. After wonderful wake-up calls of 'tea sahib', we dressed leisurely and gradually emerged from our tents into the warm glow of the rising sun. We tucked into a large breakfast laid out for communal dining – porridge, omelettes, chapattis, marmalade on toast and hot chocolate.

Then we were on the trail, in order of age or seniority. The youngsters had yet to understand that every day was a race. At 10 am, after a 2½-hour speed-walk, we stopped for lunch and a two-course meal (hard-core trekking). The older and wiser individuals remained standing in readiness for the afternoon's competition, while the youngsters foolishly sat down, not realising they might be slow of the mark. Why race? Why indeed!

The rest of the walk to Chiruwa (1,270 m) (figure 3) ended with peppermint tea alongside the roaring Tamor Khola, with our camp set up just beyond in the paddy fields. A welcome dip in the river was followed by the local 'pub', where we drank San Miguel beers and over-indulged in *tongba* – a warm millet beer (figures 4 and 5). While the Sherpa of Khumbu are enthusiastic consumers of *rakshi* (fortified rice wine) and *chang* (rice beer), the Limbu tribes of eastern Nepal prefer *tongba*. Normally served in wooden pots, it is prepared using hot water poured over a mash of fermented millet seeds. A long bamboo straw filters out the seeds,

Tongba pots

allowing one to slurp up a warm liquid that is somewhere between beer and wine in alcohol content. Rather tipsy, we staggered back in the pitch black along pot-holed trails, tripping, cursing and praying to be spared a fracture. Dinner was in a big blue tent followed by an early bed – sedated by *tongba*. The monsoon rains continued all night.

The second day was a mere 2½ hours at our high speed. It was another cloudy start, with puffs of mist rising below the deep shrouded valleys covered in tropical vegetation and ubiquitous leeches. At Tapethok, a newly created Kanchenjunga conservation area had a checkpoint where we crossed to the west of the river on a spectacular suspension bridge. I had started last to ensure the camp was properly cleared but then joined the race, finally catching the front runners, Chris and Ang Tsring (figure 6). We re-crossed the river and by 10.30 am had arrived at Sakathum (1,576 m), our camp for the night (figure 7). The good exercise, great friends and mountain air magically relaxed our minds and bodies. 'Dream time' enveloped us till the evening experiments. Revelries followed, as Sherpanis sang and danced to drums in the adjacent filthy shack.

The third morning in the jungle revealed a sodden camp with flood water under the tents. Was there no end to the monsoon? It often finishes in a great storm. As the easterly blowing monsoon is stalled by warmer westerly trade winds, it creates tropical cyclones over the Bay of Bengal that move north to the Himalayas. Could such a weather system hit us?

Our morning route was on a narrow trail that wound along the north bank of the Ghunsa Khola. From there we ascended steeply out of the valley past spectacular waterfalls

to high above the river. Guidebooks had described it as 'the most intimidating' trek in Nepal'. The path was cut into the sides of cliffs, with drops of over 60 m. A careless nudge of a rucksack against overhanging rocks would tip an unwary traveller over the edge. Great care was required.

The vegetation changed from tropical jungle to arable farmland but it was still leech territory, as we frequently discovered. We ascended in clearer skies to the Tibetan-type settlement of Amjilosa (2,308 m), a loosely defined terraced village with several scattered tea houses and campsites (figure 8), as well as yak dung

pancakes drying on sunny rocks (figure 9). Below were views over rhododendron-covered hills down to our previous camp.

It had been a very good trek so far, but at dinner we received bad news about the missing medical equipment. It was still in Kathmandu. Captain Tek had sent a letter by plane to Suketar, which a porter brought to Amjilosa. It said that both boxes had arrived the day after we left, but clearance by customs had stalled without our written permission and knowledge of the contents. Mahesh suggested that the best plan was to send a message to the police station in Ghunsa, two days ahead. They could radio to Kathmandu and authorise Captain Tek to release the equipment. Since it would take six days overland to deliver it to our proposed base camp beyond Lhonak, we realised that helicopter transport to Ghunsa or Lhonak might be necessary. Our missing items included the Propak and capnograph (gas analysers) that were essential for several experiments. Although it was a great relief to know the boxes were in the country, we decided to wait until the morning before making a final and expensive decision on a helicopter.

Over breakfast with the help of Maggie, Chris and Tim, I wrote the following message: *'8th October. To Captain Tek or Chrisna; Badoutumbu, Specialist Trekking and Expeditions. Take two metal boxes out of customs belonging to BMRES (Dr Bradwell and Dr Beazley) as soon* *as possible and send by helicopter to Ghunsa on the 9th or 10th or Lhonak on the 12th or 13th. Please confirm message to Ghunsa police station of the two boxes and to which village? Payment of helicopter guaranteed by BMRES (approx. $10k).'*

Under a light sky and with a heavy heart, I was last to leave camp, accompanied by Alex, Mahesh and the remaining porters. No haste today, I said to myself: enjoy the countryside and relax, there is nothing else that can be done. We dawdled through a huge rhododendron forest that was interspersed with oaks and towering magnolias covered in epiphytes. Rushing side streams, cascading through the dense undergrowth, fed the Ghunsa Khola. We trod cautiously over rickety plank bridges and admired the multiple waterfalls enriched by overnight rains. After a particularly large cascade, the trail began a grinding climb to our night stop at the Sherpa village of Gyabla (2,730 m), located in a beautiful meadow. Ahead, our first snow-capped mountains peeked out from the clouds.

The night was cold with clear skies. I noted in my diary *'the monsoon is over but it normally finishes with a big storm – clearly not this year'*. How wrong I was!

The following day we again trekked alongside the river and through more rhododendron forests to Ghunsa (3,595 m). There are 36 different species of rhododendrons in Nepal, most of them found in the Ghunsa area. This was the largest of the villages we passed through and was somewhat westernised, with cobbled streets, a police station, a small hydroelectric plant and communications with the outside world (figure 10). It was a good place to acclimatise and gave us a chance to wait for the missing equipment. Fragmentary information relayed via the police station suggested that the boxes would arrive by helicopter the following day.

That evening, much to our surprise, Sarah developed mild mountain sickness. This was despite our slow ascent and the fairly modest altitude. She normally acclimatised well, so we were at a loss to know why she was worse on this occasion, unless the atmospheric pressure was exceptionally low. It was fortunate that we had a rest day.

Our first full day at Ghunsa dawned brighter with clear skies, a sure sign that the weather was settling for the winter. Further good news was that the two medical boxes had been flown to Suketar and were now chasing us up the valley via porter relays. Thankfully, there would be no expensive helicopter. Expecting their imminent arrival, we agreed to wait another day, which left time for a good walk.

A trail from the campsite led towards Jannu (7,710 m), a huge westerly outrider of Kanchenjunga. With Chris, Pete and Maggie, I walked alongside the Yamatari Khola, in a beautiful pine forest to the tip of the Yamatari Glacier. Rounding a corner on a lateral moraine, we were greeted by spectacular views of Jannu and its neighbours. The 'throne room of the gods' as it is known (figure 11). The rewards for our rapid ascent and run back were bad headaches.

Jannu

Arriving back in camp, it was all action. The generator was running, experiments were starting on the

Certec hyperbaric bag and the bicycle was assembled. As we worked, our missing equipment appeared on the backs of two porters. Mahesh recounted their travels. After being cleared through customs in Kathmandu, they were flown to Suketar then carried by a relay of porters, with Sherpas escorting them through the night by torchlight. Miracle of miracles, they had arrived. We had finally got an expedition. But we had medical problems. Maggie developed facial oedema, headache and nausea from mountain sickness (figure 12). The extra altitude at Jannu Glacier had affected her. It was a good decision to have a rest day at Ghunsa.

There was more rain on the third night and we awoke to a misty morning with some ominous high cirrus clouds. We were still waiting for those famed clear autumn skies. Thankfully, Maggie and Sarah seemed better and they were determined to proceed to Kambachen, 400 m higher.

After some sort of awful porridge for breakfast, we packed the equipment boxes and checked the porters' loads. We wondered how they might cope at altitude, but as we slowed, they only seemed to get stronger. For example, the 40 kg generator was secured in a panier on some boards and a porter easily carried it up the trail.

Thankfully, the ascent was considerably more pleasant than the morning promised; low cloud with minimal visibility cleared as the sun rose. We climbed above the last of the trees onto alpine pastures, with patches of recent snow, before arriving at the scruffy hamlet of Kambachen, reminiscent of Pheriche on the Everest trek. Used as a summer pasture, it comprised a few stone houses, yak sheds and a 'hotel' with a shop selling the essentials – vodka, brandy and beer.

We hung around in the frigid air waiting for the tents, the weak sun hiding behind high cirrus clouds. Porters arrived in dribs and drabs, some of them suffering from the altitude. Since our trek was one of the first of the season, and they were from the lowlands, they had yet to become acclimatised. We wondered if acetazolamide might make them feel better. As it was helpful for us, surely it would help them. After discussions with Mahesh, Alex and Peter Hillenbrand, we agreed to give a few of them 250 mg and see how they responded.

As evening darkened, John Simmons tried to power the electric lights from the generator. Irritatingly, it wouldn't start. I got some of the blame. I had insisted on bringing a tried and tested generator from the Everest expedition, rather than a new one. It had served us well at Gorak Shep, but not this time. I lay in my tent as it coughed and spluttered as John repeatedly pulled the starting cord. If it was broken, many experiments would be compromised. The tension mounted as John tried his best to make it work. Bloody thing. But all it needed was a good service. After a clean-up – voila! Let there be light – to cheers of approval.

As we chatted over dinner, it seemed that the porters given acetazolamide felt well, but others who had been given nothing had developed symptoms of mountain sickness. More tablets were duly dispensed by Peter Hillenbrand and Robert. After dinner, I went to the Kambachen yak hotel for a beer, only to be met by a stony silence. Some younger members of our group were angry about prescribing acetazolamide to porters. Had we got ethics committee permission, they demanded to know? Had they signed consent forms? Had they understood what was going on? Shouldn't it be placebo-controlled and randomised? An intense debate followed. The protagonists, myself included, felt it would be reasonable to help them avoid mountain sickness, but others accused us of only being interested in ensuring the equipment got up the mountain, not the porters' health.

We had seen a porter die six years earlier descending the Amphu Lapsha pass. I feared a repeat of such a disaster, particularly with 700 m altitude gain the following day. While most older members supported the trial, the youngsters did not, with Jim and Damian being particularly critical. Someone compared me with Dr Mengele, the 'angel of death' in Hitler's concentration camps. Booze-fuelled, perhaps, but a criticism too far. The arguments swung back and forth for an hour until we agreed to proceed. I went to bed very upset. I mulled over the debate much of the night. Was I out of touch with the troops? Was there a pupil/headmaster resentment with me on the wrong side of the ethics?

Next morning, Pete offered reassuring words as we collected clinical histories from the porters. They were certainly well looked after, all warmly dressed in orange cags and over-trousers accompanied by new gloves, socks and hats. With a Sherpa interpreting, we found that all porters on acetazolamide had no mountain sickness and they believed the loads were lighter. But could that really be possible on only 250 mg?

Still feeling bruised, I avoided the youngsters at breakfast, leaving camp in the protective company of Peter Hillenbrand, Pete Forster and John Milles, reassured by their calming words. As we climbed up a mist-shrouded moraine in a slight snowfall, I moved through the group to touch base with Damian. He had been my most vocal critic the previous night but now seemed completely relaxed about the whole affair. Alcohol and hypoxia can be a potent mix.

It remained cold and misty as we ascended up the narrow path to reach Lhonak at 4,780 m. It was another summer yak pasture, even more remote and dilapidated than Kambachen (figure 13). It comprised a few stone sheds with 20 or so trekkers' tents, plus a tea-house crammed with visitors hiding from the poor weather.

Rather than have tea or wait for the tents, Chris, Robert and I decided to check out our next campsite. Doug Scott had suggested looking near Broken Glacier to the north. In low cloud and drizzle, we trudged into a narrow canyon containing an icy stream with snow-covered rocks. After an hour in the freezing gloom negotiating slippery boulders, we turned around. It would be a difficult ascent in dry weather but almost impossible for heavily laden porters. We returned to Lhonak to find our tents erected but covered in snow.

After dinner we went to the tea house – 'Mrs Miggins's', as it became known (after Mrs Miggins Pie and Coffee Shop in *Blackadder*). Pete Forster noted in his diary:

"I spent the evening sitting like a bit player in a Bruegel painting (or perhaps 'The Potato Eaters by Van Gogh'), sipping brandy, on a bench under rafters, festooned with smoked yak cheese, black sausage and animal entrails. Smoke from the open fire filled the filthy pungent room. Mein host was drunk and curled under a blanket on the corner of a bench seemingly to escape the wrath of his wife. Extraordinary scene on a Wednesday evening for a chap from Halvergate, in remote East Anglia. Eventually called to the evening meal – excellent potato and tuna, etc. Chinese brandy at 220 rupees (£2.20) per bottle and good company."

As the night progressed, Sherpas, porters, all our group and other tourists crammed into the small room to eat, chat and make a lot of drunken noise.

Next morning the sky was partially clear, the warm sun melting a sprinkling of snow. After discussing those who had mountain sickness, Pete, Rob, Chris and I set out with Ang Tsring and two Sherpas to try again for a base camp above 5,000 m. Having ruled out the route to Broken Glacier, the yak pastures at Pengpema were our second choice, eight kilometres up the side of Kanchenjunga's northern glacier. Jim had hoped to join us but was suffering from nausea and a headache.

We held a good pace as we marched eastwards above the huge glacier, perhaps a mile across, with the mountain's massive north face gleaming in the sun. To our surprise, Pengpema was a hive of activity, with dozens of people milling around –climbers, Sherpas, porters, trekkers and camera crews plus satellite dishes, telescopes and even TV studios. It was being used as the base camp for a Korean attempt on Kanchenjunga. The excitement of a summit attempt in actual progress was being beamed live to a huge audience in South Korea.

Although interesting, we wouldn't welcome inquisitive reporters enquiring about our experiments, so we decided to move higher. To the east of Pengpema, the route was obstructed by a large rock fall. Ang Tsring explained that beyond it were more pastures and potentially a good base camp. It was quite a struggle climbing up the 100 m of broken boulders but, cresting the ridge, we saw the promised green fields. On closer inspection, the site seemed perfect. It faced south towards the magnificent face of Kanchenjunga, was sheltered from the wind, and a clean stream of melt water ran off the south side of Drohma peak.

Decision time was upon us: ascend to the new campsite or remain at Lhonak where the altitude was a little too low. After dinner we mulled over the issues. We had a few with mountain sickness who would be worse with a further ascent of 350 m; the weather was still unsettled; and our recently arrived medical equipment had yet to be fully tested. Hypoxic brains work slowly, so we delayed our decision until the morning. But there were good reasons to proceed. The expedition had cost over £40,000, so we had to perform our planned tests, and preferably above 5,000 m for reliable results. But it must not be dangerous. Providing that the decision makers, Pete Forster, Chris, Alex and I, were in agreement, we would move upwards.

The morning brought sunshine, high cirrus clouds and welcoming 'bed tea'. But first the ward round. Maggie and Sarah were still poorly; they were up for breakfast but had facial oedema and headaches. Sarah was worse, with photophobia and mild ataxia, but she was in complete denial of her clinical signs, as was Maggie. She doubted our opinion both about Sarah and herself and refused medication or any suggestion that she should not ascend. She was not being rational. Not a good time to have a confused medical officer. With a little persuasion, Sarah agreed to take 500 mg of acetazolamide and we decided to ascend.

I hung about the camp until all the boxes, porters, Sherpas and members were moving upwards. Going last, I could encourage the stragglers and perhaps help the poorly. Peter Hillenbrand (our deputy medical officer) was struggling. Often an early sufferer from mountain sickness, he was going slowly. He was accompanying Maggie, who was still puffy and wobbly and not thinking very clearly. She had given Belinda acetazolamide in the belief that her nausea and colic were signs of mountain sickness rather than gastroenteritis. Oh dear!

After three hours we arrived at our lunch stop. This had been set out near the Koreans at Pengpema, where our rather miserable and cold group sat around a tarpaulin waiting for hot food. The sun was gone and a chill wind blew up the valley. The Korean's final summit attempt was underway, while telescopes searched the mountain's upper slopes for two missing climbers.

After an hour of eating lunch amid darkening skies, we plodded on, over the rock fall with its stiff ascent to our planned campsite near the stream. Numerous porters milled around sorting out our food, equipment and tents.

While waiting for the tents to be erected, we had time to reconsider our ill friends. With a little persuasion, Maggie agreed to take 500 mg of acetazolamide and to let Peter Hillenbrand take over her medical duties. In addition, Lee and Colin were unwell. By the evening they were worse and in need of treatment. After a medical conference with Pete Forster and Brian, they were given intravenous dexamethasone, as was Maggie, together with acetazolamide.

Their poor response to the ascent was unexpected. We could not understand why so many were ill despite the relatively slow ascent profile. Was it the exercise? Could it even be low barometric pressure? While our maps indicated a height of 5,143 m, our barometric watches suggested 5,343 m. If the pressure was really that low, it could mean a storm was on its way!

The medical team met to discuss possible options if people worsened overnight, but they were rather limited. We could use the Certec hyperbaric bag and help them down in the morning, but it was only big enough for one person. The option of taking them over the rock fall at night was dismissed as too risky. Even then, descent to Lhonak might not be sufficient for recovery and Kambachen, 1,100 m lower, was 25 kilometres away.

It was agreed that, provided there were no crises overnight, the patients would be reassessed in the morning, but it was very worrying. We slept as though 'on watch', hearing every cough, groan and unzipping of tent flaps. Thankfully, though, there was no cold scramble to a medical emergency. By morning, those treated felt rather better. A few others, including Jim, Tim, Alex and Robert, were not particularly well, but did not need treatment.

Breakfast was a cold, sombre affair with the camp encased in dense cloud. Even the nearby rock fall was hidden. And it was ominously quiet.

The experiments started. We planned to use the hyperbaric chamber to assess the effect of added oxygen and carbon dioxide saturations. However, the two capnographs (carbon dioxide monitors) were broken. One had a damaged multi-pin plug while the other had a non-functioning cathode-ray tube. These were the instruments that had been stuck in Kathmandu. We had moved heaven and earth to locate them and rush them to Lhonak and we had almost hired a helicopter at cost of $10,000. Now we discovered they didn't work!

We struggled through the day coaxing everyone through the other tests – PASAT, wobble-board and muscle measurements, with exercise tests planned for the following morning. At least we had four more days to complete the studies – or so we thought.

At dinner the cooks presented an incredible wedding cake to Sarah and Tim plus two bottles of brandy (figure 14). What a great way to spend a honeymoon: cold, unkempt and suffering from mountain sickness. Nevertheless, we toasted the happy couple and to 'sunshine tomorrow'. As we shivered our way back to the tents, with everyone set for the next day's experiments, it started snowing. It was now well into autumn, when clear days and cold nights were expected, but certainly not snow.

Towards midnight, I looked out to see a couple of inches of snow on the tents. An hour later, I awoke with a start to loud banging and was briefly scared of an avalanche, only to hear a friendly voice. The Sherpas were banging the flysheets to remove snow, fearful that the tents might collapse. An avalanche rumbled in the distance, followed by silence, all noises deadened by the softly falling snow.

Our camp was potentially in a very dangerous location. Behind us, steep slopes rose 1,700 m to the summit of Drohma peak (6,850 m). Fearful questions rattled through my mind. Could it be avalanche prone? What depth of snow would be unstable? Was the snow deeper higher up and would wind produce an unstable slab of blown snow that could slide off?

The slopes above appeared to be mostly scree and sloping rocks, with little possibility that fresh snow would bind to underlying surfaces. Our tents were directly under the huge slope, while the Sherpas were camped 100 m further away at the edge of the glacier. We had camped by the stream for convenience, but they had camped on the moraine's edge for safety.

Killer storm. Day 1: Descent

I slept fitfully, listening to the intermittent banging on the tents and distant avalanches. They were probably falling from Kangchenjunga several miles away across the glacier. We knew from the Korean climbers that it had been snowing for several days high up. First light and bed tea revealed mist and still more gently falling snow. It was now four inches deep. Would this mean a foot or more on the slopes above us?

Gloomily we congregated in the mess tent to discuss our predicament. To make things worse, Jim was now poorly. He had awoken at 3 am with headache, vomiting and diarrhoea. His tent mate, Pete Forster, offered a Voltarol suppository for pain relief, which allowed him to sleep but he clearly had mountain sickness. In the morning, he was given acetazolamide but promptly vomited. Intravenous dexamethasone followed – the fourth person to receive such treatment, 20% of the group! The expedition was poised on the edge of failure. If we descended, we would be in less danger but we would throw away the chance of any experimental results. But safety had to came first.

Ang Tsring clambered back over the rock fall to see if the Koreans could give us a reliable weather forecast from their satellite phones. It would be a couple of hours before he returned. In his absence, we had breakfast and set up experiments in the Arctic tent, still hoping for the weather to improve.

When he returned, the news was bad. The forecast was for three days of heavy snow. He thought that its depth on the rock fall was already becoming dangerous. We held a crisis meeting with everyone. Most agreed that we should descend to the Korean base camp as soon as possible. A few strong voices argued for staying but the majority view was accepted. We would make an emergency evacuation.

To add to our difficulties, we had a limited number of porters. Many had been sent down because they were not needed while we remained at the top camp. This meant there were too few to carry everything. Our best option was for each fit person to carry their personal gear while Sherpas and porters would carry the tents so we had enough camping equipment for the night.

Within an hour we were ready, only to find that the cooks, encouraged by Damian, had prepared lunch. We ate a little of the food then, in single file, trudged towards the rock fall. Clearing a path through a foot of snow, the Sherpas led as we ascended the col, slipping and sliding over its treacherous rocks (figure 15). Carrying 25 kg at over 5,000 m was very strenuous. As I crested the ridge, I looked back to see Peter Hillenbrand struggling 200 yards behind. Gasping in the thin air, I dumped my bag and waded back down to help him. His bag was even heavier than mine and the effort was exhausting. It took 1½ hours to reach Pengpema, a mere 2 kilometres away. We gathered around a yak hut alongside Korean climbers still waiting for news of their two missing friends.

I had resolved that we should descend further. As leader, it was rare for me to make undemocratic decisions on expeditions but I didn't want to waste valuable daylight on a pointless debate. Dissenting voices would be ignored. As soon as everyone had arrived, I announced the descent must continue to the safely of Lhonak. "The senior members of the group have decided we will go to Lhonak," I stated with authority. "We have ill people and the snow storm is worsening."

In a brief discussion, it was agreed that no one should be alone because of the low visibility but resolve quickly evaporated. Soon I found myself alone. There had been a maze of footpaths over the huge boulder-strewn pastures that led to Lhonak, but all were obliterated by the fresh snow. Footprints were rapidly covered and visibility was at best 100 m. With 6 kilometres to go, it was easy to misjudge the distance and overshoot the few stone yak sheds at Lhonak. I struggled in the silence of the steadily falling snow. With mounting anxiety, I realised I had mistakenly drifted to the south and followed a track down the steep moraine onto the Kanchenjunga glacier. The early efforts of helping others had drained my strength. Realising my error, I struggled back up a steep snow-filled gully to the top edge of the moraine. After a final exhausting scramble, I lay down on the top gasping like a stranded whale. I wondered who else was lost. As dusk fell, I saw the stone shacks of Lhonak and safety. All the team had arrived; I was last.

If it was tough for us, it was even tougher for the porters. They carried loads of up to 60 kg just so that we would have enough tents and food. While we were all in camp by 5 pm, they continued to arrive until 1 am as it snowed continuously. Some did the journey twice. Furthermore, few could afford boots. They normally wore flip-flops but the flat soles slipped on the fresh snow, so they walked in socks to get a better grip (figure 16).

We spent the evening in the gloom and filth of Mrs Miggins's, huddled together for warmth. Our Sherpas supplied a most welcome rice and dhal supper, supplemented with salted boiled potatoes cooked over the wood and yak dung fire. A young urchin scampered between us and the cooking pots, covered in dirt and goodness knows what else (figure 17). What a contrast for that little chap's opportunities at 5,000 m, compared with city life in Britain.

As for our ill ones, the lower altitude was helping. Even Jim felt better, and was back to his usual ebullient self, leaving his earlier illness but a fond memory for Pete. We finished off with our usual bottle of Chinese brandy.

Many of the tents had arrived by 9.30 pm but it was three people to each one since some were still at Pengpema. Fortunately, there was a yak shed that could sleep four (50 rupees each per night – about 30p). I went for the yak shed which I shared with Pete, Maggie and Brian. Our beds were on boards raised above the ground by turf. Walls were lines of rough-hewn rocks, sealed externally with splodges of yak dung, while snowflakes squeezed through a wood and slate roof and drifted onto our faces. A low stone wall partitioned our quarters from a family of four. They cooked on an open dung fire that rapidly filled the upper half of the room with acrid smoke until it escaped from the half-open door. This let in a cold lower layer of air that mercifully was breathable. All night long, the wooden door creaked on its rusty hinges as fresh snow whirled around our bivouacs.

Day 2: Disquiet

We had escaped from the dangers higher up but into what? I lay in the dark listening to the avalanches, fearing we might be in their path. High cliffs to the north might offer some protection but what was above them? I listened to the deep breathing of the others, Maggie's more rapid than others, as well as the creaking of the roof from the heavy snow and the family sounds next door.

Were those with mountain sickness going to recover with this small reduction in altitude? Would more be sick? Had it been right to come down from our high camp? Would we obtain any scientific results? Decision making was easy at sea level but at 5,000 m it was a different ball game. Was I making errors of judgment? Was it me who had mountain sickness that was distorting rational thinking? Like all of us, my brain was low on oxygen. Others had disagreed over giving acetazolamide to the porters and about the decision to descend. Was I the right person to be in charge? I had not had to make life-or-death decisions on any previous expedition.

Such thoughts churned through my hypoxic mind all night. The morning brought no relief. It was another cold, sunless day with endless snow. I sat much of the day in the yak shed watching Maggie perform clinical examinations in the cold. Some of us were acclimatising while others suffered quietly in their tents.

Through the afternoon the remaining tents and equipment come down from Pengpema, thanks to Sherpas and porters making return trips. A group of Germans and Austrians briefly stopped on their way down, fleeing from the storm. In late afternoon the Arctic tent arrived so we could have dinner together. All day long Sherpas cleared snow off tents and our yak shed to stop them collapsing. After dinner, fortified with Chinese brandy, we packed into Mrs Miggins's to discuss our predicament. Mahesh and Ang Tsring felt that we could probably descend in the morning. Sherpas would clear tracks through the snow while we followed roped together. Chris could lead on one rope, Ang Tsring another – perhaps four ropes of five people in all. But we would have to be beware of avalanches. Several sections were prone to snow and rock falls, and we would need to move as quickly as possible to the safety of protective cliffs. Some of the group had never been in snowstorms in the high mountains, or roped-up. It would be dangerous, but at least it was a plan.

Outside the snow continued to fall. As we went to bed, it was 40 cm deep.

Day 3: Dissent

Overnight the wind freshened, spinning snow in eddies all around us. By dawn it was 60 cm deep, with zero visibility. Tents, huts and yaks were half-covered, with ridge poles bent under the weight of fresh snow. Ang Tsring confirmed our fears that the route down to Kambachen had become too dangerous. Our alcohol-fuelled talk of descent the night before was dashed by reality. After a gloomy breakfast, the exhausting effort of clearing the tents had to be commenced before they collapsed. It was all fit hands to shovels, spades, plates and any useful items. This was no honeymoon.

Sleeping tents, mess tent, yak shed and all paths between them were covered as quickly as they were cleared. The 50-metre trip to the loo tent became an exhausting expedition. We put up the Arctic tent for safety as it was designed for just such an emergency. Inside, the mountain sickness sufferers huddled, frightened about the worsening blizzard. The numbers clearing the snow gradually declined as spirits fell until just a few remained – Pete, Maggie, Chris, me and a few others.

At some point in the morning, when the storm was at its peak, I was summoned to the Arctic tent to sort out 'the problems'. I said I would come when I had finished clearing snow around the remaining tents. This provoked a ridiculous 'strike' by some of the group, who retired to sulk in the Arctic tent. Eventually, I went inside, where a dozen rebels demanded that I account for the mess we were in and explain what I was going to do about it. The yak shed that I was sleeping in, which most people had rejected as being too disgusting, was now elevated to the status of presidential palace and the only safe place to be. As for the tents – "Every time we clear them, the snow covers them again – so what's the point?" was one comment.

I was astonished, lost for words.

Pete came to my rescue and explained with studied patience: "One: tents covered in snow collapse. Two: snow continues to fall. Three: tents need to be cleared. Let's make an analogy: if we were all in a small open boat and water was splashing over the sides in a storm, everyone bails, otherwise the boat sinks and we all drown."

Jo, frothing at the tent protests, offers to resign his leadership (a semi-serious suggestion noted in Pete's diary).

Chris pitched in to support the boat analogy. The petulant protests faded. I offered the rebels the luxury of the yak shed if they wished, or the Arctic tent, but they all declined. (That night, the tent collapsed onto four sleeping porters. Thankfully, no one was hurt.)

The storm continued throughout the day. Even the mighty yaks had to be brought down from their 'summer pastures'. They were mustered through our tented village, taking huge leaps, their youngster struggling behind (figure 18).

Yaks in the snow

In late afternoon, with one minute's notice we were evicted from our presidential palace as the space was needed for some yak calves. I moved in with Pete but the collapsed tent had first to be dug out, then one for Maggie. As night fell, we all congregated in Mrs Miggins's for drinks (figure 19). Pete was on fine form, keeping us in hysterics with his wry observations on Mrs Miggins pie and knocking shop – 'a stygian den of iniquity':

Does Lhonak 'boast' the highest operating whores in the world? High-altitude whores? Three girls were engaged in a brisk trade with porters. Sad embellishments of high heels (essential in deep snow) with inevitable (and appropriate) sunglasses. Where is there to lie down (in private) – or is business conducted in the vertical? One Sherpani presented to Dr Maggie with sore eyes – snow the apparent cause, but likely to be diplococci or chlamydia – 'eyes like a petri dish'. Girls follow the camps down to Kambachen. The golden goose descends as does the service industry!"

We dissolved in mirth despite our precarious predicament.

On the advice of Mahresh, we agreed that even if tomorrow were fine, we would stay. The freshly fallen snow would be too unstable. After final drinks with Peter Hillenbrand and John, it was bedtime. Ang Tsring, half our size, piggy-backed Damian and me to our tents. That night I had the first decent sleep for several days, exhausted from shovelling snow and with fewer worries about illness as we acclimatised.

Day 4: Respite

Overnight, 20 cm of snow fell. Then, finally, it stopped. When going to the loo, outlines of huge peaks were visible against the stars. Roars of distant avalanches resonated around the valley. I felt spindrift on my face as one petered out across the mile-wide glacier.

The morning was wonderfully clear. Sun lit up the sparkling peaks, showing off their winter clothes, while snow layered our camp, tents half-hidden in their deep pits of cleared trenches (figures 20 and 21). The familiar 'tea sahib' call was heard at 7 am, as we emerged to blinding sunlight among the magnificent whiteness. What joy to have come through the storm to such a beautiful day.

Stories circulated about the Korean climbers who had descended from Pengpema. They had abandoned all hope of finding their two friends. Their base camp tents had been crushed and they had no food or drinks. Leaving after midday, it had taken ten desperate hours to descend five kilometres through chest-high snow. They were lucky to have made it down.

Meanwhile we had work to do – a research expedition to resurrect. Chris was imbued with new enthusiasm (figure 22). He turned on the Niroscope and started testing people after giving them 500 mg of acetazolamide. I sat behind Mrs Miggins's in perfect weather measuring urine proteins using the nephelometer (figure 23). There was no chance of performing exercise tests, but results came quickly from Chris's experiment, which showed large increases in cerebral blood flow after acetazolamide.

But what next? What should we do over the remaining days of the expedition? Re-ascent to the high camp was impossible and time was pressing. We had to be back at Suketar for the return flights to Kathmandu in five days. We checked the descent route with Ang Tsring. The Sherpas could start clearing the trail immediately with yaks leading the way. We could probably follow the next day. There would be avalanche danger but if we started early and moved quickly, it should be safe.

Their first attempts failed. Laden porters returned exhausted from wading through waist-high snow. The Sherpas returned in the evening having got only half-way to Kambachen. There was deep snow for several miles, with many avalanche trails across the route.

As we sat in Mrs Miggins's with the Koreans in the evening, they showed us a news clipping:

'Kanchenjunga Kills Two. The South Korean Expedition on Kanchenjunga has the first casualty news for the autumn season of climbing in the Nepalese Himalaya. Mr. Han Do Kyu (35) looking after the transportation of the expedition, and Mr. Hyung Myeong Keun (31), have been swept away by a snow avalanche at Camp II above 6,000 m to death on 14 October 1999. However, their compatriot, Mr. Oh Dong Jin miraculously survived the avalanche. He was flown out to Kathmandu by chopper and is being treated in Nepal's teaching hospital.'

We shared a bottle of Nepalese Bagpiper whisky and prepared for an early exodus.

Descent

We were up early to beautiful clear views, although it was very cold at -20°C. All the gear was quickly packed while Sherpas dug out the tents. Breakfast was in the open, with a hand-out of packed lunches given the pressing need for urgency. Chris exhorted us to make all speed as the avalanche risk in the afternoon would be very high. We left at 8.15 am along the snow gulley cleared by Ang Tsring, his colleagues and yaks. Porters led the way in a 'porter jog' with bent knees and fast shuffles in their flip-flops. Bafflingly, they had no sunglasses despite the intense ultraviolet light. I hung around at the back feeling strangely weak. Was the dose of acetazolamide sapping my strength? Others wondered the same.

With descent and the rising sun, we warmed up, shedding layers of clothing as we went, always conscious of the steep, snow-covered mountains above. We moved as quickly as possible, hiding behind small protecting cliffs, repeatedly looking upwards for early avalanches or bouncing boulders loosened by the midday sun. There was great danger with us all stretched out over a couple of miles.

We were in Kambachen by 1 pm, knackered from our energy-sapping descent through the steep snow. After lunch, I lay in my tent ruminating on our escape from the storm. This was the first trip when safety had overtaken research. We were all alive – thank God. Pete Forster had been particularly helpful in his advice and support. It could have been so much worse.

Below Kambuchen, the route was easy. We followed our ascent route, stopping overnight at Ghunsa, Amjilosa and Tapethok. Every day it was sunny, the path was easy and we were happy. The ill recovered, the monsoon was over and bonhomie returned. At Ghunsa we met with a team of tough-looking Russians who had attempted Jannu, but, like us, they were beaten by the storm. A game of football ended four-all.

But danger was never far away. Jim Evans slipped on a thin coat of ice, performing a very impressive series of summersaults five metres down a rocky embankment to the Ghunsa Khola. An injured toe, bruised back and hurt pride caused him to faint, but with ten doctors in attendance, a correct diagnosis of 'nothing serious' was rapidly made and on we marched. But more hazards were ahead. The path below Amjilosa included a ledge cut into the cliff side that needed great care. Colin, sometimes in a world of his own, slipped on the edge above a 60 m cliff. As he fell, grabbing desperately at the grassy edge, John Simmons caught his hand. He had seen Colin stumble and, with lightning speed, had caught him in the nick of time. Colin was lucky to be alive. After a few stitches to a cut knee from Chris, we marched on. Most mountain accidents occur on descent when climbers are tired or relaxed and danger seems past. We had escaped a killer storm intact. Now was no time for silly falls.

On the third day we passed Sekathum and arrived at Tapethok in the early afternoon to a sunny camp by the river with beers at the local bar. The drive of the expedition was over, and the pressure was finally off. With time to spare, old disagreements resurfaced. There were scores to settle. And so it came to pass. The prefects versus the pupils. The views of junior doctors against consultants. Over drinks, Pete Forster, Peter Hillenbrand and myself sat opposite Damian and Jim, one recently qualified and the other a student. Damian insisted that physicians had no clinical acumen compared with general practitioners or even junior hospital doctors. Jim egged him on. The basis of their argument was that consultants had the benefit of every possible investigation. It was typical of know-it-all young doctors. Completely daft. I went to bed irritated by petty arguments when we all should have been thanking our lucky stars.

Side trip to a Hindu shrine

Because of our early descent, we had a spare day. Mahesh suggested climbing Pathibhara hill (3,795 m) rather than following the Tamor Khola to the airport. We could camp on its summit for a Himalayan sunrise. The suggestion mainly fell on deaf ears but Chris, Pete, Jim and I were ready for some action and we could escape from niggling irritations in the group.

We left the main group after breakfast with Ang Tsring, Keeper, a cook and three porters. We passed well-manicured rice terraces, bamboo woods and subtropical rainforest as we slowly gained altitude. Our 15 kg backpacks were a struggle, despite our relative fitness, and by 1 pm we were tired from the relentless pace. Then Ang Tsring announced we were on the wrong ridge. We had started the ascent before reaching the proper path and were climbing Megung rather than Pathibhara by mistake. Our guides disappeared to find the correct route.

Two hours later they returned to lead us upwards in light drizzle through rhododendron forests, high pastures and finally alpine conifer woods. As darkness fell, we donned head torches and continued to follow our leaders. By 6.30 pm and at 3,200 m, we were completely knackered and slumped on the floor of a cattle shed hiding from the rain. Chris had a cold, Pete and I were exhausted, and Jim alone felt fit. Ever-energetic, Ang Tsring left us to run back down the trail and guide our porters, who had no head torches. As we set up camp, we heard sounds of another encampment nearby. Wandering over in curiosity, we were astonished to see the rest of our group. What on earth?

They explained that they had left later, walked slowly but hadn't got lost. The tortoises had won while the hares were wiped out. We sloped back to our shack with its leaking roof as the cooks prepared our gruel in the filth. It was an early bed and a chastened sleep.

The morning brought perfect weather and fabulous views of Kangchenjunga, Jannu and the great Himalaya chain. Having recovered overnight, we enjoyed a magical walk up through rhododendron forests to the summit of Pathibhara (3,795 m), a Hindu shrine. Pilgrims were everywhere, with sacrificial rituals in full swing – goats having their throats cut, and pigeons and chickens being beheaded in the name of the gods. Blood and body parts littered the ground. Oh religion! We were grateful that we had not camped on top the previous night. However, near the summit we found a glorious place for an early lunch and a mountain panorama (figure 24).

There was a further surprise. On the far side of the hill there was a beautifully constructed broad brick path that led all the way to Suketar. It was in perfect condition, with hundreds of devotees travelling up and down. Ang Tsring explained that Pathibhara was one of the most important Hindu shrines in Nepal, even visited by the royal family.

We started our descent at a leisurely pace to the admonishing tones of Ang Tsring's 'slowly, slowly'. But soon temptation got the better of us. The pace quickened until we were running down like the proverbial bats out of hell. The countryside flashed past unnoticed. A tea house that was supposed to be our night stop was a mere breather before the next downhill sprint. By 4 pm we were at Suketar airport, still a day ahead of schedule.

Happy to be 'off trek', happy to be safe, and happy from the exercise, friends, Sherpas and porters dived into San Miguel beers at the airport 'hotel'. We sat outside in the setting sun delighting in any old arguments about religion, marriage, statistics and scientific methods.

We camped in the village square to the annoying sounds of barking dogs and porters partying till 1 am. Welcome back to civilisation! But all was not well. Dawa Dorje, Mahesh's brother, had been killed in an avalanche on Dhauligiri. We offered our condolences but that was the terrible risk they took.

On our spare day, many of us walked to the town of Taplejung (700 m below) to confirm our flights to Kathmandu. We had 14 for the following morning and six for the day after – dangerously close to our return flight departure, one day later. The town itself was of little interest, even though it was the regional administrative centre with 25,000 people. There were dozens of typical Nepalese shops that sold everything, mostly junk. But there were a few restaurants with tasty fried *momos* (Nepalese dumplings) and, in the street, a single telephone box. We took it in turns to phone home for the first time in 3½ weeks.

Back at Suketar airport we drew lots for the six places on the second flight, with Alex insisting I went on the first flight to smooth out any remaining issues in Kathmandu. With dinner over, it was then my job as leader to personally thank 31 porters, six kitchen staff and six Sherpas, paying out generous tips with lots of *dhanyabaads* ('thank you' in Nepali). They seemed happy but Damian argued about the amounts – he wouldn't give up.

We were up with the dawn for final packing of rucksacks and medical boxes. In clear skies, we saw our plane coming over the foothills, land and come to rest. Happy tourists disembarked, just like we had three long weeks ago. Some were heading to Pengpema, others had bikes, using the airlift to gain height for a long descent to the plains.

Our flight took off to cheers from us and waves from the six left behind. The big mountains receded as we headed south for our first stop at Biratnagar, where we had a four-hour stopover in the tiny but busy airport. On the floor were scattered local newspapers announcing the death of two climbers on Dhaulagiri – not just Dawa Dorje, Mahesh's brother, but also our friend Ginette Harrison. They had been swept away in an avalanche following the storm that had trapped us. Her death hurt us all.

After a four-hour wait, an ancient British Avro took us to Kathmandu where we were bussed to the Narayani Hotel. More papers and news from home mourned Ginette's death. We ate at KC's and held a wake for Ginette. Then to bed for the first time in a proper room for 3½ weeks, although I preferred my sleeping bag.

It was fortunate that we had a spare day. The second flight, with our last six companions, was due in the afternoon but it failed to show up. John Milles phoned us at the hotel to explain there was no onward flight from Biratnagar. They were stuck 300 miles away with a possible flight the following day, meaning they would miss the plane home. They had arrived at Biratnagar airport at 9 am, in time for a connecting flight to Kathmandu at 11 am, but it was progressively delayed until 5 pm then cancelled. Anxious passengers searched for taxis outside the airport but none was prepared to drive them overnight to Kathmandu.

By chance, John Milles, who had a penetrating Eton accent, was overheard by an ex-Gurkha. Thinking John was perhaps an army top brass, he approached him and offered to drive them to Kathmandu; 30 minutes later, a brand-new, long-wheel-base Land Rover appeared and all six piled in.

They drove through the night, at breakneck speed on narrow winding roads, arriving at the Narayani Hotel at 7 am, just as we were eating breakfast by the pool. It was a happy reunion until we mentioned Ginette. They too were horrified.

Finally, it was home time, with an uneventful Gulf Air flight to Bahrain and London Heathrow. We arrived with all our personal bags and all medical equipment boxes intact. It was a satisfying end to a very demanding trip.

And what if? What if we had stayed at the top camp with 4–5 feet of snow beneath the steep slopes of Drohma peak? What if it had avalanched? What if several of us had been killed or perhaps some students? We could imagine the headlines:

"Doctors wiped out in Himalaya disaster. 15 senior specialists and five students wiped out in huge avalanche." Or:

"Irresponsible doctors experiment on students who are left to die."

We had a lucky escape.

At the Lake Louise Hypoxia Symposium in April 2001, I presented an obituary on Ginette. She was one of three great British female Himalayan climbers, alongside Julie Tullis (who died on K2 in 1986) and Alison Hargreaves (who died on K2 in 1995). Another obituary was on Stuart Alexander (Alex) Lowe and his climbing friend David Bridges, who died while climbing Shishapangma two weeks before our great storm. Lowe was widely considered one of his generation's finest all-around mountaineers while Bridges was one of the best mountaineering cameramen.

Postscript

Despite the storm and our desperate escape, we managed to collect some useful data on the benefits of carbon dioxide on cerebral blood flow. The benefits of acetazolamide on high-altitude Nepalese porters was shown in a controlled trial a few years later.

[#]Lonely Planet – Trekking in the Nepal Himalaya, p 383, 9th edition 2009, Published by Lonely Planet Publications Pty Ltd, Bradley Mayhew, Joe Blindloss.

Publications

1. Bradwell A, Major R and BMRES. Portable nephelometer for specific protein testing in remote locations. 12th International Hypoxia Symposium. High Altitude Medicine and Biology 2001; 2:103, 99.
2. Hillenbrand P, Pahari AK, Soon Y, Subedi D, Bajracharya R, Gunrung P, Lal BK, Marahatta R, Pradhan S, Rai D, Sharma S and BMRES. Prevention of acute mountain sickness by acetazolamide in Nepali porters: A double-blind controlled trial. Wilderness and Environmental Medicine 2006; 17: 87-93.
3. Imray CHE, Brearey S, Clarke T, Hale D, Morgan J and Walsh S. Cerebral oxygenation at high altitude and the response to carbon dioxide, hyperventilation and oxygen. Clinical Science 2000; 98(2): 159-164.
4. Imray CHE, Clarke T, Forster PJ, Harvey T, Hoar H, Walsh S, Wright AD and BMRES Carbon dioxide contributes to the beneficial effect of pressurization in a portable hyperbaric chamber at high altitude. Clinical Science 2001; 100(2): 151-157.

Fig 1. Suketar airport

Fig 2. Phurumba

Fig 3. Chiruwa

Fig 4. Tamor khola

Fig 5. Tsompa, Robert, Jim, Damian and Tom

Fig 6. Ang Tsring, Chris and Jo

Fig 7. Sakathum

Fig 8. Amjilosa

Fig 9. *Alex with drying yak dung*

Fig 10. *Ghunza*

Fig 11. *Jannu and Phole peak*

Fig 12. *Maggie with facial oedema*

Fig 13. *Lhonak*

Fig 14. *Wedding cake*

Fig 15. *Over the ridge to Lhonak*

Fig 16. *Porter 'boots'*

Fig 17. Child living at 5,000 m

Fig 18. Yaks in the storm

Fig 19. Alex, John Simmons and John Milles

Fig 20. Kanchenjunga and tents after the storm

Fig 21. Sun warms camp and 'president's palace'

Fig 22. Chris experimenting in the yak shed

Fig 23. Jo testing urine behind Mrs Miggins

Fig 24. Pathibara and Kanchenjunga

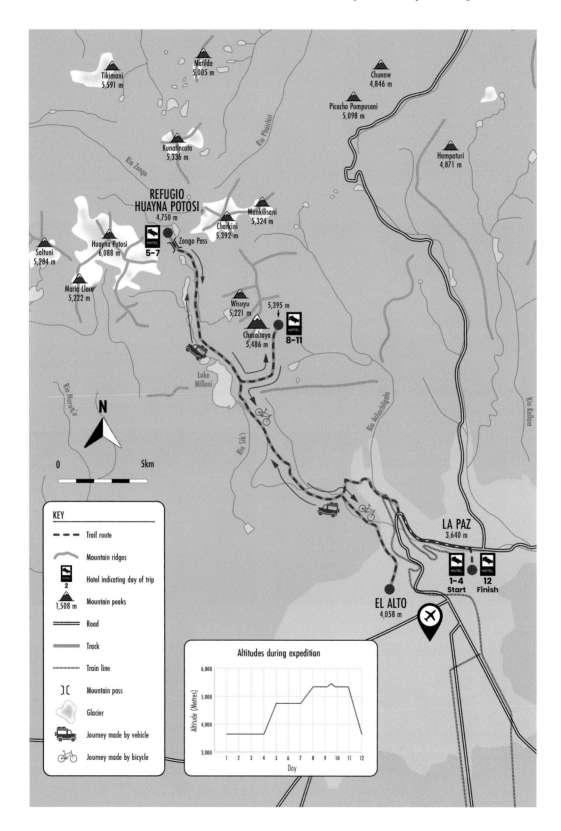

Chapter 10
Chacaltaya, Bolivia – June 2002

Chacaltaya lodge and ski-lift

The Sofa of Death

'It had been absorbed into my subconscious many years before that physical discomfort was a valuable penance.'

> – Joe Tasker on the influence of his religious
> upbringing on his climbing career in: *Savage Arena.*

Summary: For some years we had been interested in the effects of altitude on exercise performance. An association with the British Army allowed us to design and build a sophisticated lightweight exercise bicycle. With five Canadians under the leadership of Joe Fisher, we flew to La Paz in Bolivia and ascended first to Refugio Huayna Potosí (4,750 m) then Refugio Chacaltaya (5,345 m), the highest mountain hut in the world. At each altitude we studied cerebral blood flow during exercise while breathing different gas mixtures and taking the vasoactive drug sildenafil (Viagra). Despite controlled ascent rates, Peter Hillenbrand ended up seriously unwell on the 'sofa of death'.

Expedition members: Maggie Beazley (medical officer), Steve Breary, Jo Bradwell (leader), Colin Chan, Ian Chesner, Tim Clarke, Phil Collins, Peter Forster (medical officer), Steve Harris, Tim Harvey, Peter Hillenbrand, Chris Imray, Brian Johnson, John Milles, Steve Myers, Kyle Pattinson, John Simmons, Alex Wright (deputy leader). Canadian contingent: Joe Fisher, David Preiss, Eitan Prisman, Ron Somogyi, Alex Vesley (figure 1).

We first met Joe Fisher (Professor of Anaesthesia at Toronto General Hospital) in February 2001, at the Hypoxia Conference in Lake Louise, Canada. He was full of ideas about breathing circuits and oxygen delivery. Using his patented breathing gadget, he claimed he could reduce the oxygen needed when climbing Everest by two-thirds while still maintaining high oxygen levels. It was one of those devices that was brilliant and incomprehensible in equal measure. We were intrigued.

We asked him if we might try it, fearful that other altitude research teams were lined up ahead of us. Perhaps we could make him an offer he couldn't refuse.

"Would you like to come to Bolivia with us next year and experiment with your apparatus?" I cautiously enquired.

"Yes," he immediately replied.

That summer, I received a phone call from Danny, an SAS soldier, seeking research ideas for his imminent expedition to Aconcagua. I can't tell you his full name; it is confidential. I might be eliminated. I agreed to a rendezvous; no blindfolds but no photos either.

We met in the garden of my house in Birmingham one sunny afternoon. He was of medium height, super-fit and spoke at high speed. His plan was to climb the highest peaks of each continent, starting with Aconcagua, as an army team-building project. However, he needed research proposals to satisfy his boss, a general. Crucially, he had persuaded the head of QinetiQ to support the expedition financially, including funding for research. At that time, they were a quasi-governmental organisation that provided scientific and engineering facilities for the armed forces.

Reluctant to mention Joe Fisher's gadget, since it was not mine to offer, I asked him if he might produce a special exercise bike for altitude studies. On the Everest trip (chapter 7), we had used the bike made by Griff Pugh for the Silver Hut studies 40 years earlier and, while technically advanced for its time, it was heavy and inaccurate. Static exercise bikes found in gymnasiums, although functionally adequate, were impossibly heavy for mountain expeditions. Could QinetiQ possibly design and build a lightweight one?

Danny thought this would be no problem. Within a few days we were invited to QinetiQ's headquarters near Farnborough, where we were introduced to Steve Harris, a keen cyclist who was in charge of an engineering section.

He suggested using a novel crankshaft that directly measured power generated at the pedals. This produced second-by-second recordings when connected to a computer and could be linked to simultaneous recordings of many physiological variables such as heart rate and VO_2max (oxygen uptake per kilo at maximum exercise).

Since Danny planned to depart in six weeks, Steve immediately set about constructing the bike. For us it was a dream come true – a bike that could replace the ancient Pugh bike and all paid for by the Army (over £20,000). We visited Steve a month later as the bike was nearing completion. Indeed, it was a masterpiece of engineering. His ideas of minimising the bicycle's weight were particularly ingenious. From the pedals, three gears in succession accelerated a 2 kg flywheel to 3,500 rpm when the pedal speed was 60 rpm. This provided the same feeling of inertia as a conventional bicycle. Other features were an all-aluminium frame, central hinges to allow folding and shoulder straps so it could be carried like a rucksack. In addition, it had a horizontal cycling position, which allowed the head to be held firmly in place while measurements of brain oxygenation were taken. We christened it the Alticycle (figure 2).

The project we proposed to Danny was to take acetazolamide and test its effects on exercise at Nido De Condores (5,486 m), 1,500 m from Aconcagua's summit (expedition 5). From there, and after a few days of acclimatisation, they could try for the top.

In mid-September, eight super-fit army types flew off to Santiago with the Alticycle to climb the first of their seven summits. The weeks ticked by but we heard nothing. Had they succeeded? What were the results of the experiments? Eventually, through Steve Harris we located Danny. Very embarrassed, he explained that the expedition had been a disaster. They had measured exercise performance at sea level without any difficulties but at altitude he had developed severe mountain sickness and had to be evacuated along with the rest of his team. Data, saved to disks, had been lost in the panic of the retreat. There were no results.

Their failure was our opportunity. We would use the Alticycle to study exercise at altitude on our forthcoming trip to Bolivia. This could be added to the proposed studies on Joe Fisher's breathing apparatus. Joe had visited us in Birmingham a few months before our expedition. Over a weekend in the physiology laboratories at the Medical School, we obtained baseline measurements of VO_2max on the Alticycle. In the evenings, Joe explained the physiology of breathing and how his gadget would revolutionise climbing of Everest. Brilliant, we all agreed. It was only a question of seeing if it worked in practice, since it was not quite ready for use. What impressed us more, however, was his ability to do ten one-armed press-ups. That, we *could* understand.

The expedition was arranged for June, Bolivian mid-winter, when there are clear skies with warm sunny days and cold nights. The plan was to first acclimatise at La Paz, move to a higher altitude for further acclimatisation before staying at Chacaltaya (5,345 m), the highest mountain hut in the world. It had been used frequently by research groups and had a good reputation for hospitality. It had never accommodated 20 people but its caretakers promised they would enlarge the attic room for our sole use. A promise to be believed when we saw it.

On the morning of 15 June, we left London Heathrow bound for Miami. A six-hour lay-over found us eating out on a glorious warm evening at the downtown Bayside Mall complex. Pete Forster kept us amused as we watched a deep red sunset. We were joined by Tim Clarke, who was working in New Zealand for a few months. We left Miami at 11.30 pm on the overnight flight to La Paz. Its international airport at El Alto (4,058 m) is the highest in the world.

Coming into land early next morning, we gazed spellbound at the beauty of La Paz huddled along a great gash in the Altiplano. Above it, triple-peaked Nevado (Mt) Illimani (6,438 m) was dramatically illuminated by the rising sun. On landing, the cabin de-pressurised to the high altitude, leaving us slightly dizzy from hypoxia as we walked into the freezing airport. All equipment boxes and personal rucksacks arrived without problems. Outside, our guide Roberto was waiting with lorry and bus. The pot-holed road from the airport tipped over the canyon rim and wound steeply downwards among decrepit cars and dilapidated houses to the El Dorado Hotel in the city centre at 3,513 m (figure 3). The modern high-rise building provided for all our needs, including a tenth-floor penthouse suite for experiments. Medical boxes were opened, equipment checked and plugged in.

Everything worked perfectly, benefiting from a stable electricity supply that was rare to find in Nepal.

Since it was Sunday, and a good Catholic Sunday at that, there was a chance to see Bolivians dressed in all their finery. Married women in colourful traditional dress with bowler hats sold food in Sunday markets and paraded in front of the Basilica of San Francisco and the Parliament buildings. Everywhere seemed sunny and benign, although not always as benign as first appearances suggested. Alex was almost robbed at a cashpoint. One of the oldest tricks around but tried, tested and known to be successful in La Paz. A man sprayed the back of his rucksack with water to distract him while trying to take his wallet. Fortunately, 63 years of life makes you canny; Alex rumbled the scam and off they ran.

*Bolivian woman in
her Sunday best*

We watched a beautiful sunset over the glaciated Nevado Huayna Potosí, the peak above our first mountain refuge. Next to it was the peak of Chacaltaya, our expedition target. It seemed close enough to touch in the clear mountain air; travel distances for this expedition would be the smallest ever.

The Canadians arrived the following morning, one day late. Being Orthodox Jews, they had refused to travel on the Sabbath, so arrived on Monday. Not just Joe and one student as he had promised, but four of them, none of whom we had met before. They all seemed very pleasant but it wasn't what we had agreed. They might fit in well but we were concerned that they might form a separate research clique. Nevertheless, Joe was paying and apologised for any difficulties. We could only wait and see. In the meantime we had work to do.

Our main experiments were centred on the Alticycle and cerebral oxygenation. Ever since the first description of mountain sickness in 1913 by Ravenhill, there had been suspicions that exercise was a provocative factor, but it had not been demonstrated experimentally. We suspected that at maximum exercise, oxygen concentrations in the brain would be lower. This could lead to worsening of headaches, the classic symptom of mountain sickness. Our plan was to exercise hard while measuring cerebral oxygenation by infrared spectroscopy with Chris's Niroscope (figure 4).

Viagra: 100 mg

We were also testing Viagra (sildenafil). Its dilation effects on blood vessels in one particular organ are well known, but it can also increase blood flow and oxygenation to the brain. We set to with our research: exercise tests, blood gasses, clinical assessments, urine collections and wobble-board. Alongside the Canadians (figure 5), we were fully occupied for the rest of the day. We emerged from the experimental room in the early evening tired and hungry. Roberto had booked dinner at a restaurant that was not entirely to our liking, as described by Pete:

'A barn of a restaurant – freezing cold, table arranged like a meeting of the board. Toxic and truly foul food; spicy, chicken bits, lamb, beef, etc. Afterwards, our Canadians had a conference on the way back to the hotel and elected to be 'cipro'd' (take the antibiotic ciprofloxacin to prevent gut rot) much to my amusement. I had no reason to be smug; barely managed to get back to hotel bog before a faecal torrent erupted. "Codeine tonight, my boy".'

Over the next two days we continued with our experiments. The Viagra test provoked as much amusement as might be expected. It was pretty obvious who was on the drug within 30 minutes and its effect lasted an hour or more. The victim had to lie on a bed and have their cerebral blood flow checked with the Niroscope, plus other measures such as blood pressure and heart rate. You guessed right; they had red, flushed faces from the increased blood flow, but no other discernible effects.

Refugio Huayna Potosí

On 20 June, four days after our arrival in La Paz, we were well acclimatised, baseline tests had been completed and we were ready for our next ascent. We would be 1,100 m higher, which was certain to provoke some mountain sickness.

With bus and lorry loaded, we wound up the busy roads of La Paz to El Alto then north onto the open Altiplano. Beautifully clear air and a bright sun showed the Bolivian Alps in their full glory, with Nevado Illimani towering in the east. Behind us, La Paz shone in perfect detail.

As we ascended, stubby brush gave way to alpine grasses, groups of llamas lifting their heads curiously as we passed (figure 6). Bright orange lakes, contaminated with metals leached from ancient mines, glowed among the rolling hills (figure 7). The road passed the turn to our top hut at Chacaltaya and rose to Paso Zongo on the east side of Nevado Huayna Potosí at 6,088 m (figure 8). The high watershed drained to the Rio Paraná in the south and northwards to the Amazon jungle.

Llama

It took three hours to reach Refugio Huayna Potosí at 4,750 m. Modern, alpine in style, with all necessary facilities, it was a haven in the high Altiplano (figure 9). Dormitories were downstairs while upstairs was a dining room, a room set aside for experiments and a lounge with a large sofa. The hotel was owned and run by Dr Hugo Berrios. He had welcomed innumerable climbers and high-altitude research groups over the years and was well known to the American 'hypoxia mafia' of Bob Roach, Tom Hornbein and Charlie Houston. The only other guest was an American climber aiming to accurately measure the height of Huayna Potosí.

After lunch, some of us walked around the nearby reservoir (figure 9) while others climbed on Huayna Potosí. There were no thoughts of reaching the summit, but they reached the tip of a glacier then ran back to the refuge. Not me; I was incapacitated with a gut infection and lay in bed.

The ever-energetic Joe Fisher and his team set up their rebreathing circuit and started testing each other while hooked up to Chris's Niroscope, reworking their protocols for the umpteenth time. By evening we were all into the research, everyone either testing or being tested (figure 10).

As the evening wore on, the 1,100 m of ascent from La Paz started to take its toll. Steve Myers developed a bad headache. As he had a central role running the VO_2max tests on the Alticycle, we were particularly sympathetic and he was prescribed acetazolamide.

Peter Hillenbrand was also a worry. Because he loved the trips so much, he repeatedly came back despite recurring doses of headaches and nausea. This time was no different. He developed a headache and by the morning was clearly unwell. For most of the day he sat on the lounge sofa nursing his sore head. Next to him languished Alex Vesley and Steve Myers, also ill.

When we returned in the late afternoon from walks, Peter had taken on a blue-grey colour. He was nauseated and weak, with a bad headache. We checked his peripheral oxygen saturations; they were down to 62% – low enough to put him in intensive care in the UK. And, ominously, he was sleepy. Was he suffering from cerebral oedema?

It was time to intervene. A dozen of us stood over his barely moving body like vultures awaiting the death of an animal. Who would be the first to attack – with treatment that is. We could give him oxygen but that wasn't the point. We were a research society and we had novel therapies to try. Was it time for Joe Fisher's special oxygen mask or Pete Forster's Bartlett inflatable hyperbaric chamber?

The squabbling chorus agreed to the chamber. Much to the consternation of the refuge staff, he was put inside and the bag inflated. They thought we were blowing him up. Using the foot pump, the bag slowly expanded then became taut, with Peter peering out through the side window. The pressure increased to two pounds per square inch, dropping his effective altitude to 3,000 m. With one of us pumping and others talking to him across the tight plastic window, he started to improve and within 30 minutes his headache was better and his oxygen saturations were up to 90%; 30 minutes later we took him out, and gave him 500 mg of acetazolamide for good measure. He tucked into supper – much to the surprise of the cooks who remarked that everyone should have been put into the bag!

Needless to say, once out of the bag his oxygen saturations fell back to 65%. We would need a team of people working hard if we were to keep him in the bag all night, so it was Joe Fisher's turn to experiment. Lying on the sofa (that Pete Forster wryly named the 'sofa of death'), he was hooked up to the Fisher mask and an array of computers (figure 11). Monitoring numerous parameters while fiddling with the mask, his oxygen saturations soon climbed to 94% on a mere 1.2 litres per minute of oxygen compared with the l/min normally recommended. Peter soon felt better. The 'oxygen sparing' device was pronounced a great success. The downside was it needed continuous monitoring. Joe Fisher and his team agreed to take 2-hour watches throughout the night. By the morning Peter was much better. In contrast, the overnight monitoring team were completely knackered. Besides, as it was now the Jewish Sabbath, our Canadian friends were reluctant to work on him all day.

There was the inevitable argument about the exact cause of Peter's illness. Did he have high altitude pulmonary edema (HAPE) or was it pneumonia? Out of caution rather than common sense, it was decided that he should descend to La Paz and perhaps have a chest X-ray. While in La Paz, a few days earlier, Tim Harvey and I had visited the famous Bolivian altitude researcher, Dr Gustavo Zubieta-Castello (figure 12). In 1970, he had founded the first clinic in the world devoted to the study of high-altitude medicine. (His views were not entirely without controversy. For instance, he believed that man had the capability of living on the summit of Everest.) The charming doctor, flanked by his son and daughter had showed us his modest facilities in La Paz and prophetically, thought we might need his help. After lunch, Peter was taken there by John Milles, Ian and Roberto.

Fortunately, the rest of us were acclimatising well. With experiments completed and Peter in La Paz, a large group set out for Huanya Potosi.

Pete commented in his diary;

'I head for the lateral moraine with the intention of reaching high camp – not aware of anyone ahead of me, although I know that Tim Harvey is behind and Tim Clarke, Steve Brearey and several others are on the left-hand moraine as I climb on the right. Wonderful walk – good pace, four stops to the ridge. Clearly marked path with tumbling glacier to my left and peak of Potosi to the right. Path changes to more vertical scramble. See Tim Harvey a long way back. Reach cairn marking high camp at 4 pm – to see Chris and Kyle playing on the snow – but do not feel cheated. A confidence building ascent for Chacaltaya tomorrow; from 4,750 m to 5,000 m in 1½ hours. Easy descent, pass others climbing up – back at refugio for 5 pm tea, cake and a hot shower.'

As afternoon turned to evening then night, we grew concerned about our companions in La Paz and their patient. The road was treacherous with no barriers at its edge. Much to our delight, John, Ian and Roberto arrived back a little after 7 pm. It had been difficult driving along the narrow roads in the dark, so we were greatly relieved to see their smiling faces and hear their story.

During the descent, Peter suddenly perked up – on arrival at Gustavo's, it was not possible to distinguish the patient from his carers. By X-ray, his lungs were not entirely clear, suggesting pneumonia (although Ian didn't believe it, and neither did radiologists in the UK when the X-rays were reviewed). It was agreed he should stay overnight for observation. With the benefit of descent, Fisher's gadget and loads of attention, Peter felt much better. Three days later we met Peter at the hotel in La Paz and he was fully recovered. Whether he really needed digoxin plus ciprofloxacin and an exercise test were mysteries that remain with Dr Gustavo Zubieta-Castello.

But particularly welcome from La Paz was a supply of Chilean red wine and a huge chocolate cake with two candles on its summit, to mark Alex's and my birthday. Partly recovered from the gut infection, I was well enough for wine and the chocolate birthday cake. Alex and I jointly blew out the candles. We had a fun night.

On the final morning, everyone had improved their morning oxygen saturations measured with an oximeter. We loaded the bus and left at 10 am, first back towards La Paz and then up a rubble and slate causeway that snaked around the mountain to Chacaltaya. The bus juddered on large boulders that seemed to push it to the very edge on exposed corners (figure 13) and there were no protective barriers to prevent us tumbling over the edge. Breath-taking views of La Paz, thousands of feet below, greeted every turn.

Chacaltaya

The refuge was on a spur of Chacaltaya mountain, with its neighbouring ski lift spectacularly poised over a cliff (figure 14). Beyond were panoramic views of the glacier-capped Bolivian Alps, Lake Titicaca, the Altiplano and La Paz; 150 miles to the far south, Sajama's white summit (at 6,542 m, Bolivia's highest peak) was just visible.

We were welcomed by the ski resort's two long-term guardians, Adolfo and Samuel Mendoza, who had been living at Chacaltaya for nearly 30 years (figure 15). Once amateur skiers and mountaineers, they now looked after a ski resort with no snow and tourists as scarce as oxygen.

Our group of 22 was the largest the refuge had ever taken. We had booked it nine months earlier and in response to our interest they had expanded the attic dormitory to take 20 beds. The first floor had two small twin-bedded rooms. Tim and Maggie bagged one while John Milles and myself were in the other, which became known as the presidential suite but it could double up as a sick bay. The ground floor had a restaurant, bar, kitchen plus a room that we could use for exercise tests. Thankfully the toilets worked but not the shower. In the winter months, water had to be brought up from a reservoir or La Paz so showers were too wasteful. Surprisingly, there was a stable electricity supply, so the huge generator that we had expensively rented in La Paz was not required.

Next to the refuge was the ski lift, the highest in the world. The term ski lift is rather misleading since it didn't lift. But it had, in a fashion, over the years. Built in 1940, and the first in South America, it had remained largely unchanged since. It was powered by a lorry engine that pulled on a long wire loop from the base of the glacier, 500 m below. The controller had to be very careful accelerating the motor, otherwise everyone was jerked off the T-bars. A further problem was that the Chacaltaya glacier had shrunk to a quarter of its 1940s size (by 2009 the glacier was gone). With no solid base of ice, skiing was only possible after a heavy snow fall. Needless to say, it was no place to ski unless well acclimatised. It was far too dangerous for newly arrived tourists in La Paz to drive to 5,345 m for a quick ski because of the risks of mountain sickness. Its future seemed bleak since the refuge could no longer rely on skiers for its revenue.

Over the next three days we settled into a routine of sorts. Experiments dominated the days for many, with the bike test being the one we all feared. It had been hard enough exercising to maximum at the previous refuge but at 5,345 m it was debilitating. Nevertheless, Chris, Colin and the two Steves made good recordings of cerebral oxygenation as we gasped on the bike. Added to these were oxygen saturations, clinical examinations, Lake Louise scores, wobble-board, blood pressures and proteinuria measurements. Alongside us the Canadian team kept themselves busy with a stream of new ideas.

In the evenings we sat around in our duvet jackets and thermal underwear. There was a wood stove but the room was too large and draughty for it to be anything other than cosmetic. We worked, chatted and drank the wine we had bought up and Peter kept us amused. Unusually, there was also phone reception since we were in line of sight of La Paz. Intermittently, we gathered news of loved ones. We learnt that there had even been a BMRES 'widows dinner' back in Birmingham.

At 5,421 m, the summit of Chacaltaya was only 80 m above the hut so we had a chance to 'knock off' a 5,000 m peak. All of us climbed it. Magnificent views of the sun setting over Lake Titicaca and the Andes made it well worthwhile.

The first night at the hut was expected to be tough and indeed next morning there were many complaints of poor sleep and headaches. At breakfast, puffy faces and slow movements were plain to see, despite the occasional cheery comment. We were all a little cyanosed but there were few complaints.

That night was the turn of Steve Harris. He was not a person to make a fuss and had diligently attended to the Alticycle during the exercise tests but he was not well. Sleep was impossible as he was suffering recurring bouts of nausea and a severe headache. Getting up to vomit, he tripped over his sleeping bag and collapsed his frail bed. I was called up from the presidential suite to find the dormitory fully awake with many clustered around him. It seemed he had mild cerebral oedema. Since it was 3 am, we thought it best to give him oxygen and 8 mg of dexamethasone intravenously. He was swopped with John Milles in my room partly so that I could keep an eye on him, but mostly so everyone else could go back to sleep.

Steve was pretty miserable and hardly slept, intermittently gasping for breath. He confessed to having felt poorly for a couple of days. Earlier, he had watched Peter on the 'sofa of death' with horror, incredulous at our light-heartedness towards a good friend who was ill. It was difficult for him. He was not medically qualified so had little understanding of our sense of humour. We were full of macho talk of near-death experiences on previous expeditions. Now that he was struck down, he feared the worst. Soothing words from me had little impact apart from 'at dawn you go down and will improve rapidly'. I promised to be part of the descent team.

Thankfully, by morning he was much better but we still took him down. With Roberto as driver and Maggie as his general practitioner, we descended the treacherous mountain road. By the time we reached La Paz, he was his usual animated self. We ensconced him in the Hotel El Dorado and had lunch with Peter Hillenbrand, who had fully recovered. After our first showers in a week, we purchased a crate of beer and a box of red wine and drove back in sleet to Chacaltaya for a cold dinner.

The third morning there were further casualties. Alex Vesley and Eitan were missing at breakfast. They lay in bed with nausea and headaches. Pete Forster was convinced all three should descend, closely attended by their doctor – him. This would ensure they had the very best of care. It was an excellent idea, not least because all the wine was gone. Who could we trust more than Peter to return with a good wine selection to celebrate our last supper?

We awoke on the final morning to bright sunshine, relishing the thoughts of descent and plentiful oxygen. Our spirits were further raised by the welcome sight of Alex, Eitan and Steve. Well recovered from their mountain sickness, they had returned for the bike ride. Earlier in the week, Pete had seized the opportunity to rent 25 mountain bikes advertised as 'the descent of a lifetime'. The route: Chacaltaya refuge to the market square in El Alto.

Inevitably, it was a race. What else with BMRES! Adrenaline flowing, tyres pumped and brakes repaired, we lined up in helmets and padded gloves, well prepared for the inevitable tumbles. The smart money was on Steve Harris, gleaned from his stories of hairy mountain rides in the Alps (figure 16). Photographs over, the *peloton* streamed down the bumpy track of rubble and slate.

As the contest developed, I held back, not wishing to show up my friends. Within minutes the leaders vanished out of sight, unfazed by the precipitous drops and the bone-

Illimani above La Paz

jarring road, leaving me trailing at the back. Once it turned to tarmac, the surface became tolerable but we soon slowed to enter the rutted, crowded streets of El Alto and its colourful marketplace – the finishing line. As four others suffered punctures (rapidly repaired by guides from the accompanying bus), I wasn't last.

All safely down and with Steve Harris the winner, we piled onto a bus for the descent into La Paz, the El Dorado Hotel and a wonderful hot shower.

We were now free of research obligations, allowing us to celebrate in the customary way in a private room of a nearby Viennese restaurant. That night it rained heavily. The morning revealed Chacaltaya and Illimani blanketed in snow. It had been a timely escape.

The desperate trips afterwards

After Chacaltaya we split into three groups: the super-elite climbing group, laden with acetazolamide, to climb Sajama; the 'B team', weighed down with beer, went to the Illampu circuit; and the Canadians, well-dosed on ciprofloxacin, headed to the Amazon.

The climbing group

Participants: Jo Bradwell, Kyle Pattinson, Steve Myers and Chris Imray

Rising above the hut at Chacaltaya, Nevado Huanya Potosí had tempted us but we had bigger ambitions. Some 150 miles to the south was Nevado Sajama – at 6,542 m, the highest peak in Bolivia. A French high-altitude research group led by Jean-Paul Richalet had spent two weeks camping on its broad summit 11 years earlier. Since the Altiplano is at 5,000 m, the ascent was a mere 1,500 m and there were tracks to the top.

We found Alberto, a rather dodgy-looking guide, in a climbing shop around the central square in La Paz and explained our mission. He was keen, said it was easy and he would find a porter. We had our own crampons, ice axes and tents to which we added food and other provisions. We hired a Toyota Landcruiser, a 4x4 that could go anywhere – probably even to the top of Sajama. Documents signed and sealed, we scrambled aboard. With a grinding of gears, and a lively but inadvertent salute of the windscreen wipers a couple of bronco lurches, we shot up the street towards El Alto and the Altiplano.

It was dusk by the time we arrived at Sajama village (figure 17). Above us, Nevado Sajama had a great plume of snow flaring off its summit like a shock wave (figure 18). Alberto recommended a bunk house with nearby bathing in natural hot springs. In the pitch dark, we located some changing shacks in a field where we donned head torches and swimming gear before shivering across a freezing grass moorland into the wilderness. At the point of giving up because of the bitter cold, an American-accented voice shouted from below. Barely visible in the scrub was a meandering creek of steaming water. Sulphurous smells and slimy mud banks were off-set by the welcoming warmth as we slithered in. At one end, boiling water bubbled from under some turf, cooling as it mixed in the slow-moving water (figure 19). From our smelly 'hot tub', we looked up at Sajama, shining in the moonlight with its long trail of cloud.

Alberto had earlier insisted that the weather would be perfect for the climb: "We are in the winter season when there are stable clear skies night and day. It is a desert with places like the great Salar de Uyuni having no rain for years. It is the climbing season; we expect the best weather."

However, it did look rather stormy to us and it was drizzling. The American in our hot spring had tried the regular route two days earlier and thought it was a killer. He recommended that we try a smaller mountain first.

Nearby were the twin volcanoes of Parinacota (6,348 m) and Pomerape (6,282 m), so we abandoned thoughts of Sajama and next morning drove to its lower neighbours. Leaving the road, we manoeuvred over the rough ash and cinders. It seemed sensible to drive as high as possible but eventually we were blocked by large lava outcrops. From there, it was a mere 1,000 m to the tops. Perhaps we could knock one off, then the other and be back for dinner the following night.

However, looking up we did wonder about the possibility of some brisk winds. The map indicated that each crater rim was about a kilometre across. Counting the seconds for clouds to transit from one side to another indicated wind speeds of 100 km per hour. Alberto said it was just an afternoon anomaly and would stop by late evening. It was certainly completely calm at our camp. Reassured, we turned to our boiling billy cans for dinner and made ready for an early departure.

It was a 3 am start with head torches, big boots and backpacks as we set off up a vague path into the steepening slope of volcanic debris. The pass between the two peaks was 3 km distant, heading due west. We gasped in the thin air, slipping backwards in the steep ash with each step and stopping periodically to remove sharp clinkers from our socks. I wallowed at the back, struggling to keep up, still hampered by the dwindling residue of a gut infection. As we slowly approached the col, we heard a strange whining noise. This increased to a moaning, then a roaring and finally a ferocious screeching. We reached the coll and were brought to our knees by horizontal wind. We hid behind some lava pinnacles out of the blast. Who had said no wind during the night? We looked accusingly at our guides in the darkness. We would make our own decisions from now on.

I pondered the inevitable. There was no way I could complete the final 700 m in those conditions. True, the wind might be at its worst on the narrow col between the peaks but I remembered the wind racing across the summit cone, now hidden in clouds. I told the others there was no chance, but they remained determined to try. I bade them success and turned back towards our camp.

While ascending, the col had been faintly visible against the stars but the route back was pitch black. A faint trail of footsteps, lit by my head-torch, marked our ascent but it was criss-crossed by others among unrecognisable slopes of ash and lava outcrops. I pressed on fearfully, unwilling to wait for friends who might descend by a different route. After several wrong turns and slow re-ascents, Landcruiser and tents emerged from the gloom. I struggled into the tent at 5.30 am in a curiously darkening night. I was exhausted and fell deeply asleep.

Two hours later there was a banging on the tent and in poked Kyle's head. It was morning and there was snow on his hat.

"Did you get to the top?" I asked expectantly.

"No of course not, it was terrible," he blurted out, looking shattered. "The wind was less above the col but worsened as we climbed and storm clouds were rushing towards us. It was impossible and the guides were useless. They had no idea whatsoever."

There were a couple of inches of snow outside and it was coming down hard. With wind buffeting the tent, he clambered in to catch some much-needed sleep. We all stirred at 9.30 am and looked out to see six inches of snow, with more swirling down the mountain. In view of Alberto's hopeless weather predictions, we agreed to abandon camp without waiting for further advice. We rapidly packed, contemplating our descent across the snowy wasteland. There was no possibility of identifying the way we had come up. And who would drive? Who had any experience driving under such awful conditions? Perhaps Chris, or me as the oldest?

"Has anyone driven a four-wheeler under such circumstances?" I ventured.

Steve replied with the immortal words, "I have driven a Chieftain tank. Will that do?"

We remembered that he had been in the commando brigade – he got the job.

Pointing the turret downhill and with the engine firing on all cylinders, he gunned the accelerator (to use military speak) as we slithered down the steep snow slope. An escape from the forces of evil; but the war banter had to stop as we approached three French climbers we had met earlier. Anyway, with brakes fully locked they were on our glissade route off the mountain. Like us, they had abandoned the climb, but they had no vehicle. We rapidly tied their equipment to the top and they clung to the outside as the nine of us bumped, slid and angled our way to the road 3 km away (figure 20). Six was a crowd inside the Landcruiser, but on the road we added in the three Frenchmen. Half an hour later we booked in at a cheap hotel in Sajama village, mentally exhausted from the drive and physically exhausted from too little sleep and the hard climb. Welcoming tea and food calmed our nerves.

The chat soon turned to the two guides who were getting drunk on *chicha* (maize liquor).

"They have to go immediately," Chris insisted, backed up by Kyle.

"Since they are drunk it would be best to do it gently," I argued. "If we are too aggressive, they might get dangerous."

Having more experience firing people than the other three, I got the job of hit man. As I pointed out in corporate 'human resources' speak: "The aim is to release them from their contract in such a way that they are not upset. Indeed, if their misdeeds are explained sympathetically, they may thank us for pointing out their transgressions and how they might improve their performance indicators in the future."

In a mixture of broken Spanish and simple English, the situation was explained. Alberto dismissed his inebriated colleague telling him to get the bus back to La Paz. That left the main culprit. I explained that he would have to catch the same bus since we were going in the opposite direction. "We will not be returning for many days and you should think of all the other clients you might be letting down."

Thankfully, to my great relief, we shook hands. I gave him their bus fares, which were immediately spent at the bar while we retired to an early bed. There was no wind and the night was utterly calm.

By an unfortunate piece of bad luck, we had clipped a rare storm. Across Bolivia over 40 people died, together with thousands of llamas and vicunas. The snow blanketed all the high peaks, making them un-climbable for many days.

The poor conditions for climbing forced us to lower our ambitions. In Europe, and indeed most parts of the world, a 5,000 m mountain is very respectable – after all, Mt Blanc is 4,887 m. Since much of the Altiplano is 4,000–5,000 m above sea level, there were plenty of easy options. Along the road to La Paz a small hump appeared 50 m above the surrounding plateau. It was on the map at 4,950 m. We puffed up a narrow track in a few minutes and fixed a BMRES T-shirt to a gnarled tree stump on a broad sandy summit. Shaking hands, we congratulated ourselves on yet another mountain triumph for the Society.

The beer group on the Illampu circuit (modified from the diary of Pete Forster)

Participants: Pete Forster, Tim Harvey, Maggie Beazley, John Simmons, Brian Johnson, Ian Chesner, John Milles (figure 21).

We took a bus from La Paz, past Lake Titicaca and descended to Sorata. Sorata was lovely: lush, warm and green, unlike anything we had seen in Bolivia before. We stayed at Casa Gunther, an old and beautiful hacienda. It was a rambling architectural tribute to late 19th century Germanic ambition. Where the previous owners had been interested in coca, quinine and rubber, the current owners of the hotel were interested in catering to the needs of a world-traveller clientele to whom they boasted, and served, 'the best breakfast in Bolivia' in a colonial courtyard full of hibiscus, date palms, succulents and evergreen vines.

By contrast, Pete's Place was a bad choice of restaurant for an evening meal before starting the Illampu Circuit. Zero ambience: poorly lit, cold atmosphere, dispiriting background music, hushed voices of the few other diners, and badly cooked food in portions offensive by excess. To add to the misery, there was a countrywide moratorium on the sale of alcoholic drinks to mark the general election the next day. Our host, Englishman Pete, matched the spirit of his establishment and took pleasure in dire warnings of banditry and knifings of trekkers.

The full trek starting and ending in Sorata is walked in eight days and includes three passes over 4,000 m and one over 5,000 m, a total of 4,260 m of ascent. Our trek was easier: two rented jeeps to take trekkers and provisions from Sorata (2,650 m) to the first pass at Paso Chuchu (4,658 m).

At the pass, we met up with our trusty muleteer, his mule boy and six beasts of burden.

Baggage was downloaded from the jeeps and uploaded onto the mules. A cyanotic boy with an impassive expression watched all this activity. In addition to the mule team, the group comprised seven of us in four tents plus a cook, a cook boy and a Bolivian student on work experience under the supervision of our guide Theodore. Theodore had shown his decision-making skills on the 4-hour drive out of La Paz when he ordered a replacement jeep as our original vehicle had inadequate brakes for country roads: a good call considering the hairpin bends on the road from Sorata to Paso Chuchu. Theodore spoke good English and was willing to share his knowledge of Inca history, civilisation and agriculture, all the while wearing his wrap-around sunglasses and bright red cagoule. With evasive answers to questions about his previous experience in the mountains, however, he did not inspire confidence as a trail-hardened Andean guide. Time would tell.

So began the trek over six days and five nights. We hiked to a campsite near Lacatiya at 3,900 m. I remember a few grimy stunted Aymara children, all very cyanosed, with a delightfully lively kitten called Caramello – or perhaps the kids were asking for sweets.

The first night and subsequent day were marked by relentless rain. On the second day there was deep snow lying over Paso Korahuasi (4,479 m) and Paso Sarani (4,600 m). Tim, experienced climber and veteran of many BMRES expeditions, had expressed concern about trekkers being ill-equipped for walking on snow; several of the group were shod in trainers and the cook was wearing flip-flops on his bare feet. Nevertheless, the cook managed to keep up with the trekkers and rustled up lunches of cheese and guacamole sandwiches as if by magic.

By the fourth day, the long grind up and over the Paso Calzada (5,045 m), walking in 2-foot snowdrifts, had taken its toll on the group, particularly on Tim, who was walking in trainers. The physical exertion was compounded by his habit of walking with cagoule unzipped and without hat or gloves in the bitter weather. Altitude sickness was unlikely to be a factor as there had been sufficient time spent on Chacaltaya to achieve acclimatisation. Walking in sodden footwear, crawling into a sleeping bag at night with cold and wet feet, sub-zero night-time temperatures, and cramming blistered feet into frozen trainers in the morning added to his misery. Further, by refusing sufficient food and drink despite the persistent entreaties of Maggie and threats of physical violence by me if he did not drink his morning carton of orange juice, Tim became weak, dehydrated and didn't pass urine for 48 hours.

As Tim noted: '*At Calzada we were very cold and tired and the animals exhausted. At the camp our sodden tents froze instantly as we set them up. I went to bed in every article of clothing in my sac, including cagoule; inserted myself into the extendable rucksack and then eased the whole lot into my sleeping bag. Maggie says I was very bad tempered, refused to eat or drink anything, was dehydrated and anuric (no urine) for about 48 hours and I flung a cup of tea at her. I remember none of this.*'

Once over the Calzada, the route descended to the sloping grasslands around the Laguna San Francisco. We had been warned that this was 'bandit country'. Sure enough, three aggressive local men attempted to confiscate a mule. We had to negotiate (in Aymaran) with the notorious local mafioso. They demanded our mules and women (Maggie) but after inspecting the goods and a lot of argument they settled for a large bottle of ketchup. Even the bandits were disappointing! (Tim and Maggie later married.)

We were permitted to go on our way but because of the threatening violence we skirted around the next village. At this point, Theodore delegated route-finding responsibilities to the muleteer, who delegated it to the mules. Spooked by the bandits, and prompted by the muleteer, the beasts set off helter–skelter across the hillside in the general direction of Lake Titicaca. The muleteer pursued the mules and was himself pursued by Milles and me and an unknown man. When men and beasts stopped, the local unknown man demanded money. Was he a landowner charging us for crossing his land? Why was he wearing a facemask? Was he holding a knife in the hand that he kept in his pocket? A settlement of 5 bolivianos (about 50p) satisfied his demands.

By the time we regrouped, we were engulfed in a storm, with poor visibility, hailstones and sleet. With Theodore undecided what to do, Brian stepped into the role of leader and insisted that unless we set up camp immediately, we risked losing Tim, who was staggering some distance behind.

By the next morning, the storm had passed. The route was downhill and the weather ideal for walking. We passed through villages with friendly locals and free-range chickens. Tim was on the mend, the party was in good spirits and chicken with rice was served at our final stop, the road-head at Millipaya, where we waited for the bus. In the village square, a gang of workmen were building the plaza. We watched them for a while. Eventually John Simmons could contain himself no longer. He picked up a shovel and wheelbarrow and for the next three hours set them an example of very hard work. Interestingly, not a single word was exchanged and they simply allowed him to do whatever he thought necessary. The bus arrived and John put down his shovel and climbed aboard. Heaven knows what they thought.

On reflection, the Illampu circuit was not the most arduous post-BMRES expedition trek but it was certainly the most wretched. However, memories fade and time heals. At the post-trek meat- and wine-gorging feast held in the Vienna restaurant in La Paz, we met with the rest of the BMRES to exchange tales of derring-do. John Milles was heard to exclaim, 'How lucky we were with the weather!'

The antibiotic group – on the road to Coroico

The Canadians: Joe Fisher, Ron Somogyi, Alex Vesley, Eitan Prisman, David Preiss.

The North Americans split up from the rest of us to tackle the Yungas trail, the toughest and most scenic of the three Inca trails that link the Altiplano with the tropical valleys. Ever-present rain, fog and desperate camping whetted their appetites for a return to civilisation. Thankfully their salvation was at hand – the North Yungas Road. Known as El Camino de la Muerte (Spanish for the 'Road of Death'), it is a 70-km road that leads from Coroico back to La Paz. An average of 26 vehicles disappear over the abyss each year. Cocaine-peddling bandits and near-death experiences on the road further improved their appreciation of western society.

A few of us stayed a fourth week. Barbara joined me from England to explore Bolivia, including Lake Titicaca, the cities of Santa Cruz and Sucre but particularly the silver mines of Cerro Rico (rich mountain) with its neighbouring Potosí, the world's highest city (4,090 m). In 1987 it became a UNESCO World Heritage Site in recognition of its rich, tragic history and its profusion of colonial architecture.

Its wealth was discovered, so legend goes, by Diego Huallpa in 1544, who lit a fire on

Cerro Rico from Potosi

the mountainside and silver flowed from under it. The Spanish jumped on the discovery and, within a year, thousands of Indians were enslaved to dig out its treasures. For over 100 years, it became an extraordinarily rich source of silver, lead and other metals. Even 2,000 km away, the Rio Plate (Spanish for silver river) was named after the precious metals flowing down from Cerro Rico. At its peak of silver production, nearby Potosí became one of the largest cities in the world.

For the Indians and imported African slaves, the mines were terrible. Miners were forced to work 12-hour days and live underground for months at a time. Up to eight million are estimated to have died in appalling conditions. Even today, dozens of miners are killed each year in the labyrinthine uncharted passages, while others die from the inevitable silicosis. Life expectancy is less than 40 years.

Despite or perhaps because of this tragic story, Potosí was recommended as a 'must-see' place in Bolivia. We drove from Sucre, the capital, up the mountains and booked into the Hostal Colonial with its lush central Spanish courtyard. Elegant maybe, but there was no central heating. As the mid-winter sun set, we could not keep warm in the thin, bitter winds blowing in off the Altiplano. At night we wrapped up in all our high-altitude clothes and huddled in our big sleeping bags under many blankets. Beside our beds, drinking water froze solid.

Tourist trips into the mines were widely advertised, with one reputable-looking outfit charging £4 for a 4-hour tour. We took our chances along with a few others. Each person was given overalls, hat, goggles, head torch and face mask. Across the road a small shop sold good-luck candles to illuminate underground statues of El Tío (the mine devil), together with coca leaves and dynamite. Barbara chose candles; I chose dynamite, not believing it was the real thing.

Candles, coca leaves and dynamite

A battered minivan drove us out of Potosí to Cerro Rico, whose triangular shape was recognisable from its profile on Bolivian coins. The guide explained that thousands of people still worked in the mines – voluntarily, he hastened to add. The majority were government employees but there were many small private companies that made good money. About 200 miners went missing every year, he reassuringly informed us, but it was not clear whether they died from tunnel collapses or absconded.

We expected a large, well-built and well-lit doorway to the mine. Instead, the entrance was hidden among a barren area of rocks on the mountainside, where the guide found a hole slightly larger than the entrance to a badger sett. Unbelievably, this was the start of our tour. One by one we squeezed down, locating a rickety ladder with our feet in order to descend into the void. Caverns, some small, others large, fanned out in every direction – sideways, above and below. Drilling sounds whirred from side passages that had veins of glistening minerals embedded in their roofs.

As our eyes accustomed to the dim lights in the low tunnels, the guide explained, "There are no maps of the mines since some tunnels are hundreds of years old. Most are being re-worked to remove lead and other minerals that were of little value in the early days. There are minor collapses of the roofs every day as miners break into old, uncharted passageways."

A dull BOOOOM shook our ears and the cavern walls. Barbara hyperventilated behind me with tear-filled eyes. A miner ran up to us and crouched on the floor. "He had just set off the explosives you heard and has run from the drilling area to escape falling rocks," our guide explained.

Helping him up, I could see advanced finger clubbing, a sure sign of serious lung disease – confirmed as he coughed blood. Although only 31, he would surely be dead in a few years.

We passed a statue of El Tío with lit candles and put ours alongside. I told the guide that we didn't have any coca leaves but I had brought some tubes that might contain dynamite. From there we descended a series of ladders and along tight passages, stooping below cracked and crumbling roofs with occasional sparkling minerals. There were untold levels below and above to the very top of Cerro Rico.

On the return journey, we stopped alongside a deafening drilling site. Behind a cloud of dust and noise was a miner with our dynamite. Unable to see him, I approached until the noise was piercing. One foot from the drill he was finally visible in the dense swirling dust. I held my breath to avoid inhaling the toxic filth. There were a dozen holes in two rows packed with dynamite, connected together with short fuses. He lit the end. We ran down a narrow passage for 40 metres to hide behind a rock wall. Just in time: with a loud bang, a pressure wave hit us, the walls shook and rocks fell from the tunnel roof.

With a shout of 'all clear', we trooped back to the drilling site. On the ground were hundreds of rocks, some containing metals so I took a small piece for examination later. We retreated to the surface, emerging from the narrow hole into the bright sun. It was hard to believe that beyond such a tiny innocent-looking entrance were innumerable miles of uncharted tunnels containing thousands of miners.

My lump of rock was galena, a lead sulphide ore worth a few pence. Finding it was their livelihood. We could walk away, but not those miners working in their Cerro Rico of hell.

Holiday over, we returned to La Paz for a final night with the gang to find out who had suffered the most. On the flight to Miami next morning, we met the American climber we had last seen at Refugio Huayna Potosí. With a dozen students he had climbed Huayna Potosí to camp high up on the summit glacier. But they became trapped in the same storm as us. Miraculously, there were no deaths as the terrible weather raged around their high camp. They only had a little frost nip on fingers and toes. It was a lucky escape.

Postscript

While the climbing had been a failure, from an experimental viewpoint it was a successful trip. Joe Fisher's mask was very efficient at conserving oxygen but its investigational form was not robust enough to be used for climbing. We also found that both Viagra and CO_2 inhalation improved cerebral oxygenation. Nevertheless, the results raised more questions than answers. We would need another expedition. Perhaps back to the Himalaya?

Publications:

1. Chan CWM, Hoar H, Pattinson K, Bradwell AR, Wright AD, Imray CHE and BMRES. Effect of sildenafil and acclimatization on cerebral oxygenation at altitude. Clinical Science 2005; 109(3): 319-324.
2. Imray CHE, Myers SD, Pattinson KTS, Bradwell AR, Chan CW, Harris S, Collins P, Wright AD and BMRES. Effects of exercise on cerebral perfusion in humans at high altitude. Journal of Applied Physiology 2005; 99: 699-706.
3. Imray CHE, Walsh S, Clarke T, Tiivas C, Hoar H, Harvey TC, Chan CWM, Forster PJG, Bradwell AR, Wright AD and BMRES. Effects of breathing air containing 3% carbon dioxide, 35% oxygen or a mixture of 3% carbon dioxide/35% oxygen on cerebral and peripheral oxygenation at 150 m and 3,459 m. Clinical Science 2003; 104(3): 203-210.
4. Johnson BG, Wright AD, Beazley MF, Harvey TC, Hillenbrand P, Imray CHE and BMRES. The sharpened Romberg test for assessing ataxia in mild acute mountain sickness. Wilderness and Environmental Medicine 2005; 16: 62-66.
5. Pattinson K, Myers S, Gardner-Thorpe C. Problems with capnography at high altitude. Anaesthesia 2004; 59: 69-72.
6. Pattinson K, Somogyi RB, Fisher JA, Bradwell AR and BMRES. Efficient breathing circuit for use at altitude. Wilderness and Environmental Medicine 2005; 16: 101-103.

Photographs by John Milles

Fig 1. Top row, left to right: *Brian Johnson, Ron Somogyi, Steve Harris, Steve Myers, Jo Bradwell, Steve Brearey, Chris Imray, Ian Chesner, Alex Wright, Colin Chan, John Milles, John Simmons, Pete Forster.* **Middle row:** *Maggie Beazley, Phil Collins.* Front row: *Alex Vesley, Eitan Prisman, Tim Clarke, Tim Harvey, Kyle Pattinson, Joe Fisher.*

Fig 2. *Steve Harris with the Alticycle*

Fig 3.
Down-town La Paz and Illimani

Fig 4. *Lt to Rt, Phil, Tim Clarke, Chris and Steve Myers*

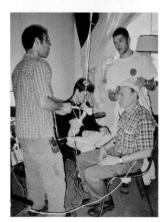

Fig 5.
Canadians: Eitan, Alex, Ron and Joe Fisher (sitting)

Fig 6. *Llamas*

Fig 7. *Contaminated lake*

Fig 8. *Nevado Huayna Potosi and cemetery*

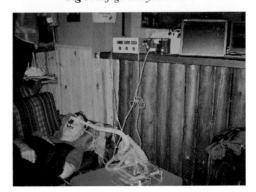

Fig 9. *Refugio Huayna Potosi*

Fig 10.
*Steve Myers with
breathing circuit*

Fig 11. *Peter Hillenbrand on the sofa of death*

Fig 12.
*Dr Gustavo
Zubieta-Castello*

Fig 13.
Up to Chacaltaya

Fig 14.
Chacaltaya lodge
and ski lift

Fig 15. *Veronica, Samuel and Adolfo*

Fig 16. *Race time at Chacaltaya; Steve Harris and Tim Clarke*

Fig 17. *Sajama village, Parinacota and Pomerate volcanoes*

Fig 18. *Storm on Sajama*

Fig 19.
Steve, Kyle and Jo
in thermal springs

Fig 20. *Escape from Parinacota*

Fig 21. *Illampu team: Lt to Rt: Theodore, John Simmons,*
Pete, Tim, Ian, Brian, Maggie and John Milles.

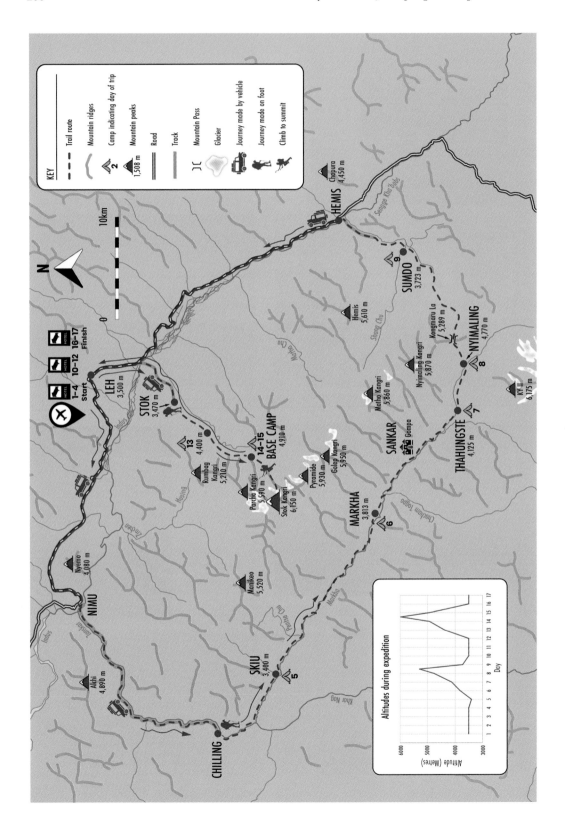

Chapter 11
Ladakh, Land of High Passes – June 2005

Stok Kangri, 6,150 m

Stok Kangri or bust

Who, or why, or which, or what, Is the Akond of Swat?
Is he tall or short, or dark or fair?
Does he sit on a stool or a sofa or a chair, or SQUAT, The Akond of
Swat?
Is he wise or foolish, young or old?
Does he drink his soup and his coffee cold, or HOT, The Akond of
Swat?..........

– 'The Akond of SWAT'
Edward Lear (1812–1888)

Summary: An expedition is always enticing if it includes a big mountain but it had been 15 years since we had climbed Aconcagua. For our 11th expedition, we targeted Stok Kangri (6,150 m) in the Ladakh region of northern India. Known as 'Little Tibet', its sophisticated Buddhist culture, warm dry summers and accessible mountains offered an ideal venue for research and climbing. After measuring bubbles entering the brain during hard exercise and an acclimatisation trek around the Markha Valley, we tackled Stok Kangri.

Expedition members: Steve Brearey, Colin Chan, Katherine Chesterman (student), Phil Collins, Mark Edsell, Pete Forster, Helen Hoar, Chris Imray (joint leader), Brian Johnson (medical officer), Emily Kewley, Ian MacLennan, Steve Myers, Kyle Pattinson, Hannah Rhodes (student), John Simmons (quartermaster), Mark Wilson, Alex Wright (joint leader) (figure 1).

In the 19th century, stories abounded of the huge Karakoram mountain range in northern India – mountains beyond the Himalaya, beyond the mighty Indus. They became the stuff of legend, reinforced through daring explorations by British soldiers and adventurers. Back home in Blighty, Rudyard Kipling's novel *Kim* and Edward Lear's nonsense poem 'The Akond of Swat' further stoked the public's obsession with Empire. The North-West Frontier of India became the centre of the 'Great Game' – the political and cultural collision between Russia, China and Great Britain.

Some 150 years later, it remains a troubled land, with armies from China, India and Pakistan contesting the high remote plateau. When we had visited the Hushe Valley of Pakistan in 1984 (chapter 5), we could hear gunfire in the upper Indus Valley aimed towards Ladakh in northern India. Intrigued by its history, and ruling out Pakistan as politically too unsettled, we chose Leh in Ladakh for our next expedition. Known as 'Little Tibet', its sophisticated Buddhist culture, warm dry summers and accessible mountains offered an ideal venue for research and climbing. Furthermore, a huge airport, built to service the Indian Army, provided easy access for tourists.

Our climbing target was Stok Kangri (6,150 m), the highest peak in the Stok Kangri range of mountains and the highest trekking peak in India. Because of its easy access from Leh, the peak is popular among trekkers and rookie mountaineers, particularly since the top can be snow-free in July and August. But the guidebooks advise novices to be well acclimatised: *'the climb can be exhausting and requires plenty of stamina, both physically and mentally'*, according to one, which sounded a final warning – *'the difficulty of the mountain is often underestimated'*.

In order to acclimatise sufficiently, we needed first to spend a couple of weeks at high altitude. For this purpose, we would stay in Leh, at 3,500 m for a few days, then take the Markha Valley trek, which circumnavigates the Stok Kangri range and includes the Kongmaru La (pass) at 5,289 m.

Having selected a mountain and decided upon our climbing plan for the three-week expedition, we adapted our research to fit in. On all previous expeditions, we had performed our studies as we ascended to high altitude. This time we would perform our studies in Leh before and after acclimatisation, and then tackle Stok Kangri.

There were three main medical projects: blood-shunting in the lungs during exercise at altitude; changes in pupillary responses; and changes in arterial parameters during acclimatisation. Although involved with the expedition's early planning, I was too busy at work to take part and reluctantly withdrew a few months before departure. Hence, this chapter is based upon the diaries of Alex Wright, Pete Forster and John Simmons.

It was a fine day as we climbed into a minibus at Birmingham Medical School in the early afternoon of Saturday 18 June, carefully adding 11 boxes of medical equipment. On our journey south, we picked up Chris, Phil, John and Kyle at Warwick motorway service station then met Steve, Pete and Emily at a Virgin Airlines desk at Heathrow Airport for our flight to Delhi. We had no problems with excess baggage as we had been gifted 150 kg extra by the airline; we only had problems with members. As the departure gate was about to close, Mark Edsell and Mark Wilson, both from London, were still missing. By a fortunate coincidence, the plane was delayed and then cancelled without any explanation.

Perhaps the pilots were drunk! Helen, who flew as a senior first officer for Virgin, defended the airline. It was a bad move. Pete mocked her without mercy for the next hour. Unwisely, she defended her position, while we laughed at his wry and cutting comments. He had a field day. We wondered if she would speak to him again on the expedition. An hour after the designated departure time, the two Marks appeared. There had been a suicide on the railway line.

After a lot of hassle, we were re-booked on a flight 24 hours later. A plane-full of irritated passengers – 300 in total – were loaded onto buses and taken to the nearby Radisson Edwardian Hotel, to be welcomed by surprisingly pleasant staff. Perhaps they were used to unplanned flight cancellations. A consolation curry supper and a couple of drinks at the bar (courtesy of Richard Branson) sent us to bed reassured that all would be well tomorrow. Poor Alex, our leader, was feeling the pressure; it was well past his 10 pm bedtime and he didn't drink alcohol.

With a good night's sleep and a convivial breakfast, optimism was high as we hung about on a surprisingly warm summer's day. The hotel provided more curry for lunch, good practice for Ladakh, and we were back at the airport for 5.30 pm. We were briskly checked through only to find that the plane was delayed for an hour, finally leaving at 11 pm. It had been a frustrating, wasted day.

The 7½-hour flight was comfortable enough – especially for Helen who, as a Virgin pilot, was upgraded to business class. On arrival, we were taken by air-conditioned coach to the Hans Plaza Hotel. Outside the temperature was 47°C, the hottest day for five years, and it was very humid in the build-up to the monsoon. The remainder of the day was for recuperation from jet lag and an outing to the Red Fort, only to find on our arrival that it was closed. In darkness, we walked back through the Old Town among the smells and visual onslaught of the third world. A massive huddling of humanity, dogs, sacred cows and their excrement.

We were awoken at 4 am and trooped onto the coach for a 45-minute ride to the airport. Jet Air quickly checked our 26 baggage items, then we were in the air right on time at 6.30 am. All very efficient – not like Virgin at Heathrow. Oh, for the third world. Please forgive our condemnations the night before!

It was a one-hour flight over the Zanskar and Stok Kangri mountain ranges to the River Indus and Leh. We descended over glistening snow-capped peaks onto a broad desert plain with green strings of agriculture following the river valleys. We were met and taken to the Mandala Hotel (figure 2) on Fort Road, barely a 3-minute walk from the city's main bazaar. Welcoming staff ushered us into a pleasant garden and served us tea and biscuits, followed by a good lunch. While the hotel was fairly basic, and being rebuilt in places, it had Wi-Fi, hot running water and mains electricity, albeit intermittent.

Satisfied with the hotel, we went to explore Leh. Being south facing, the whitewashed city positively shone in the intense sun, while in the distance the Stok Kangri range provided a perfect backdrop (figure 3). Dominating all was the abandoned royal palace (figure 4), a 16th-century miniature version of Lhasa's Potala Palace. The impoverished royal family had moved out in the 1940s to live in the nearby Stok Palace. Below, the Old Town was a maze of narrow lanes and rickety whitewashed houses with wooden decorations. Buddhist gompas (monasteries), stupas (hemispheric funeral mounds) and chortens (relic shrines) were everywhere, but there was also a large Muslim mosque. Between the religious symbolisms, every imaginable shop and cheap hotel served the booming tourist industry. It was a very attractive, energetic city.

Our plan was to spend three days in Leh on experiments, then repeat them after trekking around the Markha Valley to assess the effects of acclimatisation. Afterwards, we would climb Stok Kangri, for which Chris was already in practice (figure 5). Having successfully hired guides for the trek, we enjoyed a jolly good dinner and drinks at the hotel to celebrate Mark Wilson's 31st birthday.

Next morning, with a little mountain sickness in the group (Mark Wilson and Alex), experiments started in earnest. However, the mains electricity was temperamental and, despite our appeals, the hotel staff refused to switch on the emergency generator. John, our engineer, was set on the job. By chance, a shop next door supplied generators. One was hired, fuelled and it sang like a bird. Remarkably, there was no petrol for sale in the city but, as resourceful as ever, John found some at the airport.

Research dominated the next three days, particularly Chris's brainchild, the project on intra-pulmonary shunting. His hypothesis was that if large amounts of venous blood bypassed the lungs (right to left shunting) at altitude, it would reduce arterial oxygen levels, resulting in mountain sickness. Susceptible individuals might be those who had larger shunts or who developed them during hard exercise. The test was simple and ingenious. A few millilitres of blood were taken from a vein, shaken in a syringe with air to make micro-bubbles, then injected back into the vein. A few seconds later, any bubbles bypassing the lungs could be detected in a carotid artery using a Doppler ultrasound scanner (figure 6). By testing people at rest and after cycling hard on the Alticycle, Chris could assess whether altitude and additional exercise caused an increase in bubbles entering the brain. The output was recorded as a pulse wave on the scanner, with any air bubbles superimposed as white streaks (figure 7), or 'chirps' on the sound monitor.

There were two other much simpler studies. Mark Wilson, a neurosurgeon from St Mary's Hospital in London, was interested in the reaction of our eyes to light. Pupil size, speed of reaction and rate of constriction/dilatation were known to slow with hypoxia and cerebral oedema. He wondered whether this correlated with mountain sickness. Measurements were made using a hand-held pupillometer (figure 8). Each person could be tested in a few minutes and results seemed highly reproducible.

The other study was led by Phil Collins, whose medical equipment company supplied sophisticated blood pressure devices. With the assistance of Hannah, Kat and Colin, Phil measured arterial stiffness from the brachial artery while pulse waveforms were recorded from changes in finger volume with each heart beat (plethysmography). The usual supporting measurements included Lake Louise acute mountain sickness scores and weights (figure 9) while Brian, our expedition doctor, performed clinical examinations.

All went well for two days but, as we prepared for the third day of experiments, the generator seized up. The owner was called and, after a thorough check, complained that the engine oil had been allowed to run dry. Poor John was blamed and it developed into an argument. After hassling over the full cost of 2500 rupees (£35), we settled on 1500 rupees for the damage. Calm was restored but it took three hours to repair. By the time it was done, the third day's tests were ruined, leaving only ten individuals fully evaluated. We worried that it might not be enough for meaningful results.

While the researchers researched, others had time to explore Leh's narrow streets and Tibetan-style buildings. Trips to the royal palace and Shanti Stupa, further along the ridge, provided spectacular views southwards to Stok Kangri (figure 10). Both monuments provided training walks in the thin air for the upcoming Markha Valley trek.

Pete, Brian and John also visited Thikse Gompa (figure 11), the largest monastery in central Ladakh, situated on top of a hill at 3,600 m. It is a 12-storey complex and houses many spectacular items of Buddhist art, such as stupas, statues and wall paintings, as well as monks (figure 12). Particularly impressive was the inner temple dedicated to Maitreya, its 15 m statue (the largest in Ladakh) covering two stories of the building. It was installed to commemorate the visit of the Dalai Lama in 1970.

Snow lion in Thikse Gompa

Evenings were spent over dinner with beers and entertainment provided by Pete at his witty best. He had an extraordinary ability to see the funny side of everything and developed different themes to keep us in hysterics. On the second day of the experiments, it was our leader's birthday (Alex). He was given a celebratory T-shirt and a magnificent chocolate cake with six candles (each one representing a decade) with 'happy birthday' scrawled on top in icing sugar. It was a happy evening.

Inevitably, some of the chat was focused on Stok Kangri, driven by Chris and Ian's climbing ambitions. It would be a good peak to 'bag', being above 6,000 m, but it was the highest Himalayan peak any of us had attempted (Chris later climbed Mt Everest). Although technically simple, it would be cold and icy so we would need high-altitude equipment and an experienced guide. For the peak and our trek around the Markha Valley, we hired Tundeep from Overland Adventures Ltd. He was a most reassuring tour operator who could arrange everything – road transport, campsites and meals – all for the very modest sum of 35 rupees (45p) per person per day.

Markha Valley trek

Having spent four days in Leh, it was time for the Markha Valley trek and further acclimatisation. It is located in the Hemis high-altitude national park, just south of Leh, and at 4,400 square kilometres it is the largest national park in South Asia. As the tourist brochure boasted, 'with its stunning high valley and magnificent views, it is one of the best

Bridge over the Indus

ways to experience the unique culture of Ladakh and perhaps see one of its 200 elusive snow leopards.

Day 1: Leh to above Skiu village (3,400 m)

At 6.30 am, six gleaming 4x4 Toyota Land Cruisers arrived at the hotel for the trip down the Indus River Valley to its confluence with the Zanskar River. The wide dusty plain surrounded by snow-capped mountains was spectacular, but rather spoilt by the endless army camps and miles of barbed wire fencing. Lots of troops with shovels and picks filed along the roads but there seemed to be a surprising lack of major equipment. The army's presence was a strong deterrent to the ever-feared Chinese invasion, but also meant good roads that benefited small villages and remote homesteads.

We followed the Indus west to its confluence with the turbulent glacial grey waters of the Zanskar River at Nimu, which signalled our turn south to the Markha Valley. After ten miles, the dusty dirt road terminated at Chilling and our first river crossing. It was a cable bridge that comprised a thick wire rope with a pulley under which hung a wood and metal mining box. This was pulled across by hand using an old hemp rope. Our guide Amchuk organised the 2-hour crossing: rucksacks first, then two people at a time with their day sacks (figure 13). Thankfully, the primitive transport was uneventful.

From the far bank it was a 3-hour trek to our first camp a little way beyond Skiu. As if released from a leash, there was a race up the valley, leaving the group strung out over several miles (figure 14). Breathless, dehydrated and tired, the front-runners arrived at the night camp by 2.30 pm, only to hide from the sun under stupas while waiting for the tents (figure 15). When will we ever learn to slow down? Three hours later, our ponies arrived. Lemon drinks all round, hay for the animals and up went the three-person tents. A nice dinner by candlelight followed, then bed as the night cooled. Older members preferred to sleep under the amazing canopy of stars, enjoying the delicate chimes of horse bells as well as the aromatic smells of horse dung and urine.

Day 2: Skiu to above Markha Village (3,813 m)

We were awoken with our first expedition 'bed-teas' at 6 am. After breakfast, we departed at 7.45 am with our packed lunches in Tupperware boxes. Steve Brearey vomited before we set off and Phil felt sick (probably due to food rather than altitude) while poor Brian lost the sole off one of his boots. For the rest of the trek, he wore one trainer and one boot. There was no race that day – we had briefly learnt our lesson and marched in orderly style, wading across rivers in flip-flops (taking care to face them upstream so we didn't lose them) (figure 16) and over small rickety bridges.

It was a 5-hour trek. There was a lunch break at midday to rehydrate, followed by a 2-hour afternoon trek, by which time melt water from ice high up had churned down the river, changing it from a shallow brook to a raging dirty torrent. We climbed up a steep hill to a monastery with a ruined fort and the campsite set among beautifully cultivated fields.

That evening was shared with a collection of admiring local boys over a cricket match. Not perhaps played to the highest standard, it was, nevertheless, most entertaining and provided plenty of photo opportunities without embarrassment. We thought that bringing cricket balls as presents would be useful another time. There followed a photogenic sunset. Everyone was in bed by 9 pm and tired after the long trek in the hot sunshine.

Day 3: Markha to Thahangtse, (4,125 m)

The morning sun lighting the valley sides had proved an inspired setting for the campsite (figures 17 and 18). It was 'bed-tea' in the cool air till the sun kissed the tent sides around 7 am. Another perfect mountain morning and a nourishing breakfast. From Markha, the countryside changed from warm and heavily wooded to alpine territory. There were several river crossings with no bridges. Great care was required in the strong current, especially as the day progressed and the gentle cool stream became a freezing torrent. Walking poles and occasional hands helped the aging and wobbly. Late-afternoon crossings were seriously dangerous.

Hankar, en route, is the highest village in the Markha Valley. Its beautiful Sankar Gompa was built high on a pinnacle of bright red rock for a monk in exchange for his prayers (figure 19). Apparently, it stored weapons kept from a war with Afghanistan – perhaps Lee Enfield bolt-action rifles from the 19th century, but there was no one there to show us around.

From Hankar it was a steady climb under the blazing sun to Thahungste. As the evening approached, the sun glanced beautifully along the valley sides but the night's cold wind drove us into our tents. We were now over 4,000 m.

Sankar Gompa

Day 4: Thahangtse to Nimaling (4,770 m)

This was the day with the greatest ascent, 650 m. As 300 m is the recommended safe ascent rate, we expected some headaches and poor appetite by the evening and particularly overnight. The trek started on a good path with several small inclines and grassy ridges followed by a slow plod on alpine slopes and moraines. There was a series of mani walls (walls carved with Buddhist prayers) and chortens en route, while views were dominated to the south by Kang Yatse (6,400 m) in the Zanskar range (figure 20).

We tramped into Nimaling camp over the afternoon, strung out by the effects of altitude, to lazily hang around or climb to the snowline at 5,700 m. The Marks made pupillary measurements on us all.

As the evening wore on, many developed headaches and poor appetite that encouraged their early retirement. Mark Edsell was the worst, with facial oedema – clearly mild mountain sickness. The night was frosty with ice forming on puddles.

Day 5: Over Kongmaru La (5,289 m) to Sumdo village (3,723 m)

This was the big day – the ascent over the Kongmaru La. Only 500 m of height gain but it would be difficult after a night of headaches and nausea. We were up early among the frozen pools for pupillary measurements, a lazy breakfast and off by 8.30 am. The slow plod of our guides kept us in a line that gradually lengthened as the laggards struggled. It was two to three hours of zigzags to the col, where multiple tatty prayer flags blew in the cold wind. We all congregated to admire the snow peaks in every direction, even as far as the Karakoram giants and K2 on the north-western horizon.

Beyond, the trail descended steeply to the Martselang Valley then followed a stream to our night stop at the village of Sumdo. We were forced into numerous crossings by recent landslides. Lower down there were patches of agriculture with the inevitable gompas and chortens, while the first village contained a café where we enjoyed tea with our packed lunches. The sun shone, the air thickened, headaches disappeared and we were happy. It was perhaps one of the most enjoyable BMRES mountain descents.

We arrived at Sumdo village after 6–7 hours, to slump outside a school building. After a quick recce, Chris and Alex purchased all the beer to be found (11 bottles) which everyone shared. Magically, whisky and gin appeared, leading to a drunken evening with much jollity. The guides, cook and crew had been excellent, even presenting us with a cake to celebrate a successful trek.

Day 6: Descent to Hemis and Leh

Before the usual early start, we tipped the crew who all seem pleased – especially one of the Amchuks, who had earned an extra 'lemon' supplement from Helen for some undisclosed assistance. Our crew had been a remarkable team. We had had good food and clean water, while the campsites had been impeccable, all provided with an easy charm and remarkable punctuality. A 7.30 am start didn't mean 7.45 or even 7.35.

The final day was an easy 4-hour descent to the road head. A spectacular widening gorge, little change in altitude and much-improved physical fitness made the walk simple and relaxing. Awaiting Toyotas whisked us back towards the main road, with a brief detour to the huge Hemis gompa. But we were gompa'd out and, despite its obvious attractions, we soon departed for the main road, past all its military encampments, for lunch at the Mandala Hotel.

Nature and culture

The scenery along the trek varied as we ascended. As Ladakh is in the Himalayan rain shadow, the monsoon fails that far east so rainfall is scant. However, snow and glacial melt water provide enough for irrigation in the brief hot summers. At each village, careful crop cultivation and well-maintained water channels produced bright flashes of green in the brown desert landscape. Beautiful to look at in the summer heat but harsh, one imagines, in the seven long months of winter.

Away from the watercourses, the mountains rose dry and stark, coloured by different chemical compounds and formed into astonishing shapes by plate tectonics and erosion. Earthquakes are a constant risk, while flash floods lead to huge mudflows and landslips. One of the most extreme storms was on 6 August 2019, when nine inches of rain fell in three hours. The effect was devastating. An estimated 300 people died, including six tourists. In Leh, many buildings were destroyed, including hospitals and houses.

Stupa

The influence of Buddhism was everywhere, from royal palaces to innumerable gompas, chortons, stupas, prayer wheels and mani walls. Small bulbous stupas were particularly in evidence and provided welcome shade from the hot sun. They were built in threes: red for wisdom, white in the middle for compassion and blue for protection (figure 15). In places, cow horns were stacked up in somewhat random fashion. They were coloured red as a sign of blood sacrifice to the gods.

On the early part of the walk, we encountered wonderful wild roses, as well as apricot, willow and poplar trees, berberis and tamarisk-like bushes scattered among the fields of bright green rice. Higher up there were wild primulas, asters, saxifrages, wild rhubarb, various vetch-like flowers and even sea holly on scree slopes. We saw a few animals, such as lizards and birds, but little sign of the 200 snow leopards that were supposed to live in the area – although we did see tracks outside the tent on the first night. Surprisingly, at one village there was a stone enclosure for trapping wolves. Lured with fresh meat, they are apparently captured then stoned to death.

Individuals and group dynamics

During nearly all BMRES expeditions, people get on well and this was no exception. Most are good friends, there is always a clear focus on research, which is highly motivating, and all love the mountains. Although there is fierce competition to be first into camp, this is all in good spirit. The rapid marches up the trails can surprise the novices, and sometimes even experienced members. After the cable bridge crossing at Chilling, the pent-up frustration of three days of experiments left many desperate for exercise. The three hours to the campsite under the beating sun and crippling temperature became a gruelling race. Most were caught up in the stampede under the hot midday heat, particularly the novices. If they had expected a leisurely amble along a beautiful wild valley, with time to absorb local culture and scenic views, they were quite wrong. Even Pete, a very experienced society member, became dehydrated and sunburnt, cursing his stupidity for getting involved in the race. Our guides were most amused by the competition.

As the altitude increased, the pace slowed and more consideration was paid to the back markers. At the start of the climb over the Kongmaru La, everyone was actually in a line. But it didn't last. After 30 minutes rest at the top and group photos, the race downhill to Sumdo village was on. There was a two-hour gap between the first and the last into camp. While those such as Chris, the Steves and Pete relished the physicality of the trek, others, such as Alex and John, adopted a slower pace so they could enjoy identifying exotic plants and examining local culture.

The students, Hannah and Kat, fitted in particularly well with their relaxed charm and were much liked for their willingness to help. But it wasn't all easy for them. Hannah in particular was not used to the daily pace from the early 'bed-tea' on awakening, a rushed breakfast, quick packing and the fast start. And it is not easy being with a group of experienced older doctors and scientists who seem to be completely in control. Knowing what and how much to eat, protecting her skin from the intense sun and avoiding painful blisters was not easy for a novice. Further debilitated by a cold and sinusitis (treated with antibiotics), she had a tough time. Since she was never one to complain, it was several days before we realised she was in difficulty and offered our help.

Health was never a serious issue but Brian, our doctor, was kept occupied with our daily troubles in a remote setting. A few people had rumbly guts. Some of this may have been from our time in Leh, but others developed diarrhoea and vomiting while on the trek. There were lots of dirty fingers on lots of dirty plates and poor washing facilities. Fortunately, no one was severely affected and all ailments were easily controlled with Lomotil. Blisters and sunburn were recurrent minor problems.

Mountain sickness inevitably reared its ugly head at the high camps. Many had headaches, poor appetite and felt weak after we ascended 650 m to Nimaling at twice the recommended rate. Mark Edsell seemed particularly prone to altitude sickness, but stoically performed the pupillary measurements with Mark Wilson despite his symptoms.

Daily organisation, food and guides

The trek company provided everything, including car transport to and from road heads, ponies to carry rucksacks, tents, cooking equipment and food. Our guide Amchuk were always happy and pleased to help with every minor issue. The cooks provided appetising breakfasts such as omelettes, porridge and muesli as well as packed lunches containing more than we could eat. A typical evening meal comprised soup, Moroccan cheese with fried vegetables or rice, vegetables, dhal and a salad with cucumber, carrots, tomatoes and momos (dumplings), followed by pineapple dessert. There was always plenty to go round. Before meals, there was hot tea, coffee or lemon drinks.

Tipping is always an issue and was hotly debated. The travel guidebooks suggested one day's wage for a six-day trek but we were not sure if the books were up to date. The last thing we wanted was to insult them. Eventually Stephen Brearey discussed the issues with Amchuk and it was agreed that we each contribute 600 rupees (£7.50), so that the leader and the chief received 1,600 rupees each and others lesser amounts. It was handed out after breakfast at Sumdo and all seemed happy. The Markha Valley trek had cost a mere £120 for everyone.

Last experiments

Refreshed and relaxed from our trek, we set about the final two days of experiments with relish. The generator behaved perfectly as we completed our research studies with practised ease. Recordings seen in the carotid artery trace of Steve Myers showed multiple bubbles at maximum exercise (figure 7). It appeared as though he had shunting in the heart (via a patent foramen ovale – a small unsealed hole between the two upper chambers of the heart). Other people showed bubbles but with a longer time delay, indicating they had lung shunts. Chris and Alex became very excited, with various papers and abstracts planned with a list of authors. It was a most satisfactory outcome. But full analysis would have to wait until our return to the UK.

Those two days also allowed us to finalise our plans for Stok Kangri. Tundeep agreed to supply transport, camping and guides. Climbing equipment was rented separately, including crampons, ice axes, ropes and warm weather gear. Ominously, however, the weather had changed. The forecast for the next few days was for grey skies, lower temperatures and rain. We wondered if there might be dangerous storms high up on the mountain. Nevertheless, buoyed up by the delightful Markha Valley trek, most people decided to climb. The two Marks went home while Alex and Hannah, looking at the weather, chose to explore Ladakh.

Alex and Hannah – culture vultures

Alex was not interested in climbing a snow peak, and never had been. He wanted to discover Ladakh's nature and rich heritage, as did Hannah. They drove up the Indus Valley to Hemis, Korzok and Tso Moriri, a lake near the Chinese border. There they saw black-necked cranes, kiangs (wild asses), golden eagles and even the famed bar-headed geese. But the weather deteriorated, with clouds hiding the peaks, including Stok Kangri. How much fresh snow was there at 6,000 m, they wondered? Had the mountaineers succeeded? Were they safe?

Further explorations along the Leh–Manali road found them in sleet, snow, low cloud and mist. Innumerable army lorries, fuel tankers, multi-coloured buses plus the occasional car made it the highest congested road in the world. Its ever-present danger from crazy drivers justified numerous roadsides warnings:

'Alert today, alive tomorrow'

'Feel the curves, do not test them'

'This is a highway, not a runway'

'Divorce speed if you are married'

'It's not a rally, enjoy the valley'

'Over-taker beware of the undertaker'

'Safety on the road, safe tea at home'

'After whiskey, driving risky'

Strange that they were written in English. Extraordinary that Britain had been in charge of this vast, remote region only 60 years earlier.

Cham dancer with a cow mask

After the high passes, it was gompa time – indeed, a two-day gompa-fest. First was the photogenic Likir Gompa dating from 1088, with its gleaming, gold-plated 20th century Maitreya Buddha (the head Lama was the younger brother of the Dalai Lama). Next up was Rizong Gompa and finally Alchi Gompa, with its famous Choskhor temple complex containing millennia-old murals and carvings. Wall photographs profiled the exotic cham (mask) dance, which was frequently performed at religious ceremonies.

Gompa'd out, it was back to the Mandala Hotel to meet the climbers.

The tough guys – Stok Kangri (6,150 m)

Since we had already spent 12 days at altitude, including climbing over the Kongmaru La (5,289 m) on the Markha Valley trail, we considered ourselves well prepared for Stok Kangri. The weather was fair, the guides were good and several of us had climbed higher on past expeditions. Nevertheless, the summit day required 1,200 m of ascent from base camp and we had a few novices. Eleven of us signed up for the four-day exploit.

At 7.30 am on the first morning, four off-road vehicles arrived to take us to the tiny village of Stok and its scattering of gompas. With horses carrying tents and bags, it was a five-hour trek to our first camp. The guide, Amchuk, set a steady pace with everyone following in a long line. The route was through a spectacular mountain amphitheatre to our campsite at 4,400 m, where tea was served in a local café. The tents arrived, leading to a scramble for places. With three to each, Pete bagged one with Kat and Helen, to much mocking. They must have felt safe with him; it couldn't have been his charm.

Chris and Pete spent the afternoon exploring the route for the following day, but went up the wrong valley. They had to cross a high ridge to join the correct route, reaching 4,700 m in the process without any difficulty. As the sun set, it became cold and windy.

The morning broke clear and bright with perfect views up the valley. Following bed-tea, an excellent breakfast and more tea, the camp broke at 8.30 am for the three-hour ascent to base camp at 4,913 m, near the snowline. While the previous day's walk had been spectacular, the second day was through a barren landscape of moraine and snow peaks. Pleasant enough in the sunshine but a cold wind bit through our jackets.

Arriving at camp, we met a Mauritian couple, flushed from summiting that morning. Simple enough if the weather held, but very cold, they warned. Several of us wondered if we had sufficient clothes, especially Pete who had left his duvet jacket at the hotel. Realising that the freezing conditions might be a problem, agitation spread through the group, with rucksacks packed and repacked to ensure enough warm clothes were carried. Tensions grew. To wear heavy boots at the start and risk blisters or walk in trainers and carry the boots? The many novices practised ice-axe braking on the steep snow fields nearby. Perhaps a Himalayan peak was not the time to be learning basic mountaineering skills. But we were in good spirits, with many climbing the first ridge to view the reassuringly simple route to the top. We were in bed by 7.30 pm to allow four hours of sleep before a midnight call and an alpine start – 1 am.

Summit day. To our surprise, we arose to fresh snow on the ground with more falling, although Amchuk and his two assistants were unperturbed. Each person struggled to drink their fill, knowing that good hydration and enough calories were important keys to success; but the high altitude had lowered appetites. Head torches were turned on, boots laced tight, duvet jackets zipped up then it was off in a line towards the first col. It was reached after an hour, with the snowfall relenting as we climbed. The less experienced were unhappy, however, having never walked up an unknown mountain in the dark.

As the route led over the ridge, Helen turned back. The fresh snow, increasing wind and the fear of altitude sickness were too much, so she descended while the return route was still visible. The rest of us descended from the ridge to a glacier with awkward ice pinnacles hidden under fresh snow. Although initially in line, we split into three groups, each ascending at different speeds. Amchuk led with Chris and the two Steves; Pete, Brian, Emily and Kat were in the middle group; and Ian, John and Phil brought up the rear. John was feeling the altitude, becoming so slow that a guide had to carry his rucksack.

As we climbed up the glacier towards the summit ridge, the slope steepened and the snow softened (figure 21). Warm damp air from the weather system had brought fresh snow overnight and melted the top layer of hard ice. Every step broke through into underlying deep soft snow. That, combined with climbing in the thin air above 5,500 m, was exhausting. At 4 am the sky lightened, showing an icy ridge that steepened sharply as it rose to the summit.

By daylight at 5.30 am, we were only 50 m below the ridge, but physically exhausted. The three in the lead group separated, each desperately trying to find the best way upwards. Chris tried to the left but fell in the deep snow. Steve Brearey, on the central snow ramp, was thwarted by its steepness. And Steve Myers, attempting a rock route, fell and had to dig his ice axe in deeply to break a long slide. If only it had been frozen, crampons would have made the ascent easy, but they were completely useless in the soft snow.

The followers watched anxiously 30 m behind the leaders, all the time being aware of dark clouds looming to the west. After a 20-minute discussion and growing apprehension about the risks, they realised there was only one reasonable outcome. With the thin air, treacherous snow and a storm coming, it was time to retreat. If the fittest three at the front were struggling even before reaching the summit ridge, what chance was there for the weaker climbers? The followers turned back, only to see the front three do the same. It was over. A complete failure. What had seemed an easy prospect had turned into a rout. Yet another expedition where we had failed to conquer a decent peak.

The 1,200 m descent was very slow, although barely five kilometres. We were all shattered and very disappointed as we returned to base camp. It was tea, a snack and into our bags by 9 am. Lunch was a brief affair since few were hungry. It snowed harder, the wind picked up and there was zero visibility. It had been a very hard climb so any thoughts of a summit attempt the following day were dismissed.

From base camp to Stok village the next day was a simple 3½-hour descent through fresh snow. It was warm with low cloud as we arrived. In the café we met other groups attempting the mountain; they were dismayed by our failure and the poor snow conditions. A German group planning the ascent thought it wise to wait for the cold weather to return.

Three vans took us back to Hotel Mandala, where it was raining heavily. We had made the right decision to turn back, although perhaps the decision had been made for us.

Alex and Hannah arrived from their culture tour. It was a happy reunion, followed by a jolly supper with Alex handing out certificates of thanks to everyone. However, there were a couple of niggling worries. All flights had been cancelled for the day due to bad weather and there was an unconfirmed story of bombs in London.

Return to the UK

The day started promisingly enough with a 4.30 am wake-up call, and three vehicles took us the short journey to the airport. But there we got stuck. Low cloud and rain made landing at the airport very difficult. Three flights to Delhi were due but the first was cancelled, then the second. The large crowd grew restive, some having missed all the previous day's flights. The mountains were hidden and the rain continued. An update on the London bombings reported 32 dead.

A 3 pm announcement finally put paid to our hopes – all flights were cancelled for the day. Poor Helen was becoming more and more distraught. She was on flight duty for Virgin Airlines in two days and her absence might lead to a reprimand. Demoralised and bored, we were taken to Hotel Rafica in Leh where we spent a depressing evening. Even free lodging for the night did little to raise our spirits. We would try the airport again in the morning.

The next morning's weather appeared unchanged. Fortunately, Helen and Steve Brearey managed to scramble onto the first flight (without any of the medical equipment – that would be for the rest of us to sort out). Tundeep hassled for us to be on the second flight by pushing us to the front of the chaotic queue, but it was cancelled for 'operational reasons'. Was that a euphemism for poor weather? Would the third now be cancelled? More and more people became agitated, with some individuals very angry, shouting and arguing with staff at the ticket desk. Poor Alex was crushed in the scramble and nearly fainted.

An 11 am announcement that the second flight had left Delhi was greeted with rapturous applause. Perhaps we could catch that final flight at 1 pm, but would we (and the luggage) all make it? Then we heard that too was cancelled – only for a plane to land with an accompanying huge cheer from the crowd. In short order, we were told to leave half our luggage behind to accommodate other passengers. We were all hassled through to the departure gate, waving goodbye to the equipment – then discovered that all the boxes were actually on board. An hour later we were in the heat of Delhi.

Our experience was a repeated feature of returns from expeditions. All seats booked months ahead, confirmed, even guaranteed, only to find local chaos and no information. But despite all the flight uncertainties, we were in Delhi and back at the very pleasant Hans Plaza Hotel. Any thoughts of visiting the Taj Mahal were long gone as we were a day late.

The flight home the next day was uneventful. Excess baggage was all accepted, thanks to Alex carefully keeping all the baggage receipts from our journey out, plus a bit of 'negotiation'. He had been a good leader of the expedition: outwardly calm, completely reliable and fully on top of the organisational requirements.

We returned to England's green and pleasant land at 6 pm. Spouses and friends were gathered at the arrivals gate for the lucky few, leaving those from the Midlands to take a minibus to Warwick and Birmingham Medical School. So yet another BMRES expedition came to an end – undoubtedly one of the most enjoyable. Great camaraderie in an exciting environment – although, yet again, we had failed to climb a decent mountain

Postscript

And what of the research? Shunting of blood in the lung did indeed occur at altitude and increased with exercise. But it seemed insufficient to cause harm and did not relate to symptoms of mountain sickness. Pupillary reflexes slowed at altitude and recovered with acclimatisation but changes were not related to mountain sickness, only to hypoxia. The same was true for the blood vessel measurements. We would have to find some different experiments for the next trip, but where to?

Publications

1. Imray CH, Pattinson KT, Myers S, Chan CW, Hoar H, Brearey S, Collins P, Wright AD and Birmingham Medical Research Expeditionary Society. Intrapulmonary and intracardiac shunting with exercise at altitude. Wilderness and Environmental Medicine 2008; 19: 199-204.
2. Rhodes HL, Chesterman K, Chan CW, Collins P, Kewley E, Pattinson KTS, Myers S, Imray CHE, Wright AD and Birmingham Medical Research Expeditionary Society. Systemic blood pressure, arterial stiffness and pulse waveform analysis at altitude. Journal of the Royal Army Medical Corps 2011; 157(1): 110-113.
3. Wilson MH, Edsell M, Imray C, Wright A and BMRES. Changes in pupil dynamics at high altitude – an observational study using a handheld pupillometer. High Altitude Medicine and Biology 2008; 9(4): 319-325. DOI: 10.1089/ham.2008.1026.

Photographs by John Milles, Alex Wright and Pete Forster.

Fig 1. Back row, left to right: *Mark Wilson, Emily Kewley, Chris Imray, Alex Wright, Steve Myers.*
Middle row: Pete Forster, John Simmons, Phil Collins, Ian MacLennan, Brian Johnson, Helen Hoar, Kyle Pattinson,
Hannah Rhodes. **Front row:** *Katherine Chesterman, Colin Chan, Mark Edsell, Steve Brearey*

Fig 2. *Mandala Hotel*

Fig 3. *Stok Kangri range from Leh*

Fig 4. *Royal Palace looming over central Leh*

Fig 5.
*Chris practising
for Stok Kangri*

Fig 6. Phil and Colin measuring brain bubbles

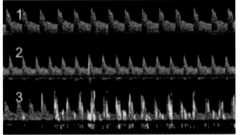

Fig 7. 1, normal carotid artery Doppler trace; 2, one bubble; 3, multiple bubbles

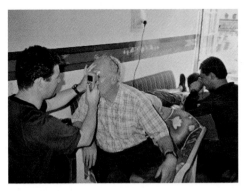

Fig 8. Pupillometry: Mark Wilson examining Ian

Fig 9.
Alex weighing
Colin

Fig 10. Shanti Stupa in front of Stok Kangri (PF)

Fig 11. Thiksay Gompa

Fig 12.
Monk in Leh
(PF)

Fig 13. Pete and Helen crossing the Zanskar River

***Fig 14.** John Simmons alongside the Zanskar*

***Fig 15.** Three coloured stupas*

***Fig 16.** Crossing the Markha River*

***Fig 17.** Camp at Markha*

***Fig 18.** Left to right: Emily, Kat and Hannah*

***Fig 19.** Sankar Gompa (PF)*

***Fig 20.** Looking south to Kang Yatse (6,400 m)*

***Fig 21.** Route from base camp to Stok Kangri*

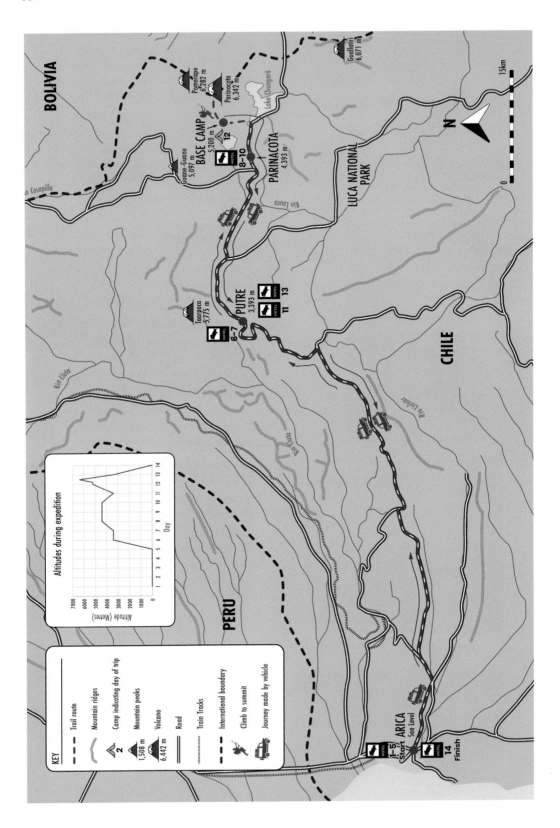

Chapter 12
Parinacota, Chile – November 2008

Pomerape and Parinacota

Evil penitentes

Getting to the top is optional. Getting down is mandatory.

– Ed Viesturs

Summary: Parinacota and Pomerape are twin dormant stratovolcanoes that straddle the Bolivia–Chile border. Two futile attempts on Parinacota (6,348 m), one during a dangerous storm after the 2002 expedition to Bolivia, only served to whet appetites for further attempts. But first came a week of research at the villages of Putre and Parinacota, with studies of gastrointestinal blood flow and colour vision. Subsequently, three people reached the summit of Parinacota, finally laying to rest the ghosts of past failures.

Expedition members: Damian Bailey, Maggie Beazley, Brynn Bird (PhD student), Adam Booth, Steve Brearey, Colin Chan, Ian Chesner, Tim Clarke, Andy Davies (student), John Delamere, Kevin Evans, Pete Forster, Faye Hext (medical student), Chris Imray (joint leader), Brian Johnson, Nick Kalson, Emily Kewley, Andy Luks, Ian MacLennan, Susannah Patey (medical student), Hannah Rhodes, John Simmons, Alison Stubbings (medical student), Alex Wright (joint leader) (figure 1).

From a report by Emily Kewley

November 2008 saw BMRES embark on another trip to the mountains, with a group of 24 members ranging in age from 22 to 72 years heading towards Parinacota volcano in north Chile, via Toronto, Santiago and Arica.

Chris Imray held a grudge. Two previous summit attempts had been thwarted by bad weather, including one on a BMRES trip to Bolivia (chapter 10). Would it be third time lucky? We had also failed to climb Stok Kangri three years earlier (chapter 11). We had waited too long for a successful ascent. After all, it was a mountaineering society.

Altitude research was the first job, with numerous experiments at Arica (sea level), Putre (3,393 m) and Parinacota village at 4,393 m (figures 1 and 2). Some measurements had already been performed in a hypoxia chamber in Glamorgan, courtesy of Professor Damian Bailey. The aim of the trip was to see if results were similar following a longer exposure to hypoxia. Studies included blood flow in the gut and brain; the effect of sildenafil (Viagra) on pulmonary hypertension and cerebral blood velocity; acute effects of acetazolamide and dexamethasone on calcium metabolism; and a visual analogue scoring system for acute mountain sickness. Damian provided professorial guidance while Kevin, his student, diligently collected samples. Andy Luks had a particularly painful experiment. He was an expert on ultrasound scanning of the heart and tested everyone for tricuspid valve incompetence (figure 3). The probe was pressed forcefully between ribs while scanning for an evanescent signal on the monitor. Not popular, and it was a shame that not one publication resulted from all the hard work.

One of the first jobs on arrival was to sort out cold storage for blood samples. Dry ice was not readily available in Arica while liquid nitrogen had to be trucked from Antofagasta in the far north. Army checkpoints and travel restrictions made supplies unpredictable. A clever solution was the use of a chest freezer. Bought in Arica, it was hauled onto a truck and powered from hotels and bunkhouses up and down the mountain. All samples were duly collected, pipetted, frozen and finally shipped (at great expense) to Seattle in the USA and the UK. It was a busy schedule.

After five days in Arica, the team drove eastwards to the small town of Putre. Two days of acclimatisation included a visit to the INCAS high-altitude research station (International Centre for Andean Studies) run by Professor Anibal Llanos. Having acclimatised, the team ascended to the tiny pre-Columbian village of Parinacota on the Altiplano. Fabulous views across the plateau to Parinacota and its sister volcano Pomerape (figure 4) welcomed their arrival: picture postcard-perfect lakes, multicoloured mountains and snow-capped summits. The climbers itched to get their climbing boots on.

The village comprised a few breeze-block buildings, one small school and a 17th-century church with old frescoes. A remote spot, empty apart from a few tourists lingering around stands selling the usual hats, gloves and tasty coca teas. A colourful tea-selling character spoke such a polyglot of international words and phrases that even the locals couldn't understand him. Everyone bunkered in a newly built but basic hostel that nevertheless had a good supply of cold water, electricity and a surprisingly good chef. Alpaca was served twice a day in every form possible. Mixed with tasty vegetables, it perfectly suited all meals.

Experiments ensued intensely for the next three days as sea-level studies were repeated to detect any changes due to altitude exposure. Spare time was spent exploring the local area, including several visits to Lake Chungará (4,517 m) with its flamingos and views of the smoking volcano Guallatiri (6,071 m).

At the end of the experimental period, the group divided, with some heading home, some to the Lake District, south of Santiago, while others climbed. Preparatory climbs on Guane-Guane (6,097 m) and Taarpacá (5,860 m) came first. Ascents with easy gradients, stunning views and warm summits boosted everyone's confidence (figure 5) for the beast: Parinacota.

From the diary of John Delamere

Nine people had a crack at Parinacota: Tim, Emily, Kevin, John Simmons, John Delamere, Ian, Chris, Adam and Damian. We planned a 2-day expedition: day one from Putre to a high base camp, followed by an early start for the summit and back to Putre for the evening. We took two four-wheel-drive vehicles, a Mitsubishi and a Chevrolet long-wheel-base pick-up. Nine of us climbed in, plus Justino and Franklin, our guides; George, our driver, stayed with the vehicles and kept in touch via phone.

We set off from Putre at 10 am for the 2-hour drive to the base of Parinacota past Lake Chungará and onto a dusty track. We stopped at the road head to the east side of Parinacota where we met a German team planning a 3-day ascent. They intended to place all their equipment near our high camp and return to the cars on the first day (to help acclimatisation), then re-ascend for a summit attempt on the third night.

We slowly hauled our gear from the cars at 4,400 m to the high camp at 5,300 m, a distance of 2–3 miles. We struggled with the large rucksacks containing sleeping bags, five litres of water, food, cooking gear and spare clothes. It took 4–5 hours to reach a large rocky outcrop on top of a moraine slope (figure 6). While it was reasonably flat and had extensive views, numerous rocks had to be cleared to make sleeping comfortable. Tim, Emily and Kevin had a tent while the rest of us slept in the open. Poor Justino forgot the poles for his tent so he slept under the tent's fly sheet. It was such an elementary mistake that we wondered if it reflected on his mountaineering skills. We had had a bad experience with guides on Parinacota when we tried to climb it before (chapter 10).

As we settled in to eat cake and biscuits, the Germans arrived. They erected a tent for their equipment irritatingly close to us, not paying any attention to our privacy. Thankfully, they soon departed back to their camp at the road head.

Chris and Adam got out their stoves to make tea and hot fruit juice in an attempt to keep us all hydrated but most of us retreated to our sleeping bags as the sun set at 8.30 pm and temperatures plummeted. Sleep was difficult. I was not sure I had drunk enough but was reluctant to take in too much and then have to get out of bed during the night. I was cold in my light sleeping bag, lying on sharp stones, without a pillow and my water bottle, kept inside the bag to stop it freezing, always seemed to be in the way. Franklin, our second guide, arrived at 2 am. George had brought him to the road head whence he had struggled up in the dark to grab an hour's sleep next to Justino under the fly sheet. We muttered among ourselves as to their competence if we had problems.

Our 4 am start was bitterly cold, even with a duvet jacket and balaclava. Breakfast comprised a little muesli, swilled down with cold water, while for the climb we had chocolates bars and biscuits plus a litre of orange-flavoured water. With head-torch on, I tramped up the moraine spur feeling very weak.

I fell in behind Tim but struggled to keep up. Toiling alongside me were Franklin, John Simmons and Ian. Why was I so pathetic? Was it the acetazolamide that I had continued on since the experiments in Putre? After 30 minutes, as we approached the snow line, Ian announced he had had enough. He would stop and wait for the sun, then go back to camp. I was most surprised since he was normally so tough and had been very keen to climb the mountain. Perhaps we were just getting too old!

John, Franklin and I caught up with the others who were waiting at the snow line – or rather the ice line. Ahead was a slope of six-foot ice pinnacles as far as we could see (figure 7). The dreaded penitentes! Spiky hard ice of every shape and size with deep ankle-breaking gullies at their bases. We tried clambering over them, swinging around them or seeking other routes, all of which were exhausting. Some we knocked down, then walked precariously across their rigid prone form; others we knocked down so the debris filled in deep holes. Some just crashed down as we pushed our way through. My feet got stuck or twisted again and again. My shoulders strained from pulling and pushing and my hips ached from the effort. Using crampons would have been even worse, with a constant risk of spiking or spraining an ankle. Initially I thought that they would slowly give way to normal hard snow but this was not the case. The whole of the mountain where snow would normally lie was covered in penitentes with no discernible path. Ghastly.

Dawn at about 6:45 am greatly improved matters and by 9:30 am the sun was beginning to shine on our faces. We moved clockwise around the face as we ascended, desperately seeking easier routes. John Simmons dropped back as Franklin and I struggled upwards. Having overcome one particularly steep icy rib of the mountain, we waited an hour expecting him to catch up but he never appeared.

By midday, I was starting to have doubts about continuing. The lead group was 100 metres above us, still in the penitentes, and perhaps an hour below the summit rim. Even if I made the rim, perhaps by 2 pm, I would be exhausted, perhaps too exhausted for the five-hour descent to base camp followed by a long slog to the vehicles. There was no sign of John and I had no chance of catching the leaders. I took the only safe decision and turned back.

I think Franklin disagreed, but he spoke no English and I spoke no Spanish. It was difficult enough explaining the simple idea of returning; clarifying which way to go was almost impossible. After much inter-personal communication of unintelligible verbiage, we commenced the descent. He favoured straight down, I favoured reversing our route in order to find John but our ascent route was impossible to find.

As we struggled down, the penitentes seemed even bigger, with streams of afternoon melt water making them ever more treacherous. Slipping and sliding on the wet ice, we skidded our way through. It seemed an age before we emerged onto a steep moraine slope of rocks on underlying ice. Franklin could see I would be slow on the slippery rubble so he walked ahead to pack up the camp.

As I was struggling down, Chris, Adam, Damian and Justino made it to top (figure 8). It had taken an hour from when they reached the rim, with penitentes right up to the summit. Tim, Kevin and Emily had reached the rim but were too exhausted to go higher.

Feeling extremely tired, I walked excruciatingly slowly to the camp to find Ian distraught. He thought John Simmons might be lost. He had watched John's ant-like progress for many hours only to see him disappear around the mountain. He now feared for his safety, even his life. Indeed, John did have a particularly awful time. Alone, exhausted and lost among the penitentes, he had turned back only to find himself above a deep rock and ice crevasse with no easy route to the moraine slopes below. But, tough and resourceful as ever, he eventually found a route down to the campsite. With John safely back we slowly descended to the vehicles at the road head.

What a terrible mountain, yet it had looked so benign from a distance! A uniquely difficult experience, with the descent as treacherous as the ascent. Maybe it was lost in translation, maybe it was deliberate, but the guides had never mentioned the penitentes when we hired them. They had only showed us photos of easy gentle snow slopes with no crevasses. When questioned, they admitted that their last clients had given up at the high camp and no one had reached the summit for several months. It was the old story – money counted for more than reality. And, of course, the crampons that we had carried all day were useless. If either guide had been up high recently, they would have known not to bring them. Nevertheless, three of us had reached the summit, three the rim, and John and I had been to around 6,000 m. And, on a further positive note, the weather had been kind and the views spectacular. Good luck to the Germans following us.

As the sun set, we departed for Putre. But, as our luck would have it, we had a puncture, further delaying a snatched supper and the welcoming embrace of a bed. It had been a very tough two days.

The next day saw everyone back in Santiago from all their adventures. A happy reunion, a fun evening and too many pisco sours. Salud!

Postscript

And what of the research? Some studies were published and others not. Perhaps we undertook too much, but lack of research outputs was compensated for by great companionship with engaging students, stunning scenery and exciting post-research adventures. Combined with good food and wine, it had been a happy group.

Publications

1. Bird BA, Wright AD, Wilson MH, Johnson BG, Imray CH and BMRES. High altitude ataxia – its assessment and relevance. Wilderness and Environmental Medicine 2011; 22: 172-176.
2. Davies AJ, Morris DS, Kalson NS, Wright AD, Imray CHE, Hogg CR and Birmingham Medical Research Expeditionary Society. Changes to colour vision on exposure to high altitude. Journal of the Royal Army Medical Corps 2011; 157(1): 107-109.
3. Hext F, Stubbings A, Bird B, Patey S, Wright A and BMRES. Visual analogue scores in assessment of acute mountain sickness. High Altitude Medicine and Biology 2011; 12(4): 329-333. DOI:10.1089/ham.2010.1055.
4. Kalson NS, Hext F, Davies AJ, Chan CW, Wright AD, Imray CHE and Birmingham Medical Research Expeditionary Society. Do changes in gastro-intestinal blood flow explain high-altitude anorexia? European Journal of Clinical Investigation 2010; 40(8): 735-741. DOI: 10.1111/j.1365-2362.2010.02324.x Publications: 2011.

Fig 1. *Pomerape and Parinacota from Parinacota village.*
Emily, Mac, Alison, Faye, Chris, Tim, Brian.

Fig 2. *Parinacota village at night*

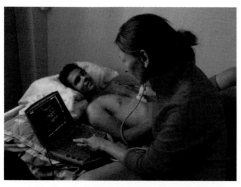

Fig 3. *Ultrasound measurements of the heart. Faye and Bryn*

Fig 4. *Volcan Parinacota*

Fig 5. *An early success*

Fig 6. *Top camp*

Fig 7. *Penitentes at night*

Fig 8. *Up to the summit on Parinacota*

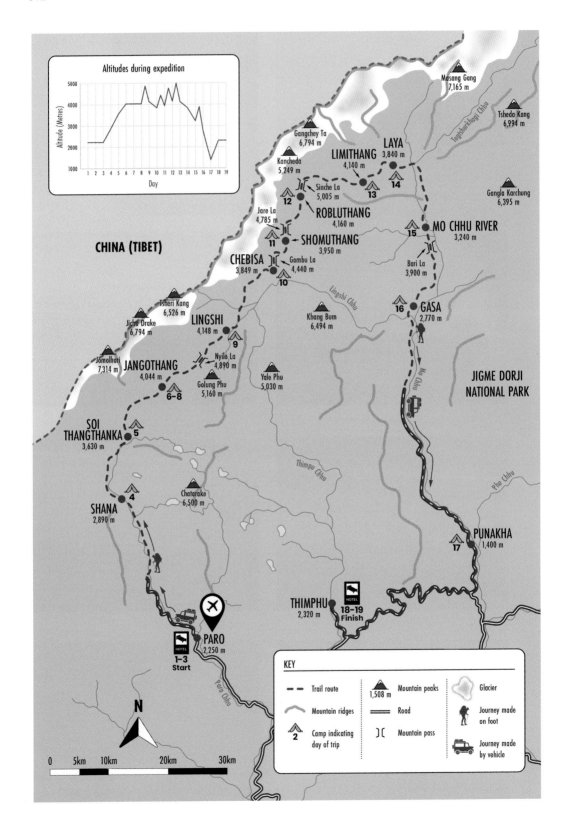

Altitudes during expedition

CHINA (TIBET)

Masang Gang
7,165 m

Tsheda Kang
6,994 m

Gangchey Ta
6,794 m

LAYA
3,840 m

LIMITHANG
4,140 m

Kancheda
5,249 m

Gangla Karchung
6,395 m

Sinche La
5,005 m

13

14

12

Jare La
4,785 m

ROBLUTHANG
4,160 m

MO CHHU RIVER
3,240 m

15

11

SHOMUTHANG
3,950 m

Bari La
3,900 m

CHEBISA
3,849 m

Gombu La
4,440 m

10

Lingshi Chhu

16

GASA
2,770 m

Tsheri Kang
6,526 m

Khang Bum
6,494 m

Jichu Drake
6,794 m

LINGSHI
4,148 m

9

Mo Chhu

JIGME DORJI
NATIONAL PARK

Jomolhari
7,314 m

JANGOTHANG
4,044 m

Nyile La
4,890 m

Yale Phu
5,030 m

Golung Phu
5,160 m

6-8

SOI
THANGTHANKA
3,630 m

5

Thimpu Chhu

Chatarake
6,500 m

4

Pho Chhu

SHANA
2,890 m

PUNAKHA
1,400 m

17

THIMPHU
2,320 m

18-19
Finish

HOTEL

Paro Chhu

PARO
2,250 m

HOTEL

1-3
Start

N

0   5km   10km   20km   30km

KEY

- - - Trail route

1,508 m Mountain peaks

Glacier

Mountain ridges

Road

Journey made
on foot

2 Camp indicating
day of trip

)(Mountain pass

Journey made
by vehicle

Chapter 13
Jomolhari, Bhutan – April-May 2012

Jomolhari

Five high passes

Mountains have a way of dealing with overconfidence

– Hermann Buhl

Summary: This was an expedition for the indulgent. A trip to entice older members from retirement and seduce the mountain senses of the young. Remote and exotic, the Kingdom of the Thunder Dragon evokes images of ancient temples, remote valleys and sacred summits. Enticingly, Bhutan has a government target of increasing gross national happiness rather than gross national product. Into this beautiful arena stepped BMRES in April 2012 for three weeks. The main altitude research was to assess oxygen levels in brain and leg muscles during hard exercise. This was performed at Jangothang (4,000 m) on the younger members of the group, those under 55. A subsidiary experiment studied lung fluid accumulation during and after exercise. Once the research was completed, we trekked north-east for seven days, crossing five passes of up to 5,000 m. Our route took us beneath Jomolhari (7,315 m), Jichu Drake (6,850 m) and Tsheri Kang (6,526 m) before turning south down the Laya Valley to Gasa and Punakha. Surprisingly, this was the first of our 13 major expeditions when an extended trek was just for pleasure. Despite the usual sufferings from altitude sickness, bowel infections and freezing temperatures, all survived to recount an enjoyable tale.

Expedition members: Jo Bradwell, Colin Chan, Ian Chesner, Sarah Clarke, Mark Edsell, Pete Forster (deputy medical officer), Helen Hoar, Chris Imray (deputy leader), Nick Kalson, Ian MacLennan, John Milles (medical officer), William Malein (medical student), Steve Myers, Kyle Pattinson, Susannah Patey, Hannah Rhodes, Owen Thomas (medical student), Yash Wimalasena, Mark Wilson, Alex Wright (leader) (figure 1).

Many expeditions are tough, with periods of considerable suffering, and enjoyable only in retrospect. But as time lends enchantment, bitterly cold nights are remembered for their beautiful sunsets and brilliant Milky Ways, smelly ablution facilities are the source of many humorous tales, while cold, inedible food becomes the best fare ever tasted. Indeed, the worst experiences often become the best memories. Not so with Bhutan. It was magical from the start.

The three previous expeditions had been journeys to high-altitude hotels or bunkhouses. For the 13th expedition, we wanted something different. It had been 13 years since Kanchenjunga, when we had taken a long trek to high altitude. Admittedly, moving from camp to camp made experiments difficult and we fled for our lives from a killer storm, but we wanted another trekking experience. They are always more fun, we get to know each other better and there is the physical challenge that everyone enjoys.

Every expedition has to start somewhere and these were some of the thoughts that led to a decision. It had been three and a half years since the previous trip but I was not really interested in another expedition. However, in the summer of 2011, Alex and Chris took me to one side and asked what it would take to entice me out of retirement. I thought for a short while before replying, "Bhutan".

Remote, exotic and expensive, this fabled Himalayan kingdom emerged from self-imposed exile only in the 1950s. It is a land of forbidden peaks and hidden valleys, where gross national happiness is more important than gross national product. Who wouldn't want to sample its delights?

Could we really afford to go there, though – and, if we could, what would we study? Alex wondered if I might be the leader but having recently retired from work and still recovering, I was in no frame of mind to take on a big project. Alex, with Chris's help, had led the three previous trips very successfully, so I declined and agreed to be a mere passenger for the first time. I imagined I could readily step back and observe without being sucked into the organisation, although I would need a project to keep me occupied. I agreed to make the expedition film.

Through the Society's monthly meeting, we decided to compare rush-and-rest exercise with a slow plod at 4,000 m using the Alticycle (horizontal exercise bike). We needed considerable financial support and were fortunate to receive a large grant from the JABBS foundation that covered all our needs.

We chose Mountain Kingdoms Ltd for our travel arrangements since they were experts on trekking in Bhutan. Steve Berry and Nikki Morgan were most helpful over the following 14 months and resolved all our research needs. The core plan for the expedition was to ascend to 4,000 m, where we would stop for three nights to carry out the research. We would then hike in the Jigme Dorji national park on the Laya–Gasa trail over the next ten days. Because Bhutan was so special, we had designed the trip with few experiments, leaving plenty of time to explore. One difficulty was the potential size of our group, as most treks appeared to consist of a maximum of 10–12 people, but with one campsite change from the usual itinerary they were able to satisfy our requirements.

At 2 pm on the afternoon of Saturday 21 April 2012, I found myself outside the Medical School for the umpteenth time awaiting a minibus to an exotic mountain location. For some weeks, I had reflected on how it might be to go on an expedition after a gap of ten years (Bolivia, 2002). The group had changed a lot – ten of the members I hardly knew. Thankfully, there were still a few of the oldies from early expeditions, such as Alex (12 expeditions), Pete Forster (11), John Milles (9), Chris Imray (8) and Ian Chesner (8).

Several of the newer members had been on trips that I had missed. I found it disconcerting that they knew each other so well, having spent weeks together in some remote corner of the world, but it reflected my long absence.

Alex was being a great leader, rushing about checking on everyone and everything, jobs that I had previously done. I forced myself to stand back and watch. Keep a weather-eye open for potential problems, I thought, and enjoy the ride. I was also conscious of being old. There were two older, Mac and Alex, but I was definitely in the aged category. I would have to look sharp and try to keep up.

The excited buzz from everyone continued as we met up with the rest of the group at the Jet Air departure gate at Heathrow Airport. Mac mentioned he had just become a Fellow of the Royal Society. That made two for BMRES (the other being Neville Richardson) plus four professors. BMRES seemed to be finally joining the establishment.

Alex had anticipated the usual excess baggage difficulties. The airline allowed each person 25 kg but 10 kg had been allocated to a communal excess baggage pool to cover the weight of medical equipment. With a bit of hustle and bustle, we got everything onto the plane without extra charges. That's always a relief and the first hurdle successfully cleared.

The flights took us first to Delhi. Overnights on long haul are always a pain, mostly in the neck and the back. I looked askance at my seat neighbours, a mother and her child who cried even before take-off, but with a small dose of temazepam and a little melatonin, a hard seat was transformed from all-night torture to a few fidgets and a groggy breakfast. There followed a short flight to Kathmandu International Airport in the evening. Not quite up to Heathrow standards, but it had certainly improved vastly since our early trips. We were welcomed by our tour operators, bundled into a small bus and rushed through the busy traffic to the Shangri-La Hotel.

Kathmandu had maintained many of its old charms and chaos but Tamil was crammed with tourists, KC's restaurant was quite run-down and there was one of many strikes by workers agitating for change. Pete Forster, Ian Chesner and I wandered around old haunts reminiscing about previous expeditions. We had first come to this hippie paradise 35 years ago.

We were a happy bunch of mates that evening in the hotel, dining on hot spicy foods and wondering about potential tenting partners. I took the conservative route and agreed to camp with John. We had been each other's best men and, importantly, he never snored, although there were recent rumours that he had taken up the habit.

Monday morning was our scheduled Druk Air flight to Paro in Bhutan. The route follows the Himalayan chain, passing nine of the 14 8,000 m peaks, but unfortunately it was midday and cloudy. In April, there is always a morning build-up of thunder clouds even if the nights are completely clear. As we lifted off the tarmac, towering clouds rose above us, lowering our expectations. Surprisingly, as the Airbus 317 reached its cruising altitude, there was a hint of some peaks and then, gloriously and magically, out came the tops – Cho Oyu, Everest and the rest of the Eastern Himalaya. As photographer-in-chief, I was temporarily awarded a window seat and stared transfixed by the beauty of the mountains, many of which I had visited. They never fail to live up to expectations. But the best of the flight was yet to come – landing in Bhutan.

Paro airport is in the only flat area of the country but is surrounded by big peaks. It has the reputation of being the third most dangerous airport in the world (the first being Lukla near Everest). Helen Hoar (four expeditions), a pilot for Virgin Atlantic (having abandoned her medical career), explained that it was a very difficult landing. At the airport's height of 2,300 m, the air is thin, there are usually lots of cumulus clouds, while aggressive thermals and steep mountains crowd the approach. We were excited and anxious. It was a big jet. The ridges seemed so close to the wing tips as the plane banked hard left, right and then left again, with the houses on the mountain sides close enough to touch. Into view, at the last minute, came the landing strip: a roar of engines, a heavy bump and we were down. Ten out of ten to the pilot.

Excitedly, Helen exclaimed, "I would love to give it go, but maybe not in my 747."

We were welcomed by the beauty and charm of the Bhutanese and their colourful, elegant buildings. "Kuzuzangpo la," greeted attractive Bhutanese girls from the airline (figure 2). "Kuzuzangpo la," greeted our guide Tshering Aku as we exited the airport.

We blinked in delight in the bright sunlight. First impression: Switzerland of the East. Bhutan has developed hugely since its emergence from isolation in the 1960s but it has retained a unique charm and culture of its own. It could easily be swamped by the cultures of India to the south or China to the north. Yet, despite having a population of less than a million and being sandwiched between the two most populous countries in the world, it has retained remarkable political and cultural independence. Britain mostly left it alone during the days of the 'Great Game' but did define its southern edge. British India started where stones stopped rolling downhill, which is largely where the border remains today. China stole some of its northern mountains a few years earlier and tensions remain, but India is its obvious benign political protector. While there is much evidence of army activity, the high summits are the only real defence against its aggressive northern neighbour.

The next couple of days were for acclimatisation, to overcome jet lag and to enjoy some exercise. These were accomplished from the stylish Olathang Hotel. It was built in 1974 on a steep hillside overlooking Paro for guests at the coronation of the present king, Jigme Khesar Namgyel Wangchuck. Dzong-like and rather grand, the hotel is surrounded by decorated wooden cottages for sleeping, scattered among a wood of Bhutan blue pines. Flower gardens, wisterias in full bloom and beautiful views over the Paro Valley (figure 3) were not the normal start to an expedition. We were getting soft.

Tiger's nest monastery

Our itinerary included visits to ancient dzongs (fortified monasteries) that still played an important part in Bhutan's Buddhist culture. We began with Rinchen Pung Dzong (translated as a fortress on a heap of jewels) in the Paro Valley (figure 3). There were 150 young monks in training, probably more than in the whole of Europe. Until 1960, all education took place in monasteries but now it is secular, with English taught as the second language.

The following day we climbed to the spectacular Taktshang Goemba or Tiger's Nest at 3,000 m (figure 4). It is said that the legendary Guru Rinpoche flew from Tibet on the back of a tigress to defeat five demons that were opposing the spread of Buddhism. The event was celebrated by building a breath-taking series of dzongs poised over the abyss. They were destroyed by fire in 1998 (perhaps by the Thunder Dragon) but had recently been restored and re-consecrated in the presence of the king. Apparently, the buildings were originally held to the cliff face by the hairs of female celestial beings who had carried the building materials on their backs. Disappointingly, their modern counterparts were a cable-car and crane.

It was a stimulating ascent to reach that rocky fastness. Buddhist symbolism was everywhere: multitudinous fluttering flags alongside the paths, together with every size of prayer wheel – the largest containing thousands of individual prayers and going 'ding' on each revolution (figure 5). Then there were automatic prayer wheels: some run by water power, others by the wind and some even by solar panels. It was *Om Mani Padme Hum* at every turn.

By the time we had seen Kyichu Lhakhang, one of Bhutan's oldest dzongs, later that evening, we were dzonged out (figure 6). But spinning prayer wheels and mountain *karma*, combined with hilarious evening banter from Pete and tasty Australian merlot, put us in the very best of moods for the expedition.

Decorated head in a dzong

Paro to Shana (2,890 m)

On the third morning in Bhutan and after a hearty breakfast, Tshering Aku, our chief guide, met us at the hotel, accompanied by his two assistants, Tshering Drox and Kinley. We paid our rather large bar bills and selected 15 kg of personal belongings for the trip, leaving clean clothes at the hotel for our return two weeks later.

Two minibuses then drove us north up the valley, chasing our luggage, which was packed into an old lorry. It was an attractive drive alongside the Paro Chhu among apple orchards, terraced green fields and whitewashed farmhouses. We reached the road-head near the ruins of yet another massive fortress – Drukgyel Dzong (2,580 m), which burnt down in 1951.

Briefly, we hung around in the oppressive heat of the day. There were not the usual 100 porters, typical of Nepalese expeditions, with Sherpas weighing each load. Instead, seven herders packed our rucksacks into double panniers astride 70 or so small horses. Tshering watched on as rucksacks, pots, pans, rice, tins and fuel were loaded, then the cavalcade clanked up the trail. We strode alongside a babbling river that competed with excited chat as the trek started. As we departed, we were joined by Yash, the last member of our team, who had arrived overnight from London only that morning.

We gently ascended past hamlets and monasteries to Phurba army camp at Gunitsawa, which is strategically located to stop smuggling of cheap Chinese goods. A large sign welcomed us to Jigme Dorji National Park, the largest in Bhutan. We eagerly awaited our first sighting of the snow leopards and tigers that were mentioned in guidebooks.

Trekking permits checked, there followed a fast walk to our first campsite at Shana Zampa (2,790 m) near a swirling glacial river. Campsites in Bhutan are highly regulated and at fixed locations throughout the country. In wet conditions, they can be filthy but there is no opportunity to move elsewhere. Fortunately, this one was in a dry open field surrounded by forest (figure 7).

We took it in turns to bathe in the freezing river to clear the grime accumulated during our competitive and sweaty nine-mile walk. We realised that it could be our last proper wash for a week.

As the evening approached, it cooled rapidly and then rained, forcing us to huddle in our tents as the porters constructed the mess tent. The latter became the natural focus of our chats, games and humour as we donned jackets and duvets for the first time. Surrounding us was all the bustle of the camp, shouts from the cooking tent, chimes from 70 horse bells and strange Bhutanese words. But the modern world still intruded. I had assumed that Bhutan would shun modern telecommunications so I had left my phone at the hotel. The smartphone-addicted youngsters knew better. Up the valley the army had set up a telecommunications network to warn of possible Chinese incursions or booze smuggling. iPhones worked perfectly.

After dinner, I lay in my tent. Camping felt much harder than 13 years earlier when we had visited Kanchenjunga. But, overall, it felt great to be back on the trail. It had been a good day.

Shana to Soi Thangthanka (3,575 m)

We were awoken at 5.30 am to a bright clear morning with horses ringing their bells. Even at this relatively low altitude it was near freezing. The camp stirred into action and, breakfasting together in the sun, we warmed to our second day on trek.

It was nearly 14 miles and 700 m of ascent to Soi Thangthanka, a day of stony paths, noisy streams and forests of beautiful oak (holly oak), juniper, birch and towering rhododendrons with, purple, red, pink, cream and orange flowers. Lichens and orchids festooned the branches. Some 65% of Bhutan is forested, much of it impenetrable and unlogged, with the largest conifers two or more metres in girth. We dawdled along the paths in that enchanted wonderland.

Our revelry was broken by a herd of yak on the narrow trail. They were descending from the Tremo La army camp near the Tibetan border and were clearly agitated by our presence. We had been warned of their nervous temperament and told to stop on the upper side of the trail, but we were in a large group scattered to both sides. There was a stand-off with our edgy adversaries who snorted and lowered their long sharp horns. Then they charged. Many of us leapt into the woods. With others, I cowered behind a large boulder as one huge beast came straight for us, only to swerve away at the last moment (figure 8).

As the forest thinned with the altitude, we caught occasional glimpses of snow-capped mountains but they were elusive, hiding in the afternoon clouds. On occasions, I rushed ahead with my camera boy Orgen (son of one of the horse men) to film our column marching over wooden bridges or through the woods.

After an eight-hour walk, we reached a large muddy clearing in the woods – our campsite for the night. We were greeted by a dirty kitchen and dining room, overused by trekkers. A smelly pit-toilet and contaminated surrounding woods were a disappointing end to a beautiful day. Below us roared a cold Himalayan river, while from above a chilling drizzle dampened our spirits. This was not the Bhutan we had expected. We feared for our research at the next campsite. It would be a difficult two days in bad weather.

Soi Thangthanka to Jangothang (4,044 m)

The next morning I opened the tent to see a clear sky and people taking photographs. Had the big mountains finally come into view? I rushed out of my cosy four-seasons Mountain Equipment bag to see Jomolhari, the second highest peak in Bhutan, shining in the morning sun. Its huge crown, dramatically white and crevassed, gleamed above the surrounding forest (figure 9). We watched the changing shadows on its huge glaciers as the sun rose, but soon clouds and a light drizzle blocked our view.

Jomolhari, 'goddess of the holy mountain', was a famous landmark for early Everest expeditions as it could be seen to the east when trekking into Tibet (chapter 15). Noticed in 1921 by George Leigh Mallory, it was described as 'astounding and magnificent'. The summit fell in 1937 to Freddie Spencer Chapman, a British Army officer, and Sherpa Passang Lama.

Several British climbers had a large influence on mountaineering in Bhutan. For instance, the surgeon Michael Ward from London made an extensive exploration of Bhutan's mountains in 1964–65, while Jichu Drake was first climbed in 1988 by a team led by Doug Scott. But now all peaks are closed. The government decided to prohibit mountain climbing after mountain villages complained that it violated the abode of the gods and would bring bad luck. Indeed, Bhutan's Gangkhar Puensum (7,541 m) remains the highest unclimbed peak in the world, with unsuccessful attempts by British and Japanese teams in the 1980s. While Jomolhari was recently climbed from the Tibetan side, it is unlikely to be climbed from Bhutan in the foreseeable future.

The routine of breakfast over, together with finger blood oxygen saturations (pulse oximetry), we ascended through the thinning forest. In turn, the higher montane forest gave way to alpine pastures and scrub overgrazed by yaks, some of which were visible as black dots high up the mountainsides.

Mani walls and gompas (temples) became less common, but to our amusement we passed a huge carved stone phallus – a monument to the 'Divine Madman' who had conquered the valley in the 15th century. Lama Drukpa Kunley (1455–1529) is one of Bhutan's favourite saints and a fine example of the 'crazy wisdom' attributed to early heroes. Although born in Tibet, he travelled throughout Bhutan as a yogi using songs, humour and outrageous, often obscene behaviour to dramatise his teaching of Buddha.

His sexual exploits are legendary, and many of the flying phalluses painted on houses and hanging from rooftops are in his name. Kunley's numerous sexual conquests included the wives of his hosts and sponsors. He is even credited with creating the curious-looking takin, or gnu goat, supposedly an amalgam of the head of a goat and the body of a cow that he happened

Takin

to be eating. When the congregation demanded a miracle, he put the bones of the two animals together and sent them alive into the meadows as a takin.

All human societies are concerned with fertility, the east as much as the west, but it seems to reach a peak of ostentation in Bhutan. Huge willies are blatantly painted in glorious technicolour on innumerable houses throughout the country (figure 10). Shops shamelessly sell exaggerated wooden carvings. Whereas people in the west might secretly buy erotic magazines and hide them from preying eyes in their homes, in Bhutan sex is openly on show.

We arrived in the early afternoon at Jangothang, our research base camp, but it was disappointing. There were hints of big mountains in the clouds but it was a dull scene, with a dreary stream meandering across flat and over-grazed meadows. Other campers were scattered around us among the all-pervading yak dung.

We camped beside the river as the experiment teams set out their equipment in a large blue mess tent. But Steve and Mark Edsell soon realised it was too cold for the sensitive electronic equipment. Fortunately, a large hut on the campsite, occupied by a trekking group, would soon be vacated. Tshering commandeered it for the following morning.

The 100 kg, 2.8 kW generator had already arrived, having been brought up by four men using two long poles. Amazingly, it had come from India via Paro and Shana and had then been carried by hand over the rough tracks that we had ascended. Even more amazingly, it worked perfectly.

It was a cold evening with no sun. Jomolhari was shrouded in clouds, providing only occasional glimpses of its lower slopes. We were thankfully warmed by a bottle of Bhutan Highland Whisky that magically appeared.

Two days at Jangothang camp

Apart from our last morning at Jangothang (figure 11), days were overcast with snow in the air, so we were grateful to have the relative warmth of the hut and its insulating wooden floor for the experiments. The Alticycle was set out in the middle of the room and alongside it the K4b^2 gas analyser for breath-by-breath oxygen and carbon dioxide measurements. Calibration gas canisters had been delivered from India thanks to arrangements made by Kyle. We were ready for our studies.

But there was something wrong. The K4b^2 wouldn't calibrate. We looked on in horror as Steve made more and more desperate attempts to understand the problem. He slowly realised that the K4b^2 had been programmed to work at sea level and not at our current low atmospheric pressures. The oxygen sensors couldn't calibrate against the gas mixtures. In addition, a cable had broken on the bike, severing power recordings to the computer. After two hours, Steve gave up. We were miserable. It would be impossible to compare the efficiency of rush-and-rest versus slow-plod exercise. The research thrust of the expedition was ruined.

However, other pieces of equipment worked, such as the Niroscope (to measure tissue oxygenation) and the ultrasound scanner. After thoughtful discussion, we decided to measure sub-clinical pulmonary oedema (fluid on the lungs) as assessed by 'lung comets' – distinctive ultrasound features – during hard intermittent exercise. We hooked up individuals to the bike with leg and head oxygen probes and added finger oximetry sensors. We then asked each person to go flat out for as long as possible, stop when exhausted, then repeat the effort until they had gone the equivalent of 6 km (figure 12). It was hard watching as they maxed out, recovered briefly and cycled repeatedly. Pink lips and skin turned blue as their oxygen levels fell and they became cyanosed. Pulse oximetry revealed the dramatic fall in peripheral oxygen saturations that, at sea level, would suggest the necessity for intensive care. Then the lung-comet team, led by Yash and Mark Edsell, rapidly exposed their chests in the cold air to measure lung water over the following two hours. We managed to study 12 people over the two days. Lung comets were twice as frequent after exercise and they lasted about two hours (figure 13).

Other minor experiments were undertaken, such as finger prick lactates by Susannah, testing of a mountain sickness app by Chris and capillary finger prick blood samples for mRNA. We were kept busy enough, although remained bitterly disappointed that the main experiment had failed.

Adjacent to the hut, in gently falling snow, I completed the video, interviewing everyone with Pete Forster and recording experiments. Others walked to a nearby high valley with a glacial lake, blue sheep and marmots.

Experiments completed, such as they were, we packed away the Alticycle, ultrasound instruments and Niroscopes, emptied the hut, and prepared all the medical equipment for its return to Paro the following day. We only retained a small 750 W generator to charge phones and cameras.

Jangothang to Lingshi Camp (4,148 m) over the Nyile La (4,890 m)

On all previous expeditions the main experiments had been performed at the highest point of the climb and often half-way through the trip, but this time was different. Since we had planned a circular route, we now had ten days in Bhutan's Jigme Dorji National Park and we were going higher. Mark Wilson had to return to his neurosurgery job in London and Steve had an interview for a reader's position at the University of Chichester, but for the rest of us it was holiday time.

On the ascent to Jangothang, I had mostly been at the back filming. Stopping to take a single photo loses 50 yards, using a tripod costs 200 yards, while taking a video doubles the distance. With the filming in the can, there was an opportunity to test my fitness.

Last out of camp with John, I decided to try and walk to the front. As the path to Nyile La steepened, I looked ahead and saw everyone straggled out over the next mile. Had I lost my old strength and speed at altitude? I turned off the camera, took a deep breath and set off in pursuit. One by one they were overhauled. The oldest first, then those a little overweight or acclimatising slowly. Surprisingly, the young students were not that fast, so after a couple of hours it left only Kyle and Chris in front. I joined up with them and, as the morning unfolded, the three of us stretched out our lead.

This was not a race; it was a walk with friends in the high Himalayas. If only it was that simple. The three of us stopped briefly beside a large cairn at a false summit (figure 14). Huge views stretched out over un-named snow slopes to the southern horizon with Jomolhari I and II and the spire of Jichu Drake (6,989 m) towering above us to the north (figure 15). A climbers' and skiers' paradise, we thought, as others caught up.

Jichu Drake was first climbed in 1988 by Doug Scott, Victor Saunders and Sharu Prabhu, who later became Doug's wife and was leader of our expedition to Everest in 1993. During the last part of the climb, their ice axes repeatedly poked through the summit cornice, exposing them to a 1,200 m drop down the west face into Tibet.

As we revved up for the race to Nyile La, Chris and I drew ahead. Around the next hill could be seen the summit cairn with its fluttering prayer flags. I increased pace, gasping the thin air, struggling at my maximum with Chris doggedly at my shoulder. Pace by pace we jostled up the final ramparts of the col. Hypoxic, aching, dizzy and barely thinking, I climbed at my limit but still heard Chris gasping at my shoulder in relentless pursuit. What was he thinking? Was he all-out too? To turn around and look into his eyes would admit defeat. The col beckoned; flags clattered in the wind. We arrived at Nyile La together and stood panting painfully as we admired a panorama of sacred summits in gloriously clear air.

But it was bitterly cold. I was in shorts and T-shirt with only a camera in my day-sack. Chris had spare clothes in his bag which he quickly put on. I jogged down the far side of the pass to hide from the biting wind, followed by Kyle, who lent me his over-trousers and a jacket. I was spent.

Well ahead of the others, we contoured down a long valley to a beautiful campsite looking up at Jichu Drake, which was gradually shrouded by afternoon clouds. Horses arrived and tents were arranged higgledy-piggledy on a gentle slope, a shrubby wood of pine trees blocking easterly winds. I realised our tent opening faced away from Jichu Drake, so I asked the porters to turn it in anticipation of a morning treat. John arrived feeling rather weak and clearly affected by the altitude. A cold evening, huddled in the mess tent, was followed by early bed. It had been another good day.

Lingshi Dzong

Lingshi camp to Chebisa (3,849 m)

Tea-sahib' arrived in the morning sun and as the tent was unzipped there was a perfect view of Jichu Drake (figure 16). But it had been a long night. John had snored, presumably because of the extra fluid in his nasal passages. By morning, his face was oedematous (figure 17). I discussed with Pete (deputy doctor to the group) what might be done. Was I more concerned about his health or his snoring? A difficult question to answer honestly.

I was aching from the previous day's exertions and content to take the day slowly. The walk was 'magical' according to the guides and eagerly anticipated. We were not disappointed. We climbed a little to a low pass then past the base of a small hill with Lingshi Dzong (built in 1222) perched on its summit. Chris, Kyle, Sarah and I walked up the steep path to the partly destroyed buildings, which provided commanding views of all the surrounding mountains and valleys. It had been damaged repeatedly by earthquakes, the most recent only a year earlier (figure 18). It had been used for centuries to guard the pass from Tibet to Chebisa and had been besieged many times but never conquered. Huge defensive walls and deep passages had served it well. A couple of novice monks were the only occupants. What could they do against a Chinese invasion?

Below the dzong was the interesting village of Limgshi, complete with local primary care centre and a tourist office – surprising in such a remote location. We walked on to a cold lunch stop in a rock house at Goyok village. Yak dung was piled majestically in many houses like food stacks in a supermarket (figure 19) while ancient juniper trees clung to crevices in the cold dry soil. Yaks ploughed the fields and Himalayan griffon vultures circled the huge cliffs above the village harbouring the sacred Goed Dzong.

We descended gently for another hour to the village of Chebisa. Camp was already set up among the multitudinous prayer flags in a central pasture with low rock houses to one side. A yak broke from its tether and strayed among the tents to hoots and shouts from us all. One swing of its head and it would rip a person asunder. A herdsman shooed it out of the camp and caught it. We returned to our cricket match against the village kids whom we struggled to beat.

But not all was well with the team. Susannah had a chest infection and Colin was struggling for no clear reason. John still had a very puffy face. The altitude was starting to take its toll.

After setting up camp, I walked with Kyle to a waterfall at the head of a valley leading to Tibet via the Lingshi La. Sacred cypress trees seemed to grow out of the naked rocks that guarded the pass (figure 20). It was a mere eight miles to the Tibetan border. Both countries forbid movement of goods and people but policing the area is impossible. We bumped into an old man with smuggled Chinese beer. We bought his total supply and shared it round. We all agreed that it had been another magical day.

Chebisa to Shomuthang camp (3,950 m) over the Gombu La (4,480 m)

We left Chebisa in beautiful morning sunlight, walked through the village and up a steadily rising path. John was still very slow so he gave the spare video camera and the camera bag to our camera boy (John was film assistant). Quite uncharacteristically, Alex was also at the back. Will took over the photography as we ascended in modest weather while watching bearded vultures and blue sheep in the distance.

I caught up with Pete at Gombu La (figure 21) and explained that our medical officer (John) was poorly, with possible heart failure, and Alex was unusually slow. He went back and agreed that John needed a diuretic (frusemide) while Alex had a chest infection. Also, Colin and Susannah were struggling. She took up the offer of a horse and rode to the top of the pass in style. Her tent-mate, Sarah, had provided a lot of psychological support over the previous few days. Increasing illness in the group was worrying and now John, our expedition doctor, was also compromised. Little did we realise that we would soon need all of our medical skills.

From the top of Gombu La, Nick, Owen and a few others climbed the adjacent hill overlooking Tibet. There followed a long descent through a cedar and rhododendron forest into a camp below Shomuthang. Beside the tents a shallow stream was surprisingly warm as it bubbled over the sun-warmed stones. Many people washed, but not me. There are two ways to deal with dirt: clean it off or lock it in. I favour the latter.

I explored the upper part of the valley with Kyle and Chris, rather slowly as I was still recovering from the race. Huge fir and birch trees filled the basin, hiding some scruffy encampments occupied by dodgy yak herders. We were warned to steer clear because there could also be folk of dubious origin from across the border.

Later that night, Tshering lit a fierce wood fire of juniper. Log fires are frowned upon, despite the profusion of local wood, but we welcomed its warmth as the cold night settled over the camp and our ill members. We agreed that the next day, Tshering would provide us with a sweeper to help the slowest. Fortunately, Susannah felt better but Colin was to be offered acetazolamide and a horse.

John snored less that night. The diuretic had not only cleared the oedema from his face but had also dried out his throat. Could the drug be used for other snorers? Since he had taken up the habit over the past couple of years, we wondered if mild heart failure had been present for some time.

Shomuthang to Robluthang (4,160 m) over the Jare La (4,785 m)

It was a cold start from our camp in the woods even with a wood fire, but the sun was producing beautiful views to the border mountains. We walked across the stream (figure 22) and up a mountain to the high col of Jare La (4,785 m). It was surprisingly warm but distant views were obscured by cloud. There followed a series of descents – first through scrub and low rhododendrons then fir and larch woods to finish among huge conifers in an ancient forest.

Once again clouds rose in the heat of the early afternoon and blocked the sun, leaving us cold. To make things worse, it began to drizzle then snow. We stopped for lunch beside a small river, Jhalethang Chhu, on the edge of the forest. On offer was a huge pot of boiling lamb curry. We ate it hungrily. It tasted good but I refused a second helping – as it turned out, a wise decision.

Rain and snow flurries continued as we trekked through the forest to a wide swampy plain that was kept as a nature reserve for the summer grazing of the famed takin. The Bhutanese believe that if you drink their fresh blood it will keep you warm for three weeks. We didn't see any so couldn't check whether this was true. After crossing a rickety plank bridge in the mist, over the freezing Tsharijathang Chhu, we climbed an extra few hundred feet to Robluthang (4,160 m). Hardly a place, more a rock shelter on a lateral moraine, but the additional 40 minutes walking would shorten the following day's long trek.

It drizzled and sleeted intermittently as we marched the last hour into camp. Yaks and horses were tethered on a long line, their bells tolling in the dusk (figure 23). The tents were cold and the evening bitter as we huddled in the cooking tent warmed by the gas stoves.

Mac was not feeling at all well. The long walks and high altitude were telling. He felt he could go no further but returning over four passes would be harder than just the one remaining. He was insistent that he must descend directly down the river valley, but that was impossible. It fell through steep gorges and impenetrable jungle with no paths. We were in a bowl from which the only escape was upwards, over the Sinche La – at 5,005 m, the highest pass on the trip. We had just been able to see it from the high point the day before and it looked clear, but conditions would be quite different now that it had snowed. It was the crux of the trek. We wrapped up tight that night wondering if we would be stopped by snow.

For a day or two, Tshering had been wondering whether our ill members would make it. We had a quiet discussion with him about those who were struggling. Reassuringly, horses would be available for the slowest but we would need an early start.

Robulathang to Limithang (4,140 m) via the Sinche La (5,005 m)

In the night, disaster struck. The 16 of us who had eaten the lamb curry at our previous lunch stop were in deep trouble. I had only needed four urgent trips to the toilet tent, but wind noise had concealed the plight of others. Many had been desperate with repeated dashes to the toilet. Others had not quite made it. There was a trail of shit from several tent entrances to the loo.

The afflicted could be classified according to four levels of severity: the lucky few who made it to the loo, those who nearly got to the loo, those who couldn't unzip their tents in time, and those who failed even to make it out of their sleeping bags. Poor Mac was in a real mess, wandering around outside in the snow in his pants and shirt. Our resident gastroenterologist, Ian Chesner, was one of the worst affected. Our group was in chaos and it was bitterly cold. It was probably a salmonella toxin from the lamb curry at the lunch stop but that did not prevent Ian prescribing ciprofloxacin to each of the stricken plus good doses of Lomotil. Four people had not eaten the curry, including Colin, but he was suffering with altitude sickness.

Gut infections are always a potential problem and can plague any group, as can chest infections. Whether to become a vegetarian is a frequent question. But with dirty fingers, dirty plates, contaminated food and finger oximeters passing around everyone twice a day, nothing is confined to individuals.

What to do? Every expedition seems to have a pivotal moment and this was it. If we stayed in Robluthang, the snow might worsen making the Sinche La impassable for several days. If we went on, the diarrhoea might become so debilitating that some of us might fail to climb the pass. Mac was in no state to move, nor Colin. It was difficult to go back and anyway the return journey time would mean missing the plane home.

Decision making by the group was interesting. Alex, our leader, was not in the right frame of mind since he was ill and refused to talk. Chris was never really consulted even though he was deputy leader. I was in a passive role on the trip while John, the expedition doctor, was only concerned with handing out pills. Ches, who had all the necessary gastroenterological knowledge for decision making on gut infections, was ill and only offered medical advice. Pete took charge, coaxing and cajoling people out of their bags to the breakfast table for fluids and some light nourishment. With a mixture of discussion, persuasion and logic, plus the availability of a couple of horses to carry the worst two, we agreed to move on.

I asked Mac, "How are you on a horse?"

"The last time I rode was on the beach when I was seven and it was a donkey," he replied. Mac was a big chap – 95 kg and 6 foot 4. The ponies were Himalayan dwarfs. It did not seem possible.

Chris agreed to stay with Mac at Robluthang until the medications started to work while the rest of us packed up and left camp, disappearing behind rocks to the side of the trail when necessary. Miraculously, the affliction abated as we gained height over the next five hours. Few additional episodes occurred, allowing the whole party to move steadily up the trail. Then, to a cheer from everyone, a small horse plus a large rider was seen coming up behind us. Big Mac came alongside with a broad smile as Chris trotted nearby.

The snow worsened, and the wind rose from a stiff breeze to a horizontal gale. John had to be pushed up and we carried Alex's bag. The two were very slow due to a mix of mountain sickness, diarrhoea and, in John's case, right heart failure. Slowly we followed the numerous cairns and prayer flags to reach a big stupa on the col (figure 24). We huddled under its lee side for a few minutes and were then blown down the far side. As the air thickened and the descent eased, we recovered our strength. Mac and Colin descended on foot, fearful of the horses slipping on the steep track down.

The descent, protected from the howling gale by the high pass, proved to be easier. We stopped for a brief lunch sheltering behind boulders but all views of the mountain panorama were hidden. It snowed for a while and the slippery boulders were difficult but it turned into a lovely afternoon. The clouds cleared, and we entered an enchanted forest – snow-covered rhododendrons, towering spruce and hemlock trees, and Great Tiger mountain (6,840 m) shining though the swirling clouds. It was heavenly. I held back with Kyle and Nick to drink in the idyllic scene. We stopped at a lonely herder's house, where an elegant woman in traditional skirt, jacket and pointy wicker hat offered us yak's milk (figure 25). This year's vintage they claimed, although it tasted older. Worse, they refilled the glass, which I had foolishly emptied to be polite. I left it full after that. Yak ribs and steaks hung from the ceiling, yak cloth hung from the walls, yak horns served as decorations; testament to an ancient culture. It was a million miles from Birmingham, apart from a child's plastic tricycle made in China.

Descending through the forest we came across Alex in a very distressed state. He was lost. As back markers, we should have kept an eye on the stragglers, but the tempting yak milk had hijacked our responsibilities. He was most relieved, having wandered alone in the forest for an hour shouting for help. Shortly afterwards, Chris arrived, also worried that we were lost.

Limithang camp was on a lovely meadow under towering cliffs at the edge of a cedar forest (figure 26). A hot wood fire welcomed our arrival. It had been a most extraordinary day. Potential disaster had been averted – all diarrhoea had stopped and we were safe. It had turned out to be a beautiful day.

Limithang to Laya 3,840 m

This was another magical day as we wandered through the lost world of Bhutan. It was only 9 km but we dawdled over the journey, taking nearly six hours. It was delightful to appreciate the beautiful forests, with huge mountains above us and a well-used path underfoot. A lammergeyer cruised by (figure 27) as we made the final ascent to Laya village. We were last to arrive. John and Alex were still suffering the effects of the altitude and I was sweeper for the day.

For the first time in a week we dropped below 4,000 m and entered the prosperous-looking town of Laya. The village was attractive, with many typical Bhutan houses, and reminiscent of an Elizabethan village film set. The villagers wore typical Bhutanese clothes, the women conical bamboo hats. There was the first shop since the Paro Valley and even a pub selling beer. But it was only a summertime village – everyone descended to Gasa in the winter.

Although the houses looked attractive from the outside, they were simply constructed, draughty and very cold. There was no heating. We huddled in a small house in the village centre drinking tea and beer. While beautiful in the sun, the town was less appealing as the streets became sodden in the afternoon drizzle that turned to rain. Mixed with yak and horse dung, rainwater cascaded in rivulets of filthy brown muck down the cobbled streets.

Nevertheless, the first night in semi-civilisation meant a party. No huddling in the mess tent waiting for food, but a boisterous night in the pub and loads of beer until closing time – midnight for most of us. The game of carom – a form of shuffleboard or finger billiards – proved very popular. The Layans were the easy victors.

It snowed as we went to bed but the sky cleared to a moon-lit night.

Laya to the Mo Chhu (3,240 m)

We awoke to a beautiful morning, perhaps the best of the whole expedition, with the sun radiating from a perfectly blue sky. Surrounding snow-capped mountains glowed golden as we arose to relish the stunning views and clear air. A fresh layer of snow on the tents, rooftops and fields was the finishing touch to an enchanting alpine scene (figure 28).

After a slow breakfast admiring the views, we descended through the village entry arch, decorated with protecting deities. A large spruce forest welcomed us as we followed babbling streams with views to Masang Gang (7,194 m) (figure 29). The group was uncharacteristically quiet after the drinking session the previous evening, but the snowy peaks shining behind the high trees – Switzerland of the Himalayas – soon raised our spirits. Alongside us, a wide band of trees was being cleared for electricity pylons. Big changes were coming to that remote and unspoilt village.

We reached the army camp of Take Hankhar after an hour for permit checks. A little later we passed a narrow path with a small sign saying 'Snowman'. This was the inconspicuous start to one of the most difficult Himalayan treks – 25 days in Bhutan's remote northern mountains. Thanks to the high altitude and deep snow, it is completed by less than half those who attempt it. We wondered if we were made of the right stuff to finish it.

A young rufous-bellied eagle perched on a treetop kept watch during a brief lunch stop, then it was on down to join the Mo Chhu and a finish at a beautiful riverside camp underneath large cliffs. It was rather cramped for us and 40 or so horses, but the rushing river gave us our first chance of a proper wash in ages, which we relished in the warm afternoon sun.

The high passes were now behind us, and the expedition was coming to an end. Around a wood fire, with horse bells ringing in the woods, we reflected into the night on our magical trip, previous adventures and the future of the Society. What would become of the group with few youngsters taking a lead (figure 30)?

River camp to Gasa (2,770 m) over the Bari La (3,900 m)

Our final day on trek provoked a mixture of relief and sadness. Although the days had been challenging, the beauty of Bhutan and our comradeship had been exhilarating.

Expecting an easy day, we slowly gathered our belongings from among the horse dung, amid the usual sound of bells. The walk started innocently back across the river. We were assured it was a short day but we had stopped several miles before the regulation campsite at Koina. When we arrived after a couple of hours, it was clear why. It was overused by both humans and horses, with deep filth and mud everywhere and a dirty wooden hut. It has the reputation of being the worst campsite in the Himalaya, which was hard to disagree with. We stopped briefly for Colin as he needed yet another horse and then set off towards the final pass.

We may have been heading downstream but the river had cut a series of canyons that were impassable. The trail clung to the side of cliffs for a mile or more but then lurched upwards to the Bari La. From a subtropical jungle start, we climbed back into a primary montane forest of huge fir and spruce trees (figure 31), resplendent with mosses nourished by the frequent mists. It was a long hot ascent to the pass, marked by the usual chortens (shrines) and prayer flags. The gradient stretched out the group as some raced for the top, only to face an hour's wait for the lunch cooks to catch up.

For a couple of hours after the pass, I meandered down towards Gasa with Pete and Ian Chesner, reflecting on our discussions the night before. Was BMRES coming to an end? Was Bhutan the ultimate adventure? Would another trip be as dramatic or enjoyable? How many of the older members would go again? Ian MacLennan, Colin and Alex had found it hard, as had John. Also, I was not sure about another trip since this one would be hard to beat.

In late afternoon, we arrived in Gasa (2,760 m), crossing the village green beside archery and soccer pitches to shouts from the balcony of a shop. The early arrivals had located the beer parlour and were hailing us. Individuals wandered in over the next couple of hours, with Alex, John and Ian struggling at the rear.

Everyone was happy to be off-trail and it was finally warm. But where was Colin? He had been on a horse so perhaps it had taken him the wrong way. Fortunately, we were in an area where mobile phones worked. He was located well beyond our camp, walking down the road believing we had gone beyond the town towards the hot springs. He was in a world of his own.

It was a lively evening at the end of a long day and a remarkable trek. The campsite was at the newly finished road-head car park just beyond the huge Gasa Trahsi Thongmoen Dzong. Bar-headed geese honked beside the nearby pond and Kang Bum mountain (6,500 m) glistened in the evening sun.

Gasa to Punakha camp (1,400 m)

We had the chance to wander the streets of the old town, the huge dzong dominating all. From its ramparts, the Bhutanese successfully fended off Tibetan invasions in the 17th and 18th centuries but it had been badly damaged by the ever-threatening earthquakes and fires. Recently rebuilt, it was the regional administration headquarters.

I had a lazy day which involved walking down a beautiful trail with Chris and Kyle in a tropical paradise, a far cry from the high mountain forests we had been in only the day before. All enjoyed the transition into the tropics, with its monkeys, orchids, rice paddies, trees and banana plantations, as we ambled to the hot springs of Gasa Tshachu. We had a welcome warm soak beside the river in the partly rebuilt concrete baths, a faint whiff of hydrogen sulphide in the air. Earthquakes and monsoon flooding had added to its dilapidated state. Busy with foreign and Bhutanese tourists, it was a strange contrast to the isolation of the previous two weeks.

After an 18 km bus journey from the hot springs to Punakha, we camped in a large stony field beside the Mo Chhu, the river we had followed since Laya. A warm wind blew through the trees and it was the last night in a tent – great.

We were happy, fit and felt strong at the low altitude so thoughts turned to a summer walk. Chris Imray asked me if I would like to do the Bob Graham Round with him. The Bob Graham Round is a mountain marathon in the Lake District, but that understates it. It is three mountain marathons in one – 42 peaks, 66 miles, and 8,230 metres of ascent and accompanying descent: nearly the height of Mt Everest from sea level. I would have found it challenging when young and foolhardy aged 67. I sought help from others in my determined rejection of the proposal. Sarah came to my aid. She agreed it was ridiculous for mortal men. Indeed, she was a fell runner and had accompanied someone on one section, finding the pace impossibly fast. I would never manage it at my age (see chapter 17).

Punakha to Thimphu (2,320 m)

We awoke to the heat of a tropical morning and the sight of everything being packed for the final time. All our stuff was loaded onto the lorries and we bade farewells to our guides, cooks, drivers and horsemen in an end-of-trek tipping ceremony. They seemed to be pleased with our generosity, but the language and cultural barrier made it impossible to be certain.

That final day gave us chance to reflect on the expedition, its successes and failings. Research is always difficult on a trek and this one proved that point, although failings of the bike and the K4b^2 gas recorder were of our own doing and nothing to do with the environment. We agreed to ask Steve Harris (who designed the bike) to repair its broken power lead and give it a thorough overhaul. And then there was the question about membership of the Society, how to recruit youngsters and who should be leader.

I mulled over these issues as we visited Punakha Dzong (figure 32). It was at the junction of the Mo Chhu (Mother River) and Pho Chhu (Father River) and the coronation site of the king. Its river setting, recent renovation and surrounding jacaranda trees in full bloom made for a magnificent sight, while inside were huge prayer wheels (figure 33) and a riot of dzong art (figure 34).

The bus took us over the Dochhu La (3,116 m), with its 108 chortens commemorating a battle, and into Thimphu, Bhutan's capital city. The juxtaposition of ancient buildings and Wi-Fi cafés, traffic-light-free road junctions and stylish hotels, pilgrims endlessly circling ancient gompas and businessmen in Savile Row suits, were signs of a city at the crossroads. Most importantly, however, the upmarket Phuntsho Pelri Hotel had hot baths and clean beds.

As everyone gathered together over evening drinks to watch a dance routine by pretty Bhutanese girls, I took on the chairman's role and summarised the wonderful trip. This led to a discussion about our older members. Several had not fared well and were slow at high altitude. I imagined that some might not return for more suffering. On our first expedition, the oldest

Pilgrim

person had been Frank Davies aged 49 and at the time we all thought him ancient. Now we had participants in their 70s and I was 67. It was time for a change in leadership. I announced my retirement as chairman and passed the baton to Chris. Alex would remain secretary and I would become ceremonial president.

We retired to the bar for Chilean red wine, followed by a nightclub. The perfect way to end an enchanting trip to the Land of the Thunder Dragon.

Thimphu

If Thimphu was the end of the trip for most it was not quite over for everyone. Rosalyn, Mary and Barbara (the wives of Pete, Ian Chesner and myself, respectively) arrived from London for a holiday. We had a happy reunion then saw the others off to Paro for their flights to London.

Although it may seem so sometimes, this narrative is not only about holidays but also about medical research. On our return to the Tiger's Nest monastery the next day, I offered Barbara some acetazolamide prophylaxis. I was mocked for being obsessed with drugs, but I thought it would help her acclimatise and improve her strength at 3,000 m. Normally, climbing a few hundred metres would be no problem but all day she felt exhausted, with no strength in her legs. I blamed the altitude but realised it might not be that simple. Some hypoxia chamber experiments suggested that acetazolamide reduced exercise performance at altitude, but there had been few field experiments. Yes, there were still questions to be answered. These thoughts sowed the seeds that led to three more research expeditions – two to the Alps and a return to Chimborazo in 2016. BMRES wasn't finished just yet.

Publications

1. Edsell M, Wimalasena Y, Malein W, Ashdown K, Gallagher, C, Imray CHE, Wright AD, Myers SD and Birmingham Medical Research Expeditionary Society. High-intensity intermittent exercise increases pulmonary interstitial edema at altitude but not at simulated altitude. Wilderness and Environmental Medicine 2014; 24: 409-415 doi:10.1016/j.wem.2014.06.016.
2. Imray C, Chan C, Stubbings A, Rhodes H, Patey S, Wilson, M, Bailey D, Wright AD and Birmingham Medical Research Expeditionary Society. Time course variations in the mechanisms by which cerebral oxygen delivery is maintained on exposure to hypoxia/altitude. High Altitude Medicine and Biology 2014; 15: 21-27. doi: 10.1089/ham.2013.1079.
3. Sagoo RS, Hutchinson C, Wright A, Handford C, Parsons H, Sherwood V, Wayte S, Nagaraja S, Ng'Andwe E, Wilson MH, Imray CHE and BMRES. Magnetic Resonance investigation into the mechanisms involved in the development of high altitude cerebral edema. Journal of Cerebral Blood Flow and Metabolism 2017: 37(1):319-331.
4. Wimalasena Y, Windsor J and Edsell M. Using ultrasound lung comets in the diagnosis of high-altitude pulmonary oedema - fact or fiction? Wilderness and Environmental Medicine 2013; 24: 159–164.

Fig 1. Back row; left to right: *Nick Kalson, Will Malein, John Milles, Ian MacLennan, Kyle Pattinson, Mark Wilson, Pete Forster, Ian Chesner, Colin Chan. Middle row: Helen Hoar, Hannah Rhodes, Mark Edsell, Alex Wright, Chris Imray, Susannah Patey, Sarah Clarke. Front row: Tshering Aku, Steve Myers, Jo Bradwell, Kinley, Owen Thomas, Yash Wimalasena, Tshering Drox.*

*Fig 2.
Kuzuzangpo La -
welcome*

Fig 3. *View from Olathang Hotel over the Paro Valley*

Fig 4. *Taktshang Goemba or Tiger's Nest*

Fig 5. *Looking up to the Tiger's Nest*

Fig 6. *Kyichu Lhakhang Dzong in Paro*

Fig 7. *Sharna campsite*

Fig 8. *Yak charge*

Fig 9. *Jomolhari from Soi Thangthanka camp*

Fig 10. *Typical house decorated with a tiger and penis*

Fig 11. *Breakfast at Jangothang*

Fig 12. *Sarah on the Alticycle with Yash and Helen*

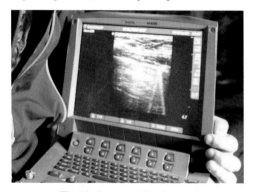

Fig 13. *Lung comet by ultrasound*

Fig 14. *Nyile La*

Fig 15. *Jichu Drake*

Fig 16. *Breakfast at Lingshi camp*

Fig 17. *John with facial oedema at Lingshi camp*

Fig 18. *Lingshi Dzong*

Fig 19.
Yak fuel at Lingshi

Fig 20.
Ancient juniper at Lingshi

Fig 21. *Gombu La*

Fig 22. *Will leaving Shomuthang*

Fig 23. *Robluthang camp*

Fig 24. *Owen and Helen at Sinche La*

Fig 25. *Yak herders*

Fig 26. *Into Limithang camp*

Fig 27. *Lammergeyer or bearded vulture*

Fig 28. *Laya camp*

Fig 29. *Masang Gang*

Fig 30. *Night writing with Kyle at Mo Chhu*

Fig 31. *Giant Himalayan spruce*

Fig 32. *Punakha Dzong and Mo Chhu (Mother River)*

Fig 33. *Giant prayer wheels in Thimphu*

Fig 34. *Dzong art*

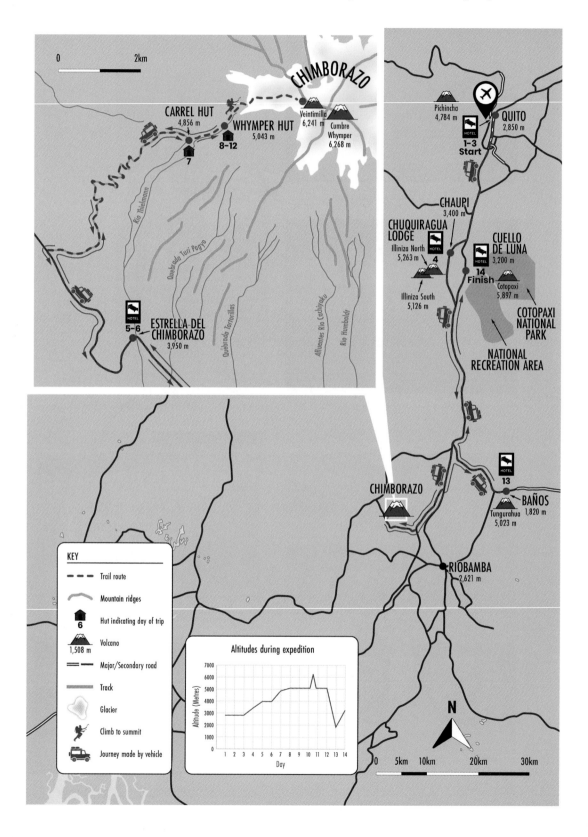

Chapter 14
Chimborazo revisited – January 2016

The summit of Chimborazo at dawn

Exercising to exhaustion

Climb if you will, but remember that courage and strength are nought without prudence, and that a momentary negligence may destroy the happiness of a lifetime.

– Edward Whymper, Scrambles Amongst the Alps

Summary: Chimborazo, sitting close to the equator, and arguably the highest peak in the world, became the target for our 14th expedition. We wanted a high hut for our experiments, no low-level studies such as in Bhutan, at a mere 4,000 m. The rejuvenated Whymper Hut (5,043 m) on the western flanks of the mountain was ideal. There, in 1979, we had shown the benefits of acetazolamide in preventing acute mountain sickness. Could we repeat that scientific success with a different drug? The hypotensive agent losartan, it was suggested, might improve exercise performance at altitude. After a 5-day ascent, we tested 20 people on an exercise bike, ten taking losartan and ten taking placebo. Daily venous bloods, oxygen samples, 24-hour urines plus psychological tests made a busy schedule. Three of us managed to climb the mountain in bitterly cold conditions.

Expedition members: Kimberly Ashdown, Jo Bradwell (experiments leader), Susie Bradwell (medical student), Patrick Cadigan (medical officer), Ian Chesner, Alex Clarke (medical student), Sarah Clarke, John Delamere (logistics), Mark Edsell, Carla Gallagher, Chris Imray (expedition and climbing leader), Brian Johnson (medical officer), Cassim Ladha, Abigail Letchford (film), Chris Lewis (medical student), Hannah Lock (medical student), Sam Lucas, Ian MacLennan (quartermaster), Will Malein, Steve Myers (engineer), Charles Newman (medical student), John Simmons, Owen Thomas, Alex Wright (deputy leader) (figure 1).

$\mathcal{D}eep$ breath in, deep breath out; deep breath in, deep breath out. Keep climbing. Ignore the leg pains and heaving chest. Keep counting: 85, 86, 87; 13 more steps then time for a rest. At least try to keep ahead of the slowest. Only 500 metres more to the Whymper Hut (5,043 m), high on the flanks of Chimborazo. I am so sluggish, since I have just completed chemotherapy for prostate cancer. In the past I would have been at the front. Now I am at the back. Susie, my 23-year-old daughter, is carrying my rucksack. My only burden is a 24-hour urine collection for proteinuria measurements, which has spilt into my daysack, soaking my balaclava.

A hundred steps completed, I sit down to gaze at the volcanic desolation: huge seams of ash and decaying lava. Green flecks of vegetation struggle for survival among the grit. Chimbo has not erupted for 750 years but it is a sleeping colossus biding its time. It is the biggest mountain in Ecuador's 'Valley of Volcanoes' and arguably the highest mountain in the world. Because of the Earth's waistline bulge, induced by its spin, its summit (6,268 m) is 2,200 m further from the centre of the Earth than the top of Mt Everest (8,848 m). Thankfully, the atmosphere also bulges so oxygen pressures are maintained, a reassuring thought in the thin air. Across the valley, Cotopaxi bears the scars of a recent explosion, while Tungurahua, its summit smoking threateningly, dwarfs the neighbouring town of Baños.

I am shaken out of my reverie by Marco Castillo, our guide: "Time to move on."

'One, two, three…' I start counting again. Ten minutes later I am at the Whymper Hut, surrounded by welcoming friends congratulating me. I arrive just as the mist clears, revealing Chimbo's mighty ice cliffs shining in the morning sun. The summit is not for me this time, but the year-long preparations have been worth it. This trip has been driven partly by nostalgia and partly by research but for the moment it is all about a beautiful mountain.

Seven days earlier, at 2.30 am on Saturday 16 January, we had been in front of the Medical School in Birmingham. Light rain was a kindly reminder of why the equator and the clear dry air of the Andes were so enticing. Ten of us were huddled in the cold alongside Helen and Patsy who were there to see off their spouses (John Delamere and Patrick). Barbara, my wife, had thought better of it and stayed in bed.

Thirty-seven years earlier, in September 1979 (chapter 2), I had stood at that very place: young, strong and keen to see Chimborazo. Alongside me now stood only two others from that earlier age, John Delamere and Alex Wright. The ghosts and memories of over 100 members who had been on 12 intervening expeditions hovered in our thoughts as we loaded the minibuses for Birmingham Airport. Remarkably, we were going to perform experiments on acetazolamide and urine, comparable studies to those carried out in 1979. I need to explain.

On that 1979 expedition to the Whymper Hut, we had shown that acetazolamide could be used to prevent mountain sickness. It worked by increasing oxygen levels in the body, thereby improving organ function and overall well-being. In the intervening years many studies had confirmed our findings, making acetazolamide a widely used medication at high altitude. However, there were nuances to the drug that we had only recently appreciated. On two expeditions to the Alps, we had found that when older members of the group (over 60) took acetazolamide their exercise performance was reduced (chapter 16, expeditions 10 and 11).

This led us to wonder whether other medications could increase oxygen concentrations but also have a beneficial rather than detrimental effect on exercise. Owen Thomas had pointed out that Sherpas, who were renowned for their amazing strength at altitude, had specific genes that helped them perform well (reduced activity of genes encoding angiotensin-converting enzyme, ACE). Similarly, white Caucasians who had 'Sherpa-type' genes were more able to climb to 8,000 m without supplemental oxygen and were more likely to reach the summit of Mont Blanc than people with more common genes. Since the effect of Sherpa-type genes could be mimicked by taking the commonly used hypotensive drug losartan, we decided to test its effect on exercise at high altitude. Could we give ourselves 'Sherpa strength' with a pill, we wondered?

It would be preferable to test our hypothesis in the high mountains rather than during a short-term chamber experiment. More fun certainly, but also more realistic from a climber's viewpoint. The Whymper Hut, high on the flanks of Chimborazo at 5,043 m, would be an ideal experiment location. Furthermore, there was the prospect of climbing the giant volcano. It would be a mountaineering challenge, but a great prize since it is the highest peak in Ecuador. We had put three climbers on the summit in 1979; could we be more successful on a second attempt?

Unfortunately, the Whymper Hut had been semi-derelict for many years so there were doubts about its availability. The Ecuadorian Army had been tasked with its refurbishment but had made little progress. However, John Paredes of Andean Adventures had recently taken over its lease, with a target opening date of January 2016, but we wouldn't know if it would be ready until we arrived in Quito. The next highest accommodation on Chimborazo was the Carrel Hut (4,856 m) but it was too small for our needs. Although it could sleep many people, there was no space for experiments. This would force us into tents where bad weather would jeopardise our studies.

Exactly on time, two minivans arrived at the Medical School to collect us, our rucksacks, 20 blue metal boxes of experimental equipment plus three white polystyrene boxes containing 60 kg of dry ice. By 3 am we were at Birmingham Airport waiting at the front of a queue for the 6 am flight to Amsterdam. We had plenty of time. The desks didn't even open for another half-hour. Furthermore, we were confident KLM would take the extra luggage since it had been booked six months earlier and guaranteed by the airline. We reflected on those occasions when a strong boot under the weighing scales artificially reduced excess baggage weight.

Our check-in desk opened, with John and myself at the front of the queue to start the loading – two bags per person, comprising one personal rucksack and one equipment box. But no! Politely and firmly the equipment boxes were refused. They had no record of our extra baggage allowance and John Delamere had no written proof. Although two check-in bags were permitted for the inter-continental leg of our journey (Amsterdam to Quito), only one bag was allowed to Amsterdam and each extra kilo would be £7. At 22–23 kg per box and with 23 boxes, that was a total of £3,542! We were told to pay at the ticket desk, which opened in half an hour. Our protestations fell on deaf ears. Behind us, the team looked on in horror. We were instructed to move aside so that others could board while we found the money. We demanded to see the manager, but she was the manager. Would we like to pay by credit card?

We could not believe what was happening after all our meticulous preparation. The team milled around during a tense hour-long stand-off. Departure time was edging closer, with the airline under no obligation to fly us.

A 4 am phone call to our contact at the travel agent followed. Not the best time of day to negotiate our way out of an impasse. A lively female voice replied. We thought we had got her out of bed but she was in Australia and, because of the 11-hour time difference, she was thankfully not upset by our call. The woman remembered our expedition and, after speaking to the KLM ticket desk manager, advised us to begin putting the team through with one bag each. As we started loading, the manager pointed out that if we had paid for the flight that day, we would be allowed two bags of 23 kg to Amsterdam and not just one. That made no sense. She relented and, with the battle won, they agreed to take the lot.

Since a few of the boxes and personal bags were large, they had to be loaded separately. Looking anxiously at the clock, we scurried around the terminal to find the 'oversize' counter where we were last in the queue. We did have two 26 kg boxes, a little overweight. I stuck my boot under the scales to reduce one to 20 kg, just for old time's sake. Some habits die hard.

We were quizzed about the contents of each box and I had no worries apart from three polystyrene boxes full of dry ice. Although within the limit for personal allowance for 24 people (3 kg each), 60 kg might take some explaining. But no one batted an eye-lid even when Susie owned up to the contents.

Departure is always an anxious time. If any of the boxes were to go missing or be delayed, it would severely compromise the research, as we had found on previous occasions. With all bags accepted, we hurried though a pleasantly uncrowded security area as the last passengers onto the plane, with just six minutes to spare. Why did the start of expeditions have to be so stressful? John Delamere had spent months painstakingly planning everything to avoid just these problems.

We had a scheduled two-hour connection time in Amsterdam for the flight to Quito. Plenty of time, but after a second de-icing we were an hour and a quarter late departing, leaving a worryingly short time in Schiphol Airport. It was only a 50-minute flight but then we circled over Amsterdam waiting for a landing slot. It was starting to look bad. As we finally got off the plane at the terminal building, I watched through a window of the aircraft as our blue boxes were unloaded. The delicate CO_2 boxes were plastered with numerous large red stickers that pronounced 'FRAGILE' and 'THIS WAY UP' but they were tossed onto a truck with everything else. It was a 15-minute fast march across the airport to the international departure gate where we arrived with 10 minutes to spare. We might make it to Quito but would the luggage?

We filed on to the KLM 777 in the sleet and misery of Schiphol Airport, only to be delayed yet again. I sat next to Susie and explained my worries. A £50,000 research expedition had almost fallen at the first hurdle. We departed 90 minutes late, crammed into small seats, but with 5 mg of temazepam and a glass of red wine, Morpheus took me.

The 11-hour flight was finally over. The plane dropped below the surrounding volcanic peaks to the huge modern airport. There were anxious moments as we queued by the baggage carrousel, but much to our relief all the research boxes and personal bags arrived undamaged – 47 in total. Inevitably, our unusual loads were spotted and hauled over for inspection. We did not have any import permits but hoped they would not be impounded. Chris Lewis was our Spanish translator. With a big smile and lots of charm he started to explain the expedition. I scurried over with the contents lists. Thankfully, they only opened two boxes, which contained cameras and bike parts – nothing remotely suspicious. I explained it was a doctors' group and showed them my university card. No bribes or tips were suggested. With smiles all round, we moved out triumphantly into the warm evening air. Pichincha volcano towered above us.

A bus took us from the airport to the modern Embassy Hotel near the town centre. Anticipating our needs, the hotel manager had set aside a seminar room especially for us, our equipment and the experiments. Our liaison officer, Javier from Mountain Expeditions, casually appeared for a quick chat. By the time we got to bed it was 3 am at home, plenty enough action for the first 24 hours.

Inevitably, we were busy during our two days in Quito making final arrangements for the expedition. We initially met in the seminar room after breakfast for Chris, John Delamere and me to present the expedition's research details. Javier followed, explaining the mountain ascent profile, accommodation and travel arrangements. Then we then came to the issue of climbing Chimborazo. Most of us wanted to try since the summit was only 1,200 m above the Whymper Hut. However, Javier stated that at the moment it was too dangerous, with no snow cover over hard ice. Not a place for novices. Chris, who had climbed Everest, was sceptical, suspecting that is was easier to put people off than to organise the climb. It was not an encouraging first morning of an expedition.

After a walk around Quito's Spanish Old Town, basking in Sunday's festive mood (figure 2), we were back at the hotel to start the 24-hour urine collections. We also checked that all the experimental equipment was intact. Remarkably, everything seemed to work perfectly, including the blood-gas analyser and the Alticycle with all its ancillary equipment. Dinner followed at the Magic Bean restaurant with liberal supplies of surprisingly good Ecuadorian cabernet sauvignon and sauvignon blanc.

The next morning, with a little help from jet lag, we breakfasted at 6 am and were then into the experiments: A venous blood team was led by Alex Wright, a blood gases team by Sarah, a urine team by John Delamere and an exercise test team by Steve, while the clinical team comprised Brian and Patrick. The target was two hours for everything apart from the exercise tests. We managed 2½ hours, which was pretty good for a first attempt. The five students pitched in while I recruited Abi and Cas to help with filming the expedition.

Particularly successful was the blood-gas analysis. On several expeditions, we had struggled with the technology. On the previous trip to Chimborazo (chapter 2), we had recruited the brilliant assistance of Bernard Coles to operate a primitive analyser but had struggled on later trips without his help. I remembered on the Everest trip that a team of people had spent several days desperately trying to obtain a few dubious results. For many expeditions we had given up measuring blood gases altogether. But since then, state-of-the-art instruments using robust solid-state electronics had been developed. We had chosen

Abbott i-STAT

the hand-held Abbott i-STAT. Tiny blood samples were loaded on small cartridges that were pushed into the instrument like a credit card into a reader. Results were displayed minutes later. A new one, at £13,000, was too much for our budget, but a second-hand instrument was bought on eBay for £3,000 and it worked perfectly. We could test all 24 of us within a couple of hours, including repeats. It was unimaginably easier to use than the earlier instruments.

However, we had other important issues to solve, the first being canisters containing calibration gases for the K4b2 gas analyser that we used for measuring oxygen consumption on the Alticycle (chapter 10). The pressurised containers were not allowed on the plane. This meant special air freight for their delivery from the UK. We had started organising this in June, giving us six months. It was just as well. It took three months just to establish that they couldn't be obtained in Ecuador. It took another month to find out that they could not be exported from England. This was because the UK supplier had a head office in the USA that only supplied its products to Ecuador directly from Texas. After four months of trying we had got nowhere. In desperation, we contacted the British Embassy in Quito and the department of anaesthetics at the University of Quito. Every attempt failed. Over a further two months including Christmas and the New Year, there was no progress. With the days ticking by, we finally arranged for the gases to be flown from Texas to a specialist importer in Quito. In a flurry of activity with extra payments for registered transport, we tracked the airway bill number across the Gulf of Mexico to Central America and finally Quito. We had two days to spare; all we had to do was collect them from the importer.

The second job was to obtain dry ice. Although we had bought 60 kg from the UK, we needed 40 kg weekly to keep our planned blood and urine collections frozen. Through a personal contact with Zurita Laboratories, a diagnostics company in Quito, we collected 40 kg from their offices with another 40 kg to be delivered to the Whymper Hut and another 40 kg on the day of our return flight. Furthermore, they had obligingly collected our precious calibration gas canisters from the importer.

The third problem was electrical power – we needed generators. Although we had been assured that electricity would be available at the huts on Chimborazo, we weren't taking chances. John had seen some in a Kiwi store so we bought two new ones plus cables for $950 and took them back to the Embassy Hotel. They started perfectly. We were very pleased (figure 3). It had taken several hours to find them, including being offered some for rent at $1,200 with a $6,000 deposit. Why would one pay ten times more than the price of a new generator just to rent? It had been a scam that John Simmons quickly spotted.

With most issues resolved by early afternoon, everyone climbed Pichincha, a large volcano looming over Quito that famously erupted in 2004 covering Quito in ash. Everyone, that is, apart from John Simmons and I. We sat in the hotel lounge chewing the cud with Javier, our liaison officer. He had a lackadaisical attitude, had not been the least bit helpful with finding generators, knew nothing about the habitable state of the Whymper Hut and said Chimborazo was too dangerous. Chris was particularly irritated and just didn't believe what he said. Nevertheless, we tried to have a civilised conversation about Cayambe as an alternative mountain. With its lower height of 5,700 m, perhaps everyone could ascend. We resolved nothing. We would put off climbing decisions until we were on the mountain and in the hands of our real guides, Freddie Tipan and Marco Castillo.

At 4 pm, the bus arrived from Pichincha and out poured our team desperate for a wee. Relief of bursting bladders and filling of urine containers came before stories of their climb. The 2-litre bottles were nowhere near large enough for the 24-hour urine collections. Before the climb, cries of anguish had been heard, with demands for second bottles. Now they were even louder. Sarah had produced a remarkable 2.8 litres by lunchtime. John Delamere, in charge of urines, dutifully aliquoted small samples into 25 ml universal containers and handed back re-sterilised bottles. Soon, all the spare containers had been handed out but there were still cries for more. We would have to find bigger pots in the morning.

Bladders sorted, they told their stories. After ascending part-way in a cable car, they had climbed to 4,800 m, including a spectacular walk to the edge of the volcanic crater. Only Cas had climbed a difficult rock route near the summit that I had ascended in 1979 with Frank Davies during a massive thunderstorm. I congratulated them on their success, for they had climbed nearly 1,000 m further from the centre of the Earth than the top of Mount Everest.

The next morning, refreshed, getting over jet lag and with thoughts of our adventures on Chimborazo, the different teams set about the daily experiments with gusto: blood pressures, venous blood samples, ear lobe pricks for blood gases, urine collections and clinical interviews for symptoms of mountain sickness. We also managed to buy eight four-litre plastic bottles for urine collections; surely, they would be big enough? Hopefully, having to carry so much urine around all day would discourage excessive drinking.

In late morning a bus took us south for two hours to the Chuquiragua Lodge in Chaupi (3,400 m). First through Quito's busy suburbs then onto the Pan-American Highway and volcano alley, which included Atacazo, Antisana, Corazón and Cotopaxi in the distance covered in cloud.

The lodge was in a field with a central restaurant surrounded by numerous small bedroom chalets (figure 4). Each charming room was named

Cotopaxi

after a surrounding volcano. Nearby were 5,000 m peaks, including dramatic views up to Illiniza, which we had climbed in 1979. The twin summits looked awesome 2,000 m above the lodge.

After lunch, we had a two-hour acclimatisation walk in the thinning air. But we had to be back for 4 pm to hand in our urines to John Delamere, with Susie acting as first assistant. Thankfully, the exercise of the afternoon meant fewer people had exceeded the capacity of their bottles. Dinner was in a large wood-panelled restaurant and washed down with elegant local wine. This was certainly not a teetotal trip.

Each morning's work was becoming more efficient: an early breakfast, then quickly into the half-dozen experiments. However, Hannah, bless her, had added a study on cognitive function – the King–Devick test. She was a student from Warwick and very keen for her own project. She had charmed us all in Birmingham with her enthusiasm and hard work. With Chris's support, the project got the go-ahead provided ethics permission could be obtained. There had been no news before departure so I assumed we were spared further studies. Excitedly, she showed me an email that had just arrived. It had been passed by the ethics committee that very day.

The test comprised reading aloud a series of single digit numbers from left to right and line by line to detect suboptimal brain function. It might be a useful tool to assess cognitive performance during the early stages of mountain sickness. We agreed it could be performed at the next three altitudes and again after the exercise tests.

Marco Cruz

Jobs completed, we headed for Estrella del Chimborazo, the hotel of Marco Cruz, high on Chimborazo's southern flank (3,950 m; figure 5). This involved a 4-hour bus journey south via Ambato and Riobamba (figure 6). To welcome us was Marco himself, who we had last met 37 years earlier (chapter 2). He had been our tour guide when we were last on Chimborazo (figure 7). Since then he had become an Ecuadorian climbing superstar. In 1979, we were sceptical of his claim to be a Chamonix guide and to have climbed around the world, but it had all been true. He had been chosen as the best mountaineer in Ecuador for many years and the top climbing instructor of his generation. As author of several mountaineering books, he was truly the father of Ecuadorian climbing.

His estanza comprised three Tyrolean-style mountain chalets full of memorabilia from around the world – dozens of photographs of famous climbers plus hundreds of old mountaineering and skiing artefacts. The world's climbing history in beautiful buildings tucked into a remote corner of Ecuador. Outside were 100 hectares of fenced-in mountainside enclosing a herd of alpacas and stone carvings of fertility rocks from the Quechuan religion (figure 8). Through panoramic windows, Chimborazo's summit glaciers glistened in the sun. It was extraordinary. Having known Marco all those years ago, I showed him a photograph of us together from 1979 (figure 7). He was just two days younger than me, having been born in Riobamba to Quechuan and Spanish parents on 24 June 1945.

Nostalgia over, we settled down to the 4 pm urine measurements, which spilled over into our 7 pm conference (figure 9). There was a vigorous debate about plans for the next few days until Marco told us about the Whymper Hut. Remarkably, it was being finished specially for us, with full meals laid on. We would be the first visitors in many years. And, with his vast climbing experience on Chimborazo, he thought an ascent was possible despite the difficult ice. There followed an excellent meal in a beautiful dining room, a hut environment similar to the very best the Alps can offer, but in the middle of the Andes. What a great hotel Mr Chimborazo had built!

The next day was set aside for acclimatisation. 'Climb high, sleep low' as the advice goes. All but John Simmons and myself marched up to 4,700 m, crossing the tiny Rio Humboldt towards the clouds that shrouded Chimborazo. While the rest climbed, Marco invited us for wine at his nearby house (figure 8), which, like the hotel, was full of historic climbing photos and other paraphernalia. On a detailed map entitled 'Nevado Chimborazo', Marco pointed out his very own glacier – Glacier Marco Cruz – that flowed towards his estanza. He explained that Chimbo has three craters, one of which was still active but had last erupted 750 years ago and accounted for much of the surrounding lava and ash debris. In 1801, the great Prussian explorer Alexander von Humboldt had travelled along the track at the bottom of his garden, but his summit attempt had failed 300 m short of the top. The mountain had been last surveyed in 2010 by a German group that had re-calculated the height of the Whymper Hut at 5,043 m, 35 m higher than in 1979. Over the last few months, the mountain had been covered in ash from an eruption of Cotopaxi, 60 miles away. Black debris had melted what little snowfall there had been over the winter. This meant that the dreaded penitentes on the summit ice cap were fully exposed. An ascent would be difficult. I wondered if any of us would climb it.

That night I lay awake anticipating the following day's journey. This was the big ascent day to the Whymper Hut. From 3,900 m to 5,043 m but at least descending 200 m to the Carrel Hut to sleep. There was bound to be some mountain sickness; I just hoped not too much.

Breakfast was again at 6.30 am, with blood gases, bloods, urines (figure 10) and clinical examinations at 7 am: the same routine, but faster and more efficient. I briefly stepped in to help with Owen's ear lobe sample since the team had failed twice. A couple of brutal stabs and a good squeeze. It was successful but I was not invited back. Everyone preferred Ian Chesner, with his warm cuddly hands and gentle ear rubbing (figure 11). Quite a hit with the girls.

We ascended steeply past metre-thick ash layers lining the road. Drizzle, mist and low scrubby grass were reminiscent of Wales but vicunas and volcanic debris reminded us of our Andean adventure. The route wound up to the Great Arenal and into Chimborazo National Park. A beautiful entrance gate welcomed us, together with passport checks, then it was up though clouds to the Carrel Hut (figure 12). Nearly 900 m of ascent in 40 minutes.

The modernised hut had recently been leased by John Paredes who, although Ecuadorian, had a broad Canadian accent from his upbringing in Toronto. Charming, energetic and organised, he had made a huge effort to accommodate our requirements. Willing hands unloaded the bus and put our overnight bags in one of the two 22-bed dormitories, leaving two of us on the floor. With the help of eight porters, we carried the medical equipment up to the Whymper Hut (figures 13 to 15). They did three trips while we struggled up the well-marked kilometre-long path just once. It was quite different from 37 years earlier when we had clambered over boulders covered in deep snow with ponies and horses carrying the equipment. The dramatic reduction in the snow on the mountain compared with our previous trip was obvious. It was clear evidence of global warming.

The Whymper Hut had areas of drying cement from the rushed attempts to finish it. We were indeed the first visitors. It was not even officially open. Completely refurbished, it was ideal for our purpose. Strange that in 1979 we had been early occupants of the original building.

The experiments were set up at the end of one bunkroom for the following morning, with urine studies in the shower area. Everything was completed by 5 pm so we descended in rapid order to the busy Carrel Hut, where we sat in the dining area, happy that everything was ready for the morning. Chris was on fine form, revelling in the high-altitude environment with tales of Everest and other adventures. A good dinner followed but there was no wine or beer as alcohol was illegal at high-altitude huts. We would have to bring up our own. By 8 pm we were mostly worn out, or suffering from the altitude, with mild headaches and poor appetites.

Climbers' monument at the Carrel Hut

Finally, the four big experimental days were upon us – seven days after leaving Birmingham. I was up first at 4.30 am to start packing my bag. I hadn't slept well, disliking dormitories with loads of people snoring, farting, clambering out for a wee, banging and wobbling the double bunks in the dark. Being on a top bunk above Mark, I swung into gyrations every time he moved. But I wasn't alone – most of us had slept poorly, with headaches and periodic breathing, and it was too hot despite being freezing outside.

I was certainly feeling the altitude. I took nearly an hour just to pack my bag and get ready for our early breakfast, which was only a slice of banana bread and inedible scrambled eggs. Few had appetites and certainly not me. Outside, the giant volcano loomed above us in the clear morning air.

I handed Susie my big rucksack, which she duly shouldered and marched off while I could barely keep up. Maybe the acetazolamide I had taken for oedema was reducing my exercise ability, although it had certainly prevented symptoms of mountain sickness. I staggered up, overtaking only a few heavily laden porters, but received a warm welcome and hot tea on arrival.

As soon as we arrived at the hut, we started the experiments. Ten people surrounded the exercise bike (figure 16) and the expensive equipment: £50,000 of K4b^2 spectrophotometers (figure 17), £20,000 for the horizontal bike, £10,000 for the blood pressure monitors, £12,000 for the ultrasound scanners, £5,000 for the power lab to link them all together and £3,000 for a Nikon camera. It took nearly an hour to test each person, with ten planned for the day and ten for the following day. The exercise was designed to be strenuous and indeed it was. Everyone became exhausted and took some time to recover.

Allied to the exercise tests were ultrasound measurements of 'lung comets', a project that followed from studies in Bhutan but this time 1,000 m higher. Mark Edsell was in charge of the experiment but was not feeling well, so Chris, Owen and Will backed him up. Meanwhile, John Delamere and Susie were busy collecting timed exercise urine samples from everyone, together with the usual 24-hour samples at 4 pm.

Other tests were slotted in around the exercise tests. Alex Wright ran the blood team of Hannah, Abi, Susie and Chris Lewis. Venous blood was collected using butterfly needles and added to tubes containing a tiny amount of thrombin to help clotting. After 20 minutes they were centrifuged at 4,000 rpm for 10 minutes (figure 18) and 2 ml aliquots of serum put into five colour-coded tubes. Within two hours all samples were frozen in dry ice.

Blood gases were measured by Sarah and her team, comprising Ian Chesner, Owen, Chris Lewis and Will. The i-STAT instrument and cartridges were kept warm in a sleeping bag overnight and, while in use, were cuddled against a hot water bottle in a polystyrene box. Minutes after taking ear-lobe samples, pO_2, pCO_2 and pH were displayed on the i-STAT. It worked like a charm.

Among the first on the bike were the climbers, Chris Imray, Chris Lewis, Owen and Cas. As soon as their tests were completed, they could attempt Chimborazo. Another early subject was Mark Edsell because he felt poorly and was keen to start acetazolamide. His oxygen saturations were only 50% while most of us were in the 70–80% range. We watched him anxiously as he was strapped on the bike and connected to the various instruments, including an ECG (heart) monitor. He started cycling. He completed the first stage of three minutes without problems, as well as the next, but as the power requirements ramped up, he clearly began to struggle. As his oxygen saturations fell to 45%, he clutched his chest in pain and his ECG became abnormal (ectopic inverted P waves, to be precise). Patrick (a consultant cardiologist), Sarah (an intensivist) and Brian (an experienced GP) watched on with increasing alarm. It was too dangerous to continue. Patrick called a halt and examined his chest. There was no evidence of heart disease or pulmonary oedema, but what to do with him?

The crisis committee (Alex, Chris, Patrick, Brian, John Delamere and me) met in the quiet of the hut lobby to decide his fate. Clearly, he had mountain sickness with a risk of further deterioration. The bike had probably made him worse. The clinicians explained that he was not very communicative but, importantly, there was no evidence of cerebral or pulmonary oedema.

We all agreed that he should be immediately prescribed acetazolamide but what else? We had no oxygen, which left the choice of dexamethasone and/or an early descent. My opinion was that he ought to descend and that I should go with him. Needless to say, I had a vested interest since I quite fancied being at a lower altitude. Dexamethasone would probably work but it would take a few hours and if it failed then a night-time emergency descent would be required. Chris was all for giving him dexamethasone but what if dexamethasone didn't work? Suddenly, with no apparent unifying process, we all agreed he should descend immediately, just at the very moment that Mark poked his nose around the door and asked to go down. A night at Marco's lodge might be sufficient for recovery but if that wasn't low enough, he could do down to Riobamba.

John Delamere, who was next on the bike, also developed problems. He had started well but half-way through the exercise test his ECG showed multiple ectopic beats both atrial and ventricular. He didn't feel in any way distressed and was most surprised to see the medical team surrounding the ECG monitor. Patrick had not wanted to bring an ECG machine since it might spot such arrhythmias, which were most likely benign. But as Sam was very worried, Patrick called a halt.

I was oblivious to John's problems for Mark and I were already walking down to the Carrel Hut, accompanied by Chris Imray and Marco. From there, we bade farewell to Chris, climbed into a jeep with Marco, bumped down over the Great Arenal to the park gates then onto the tarmac road of the old Humboldt Pass. As we descended past Estrella del Chimborazo, Mark was still non-communicative and his headache was no different so we carried on to Riobamba. As we entered the town, two hours after leaving the hut, Mark suddenly brightened up and started talking. The lower altitude and higher oxygen levels had done the trick. We found a high-rise hotel near the city centre and signed in. Over a meal with Mark, who was back to his normal chatty self, we discussed the stress of the exercise test and the worries about others. It had been a long fraught day.

The two of us slept well at the lower altitude and delighted in a morning with no urines, no bloods, no ear pricks and no exercise tests. But up on the mountain it was the second day of the studies. How were they getting on, we wondered? Was I needed for some crucial piece of advice? But I was kidding myself. They would manage perfectly well without me – perhaps even better. But I missed them all and the camaraderie.

Marco collected us at 10 am and drove us to Estrella del Chimborazo, where Mark could acclimatise for another day. The mountain lodge was empty so we booked into the nicest room. All was quiet. It was a new experience for me to be excluded from an expedition.

Although I was at peace with the world, all was not well at the Whymper Hut. They had just prepared everything for the second day of exercise testing, the bike calibrated, all monitors attached to the first subject, lung water assessed. Then disaster. As the first victim started pedalling, the power recordings from the electronically coupled crankshaft stopped. Electrical connections were systematically checked, but anxiety gradually grew as the fault seemed to be in the bike's electronic unit. Finally, anxiety blossomed into full-blown consternation as the fault was traced to the electronic chip at the heart of the device.

As a team we were experienced at mending mechanical faults and being imaginative about finding alternative ways to obtain results, but a complex electrical fault was beyond our skills. The core of our expedition experiments looked doomed. Months of work were about to be ruined. We had no replacement power crank, whereas nearly everything else was duplicated. We were in a real fix.

Cas came to the rescue. He realised that, while the wiring looms in the device were properly connected, the electronics were locked, perhaps because of a power surge from the generator. The central processor would need resetting. Remarkably, he had brought a USB electronic toolbox. Also, a week before the expedition, John Simmons had suggested bringing a soldering iron. I could see no reason why, but chatting it through, we thought it might be useful. After heating the soldering iron using the transformer from the centrifuge, John very carefully removed a small battery from the bike's recording unit to expose the central processor chip. Cas downloaded a program from his toolbox and reprogrammed it. It was re-soldered and worked perfectly. Truly remarkable. It had taken four hours. The exercise team then managed to catch up on the tests over the afternoon and evening.

Earlier, Cas had mended the i-STAT blood-gas analyser. Sarah found that it would not calibrate properly and Cas overheard. Diagnostics on the instrument said that the terminals on the cartridges were not making contact. He noted that the cartridges did not seem to click properly into the dock. Looking into the instrument, it was apparent that one of the contacts had flicked out of place. Using a fine hair-clip, he pushed the small bar back while pressing the cartridge release button. A new cartridge was inserted and the instrument worked perfectly. Using an array of tools, a new software package and a hair-clip, Cas's capable hands had saved our research.

Contentedly ensconced in Estrella del Chimborazo, I was blissfully unaware of all these problems. Around 3 pm a bus came to collect us and by 4 pm we were back in the Whymper Hut. Relaxed, benefiting from two days at lower altitude, I walked in on a silent and glum group. They explained how the expedition had been on a knife-edge the day before, but perhaps more importantly, they were suffering from two more days of high-altitude exposure than me.

To deter tourists from interfering with the experiments, we put a big bold **'PRIVATE'** sign on the hut door. Since the hut was not officially open and we had booked all the space, we assumed we had full rights to its use, but this did not prevent curious climbers from entering. One American walked right past the exercise tests and into the urine room. He was stopped and told it was private but the Yank was upset and complained to someone he knew at the ministry. John Paredes was told off roundly while Alex had to write an apologetic letter to the Ministry of Tourism. He explained that we were undertaking clinical studies with confidentiality issues. Alex's letter did the trick.

We had planned two sets of exercise tests. The first was to compare losartan with placebo while the second set, over two more days, was to see if acetazolamide reduced exercise performance when given acutely. However, a bigger question on that third day at the hut was who would climb Chimborazo?

We had been full of bravado in Birmingham, but the reality of that huge volcano, its dangerous ice cliffs and the thin air deterred all but Chris Imray, Owen, Cas and Chris Lewis. Freddie Tipan and Marco Castillo would be their guides. Since Chris Lewis was inexperienced and there were only two guides, it was felt he should have his chance a day later. The five climbers for the first assault prepared for a 2 am start.

At 9 am the following morning, three climbers were visible descending from Chimborazo (figure 19) but there was no sign of the other two. We watched as they struggled on the ice slope leading down from the summit; then, an hour later, a lone figure staggered down to the hut. It was Cas. He was exhausted and suffering from mountain sickness; 6,000 m had been his limit, well below the summit. Hours later the others appeared, carefully picking their way down the path. They had climbed to the top, but only a secondary summit. The 'Whymper' summit at 6,263 m was only a little higher but it would have meant a long climb over rugged, impossibly exhausting penitentes.

Owen described the climb:

"What have I let myself in for?" It's 4 o'clock in the morning with the temperature a biting −20°C. I am at 6,000 m climbing at an oxygen pressure half that of sea level. Up ahead is our target: the summit of Chimborazo. As we climb in the dark, a faint mist melts away under a full moon while on all sides there are faint impressions of surrounding mountains. Hard glacial ice, narrowly lit by head torches, extends into inky shadows. There is a sense of profound isolation.

A tug on the rope; I am still gasping for oxygen but it's time to move again. The guide is better acclimatised than me, he seems barely out of breath. I look down nervously at my bright yellow crampons against the hard ice. Will they grip? The lack of snow on the 45° ice makes it too steep for all 24 points to bite at one time. I can only use the front four, forcing me onto tiptoe. With calves screaming in pain I only manage 20 steps before the guide's pace again proves too much. Each step sends shockwaves of pins and needles up my legs. This is a side effect of acetazolamide taken for experiments. With a half-life of 12 hours, I had hoped to excrete enough by now. It was becoming painfully obvious that it is still active in my body.

Five hours into the ascent, climbing has slowed to a crawl. I am well beyond my aerobic threshold; my respiratory rate is above 50 per minute and I am coughing repeatedly. Alternating panting and coughing, I suddenly notice dark specks in the snow. Am I coughing blood? Is this high-altitude pulmonary oedema? I panic but a nervous closer inspection reveals the black particles of a chocolate-chip brunch bar. Dismissing the foolishness, I look up the ice face and continue. I am climbing with Chris Imray, one of the world's experts on frostbite prevention. With the temperature dropping lower than anticipated, I fear his expertise may be needed.

Javid, one of our guides, shouts, "Cas (the third member of our group) needs to go down." He is confused, with headache and nausea. Cerebral oedema is a real concern. So far during the climb he has been incredibly strong. I had expected him to be the least affected by high altitude but he is becoming delirious so rapid descent is needed urgently. Javid clips Cas onto his rope, and both descend into the gloom.

With trepidation, I turn and continue upwards. On the equator, the overhead sun causes towering pinnacles and gullies of ice (penitentes) that are exhausting, and force us to ascend in line. The summit nears; the gradient decreases. The Sun's rays kiss the horizon in shades of pink and yellow as I climb onto a narrow ice ridge. Jagged volcanic peaks are silhouetted above the cloud line on the horizon, faint smoke rising from a volcano to the north. We are at 6,241 m (Veintimilla summit). The Whymper summit is a dreadful half kilometre further but only 27 m higher and not worth the extreme effort. After a brief grim celebration, we commence our descent.

Back at the Whymper Hut, the pain is forgotten, leaving excitement and the deeply satisfying pleasure of success. Despite no clinical symptoms or signs, my chest ultrasound scan shows sub-clinical pulmonary oedema. This may be far more common in high-altitude climbers than is realised."

The next day Chris Lewis climbed to the same subsidiary summit (figure 20).

But I missed their return for I was already half-way down the mountain again. On that fourth morning at the hut, I was approached by Patrick, who was worried about deteriorating eyesight. He had developed blurred vision shortly after his stint on the bike. The diagnosis was unclear but a retinal detachment with all its serious consequences had to be excluded. Patrick insisted I went with him to a hospital. He thought I would be the best person to talk my way into a hospital consultation. Since I had promised not to leave Susie again, we three packed our bags and bade farewell to our friends for the second time. Leaving the exercise team to finish their studies, we walked down with Marco Castillo and porters carrying our full bags. There would be no returning.

At the Carrel Hut we met John Paredes who offered to take us to Riobamba in his jeep. On the way down, he told his story. Although born in Guayaquil he had been bought up in Toronto. He had made money running a number of retail outlets and now was putting his enterprising nature into an Ecuadorian venture. As a business opportunity, he had taken a lease on both the Carrel and Whymper Huts in August, together with a café at the park entrance. It was he who had made the Whymper Hut ready for us on time and had fixed up beds, heating, electricity and meals. His energy and friendliness had made our expedition a success.

He drove us to Riobamba to rest briefly at his home with his Ecuadorian wife and young child. From there we took a taxi to a private hospital in Quito. In its marbled-floor emergency department, we were met by a charming unrushed casualty officer then a consultant ophthalmologist, and all within the hour. A side room had all the latest gadgets, which revealed a small vitreous haemorrhage. The treatment: sit upright for the next three weeks. There was palpable relief all round.

By now it was late evening, so it was back to the Embassy Hotel and a meal at a local pizza place. Next morning, Patrick's vision was a little better and he was much happier. We hired a van to take us to Baños. In perfect weather, we passed the still smoking Cotopaxi, ash covering its upper glaciers, as well as Illiniza, Antisana, Cayambe and Tungurahua, before arriving at the spa town of Baños. We stayed in luxury at the Jardinier de Camareros Hotel, with afternoon beers followed by dinner and wine at the Swiss Bistro. Patrick was much happier, keeping us entertained with his stories and jokes.

Tungurahua

While we were supping the delights of lower altitudes, the others completed their morning tests with great efficiency and walked up to Chimborazo's El Castillo ridge at 5,525 m. In perfect weather, many great volcanoes were visible, including Cotopaxi and Tungurahua. It was then back to the hut, where they packed everything and descended to Estrella del Chimborazo for the night.

We had allocated the last two days of the expedition for recovery at low altitude, so everyone descended on Baños (1,820 m) for a day of walking, river-rafting or just chatting: free from experiments. The thick air, rich forest smells, the buzz of cicadas and fine Chilean wine rejuvenated us. Above us loomed Tungurahua (5,023 m), still smoking from a huge eruption in 2014. In no time at all the suffering was forgotten.

We had a final night at Cuello de Luna in the Cotopaxi National Park, a 2½-hour drive towards Quito. It was dark and cloudy when we arrived, so there was no sign of Cotopaxi, but we had a very congenial evening dinner in a beautiful wooden hacienda.

There remained only the uncertainty of the return flight and our excess luggage. Once again, on our arrival at the departure gate, KLM had no knowledge of our extra allowance of two 23 kg bags each. To add to our irritation, they were only allowing 16 of us to fly. Chris Imray calmly explained that he was a surgeon and was on duty the following day. They had to let him on. Other passengers could be left behind, he argued – why us? After an hour of repeatedly complaining, we persuaded them to relent, but we were hassled all the way to the plane. Patrick was repeatedly checked for explosives. He was taken into a security tent with his pack, which they thought looked dangerous on an X-ray scanner. Surrounded by aggressive police and security guards, he thought he was lucky not to be jailed. Finally, and grateful to be free men, we were ushered onto the plane to be enveloped in the reassuring security of a KLM flight to Amsterdam. It had been a fortnight of suffering for a lifetime of memories.

"Where can we go next?" was on everyone's lips.

Postscript

Our research showed that we could not turn ourselves into Sherpas. Losartan did not make us super-strong high-latitude athletes as we had hoped. There was no difference between the placebo and the treated group for exercise performance, blood oxygen saturations or neuro-cognition. It did seem to improve sleep a little and reduced exercise proteinuria but, overall, the results were disappointingly negative.

Publications

1. Lewis CT, Malein WL, Chesner I, Clarke S on behalf of the Birmingham Medical Research Expeditionary Society. High altitude arterialised capillary earlobe blood gas measurement using the Abbott i-STAT. Journal of the Royal Army Medical Corps 2018; 164: 335-337.
2. Talks BJ, Bradwell SB, Delamere J, Rayner W, Clarke A, Lewis CT, Thomas OD, Bradwell AR. Urinary Alpha-1-Acid Glycoprotein is a Sensitive Marker of Glomerular Protein Leakage at Altitude. High Altitude Medicine & Biology 2018; 19; 295-298.
3. Clarke A, Ladha C, Wright A et al. Losartan may attenuate altitude-related sleep disturbance. BMJ Mil Health Epub ahead of print: doi:10.1136/jramc-2019-001308.
4. Joyce KE, Delamere J, Bradwell S et al. Hypoxia is not the primary mechanism contributing to exercise-induced proteinuria. BMJ Open Sport & Exercise Medicine 2020;6:e000662. doi:10.1136/
5. Lucas SJE, Malein ML, Thomas OD and BMRES. Effect of losartan on exercise at high altitude (5,035 m). BMJ Open Sport & Exercise Medicine. Submitted.

Photographs. CL: Courtesy of Chris Lewis

*Fig 1. **Back, left to right:*** *Cas Ladha, Carla Gallagher, John Delamere, Sarah Clarke, Sam Lucas, Susie Bradwell, Owen Thomas, Hannah Lock, Brian Johnson, Alex Clarke, Jo Bradwell, Patrick Cadigan, Steve Myers, John Simmons, Chris Lewis, Ian MacLennan, Ian Chesner. **Front:** Charles Newman, Abi Letchford, Kim Ashdown, Alex Wright, Freddie Tipan, Chris Imray, Mark Edsell, Will Malein.*

Fig 2. Quito festivities

Fig 3. Generators for sale: John, Steve and Ian

Fig 4. Chuquiragua Lodge

Fig 5. Estrella del Chimborazo

Fig 6. *Chimborazo from Riobamba*

Fig 7. *Marco and Jo in 1979 and 2016*

Fig 8. *Marco's house and Quechuan fertility rock*

Fig 9. *Evening conference at Estrella*

Fig 10. *Urines with John Del, Alex Clarke and Owen*

Fig 11. *Ear-lobe samples for blood gases*

Fig 12. *Carrel Hut*

Fig 13. *Hannah, don't drink so much; the urine bottle is heavy*

Fig 14. *Nearly at the Whymper hut: John Delamere and Patrick*

Fig 15. *Whymper hut below Chimborazo's summit glacier*

Fig 16. *Exercise test*

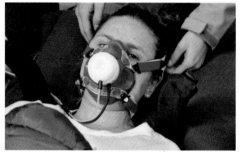

Fig 17. *K4b² gas analyser on Susie*

Fig 18. *Alex Wright centrifuging blood samples*

Fig 19. *Descending from the summit*

Fig 20. *Chris Lewis on the summit (CL)*

Fig 21. *Four summiteers: Chris Lewis, Owen, Freddie and Chris Imray*

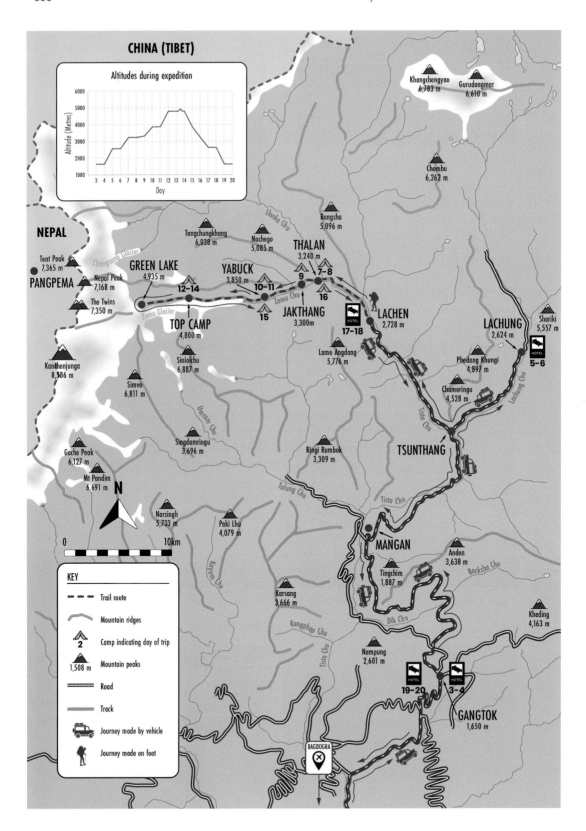

Chapter 15
Remote Sikkim – October 2019

East face of Kanchenjunga

A surfeit of beer

For the stone from the top for geologists, the knowledge of the limits of endurance for the doctors but above all for the spirit of adventure to keep alive the soul of man.

– George Mallory

Summary: We undertook a three-week trek to the remote north-east side of Kanchenjunga (8,586 m), the world's third highest mountain. In all, 64 Sherpas and porters helped us reach Green Lake, site of the base camp for the Indian Army ascent in 1977. We suffered blood, urine and interoception studies on the ascent, together with the waning monsoon until two days of clear weather at the top camp revealed Kanchenjunga in its full glory.

Expedition members: Kim Ashdown, Chris Bradley (MSc student), Jo Bradwell (leader), Catherine (Cat) Campbell (medical student), John Delamere, Mark Edsell, Hannah Lock, Kelsey Joyce (PhD student), Cas Ladha, Stephanie Larcombe (medical student), Abi Letchford (deputy medical officer), Chris Lewis, Rebekah Lucas, Sam Lucas, Will Malein (medical officer), Kyle Pattinson, Ben Talks (medical student), Owen Thomas (deputy leader) (figure 1).

The changing of the guard. The youngsters were taking over. Only John Delamere and I remained of the 17 keen young doctors that took to the Himalaya in 1977 (chapter 1). There were eight oldies on the last trip, to Chimborazo: now just two. On the first trip, Frank Davies was 49 – ancient in our eyes – yet I was now 74. What were the five students thinking? At their age, I would never have gone with a group of aging doctors, some 50 years older, even to the Himalaya.

Three of the students were studying medicine in Birmingham. Ben and Cat had won Arthur Thompson Trust travelling scholarships based on keen involvement with BMRES over the past three years. Ben had several publications, including one on urine proteins at altitude, and a distinction in research from the Medical School. Stephanie had joined recently but with an interest in research based upon a PhD in neurosciences from Oxford. In equal measure, Chris Bradley and Kelsey were worthy student participants: Kelsey was studying for a PhD on altitude proteinuria and Chris for an MSc on the effects of acetazolamide on breathing, and both were in the department of Sport and Exercise Science at the University of Birmingham (Sportex). The last new member was Sam Lucas's sister, Rebekah, who worked as a research scientist at Sportex.

Not too many experiments were planned. Bloods and urines by John, of course. It was a rite of passage − it wouldn't be an expedition without urine collections, ear pricks and blood samples. A more novel study was Kyle's on the interoception of breathing. Interoception is the body's perception of its inner functioning − as opposed to exterior perception. For example, few are aware of their own breathing except when it is problematic, such as in people with asthma, who are particularly conscious of their respiratory difficulties when they have an asthma attack. Kyle's project was to test individuals' sensing of their own breathing before and after ascending to 5,000 m (when breathing is challenging for many days because of oxygen deprivation) and to assess whether their perception of it had changed.

The baseline studies in Birmingham were on the two weekends before departure. Bloods and urines were collected and breathing perception measured.

Day 1. Departure date was Friday 4 October, for a 9.30 pm flight from London to Delhi by Air India. Nine of us left on a minibus from the Medical School, the departure point for 20 trips. Towed behind us was a trailer with 14 boxes containing equipment for experiments. Ian MacLennan and Alex Wright saw us off. There followed a slow journey in the early weekend traffic to Heathrow Airport, Terminal 2.

The flight departure is always a pressure point. Would the excess baggage be a problem? Would we have to pay extra charges? Thankfully, this time there were no issues. The medical boxes were accepted, although all had to be cleared through the over-sized baggage channel. It took only an hour. We wished them safe passage to Delhi. Relieved, we filed through the customs check with time to spare.

The travel arrangements had been through Mountain Kingdoms Ltd, a company that we had used successfully on previous trips. Steve Berry, the MD, advised us on a trek that would get us to 5,000 m. The Karakoram, our first choice, was risky since there was fighting on the Kashmir border, which left Sikkim, our second choice. Tim Harvey (a founding member of BMRES) had recently visited and said the area provided stunning views of Kanchenjunga, the world's third highest mountain. We had been to its north side in 1999 (Chapter 9) but a huge storm had hidden it from view and we had had a frightening escape. Perhaps we could see it from the east side instead.

The recommended high camp was at Green Lake, a frozen body of water five miles east of Kanchenjunga. It was remote, quiet and had wonderful views of the mountain.

The area would also provide interesting historical perspectives. Kanchenjunga and Sikkim were well known to Victorian high society, with nearby Darjeeling offering a refuge from the summer heat of Kolkata (or Calcutta as it was known then). The mountain was thought to be the highest in the world until 1852 when Mt Everest was identified. The famous plant collector, Sir Joseph Dalton Hooker, future president of the Royal Society and a close friend of Charles Darwin, had visited the area in 1848. Furthermore, the pre-war Everest expeditions that included Mallory and Irvine had taken our proposed route through the towns of Gangtok, Tsunthang and Lachen.

With a year to go, we put down a 10% deposit on the Mountain Kingdoms' trip with a departure date of October 2019. This was the longest pre-planning of any BMRES expedition. As with any date so far into the future, there is never a rush until the last minute. Planned ethics applications were late and indeed one was approved only two days before departure.

Day 2. After the 8-hour flight from London, we descended into the midday heat at Delhi's modern airport – quite some transformation from the 1970s and our first BMRES expedition. Our luggage arrived promptly, all 33 bags and boxes of it, but we had become too complacent. Our last three trollies, loaded with many medical boxes, were stopped at the customs check, just after I had passed through with all the relevant documentation. A frantic half-hour of texts followed, back and forth between those held up inside and Owen outside the airport. The combination lock numbers were relayed and the boxes finally opened to reveal the contents lists on the inner side of the lids. That was not enough. The officials wanted all the equipment invoices, of which we had none. Sam and Becky accompanying the boxes came to the rescue. They showed their university credentials and ethics permissions and explained it was a research expedition. Grudgingly they were allowed to proceed. My mistake – I should have been last, not five yards ahead.

Outside stood a fancy bus to take us to the nearby airport Holiday Inn, an ultra-modern building. We were provided with a group lunch at a 40% price reduction and ate our fill for 1,000 rupees (£12) in a beautiful glass-panelled dining room. Some of India had really modernised. While dining we met Chewang Motup and his wife Yanduk who ran RIMO Expeditions Ltd, a company that Mountain Kingdoms had engaged to organise our trip. They explained that while the monsoon was finished in Delhi, further east in Sikkim it was still pouring with rain and many back roads were impassable. Those roads might not be repaired by the time we arrived up-country in three days' time.

We were immediately impressed with Motup. He had 30 years' trekking experience and seemed to take real responsibility for our expedition's success. He had been *sirdar* on innumerable trips, including several with Chris Bonington and Doug Scott and he knew Alan Hinks well (the only British climber to have ascended all 14 8,000 m peaks). He was a member of the Alpine Club and a frequent visitor to the UK. He was even knowledgeable about the history of Britain's 'great game' with Russia and China in the 19th century.

Outside the modern time capsule of the Holiday Inn and a newly built metro, the old India showed its face. Crowds of people in typical Indian dress hung about, with flashes of bright colours in girls' saris and the occasional well-dressed businessman. Connaught Place, Lutyens' famous British Empire-style buildings, still had their rugged elegance, albeit somewhat unkempt and uncared for. Surrounding them, modern skyscrapers towered over buildings that had once done the towering. A Bollywood-style dance show boomed from 'The Inner Circle', while around it raced endless tuk-tuks, Lee Enfield motorbikes and cars to complete the cacophony.

Dusk descended fast, with the tuk-tuks continuing on their circular racecourse, hassling us for lifts if we stopped for a moment. The Saravana Bhavan restaurant, a dinner suggestion by Kyle, was a scruffy affair offering strange food supplemented with endless bottles of cooled water to help sweat away the evening heat. With dinner finished, it was back to the ultra-modern and under-used metro and the welcoming embrace of the Holiday Inn bar and a few bottles of Burgundy.

Day 3. The following morning, we were back to Delhi Airport for the 1,200 km flight to Bagdogra in West Bengal. We hassled all the bags and boxes through the gate with little proof of the excess baggage allowance except for '2LB' printed on the ticket receipt (abbreviation for two large bags we presumed). Despite moaning about the volume and the weights, the gate clerk eventually gave way. The force was with us as we boarded an Airbus A320, stressed but on time.

An hour into the flight, the great Himalayan mountain panorama appeared among large cumulus clouds: Dhaulagiri, Annapurna, Manaslu, Shishapangma, Everest and its great outliers, and finally Kangchenjunga partly hidden in a huge cumulonimbus tower. The monsoon was not finished! We descended into a smoggy haze of pollution and rainforest clouds at Bagdogra, the military airport serving Sikkim. Modern passenger jets contrasted with the shanty town and shabby buildings from a bygone colonial age. It was a small but clean airport, with a single baggage carousel that spewed out our 18 bags and 15 boxes. We were still fully intact. Outside, we were enveloped by a hot, humid, bustling Indian atmosphere with all its human and jungle smells. We were greeted again by Chewang Motup and his assistant, Tsewang. Charming, calm and quietly spoken, they gave us every confidence that we were in good hands.

From the airport at 160 m altitude, it was five hours by car to Gangtok, capital of Sikkim state. We were loaded into five taxis, with a small lorry for the bags. After a

Sikkim flag

brief lunch stop, it was north into the jungle alongside the huge Tista River, swollen with rains. Landslides and road erosion were ample evidence of the monsoon's huge impact. At one gap in the roadside barrier above the torrent, four people were gesticulating excitedly downwards. A car had just tipped over the edge. Our driver only briefly edged his foot off the accelerator as we drove on into the dusk.

The border town of Rongphu guarded the entrance to Sikkim state. It was manned by smart troops in very English-looking army uniforms. We needed visas and passport photos to enter. Prearranged, but Indian bureaucracy being what it is, further photos were needed. This entailed two hours of negotiation and cajoling by Motup while we wandered the main street to the sounds and sights of the Hindu festival of Durga Puja. This celebrated the Mother Goddess and the victory of the revered warrior goddess, Durga, over the evil buffalo demon Mahishasura.

We were in remote India.

Visas stamped, triple-checked and recorded for posterity, we continued in the dark to Gangtok (Nepalese for 'hilltop') at 1,650 m, and the Chumbi Residency Hotel, charming if somewhat basic.

On our arrival it was urine time and the start of the experiments. John and Kelsey were collecting both 24-hour and early-morning urine samples. Kelsey wanted to assess excretion of alpha-1-acid glycoprotein (a sensitive marker of hypoxia), while John was measuring the hypoxic diuretic response during both ascent to 5,000 m and the following descent, in other words, throughout the trip. That meant weeing into plastic bottles for almost three weeks. In parallel, hypoxia was to be measured from ear-prick samples using the Abbott i-STAT portable analyser together with finger pulse oximeters. Kelsey had borrowed 18 watch-sized oximeters from the Mayo Clinic, her previous employer. In use, the second-by-second recording device was worn on the wrist while the sensors were strapped to a finger using a sticky finger bandage. All the experiment boxes were placed in one of the bedrooms, as each of us clutched a brown three-litre urine pot with a bright yellow top, our constant companions from now on. We were also handed 200 ml early morning urine (EMU) pots.

As John was preparing the urine bottles with 0.5 ml of sodium azide preservative, three large polystyrene boxes containing 50 kg of dry ice appeared in the hotel foyer. This was a great relief. The serum and urine samples had to be frozen. From previous experience, we chose dry ice as the coolant but the nearest manufacturer was in Kolkata 425 miles to the south. While it was only one day by road from Kolkata to Gangtok, our final destination at Green Lake was many days more remote, so the dry ice might take five days by road and porter. From previous experience, we needed 30 kg every five days to keep the samples frozen, so we would need to start with four times more (120 kg) in the heat of Kolkata to take account of evaporation. This huge amount, together with dedicated road and porter transport, would cost over £4,000, and any part of the supply chain could easily be disrupted. Many doubted that such deliveries were possible in remote Sikkim.

Day 4. I shared a room with John, who set a 7 am start for collection of early morning urine samples. By 7.30 am, Kelsey and John had a full team operating. Meanwhile, ear pricks for i-STAT blood gases were run by Kim and the two Chrises, Sam operated the centrifuge as Owen took bloods, and others pitched in on different jobs. Our 'group doctors', Will and Abi, sat in the foyer taking clinical histories and examinations.

On a flat stretch of road near the hotel, Cas and Ben marked out a 50 m track for high-speed walking – 6 minutes as fast as possible. A Fitbit-type sensor placed on people's backs recorded every step and slip. The test? To see if walking deteriorated when the exercise was repeated at high altitude. In the surrounding jungle, exotic birds sang, insects buzzed and huge spiders devoured their prey.

By 1 pm, all was finished, just in time for lunch and an afternoon downpour – the monsoon was still active. Those venturing on a walk to the local temple were drenched.

By now, only one outstanding problem remained – the electricity source for the experiments. Mark, Cat and I had a project to minimise the use of fossil fuels by using solar panels and battery power. A Utah-based company called GoalZero produced a portable power station (a fancy name for a lithium battery) with 1.4 kWh storage capacity that was charged using 200 W solar panels. I had ordered one from the GoalZero distributor in The Netherlands, only to be told two months later they had none. Furthermore, GoalZero refused to deliver it from their office in Salt Lake City for fear of it exploding on an aeroplane. Amy (my PA) saved the day. She ordered one from Amazon that arrived in Birmingham two days later, accompanied by two lightweight (4 kg) 200 W solar panels. Fully charged, it worked perfectly, running the 350 W blood centrifuge with ease. All we needed was to get it to Sikkim, but Air India and British Airways refused to take it. Eventually a specialised air transport company agreed to fly it to Kolkata. It was dispatched a month before our departure. However, first it was stuck in London for a week then it was held up in Kolkata, as it had the wrong import licence and customs refused its entry. With lots of arguing, it was released with a week to spare, only for the Hindu festival of Durga Puja to shut down all transport from Kolkata to Gangtok. I had learnt of its hold-up while on the bus to London Heathrow, and feared that six months of effort were in vain. Showing considerable initiative, Motop's company sent a special driver the 425 miles from Gangtok to Kolkata to try and prise it out of the hands of over-bureaucratic customs officials.

We also planned to have a low environmental impact expedition. We travel to remote regions for their unspoilt beauty, pure air and cleanliness, only to pollute them with plastic, paper and excretion waste, in addition to our carbon dioxide production. Mountainous regions are particularly prone to damage and must be preserved in a pristine state for future generations to enjoy. Carbon dioxide emissions are simple to control – buy carbon offsets – but human waste is far more difficult. Hence, we planned to remove all rubbish and use low-impact materials.

At 6 pm we had a conference so that everyone was familiar with the following days' travel arrangements and experiments. Cas and Kyle clashed over time slots for their research in Lachung. Cas seemed quite unfamiliar with the research arrangements despite them having been agreed a year earlier. Then, miracle of miracles, in late afternoon, the battery arrived from Kolkata. Our expedition was ready. We had a happy dinner and an early night.

Day 5. By 5.30 am the experiments bedroom was already a hive of activity. All early-morning urine pots promptly arrived for 4 ml to be removed and centrifuged to remove cells (ethics permission insisted on this so no DNA could be extracted to identify individuals – crazy new requirements). Bloods followed, with measurements of brain natriuretic peptide on the i-STAT. Up to 10 people were on blood-taking duties, including centrifuging, urine collections and re-allocation of dry ice to fewer boxes. Meanwhile, melodic Buddhist chanting of *Om Mani Padme Hum* persistently resonated around the hotel entrance hall, soothing our spirits. Outside, low clouds hid Kanchenjunga and surrounding peaks.

Breakfast was at 7 am and all big bags were packed and outside rooms by 8 am for our day's journey. From Gangtok (1,650 m), the road descended 500 m to the Tista River at Mangan then rose steadily to Tsunthang, before finally climbing to 2,624 m at Lachung. As predicted, it rained all day, not torrentially but steadily worsening as we entered a cloud forest dripping with orchids and tree ferns. The road narrowed to little more than a single track with passing places, yet there were stretches of well tarmacked roads between rubble-covered remnants of good surfaces that had been washed away in the monsoon.

Indian Army activity, border posts and innumerable troop lorries testified to our closeness to the Chinese border – a mere five miles east of Lachung. The Chinese had built huge roads that ran along the Tibetan plateau and produced a constant fear of invasion. A year earlier, the Chinese had built a road into north Bhutan before they were discovered, leading to a stand-off, then retreat as they were pressed by the Indian Army.

In heavy rain, we drove into the front courtyard of a half-timbered hotel, modern and pleasant-looking, if somewhat basic (figure 2). To avoid getting soaked, we quickly hid inside the front entrance, while bags and boxes were taken off the small lorry by the porters and rushed inside. With noisy discussions and debate, a lot of which was 'much ado about nothing', sleeping arrangements and enough research rooms were found and calm was restored. Experiments were completed efficiently before a most tasty dinner and our evening conference in the lounge, where we had a philosophical discussion about research papers and joint authorship. We agreed that no person would be forgotten when results were published.

Outside it continued to pour, with occasional lightning. Shortly after a particularly loud bang, Ben came in complaining of a broken laptop charger. I checked the GoalZero battery charger, which was plugged into the hotel socket, and Kyle tested his charging tower. They were bust, which was confirmed by his circuit tester. The chargers had been burnt out by an electrical surge. The hotel manager confirmed that the hotel generator occasionally caused problems. It had been a long and stressful day.

Day 6. We had allowed a rest day in Lachung for acclimatisation, and many were busy with Kyle's interoception studies. Four had been completed on the previous evening but, since each test took 90 minutes, it would take all day for the remaining 14 people. Under Kyle's supervision, Ben, Chris, Cat and Stephanie paired off with an individual under test. First were ten questionnaires about breathing and one's awareness of it, followed by the test itself, which seemed more difficult than previously – possibly an indication of the altitude.

Meanwhile, the blood teams set to, while the centrifuge was powered from the half-charged battery as we were fearful of using the hotel sockets. Six spins for the bloods and urines reduced its storage capacity by 10%. There would be another 5% reduction for the urines in the afternoon. At that rate the battery power would last only three days unless it could be recharged.

Around 8 am, with the sun shining strongly, we plugged a 200 W solar panel into the battery's charging socket and, much to our relief, it worked. Because everyone was frightened of burning out their computers and phones, all now wanted to plug into the battery but its capacity was limited, forcing its restricted use. Despite the hot sun, by midday it was still only 70% charged.

Many walked to view the town in the warmth of the morning sun. It comprised several thousand inhabitants living in attractive if somewhat dishevelled multi-storey concrete dwellings that rose up the sides of the wide 'alpine' valley towards huge snow-capped peaks. Dominating the town was a large army camp, a useful deterrent to Chinese incursions.

After lunch it started to rain. This forced Cas to move his high-speed walking test from the front drive of the hotel to the front lobby, much to everyone's amusement. Not quite the 50 m that had been the length of the first walk in Birmingham or the second on the road in Gangtok, but a mere 20 m. Observations might take some imaginative interpreting!

A game of cards developed in the evening, while the principal investigators tended their data. At the evening conference, Motup emphasised the importance of drinking a lot of water – quite why was not clear, but it supported the millennials' obsession with drinking (the younger members were fixated on their water consumption based on some misconception of how much was needed per day). None seemed deterred by the idea of carrying the resulting huge amounts of urine on the trek, despite risks of spillage.

Day 7. The rain hammered down all night but by the morning it was clear, the sun glistening off fresh snows on the sharp peaks of Shariki Danenchung (5,557 m) towering over the town. By 5.30 am, a row of 18 bottles were lined up in the corridor outside room 106, topped by full early-morning urine pots. In Birmingham, we had increased the urine bottle sizes from two to three litres after the Chimborazo expedition, to accommodate vigorous drinkers, but even this was insufficient: Owen produced 3.7 litres, with others not far behind.

The blood team started their work, while Will and Abi conducted medical examinations in the hotel lobby. With everyone's efficiency improving, all experiments were complete by 7.30 am. The only worry was the battery, which failed to power the centrifuge even though it was 70% charged. Anxiously, we used the hotel's dodgy power supply instead.

With breakfast over, 18 personal bags, 12 metal boxes, four white polystyrene boxes, a generator, two petrol containers and a dry ice delivery box were quickly collected into the hotel lobby. All were loaded onto our small lorry, while we piled into five cars and drove in file back down our ascent road to the river junction at Tsunthang. In bright sunlight, we passed huge waterfalls with distant views of snow peaks that had been swathed in cloud on our ascent. We then turned north-west to follow the main Tista River valley, where army vehicles ploughed up and down the monsoon-damaged rubble road. After a few miles, we drove through a military camp where cameras were strictly forbidden. In the central part of the camp, a huge rockslide that had crushed innumerable army sheds and killed two soldiers was being picked over by large diggers.

Beyond the camp we passed through the prosperous-looking Lachen (2,728 m) ('big pass' in Nepalese), only to stop beside a steel army bridge over the Zemu Chu. It was the start of our trek and, according to historical reports, the point where Sir Joseph Hooker crossed from India to China in 1848. Even today, lands north of the bridge are claimed by China.

A group of 50 porters milled around weighing and dividing our luggage into 20–25 kg loads. They were mostly from the lowlands around Gangtok, Darjeeling and West Bengal and, unlike Nepalis, were unable to carry 70 kg loads. Doubling their daily payment from 1,000 to 2,000 rupees did double their strength, although they were likely to take twice as long.

In addition to the porters, there were ten kitchen staff, two cooks, a newly acquired liaison officer (Lakpah) plus Motup himself – 82 people in total. An exceptionally large group for that remote area – the remotest place we had ever been. The liaison officer had been imposed on us because we were a medical research group (suspicious for some reason), added to which we had the privilege of paying for him and his fancy tent. But there was no choice. Indeed, three days before arriving, our whole adventure had been at risk. Except for the timely intervention of Motup, who contacted a friend in the army, the whole trip would have been banned by the military.

Lakpah's specific job was to ensure we didn't provoke an incident with the Chinese. Cas had brought a drone for photography but its use was strictly forbidden. A recent US group had operated a satellite phone (prohibited throughout India) to communicate with each other but the signal had been spotted by the army at Lachen. It was confiscated and they were fined heavily. This further emphasised India's intense anxiety over the Chinese.

Also waiting for us at the bridge was a large broken polystyrene box containing dry ice: the second of four deliveries. Two additional dry-ice boxes had already been sent ahead to Thalan, our next camp. Since we seemed to have plenty and it was difficult for the porters to carry, we made the risky decision to leave it behind.

Lunches were distributed, day-sacks packed and porters loaded, allowing us to descend from the bridge down to the roaring Zemu Chu. With Lakpah in the van and Motup sweeping, we walked along the river's edge. Within a quarter of a mile, the path had been washed away, forcing us up a steep boulder-strewn bank. Huge rocks hung precariously over the makeshift path; underfoot, a misplaced step on loose rocks would plummet us into the river. Treacherous exposed trails, fallen trees and rickety wooden ladders were an ever-present danger (figure 3), with several people stumbling. Heavily laden porters struggled with their voluminous boxes over the slippery surfaces, delicately climbing over unstable rocks and ducking under avalanche-felled trees.

For two hours, we clambered along the sides of the river but then entered an enchanted forest. Massive Himalayan spruce and hemlock spread up the sides of the valleys – un-logged primary forests and, judging from their inaccessibility, largely unexplored.

By late afternoon, it started to rain as we reached a small forest clearing at Thalan (3,240 m). In the cooling evening, we sat miserably in the mess tent awaiting bags and boxes for our first night under canvas. The 4 pm 24-hour urine collection time came and went and still we had no personal bags. While much equipment such as tents and food had been sent ahead at Lachen, our own bags had travelled with us and, inevitably, were carried upwards more slowly than we walked. The last porter arrived after 7 pm. Motup and his colleagues, to give them credit, looked after them all, guiding the late ones into

Himalayan spruce

camp with a string of borrowed head torches. Because of the limited space for camping, they slept under lean-to sheets against collapsed sheds while others huddled together in the mess and kitchen tents. It was a hard life at 1,000 rupees a day but it was three times the payment of jobs down the mountains.

Since Yash had cancelled his trip at the last minute (we should have been 19 members), there was one tent spare, allowing John and Mark to sleep alone while the rest of us paired off equitably. Most of us knew each other well and the debutants such as Stephanie, Kelsey and Chris soon fitted in.

At our daily conference over dinner, Motup pointed out the struggles the porters were experiencing and some would have to carry double loads if we were to reach Jakthang camp the following night. Since the path was difficult, they were in a rebellious mood and a strike was possible. With our altitude-induced headaches, persistent drizzle and the porters' late arrival, we agreed to have a rest day and one day less at Green Lake, our top camp.

Day 8. Next morning, a few individuals had persistent mild headaches suggestive of early mountain sickness. Thalan was 600 m above Lachung, making for a rather fast ascent profile; 300 m per day above 3,000 m is the recommended maximum but over the next few days we were planning to exceed this. We were therefore anticipating a few problems from the altitude.

Because of the rest day, we delayed urine collections until 7 am (figure 4). I awoke to the sound of an 850 W Honda engine singing in the morning sun, powering all manner of phones, computers and camera batteries because the big battery was useless. Although it was still 35% charged, the cold night had stopped it working. To warm it, we found a sunny spot on top of a crushed metal shed (destroyed by the previous winter's heavy snowfall) and connected a solar panel, with Chris Bradley moving it repeatedly to track the sun. It charged at 7–10% per hour.

After a happy breakfast in the mess tent, we hung about warming ourselves in the sun as porters busied themselves by carrying supplies up to Jakthang for our arrival the following day. In the afternoon, clouds built up, dampening spirits. The rain arrived bang on cue at 4 pm as porters returned from dumping supplies.

The battery had charged to 72% despite minimal afternoon sun. Warmed with hot water bottles, it readily powered the centrifuge at the 4 pm urine collection time. Only a 5% drop in charge from three spins. We were pleased that it reduced use of the petrol generator but it was an expensive luxury. Cumbersome to handle and slow to charge, it was clearly much harder to manage than a simple pull on the generator handle. Battery-powered medical expeditions were unlikely to catch on any time soon.

The rain drove everyone inside, either to play cards or to attend to research projects. The camp became a desolate place; wet and slippery underfoot, with constant drips on the tents from the overhanging forest, even when the rain ceased. Yet, despite the damp conditions, the mood was good; morning headaches had abated, experiments were completed efficiently and we were finally on trek.

Day 9. That night it rained almost constantly, barely stopping before bed-tea appeared at 5.30 am. Bloods, urines and health checks were completed by 8.30 am (figure 5) and we watched from the mess tent as 50 porters departed with their heavy loads. As we left the camp, we soon re-entered the magical forest containing innumerable 500-year-old spruce trees, some charred and hollow from lightning strikes, others festooned with orchids, bryophytes and liverworts (figure 6). The route was marked by a well-constructed stone path (figure 7), built by the Indian Army in 1977 and maintained by staff from the Kanchenjunga national park. However, fallen trees sporadically blocked the way, and everything in that Himalayan temperate rainforest dripped. Motup informed us that there were 22 different species of rhododendron and the occasional Ent.

After a couple of hours trekking up and down steep slopes, we entered a clearing at Jakthang camp (3,300 m), with the Zemu Chu roaring in the background (figures 8 and 9). With 60 willing porters, a grassy area was cleared, tents erected, lunch cooked and appetites satisfied. A small concrete-based open-sided shed provided shelter from the drizzle and was used as a laboratory. A cold evening followed, a full moon shining intermittently through mist that cascaded over the trees from lower altitudes. We had our earliest dinner at 6.30 pm, shortly followed by bed.

Day 10. During the night, Kyle and Will were awoken by urgent gut rot – always a hazard on treks and always miserable for those suffering souls. Motup had insisted on constant hand cleanliness using a dilute potassium permanganate solution. This was contained in a small water butt that was placed outside the mess tent around meal times. But with two cooks, ten cook boys and 50 porters, 620 fingers and thumbs can't all be clean all of the time. It was probably a staphylococcal toxin from the evening's dinner. Thankfully it settled during the day and no one else was affected.

It was a mere six miles to Yabuk, although an ascent from 3,300 m to 3,850 m, and followed by a rest day. The old stone pathway, a thread in the huge wilderness, led us up through the spruce forest into bamboo thickets, magical rhododendron woods and the occasional rock fall. Many alpine flowers speckled the path, offering welcome succour to the few insects that hunted in the cold autumn air (figure 10). Above the dense forest, the path rose steeply to a ridge and our campsite in a low rhododendron grove. With a cold

Himalayan balsam

easterly wind whisking over our heads, we ate lunch while the porters constructed the camp, including a blue mess tent for the urines and bloods. Then the cloud descended, encouraging many into their sleeping bags.

This was the worst weather start to any BMRES expedition. We were half way through and had not enjoyed a single really nice day, merely a few warm mornings. But, despite the weather, there was a lively spirit, lifted with a little help from the bottle of whisky that Ben and others had bought in Delhi.

Evening discussions came around to acute mountain sickness. Motup claimed there were over 20 deaths in Leh alone last year. This was mostly because Ladakh is so easily accessible, with innumerable lowland workers, tourists and army personnel visiting seasonally. This prompted thoughts as to how we were faring at nearly 4,000 m. Out came a finger oximeter to measure blood oxygen saturations (figure 11). Most individuals were above 80% saturation but Cat was a clear outlier at 74% and she had had a headache in the morning. Would she need acetazolamide, we wondered?

Day 11. Overnight it rained and the morning was cloudy and drizzling. Despite the miserable weather, it was urines at 7 am with everyone pitching in to help with ear pricks, bloods, interviews and gait tests. Cat's oxygen saturations were still only 74%. With due consideration by Will and Abi, we agreed on 125 mg of acetazolamide twice a day. She offered little resistance (figure 12).

There were no mountains visible, just low mist gradually dispersed by a weak sun. A butcher bird glared down from a guide rope (figure 13). The solar panels were displayed but charged the battery at a meagre 30 watts (compared with a maximum of 200 watts) and it was too cold to run the centrifuge. The generator was started and hummed away, surrounded by an array of charging phones, computers and cameras. Groups sauntered up the track to check tomorrow's walk, while Cas's 25 m track threaded through the middle of the tents. Ben and Cas recorded the walks while many watched on, criticising poor style or running with knees bent. But I worried about the weather. This expedition was 'type-2 fun', as noted by Hannah – only enjoyable in retrospect.

The day was enlivened by Cas's birthday. Hannah and Abi had cleverly constructed a card from the front cover of a climbing magazine with juicy comments inside, much to his delight. For dinner there was a cake with two candles and a litre of whisky that didn't last long.

We had planned two nights at a higher rest camp for acclimatisation with a final move to Green Lake. However, the former was relatively close and the latter had no reliable water so we opted for a top camp at 4,800 m. This entailed a six-hour walk with an ascent of 950 m. It would be high enough for experiments and be easier for the porters who, after dropping their loads, could return to Yabuk, leaving us in the hands of the Sherpas. The downside was that some of us would struggle with the altitude gain.

At 8.30 pm, and to much delight, the moon and high mountains partially emerged from the clouds, leaving us gazing at the array of stars with high hopes for a clear morning.

Day 12. Hopes were soon dashed. Come 5.30 am, exposed low clouds hung over the tents, although they did seem thinner than before. Sure enough, over a couple of hours, sections of mountains appeared in the cold, dank air (figure 14). The camp was on the move by 8.15 am, forming a long thin file through the scrub rhododendron woods. A few deformed spruce trees, dwarfed by wind and cold, covered nearby drumlins, before giving way to alpine shrub as we ascended the stone path. Over three hours we climbed steadily as the clouds cleared to reveal an unsurpassed mountain amphitheatre. Kanchenjunga rose magnificently to 8,586 m while lancing skywards above us was Siniolchu (6,887 m) – 'the most beautiful mountain in the world', according to the early explorer Douglas Freshfield in 1899. Behind, we could see for the first time the huge peaks that had towered above our earlier camps. Further to the east, perhaps 80 miles distant, a large rounded peak rose over the Sikkim/China mountain wall. It was Jomolhari (7,315 m), the Bhutanese peak we had camped beside two expeditions ago.

We climbed up a steep moraine ridge to gain a sensational view of Kanchenjunga's massive east (Zemu) glacier, perhaps a mile wide, which was enlarged by glaciers pouring off Siniolchu, Tent and Nepal Peaks. As the ice tumbled down the mountains, its colour morphed from white ice seracs to dark grey from a thick covering of rubble. Beneath, cubic kilometres of ice were squeezed down the mountain to form the Zemu River, which we had followed for several days. Beside the sharp moraine edge was a wide, flat grassy area and in the distance our top camp in an early stage of construction.

Becky, Sam and Kim were feeling the effects of the rapid height gain. Handing their day sacks to the Sherpas, we slowly walked the last mile into camp, at 4,800 m, which we reached by early afternoon. The cooks prepared lunch while we unpacked the experimental equipment and solar panels. Above us, the huge mountains were slowly engulfed in clouds. A large dome tent was put up after innumerable attempts to much amusement and a vigorous cricket match started that included the Sherpas. Will had bought a cricket bat in Lachen together with a soft ball. We played among the tents, experiments and azalea bushes.

With the setting sun the air rapidly cooled, sending us inside. A tent round of medical examinations by Will and Abi identified five people suffering from mild mountain sickness but only Mark acknowledged the need for acetazolamide. That night's oxygen saturations around the dinner table showed most in the 80s with 67% the record low. Cat's were in the 80s and she felt better. Acetazolamide had worked well.

Day 13. That night the sky cleared, urine pots froze solid and a frost covered the tents. Inside, lying on my huge Mondo King Thermarest (self-inflating mattress) and swathed in a four-seasons Mountain Equipment sleeping bag, I was cosy. High-altitude gear had improved massively since our first expeditions. It was glamping, not camping.

A perfect morning greeted our eyes, with many up at 5.20 am to gaze in wonder at a beautiful dawn. The sun's first rays touched the top of Kanchenjunga with a red glow (figure 15), which changed to pink, orange, yellow and white in spectacular fashion. Eight days of drizzly rain and cloud had all been worthwhile. We lingered in the morning glory as Siniolchu (figure 16), Gocha Peak, Kanchenjunga's five summits, the Twins, Nepal Peak, Tent Peak and Pyramid Peak caught the sun. In the opposite direction, Jomulhari in Bhutan was silhouetted against the brightening sky.

This was the first of the two working days at top camp. Tasks started with urine collections but continued well into the afternoon, with bloods and ear pricks for blood gases and other tests. Solar panels charged the GoalZero battery and every other gadget that needed electrical power (figure 17). Cas and Ben organised the walking test, again right through the camp, and another lively cricket match occupied the afternoon. Interviews and experiments were recorded for the expedition video in glorious sunshine. The only cause for concern was the dry ice. It should have arrived in the afternoon but none had appeared. To stave off our worries about the blood samples thawing, two Sherpas climbed down the dangerous moraine slope to the Zemu Glacier and came back with great chunks of ice that were placed around the sample boxes. We would need more ice for the descent if the dry ice failed to appear. Dinner was at 6.30 pm, the temperature dropped and snowflakes flickered past our head torches in a starless night sky.

Day 14. It was a freezing night with early morning tent banging by the Sherpas to shake off the coating of snow. But once again, the sky was crystal clear, the sun's glow over Bhutan to the east beaming orange light to the top of Kanchenjunga. A dozen of us climbed up the glacier moraine to wonder at nature's beauty. The mountain gods smiled upon us for our second day at top camp.

While the two on acetazolamide had improved, Becky, who had refused treatment, had a bad headache overnight and was nauseated. At breakfast she hardly spoke. Her peripheral oxygen saturations were only 75%. Better late than never, she was given 250 mg of acetazolamide. As sometimes happens, this only worsened her headache. Will and Abi wisely gave her 4 mg of dexamethasone and with Abi and Hannah helping, she descended 950 m to Yabuk, our previous camp.

Many of us ascended the gentle grassy slope to Green Lake (4,935 m) – or rather 'green puddle', since its feeder stream was dry. Apart from lack of water, it would have been a magnificent campsite beside the Zemu Glacier with views up to Goucha Peak (6,127 m) and Kanchenjunga's massive east face. Nevertheless, we delighted in a lunch hour gazing into the 'Throne Room of the Gods' (figures 18 and 19).

It was the high point of the expedition. We sat in the sun reflecting on BMRES expeditions around the world and what might be the next adventure. I looked across wistfully to the Twins and Nepal Peak thinking of Pangpema just beyond. I was the only one who had been on that ill-fated 1999 expedition to Kanchenjunga just 20 miles to the west of our current position (chapter 9).

On arriving back at camp, our much-needed dry ice had finally arrived. Motup had brilliantly managed to persuade the porters to bring it up – and just in time, for there were only a couple of fist-sized lumps remaining in our sample boxes.

Over lunch there were smiles all round as Motup recalled tales of derring-do, the Pundits (early native explorers), the Tsangpo river exploration of 1998 and other Himalayan history. He was a real star and the best *sirdar* we had ever had.

Day 15. The next morning was cloudy and cold, offering little incentive to get up before dawn for possible mountain views. The camp stirred slowly to calls from John and Kelsey for morning urines at 5.30 am. They had worked hard without a hint of complaint, as indeed had the whole blood team: a very coordinated and selfless group. With Abi having accompanied Becky down at Yabuk, Kyle took over the morning's medical examinations.

By 9 am we were ready to descend into misty dank weather. Over 3–4 hours, we followed the narrow stone track alongside the Zemu Glacier, briefly climbing to the moraine rim. We descended past the ice snout with its emergent river, down through the dwarf rhododendron woods and finally to the upper end of the spruce forest. Only a distant glimpse of a soaring golden eagle was notable on that cloudy day.

At Yabuk camp, we were greeted by a rejuvenated Becky, fully recovered from mountain sickness – 4 mg of dexamethasone and descent had done the trick.

Golden eagle

Alongside the tents were two polystyrene boxes of precious dry ice, perhaps 20 kg. One more delivery at Lachen in three days should be enough to ensure the samples arrived home frozen. The weather remained dismal and damp through afternoon tea and dinner, although our general mood remained remarkably positive.

Day 16. On the morning of the final full trekking day, the weather brightened, allowing experiments and breakfast in the sun. There followed a six-hour walk to Thalan, covering two of the ascent days in one. Up and down the switchback path we walked, through dense spruce forests and past tumbling waterfalls, with a stop for lunch at Jakthang, our second day's camp. The afternoon took us in thickening air to the tiny camp at Thalan, with its bubbling stream, where tents were already erected under rain-soaked trees. It was a quiet, cold dinner in the mess tent that night and an early bed. Nine days of exercise were telling.

Day 17. Before departure from camp, Motup organised a clean-up. Each of us was issued with a small blue bag and sent scurrying around searching for plastic and other debris that in total filled two huge canvas bags. It was the first expedition on the route to have removed more rubbish than it had brought. Motup had been previously involved in Everest Base Camp clean-ups and, as with us, was very keen to maintain the route's pristine environment.

Experiments were now being undertaken with maximum efficiency, so by 8.30 am we were finished, champing at the bit for the final walk. As we were now well acclimatised, it allowed us to better admire the magnificent forest of 500-year-old Himalayan spruce and, lower down, hemlock and cedar trees.

The last trekking day was a short walk to the road head then a further half-mile to the prayer-flag-infested steel bridge, where our 64 staff awaited their tips. The tip-giving ceremony was in a leech-infested field beside the Zemu River. Becky had collected £150 from each of us. This had been converted to rupees – 230,000 in total. These were divided on a large tarpaulin by Owen and Chris into parcels of rupees for each person – 1,500 for porters, 6,000 for cook boys, 7,500 for Sherpas, 12,000 for the assistant cook, 15,000 for the chief cook and 18,000 for the head guide. Even the liaison officer, who had been forced upon us, was given 5,000.

In a ceremony starting with the lowest paid, we handed out their tips. Stephanie, Kim, John, Will then Owen and finally myself took turns to offer our gifts. One by one each recipient came forward with a 'namaste' and 'dhanyabad' ('greeting' and 'thank you' in Nepalese) to collect their rewards from under our umbrella, like collecting gongs from a viceroy under a ceremonial awning (figure 20). Finally, Motup was given an envelope containing $500 that he gallantly refused, for a while.

Formalities over and with everyone seemingly happy, we were allowed to escape from the persistent rain into jeeps that took us to Lachen, a few miles downhill. There, we were driven up a steep road at the back of the town to the Apple Orchard Hotel and welcoming cherry brandies, tea, biscuits and three boxes of dry ice. Reminiscent of a Lake District hotel, the Apple Orchard was a delight, particularly after a mostly wet ten days in tents. Spacious rooms with showers and firm beds meant we were back in civilisation (figure 21). We had barely seen a soul.

Phones pinged and buzzed – electronic reminders that emails, WhatsApp and the modern age were back. A clean-up, beer and cheerful chat accompanied a happy meal and early bed, with rain tapping loudly on the tin roofs. The only concern was that the amount of alcohol consumed might interfere with experiments. The agreement had been 'alcohol in moderation' so that urine volumes and interoception studies were not compromised. Naturally, we drank far too much beer.

Day 18. A full day at the hotel was allocated to interoception studies, carried out in three separate bedrooms. It was a difficult test, torture without pain, at the very limits of perception. And for the unfortunate few, because a valve had been missed from one of the circuits, their tests had to be repeated. Urines were collected and measured on the front porch of the dining room while bloods, ear pricks and medical examinations took place in two other bedrooms. The research side of the expedition was dragging out to the very end.

There was a little time to explore that remote village. It has five feet of snow in winter, six feet of rain in the monsoon and an ever-present risk of landslides and flash floods. Nevertheless, it seemed prosperous, driven by a bourgeoning Indian tourist trade, army money and agriculture. Not quite 'Switzerland of India' but certainly attractive, with exotic birds and magnificent trees.

That evening John watched in horror as beer drinking began in earnest at 4 pm. His diuresis studies would be ruined by alcoholic over-indulgence. For a second night I was called in to control the intake. As on so many occasions before, returning to civilisation led to a boisterous release of pent-up tensions, making any pretence of restraint impossible. A drinks tally from the bar bill showed most had exceeded their promised limit. Only studies back home would reveal how much the descent urines had been compromised by poor self-control.

Day 19. The next morning, we undertook the six-hour drive to Gangtok, mercifully another 1,100 m lower. Driving in convoy, four people per car, we toiled down the crazy, narrow, collapsing roadways. With a brief stop to gaze up at Kanchenjunga's summit as it appeared mystically and impossibly high above the clouds, we entered Gangtok and unloaded at the fancy Nor-Khill Hotel, once frequented by kings and Dalai Lamas. The 4 pm urine collections were in a dance room, its beautiful wooden floor protected from urine spillage with a large tarpaulin. Mark and I spend a couple of hours in the extensive markets finding interesting prizes for the following evening's final dinner.

Red panda

Day 20. We were awoken by honks, toots, traffic buzz, music and innumerable dogs barking. 'Dogs on roof tops, dogs on the tiles, dogs on the streets, dogs with piles' as the rhyme goes – overcrowded India! Then it was time for final bloods, early morning urines and medical examinations, all much easier on comfortable sofas than on hillsides with freezing hands. All were completed by 8.30 am, clearing the day for some tourism. Many went to the bazaar on the central pedestrian precinct while I went with Kyle, Will and Mark to Sikkim state zoo 400 m higher up the hillside in the cloud forest. Leopards, red pandas, yaks and ungulates in large pens were hardly memorable but I made friends with a very attractive juvenile Himalayan vulture – the biggest bird in the region. A long return walk on concrete paths through the town revealed the huge extent of Sikkim's capital city, which sprawled down the mountain ridges for several miles.

At 4 pm, the end of experiments came with completion of the 24-hour urine collections, followed by celebratory drinks in the bar. For our final dinner on the Tibet Road, our seven girl members were all dressed up while Chris Lewis and Ben had bought Indian clothes, one worn by Brahmins and the other from a lower caste. We didn't understand what the difference meant, but the Sikkimese did and were most amused as the happy couple cavorted along the road.

We had a happy final meal with no restrictions on beer or wine. After a toast to the Queen, Mark and I announced the following expedition awards:

1. Dedication to urine collections: Kelsey; a bottle of cherry brandy.
2. Best student prize: Catherine; a bottle of cherry brandy.

3. Best hair award: Kim for having beautiful blond hair and plaiting others' hair; a packet of hair broaches.
4. Smiley award: Sam; a plaster cast of a fat, jolly smiling Buddha.
5. Wimp award: Kyle for always moaning when giving blood and having ear pricks; a comfort baby blanket.
6. Most tactile award: Chris Lewis; a hair piece to add to his beautiful long black hair that the girls liked so much.
7. Worst sufferer from mountain sickness award: Becky; a packet of paracetamol.
8. Best medical practice award: Will and Abi; a shared bottle of cherry brandy.
9. Best moustache grown on the expedition award: Owen; a wooden comb.
10. Motup award: to Motup for being the best *sirdar* of any BMRES expedition; a cubic perspex paperweight containing a sitting Buddha and SIKKIM in large letters.

Day 21. The last day in the mountains was upon us: time for final bag packing and cramming of gifts into already overloaded Mountain Kingdoms holdalls. Squeeze some extra items into the blue equipment boxes, no one will notice! Owen was more relaxed than I was about the packing and was now in charge. The last of the dry ice was allocated to the polystyrene boxes containing our samples, along with a dozen ice-gel packs cooled to $-80°C$ overnight.

Sam smashed the remaining dry-ice blocks outside the hotel and put the debris under the sample trays to prolong their freezing time and hide it from prying customs officials (dry ice was forbidden on the flights). It was 40 hours to a freezer in Birmingham via an overnight stay in Delhi. We hoped for a comfortable safety margin but Delhi's temperature was over $30°C$, so we couldn't be certain. Kelsey needed reassurance, amply provided by me. Fingers crossed.

Five taxis and a small truck transported us the five hours to Bagdogra airport on the most potholed road ever. We passed huge monsoon landslides that had wrecked the road, with no evidence of any repairs since we had ascended. Lingering rains still soaked the roadside villages, while watchful gibbons begged food from passing cars. We halted briefly at Rongphu to have our Sikkim visas stamped to confirm our group exit. There we bade farewell to Chris Lewis, who had plans for a few days in Sikkim before weeks of travel around India and Nepal. Then it was down past huge hydroelectric reservoirs damming the green glacier waters of the Tista River, some of which had tumbled down from Kanchenjunga, and past the Coronation Bridge, built in the 1930s, that leads to Bhutan.

Suddenly, we were on the plains, on the India plate subducting under Tibet. 'British India started where rocks stopped rolling downhill,' it was said. A railway line marked the transition from massive, steep, jungle-clad mountains to flatness and with it the massed humanity of West Bengal – 80 million people in a state that includes Kolkata, the old capital of British India. Our cavalcade slowed, not because of potholes and landslides but from the sheer volume of people and jumbled careering traffic, some going in the wrong direction on dual carriageways. It was a one-hour crawl through the town of Siliguri to Bagdogra airport, where we found some semblance of order. Sixteen of us filed into the departure hall, together with 16 bulging bags, 11 blue boxes and four ice boxes with their precious samples bound for Delhi and London. I remained behind to meet Barbara and catch the 'Toy Train' to Darjeeling. I shook hands with everyone, my responsibilities discharged.

The band of brothers had come to an end. The 'Fellowship of Sikkim', echoing Tolkien's 'Fellowship of the Ring', was over – until next time. I was looking forward to a quiet fortnight in the Himalaya. Two days later I received news that the blood and urine samples were safely frozen in a refrigerator at the university. And we'd incurred a $100 fine, because the medical boxes had exceeded their weight limit, being overloaded with gifts.

Publications

1. Joyce K, Delamere J, Ashdown K, Bradley C, Lucas R, Thomas O, Lock H, Talks B, Malein W, Lewis C, Cross A, Letchford A, Bradwell AR, Lucas S and BMRES. Nocturnal oxygen saturation is related to increased urinary alpha-1 acid glycoprotein during ascent to 4,800 m. July 2020 25th annual ECSS Congress.
2. Campbell CA, Edsell M, Joyce KE, Lucas R, Bradwell AR and the BMRES. Assessing the environmental impact of field-based medical research. ISMM 2020.
3. Ladha C, Blake C and Talks, B. Feasibility of automatic prediction of Acute Mountain Sickness (AMS) using wearable sensors. Measuring Behaviour 2020.
4. Joyce K, Lucas S and Bradwell AR Acetazolamide can impair exercise performance; it depends upon the cohort studied. Journal of Applied Physiology 2020; 128: 1457 doi:10.1152/japplphysiol.00173.2020.

'Toy train' in Darjeeling

Fig 1. Yabuck camp. Back row, left to right: *Ben Talks, Cas Ladha, Will Malein, Kyle Pattinson, Chris Bradley, Owen Thomas. Middle row: Chris Lewis, Stephanie Larcombe, Catherine Campbell, Hannah Lock, Abi Letchford, Sam Lucas, Jo Bradwell. Front row: Motup, Rebekah Lucas, Kelsey Joyce, Mark Edsell, John Delamere, Kim Ashdown.*

Fig 2. *Hotel at Lachung*

Fig 3. *Alongside the Zemu Chu*

Fig 4. *John at Thalan testing urine*

Fig 5.
Health checks at Thalan

Fig 6. *Enchanted spruce forest*

Fig 7. *Up to Jakthang*

Fig 8. *Beside the Zemu Chu at Jakthang*

Fig 9. *Jakthang in the morning*

Fig 10. *Alpine flowers*

Fig 11. *Pulse oximeter and wrist recorders.*

Fig 12. *Cat, "The cap's come off my urine bottle."*

Fig 13. *Butcher bird*

Fig 14.
Laboratory tent
at Yabuk

Fig 15*. Kanchenjunga at dawn*

Fig 16.
Siniolchu, Kelsey
and ice boxes at
top camp

Fig 17*. Mark with GoalZero power pack and solar panels*

Fig 18*. Kanchenjunga, Zemu Glacier and Green Lake*

Fig 19*. Top camp beneath Tangchungkhang*

Fig 20*. Tips ceremony*

Fig 21*. Apple Orchard Hotel in Lachen*

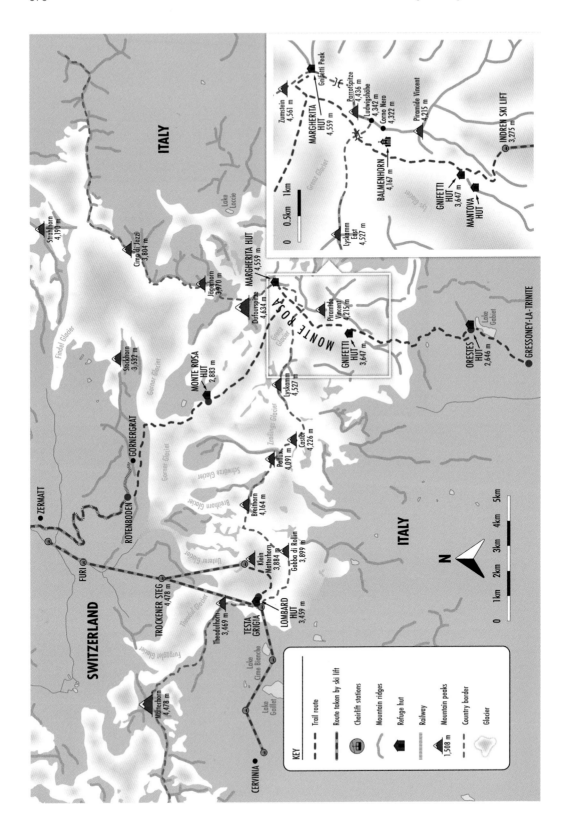

ITALY

Lake
Loccie

Inset map:

Zumstein
4,561 m

Gnifetti Peak

Parrotspitze
4,436 m

Ludwigshöhe
4,342 m

MARGHERITA
HUT
4,559 m

Corno Nero
4,322 m

Piramide Vincent
4,215 m

INDREN SKI LIFT
3,275 m

lift

Grenz Glacier

BALMENHORN
4,167 m

Lys Glacier

GNIFETTI
HUT
3,647 m

MANTOVA
HUT

0   0.5km   1km

Lyskamm
East
4,527 m

Strahlhorn
4,191 m

Cima di Jazzi
3,804 m

Jägerhorn
3,970 m

MARGHERITA HUT
4,559 m

Piramide
Vincent
4,215 m

MONTE ROSA

Grenz Glacier

GNIFETTI
HUT
3,647 m

GRESSONEY-LA-TRINITE

Dufourspitze
4,634 m

Stockhorn
3,532 m

Findel Glacier

MONTE ROSA
HUT
2,883 m

Lyskamm
4,527 m

Lake
Gabiet

ORESTES
HUT
2,646 m

Gorner Glacier

Zwillinge Glacier

Castor
4,226 m

GORNERGRAT

Pollux
4,091 m

ZERMATT

Gorner Glacier

ROTENBODEN

Breithorn
4,164 m

Schwärze Glacier

Breithorn Glacier

ITALY

Unterer Glacier

Klein
Matterhorn
3,884 m

Gobba di Rollin
3,899 m

5km

N

4km

FURI

3km

TROCKENER STEG
4,478 m

Theodul Glacier

Theodulhorn
3,469 m

TESTA
GRIGIA

LOMBARD
HUT
3,459 m

2km

1km

0   1km

Furggler Glacier

SWITZERLAND

Lake
Cime Bianche

Matterhorn
4,478 m

Lake
Goillet

KEY

Trail route	
Route taken by ski lift	
Chairlift stations	
Mountain ridges	
Refuge hut	
Railway	
1,508 m	Mountain peaks
Country border	
Glacier	

CERVINIA

Chapter 16
Alpine adventures

The Matterhorn from Zermatt

There is probably no pleasure equal to the pleasure of climbing a dangerous Alp;
but it is a pleasure which is confined strictly to people who can find pleasure in it.

– Mark Twain

Summary: While the main focus of BMRES was the Himalaya or Andes, week-long trips to the Alps provided short experimental test-beds for new ideas or filled in gaps from previous projects; but they also allowed us to ski and climb. We chose two locations – Testa Grigia (3,459 m), which sits above the best skiing in the world at Zermatt and Cervinia, and the Margherita Hut (4,559 m), which allows spectacular Alpine climbing. As there was a repetitive element to the trips, only a few have been described in detail.

Expedition	Location	Date
1.	Testa Grigia	1987: 27 March –11 April
2.	Testa Grigia	1988: 8–17 April
3.	Margherita Hut	1989: 15–22 July
4.	Testa Grigia	1992: 3–10 April
5.	Margherita Hut	1994: 12–21 August
6.	Testa Grigia	1995: 31 March – 9 April
7.	Aberdeen	1996: 26 May – 2 June
8.	Testa Grigia	1998: 20–30 March
9.	Testa Grigia	2003: 25 April – 4 May
10.	Testa Grigia	2013: 5–14 April
11.	Margherita Hut	2014: 11–20 July

1. Testa Grigia 1987: 27 March – 11 April. See Alpine Interlude (pp 121–134).

2. Testa Grigia 1988: 8–17 April

Expedition members: Jo Bradwell, Ian Chesner, John Delamere, Pete Forster, Tim Harvey, Chris Imray, Jörgen Jensen, Niels Lassen, Calman MacLennan, Ian MacLennan, John Milles, Neville Richardson, John Simmons, Mike Winterborn, Alex Wright.

Our Alpine adventures oscillated between the Lombard Hut at Testa Grigia and the Margherita Hut on Monte Rosa. Although both are located on high mountain prominences near Zermatt, they could hardly be more different. The Lombard Hut (3,458 m) is on a busy ski col between Cervinia in Italy and Zermatt in Switzerland and has all the attractions that a rustic ski lodge can offer: tasty food, easy access to ski lifts and year-round accommodation (figures 1–8). In contrast, the Margherita Hut (4,559 m) is the highest and one of the most remote buildings in Europe. Located on the very summit of a mountain (figures 9 and 10), it can only be reached by climbing, is open only in summer and, even then, is frequently inaccessible because of storms. Furthermore, the 1,100 m difference in elevation between the two huts has a huge physiological effect. The Lombard Hut is barely high enough to provoke mountain sickness, whereas the Margherita Hut sees many cases of high-altitude pulmonary and cerebral oedema, some requiring helicopter rescue.

Because of our love of skiing, the Lombard Hut (later bought from Marcello Lombard by the Cervinia Guides) became the obvious location for pilot studies for larger expeditions or to provide results at intermediate altitudes. When it came to climbing and stand-alone altitude experiments, the Margherita Hut was the perfect mountain paradise, but it was more difficult to access and required some luck. On the three occasions we visited, we had perfect weather, but it was by the skin of our teeth. Other research groups lost their research weeks as storms failed to clear or had life-endangering helicopter crashes in the ever-present winds on its high ridge.

On our first trip to Testa Grigia, in 1987, we performed a pilot study of cerebral blood flow using Niels Lassen's xenon technique (Alpine Interlude, pp 121–134). On our second visit, we compared the impact of 0.4 g methazolamide with 1.5 g acetazolamide on blood oxygen concentrations. Results showed that methazolamide was faster acting but the difference was insufficient to recommend its use over acetazolamide. The research was not demanding, so it was carried out in the evenings, leaving all day for skiing plus time for tasty Italian dinners. During a very pleasant week, there was one incident that stood out: we lost Mike Winterborn.

Mike was a stalwart member of the group, enthusiastic, obliging and interested in others, but always slow. He was usually last to get ready for skiing and usually last back. One evening, in particularly bad weather, he failed to return. He had last been seen at lunch. As he had arrived late at a pre-arranged restaurant and the rest of us had finished, we left him eating and he hadn't been seen since. In the afternoon, winds had quickly built to a blizzard with more than a foot of fresh snow, so all the ski lifts had closed early.

Drinking beers in the hut at 5 pm, we noticed his absence. We joked a little about his misfortune and thought he might yet turn up, but by 6 pm we realised there was a problem. If he had missed the lifts, he would have descended to a hotel in Zermatt and telephoned – but he hadn't. Where could he be?

As night fell, the storm intensified. The wind howled around the hut with a beating intensity: the building shook, the windows rattled, the door clattered, and unknown things banged and crashed outside. Poised as we were over the abyss, we wondered what small additional force it would take to move the hut a metre or so before a final plunge into Italy, 1,200 m below. No one could survive in that blizzard. Visibility was down to 20–30 metres and it was all but impossible to move against it. And there was still no word from Mike.

The hut manager checked all the windows to ensure they were fully sealed and locked the door to prevent it being flung open by the gale. We told him about our missing friend. He agreed with us that no rescue could be attempted even if his location were known. But we started to become worried. Mike could be infuriatingly determined. Whatever the physical difficulty of a long walk, a climb or skiing, or how far behind he had fallen, he never gave up. By 8.30 pm, we had reassured ourselves that he must be in Zermatt.

We ate our meal with half an eye on the door. It banged and shook particularly hard on a couple of occasions, but no human sound could be heard above the gale. Then, a circle slowly appeared in one of the snow-covered windows. A face appeared and pressed itself against the glass. Was it an apparition? Was it a snow troll? No, it was Mike! We rushed over, unlocked the door and fought our way against the blizzard to the figure at the window. Mike, covered from head to foot in snow, slowly turned his head. He was alive and smiling.

We were half-exhilarated and half-furious with him. Why was he out in that hellish night? Why hadn't he stayed in a hotel? Slowly, he warmed up. He was plied with wine and food as he told his story.

The first of four sequential drag lifts from Trockener Steg to Testa Grigia had taken him onto the glacier but then had stopped. Bad visibility had prevented the lift operators from seeing this lone figure, and all ski patrols had long descended. So he had decided to walk. He had remembered the story of Neville and I climbing up with the radioactive xenon gas a year earlier and realised it was possible (see Alpine Interlude). In our case the storm had abated but in his case it had worsened. He became bitterly cold walking up the T-bar track carrying his skis, but by the time he had realised his predicament, visibility was too poor for him to find his way down. He used the small sheds at the start of each section to hide from the wind, recovered somewhat, then proceeded to the next lift. Nearing the top, the storm intensified further as the wind funnelled over the pass. Finally, just able to see the hut lights, 30 metres away from the end of the ski lift, he half-crawled and half-walked to the hut. He tried the locked door several times, banging and shouting, but no one heard. Finally, he managed to attract our attention by clearing a snow-obliterated window and pressing his face against the glass.

He had survived unscathed, but it had been a close-run thing.

3. Margherita Hut 1989: 15–22 July

Expedition members: Jo Bradwell, Ian Chesner, Jonathan Evans, Pete Forster, Tim Harvey, Chris Imray, Niels Lassen, Ian MacLennan, Calman MacLennan, John Milles, Simon Morrissey, Bjorn Sperling, Mike Winterborn.

Our trip to the Karakoram in 1987, to study cerebral blood flow, had left several unanswered questions. Tim Harvey wanted to confirm his CO_2 rebreathing results and we needed a cheaper method of measuring cerebral blood flow than using radioactive xenon. Niels Lassen suggested Doppler ultrasound measurements of the middle cerebral artery. In addition, Simon wanted to study brainstem-evoked potentials (a simple nerve response) for assessing mountain sickness.

Testa Grigia was not high enough for the experiments so we chose the Margherita Hut at 4,559 m. This is an astonishing construction run by the Italian Alpine Club (figures 9 and 10). It was opened in 1893, in the presence of Margherita of Savoy, Queen of Italy, to whom the hut is dedicated. The hut soon became an important research centre for altitude medicine under the direction of Angelo Mosso. The original hut was dismantled in 1977, to be replaced by the current building, which opened in 1980. And a note for those interested in exotic marriage venues: in 2017, it was authorised for marriage ceremonies, although couples wishing to tie the knot are not allowed to arrive by helicopter – they have to climb.

There are three traditional climbing routes, each taking two days. One is from Zermatt via the Monte Rosa Hut, another from Gressoney via the Gnifetti Hut, and the third from the Resegotti Hut along the difficult and technical Signal Ridge. All require physical fitness and a good knowledge of alpine techniques. The alternative is to take a helicopter.

We drove from Birmingham to Switzerland in a minibus, collecting Niels and Bjorn at Cologne railway station on the way, then stayed at the Hotel Malva in Zermatt. Next morning, half of us flew by helicopter to the Margherita Hut while the other half took the Gornergrat train to Rotenboden then walked across the Gorner Glacier to stay at the Monte Rosa Hut for the night. A misty start the following morning made route finding on the Grenz Glacier difficult, but we were assisted from half-way by Oswald Öelz, a Swiss professor of medicine who was famous for climbing Mt Everest and other Himalayan giants. We arrived at the Margherita Hut to a scene of devastation. Those who had flown in the day before were very ill from mountain sickness, particularly Chris and Simon. Both had needed dexamethasone to relieve early cerebral and pulmonary oedema. In complete contrast, those who had stopped at the Monte Rosa Hut on the way up had only mild headaches.

We stayed at the hut for three days, keeping ourselves busy with the various experiments, but there was a little spare time for climbing. There was a choice of easy walks over the ice-cap or innumerable serious rock and ice routes. While everyone was frightened of joining Oswald Öelz on the north face of Lyskamm, five climbed the Dufourspitze: Mike, Tim, Pete, Simon and Chris. Mike, aged 53 and Tim, aged 47 shared a rope, hence:

> ***A hundred years on a rope.*** *Tim Harvey; The Lancet 1994; 343, 612.*
> *The pilot fights to keep our tiny helicopter hovering over the narrow ridge just below the summit. At over 15 000 feet the air is thin and the wind keeps blowing us off the edge.*

The snow arête is no more than a couple of metres wide. "Jump," shouts the pilot and his navigator leaps out to show us the way, landing precariously with one leg in Switzerland and the other in Italy. Unweighted, the Alouette jerks upwards and lurches over the void. Unnerved the pilot opts for a landing on the glacier below. We trudge up the last few hundred feet to the hut passing the navigator scrambling down. Yesterday we were at Calais and now we stand on the second highest peak in the Alps.

The Capanna Regina Margherita on the very apex of Monte Rosa was built as a physiology research laboratory in 1893 for the great Angelo Mosso. Now it is filled with the latest high-tech computers, 2D echo, liquid nitrogen, and solid CO_2; presiding over all is "Der Bulle", the extraordinary Oswald Öelz, Everest summiteer, polymath, polyglot, professor of medicine, wit, and friend.

The classic symptoms of altitude sickness start typically on the second night with thundering headaches, nausea, ataxia, dyspnoea, and vomiting. Radiographs show bat-wing pulmonary oedema and the partial pressure of oxygen in arterial blood would guarantee a place on any intensive care unit. But we are already in capable hands. 36 hours later, Dopplered and echoed, bled and infused, fortified with acetazolamide and dexamethasone, frusemide and frascati, we feel well enough to attempt the famous traverse of the Dufourspitze – the other summit of Monte Rosa, along a 2-km undulating knife-edged ridge of snow and ice. It is a climb that tests the adrenals, sphincters, and nerves: a slip to the left is a 5,000 ft plunge to Zermatt; a slip to the right is 8,000 ft down to Italy. The views are surreal: the summit of the Matterhorn is 500 ft below. 14 hours later we stagger back triumphant – to ironic congratulation from Öelz on setting a new record (slow) time for the traverse. And with our combined ages (climbing with Mike Winterborn), we have shared a hundred years on a rope.

There are so many grey days, months, and years that slip by without leaving any mark on the memory, but these brief moments of adventure, peril, beauty, terror, exhilaration, achievement, trust, fellowship, and friendship are etched on the soul for ever.

Experiments and climbing completed, we took a helicopter down to Zermatt and had an uneventful drive back to Birmingham.

4. Testa Grigia 1992: 3–10 April

Expedition members: Jo Bradwell, Patrick Cadigan, Ian Chesner, John Delamere, Peter Dykes, Pete Forster, Tim Harvey, Chris Imray, Ian MacLennan, Neville Richardson, John Simmons, Geoff Tsang, Alex Wright.

For research projects, acetazolamide was never far from our thoughts because of its clinical effectiveness against mountain sickness. Many other drugs were tried and were of no use, but one success was nifedipine. It is normally used for controlling blood pressure, but Oswald Öelz and Peter Bartsch showed it helped in the treatment of high-altitude pulmonary oedema. Whether it might be of benefit for less severe mountain sickness was unknown. Hence, in a pilot study at Testa Grigia, we compared it with acetazolamide.

We flew to Geneva, took a train to Zermatt, ascended the ski lifts to the Klein Matterhorn and skied down to Testa Grigia carrying all our research boxes. We skied hard, drank hard and researched hard. John Major beat Neil Kinnock in a general election, John Milles was in love, having to sit down at the mere mention of Eileen's name, and a huge landslide blocked the railway line below Zermatt, slowing our return home. Once again, acetazolamide beat the competition. Quite some drug.

5. Margherita Hut 1994: 12–21 August

Expedition members: Maggie Beazley, Jo Bradwell, Tim Harvey, Helen Hoar, Chris Imray, David Lewis, Ian MacLennan, John Milles, Jon Morgan, Nev Richardson.

The next three trips, each a week long, focused on capillary permeability. Our interest stemmed from trying to understand the mechanism underlying mountain sickness: what linked cerebral oedema, pulmonary oedema, facial oedema and protein loss in urine? Was there a generalised leakage of fluid across all vascular membranes and, if so, why did it occur? We teamed up with a group led by Professor John Tooke from Exeter University who were experts on measuring capillary pressure. One of his medical graduates, David Lewis, provided some of the technical expertise.

On the first of the three trips, we went to the Margherita Hut. We drove to Zermatt where we stayed in Hotel Mischabel for two nights measuring baseline fluid leakage in our legs. This was achieved by partly constricting blood flow in the thigh with a cuff and measuring its expansion over 30 minutes (limb plethysmography). To ensure accurate measurements, the temperature of the body and legs had to be carefully controlled since cold air would reduce blood flow. This was achieved by using a temperature-controlled box constructed from prefabricated polystyrene sheets. This was erected in the hotel's garden (figure 11). After flying to the Margherita Hut by helicopter, the measurements were retaken (figure 12). Results showed that there was increased leakage at altitude, which was greater in those with mountain sickness. This correlated with increased proteinuria, indicating a generalised process.

An additional study, which was particularly annoying, was performed by Peter Bartsch's group (a competing Swiss research team). They assessed the role of CO_2 in stimulating breathing while we were at the Margherita Hut, the results of which were in conflict with Tim Harvey's previous study published in *The Lancet*. Scientific arguments went to and fro for many years. Perhaps the effect was less than we had reported, but not negligible.

At the end of the week, our equipment was flown to Zermatt by helicopter while we descended on foot. Despite perfect weather, many initially took the wrong route, towards dangerous cliffs. Nev, Maggie and I watched from the hut in horror. Thankfully, they climbed back an hour later to take the correct path.

The three of us had waited until last to ensure that all the equipment was safely collected by helicopter, but it was late – after 1 pm. The intense afternoon sun was melting the glacier ice, making it dangerous. Maggie led on a tight rope with me in the middle and Neville at the back, ready to stop any fall. We slowly eased down the rotten ice, striding over exposed crevasses with extreme caution in case an overhanging lip broke away. Maggie jumped over one particularly large chasm, only to find she was not attached to the rope. Despite our extreme vigilance, the knot had come loose. Such is how accidents happen.

Because of our late departure and the soggy ice, we missed the last train down from Rotenboden at 8 pm and had to walk all the way to Zermatt – nearly 3,000 m of descent, and one of the longest possible descents in the Alps. With little food and water, it was exhausting. We arrived at midnight, only to find the hotel locked up. Following a shout up at a window, Chris let us in. We went to bed knackered.

The next day we ceremonially burnt the polystyrene box, not wishing to lug it back on the minibus. Anyway, it was partly damaged. After lunch, we drove to Berne for a delightful meal then headed onward to Calais for the midnight ferry.

It had been a most memorable nine days.

Lewis DM, Bradwell AR, Shore AC, Beaman M, Tooke JE. Capillary filtration coefficient and urinary albumin leak at altitude. European Journal of Clinical Investigation. 1997; 27: 64–68.

6. Testa Grigia 1995: 31 March – 9 April

Expedition members: Maggie Beazley, Jo Bradwell, Patrick Cadigan, Ian Chesner, John Davidson, Louis Davidson, Alex Dykes, Chris Dykes, Peter Dykes, Pete Forster, Peter Hillenbrand, Tim Harvey, Brian Johnson, David Lewis, Ian MacLennan, Jenny MacLennan, John Milles, John Simmons, Sarah Walsh, Chris Weiner, Alex Wright.

Eight months later we were back to the Alps for another study on capillary leakage, this time at Testa Grigia. It was basically a repeat of the Margherita Hut study but superimposed on exercise tests which we knew led to urine protein leakage. David Lewis again provided the technical expertise for limb plethysmography, while Sarah, myself and others operated the Pugh exercise bike that we had taken to Mt Everest. We bought another temperature-controlled polystyrene box, regretting that we had casually burnt the first one.

We skied hard, ate hard and drank hard. The excellent wine at the Lombard Hut was irresistible, although we would have drunk anything. Judge Davidson and his wife (friends of Ian MacLennan) were well up to the game, even dancing on the tables in the evening. We could barely keep up.

Our skiing was fast and furious, if not always terribly elegant. Start time was 8 am, as soon as breakfast was done and an hour and a half before any other skiers ruined perfect overnight snows. Woe betide anyone who was slow – we were gone. Chris Dykes, Peter's 17-year-old son, fancied himself as an expert skier and was wondering whether he should take it up professionally. He certainly had good style, but speed and robustness were less in evidence. He couldn't keep up with our relentless pace and derring-do. We had lost him in our wake by lunchtime on the first day. His dad was distraught. I had been charged with looking after him, but being with mates came first. I don't think Peter ever quite forgave me for losing his only son. Thankfully, he turned up at the hut in the evening. With guides, we repeatedly skied off-piste on the glaciers, with the most adventurous tackling the glaciers between Castor and Pollux, two nearby 4,000 m peaks.

High winds blew over Testa Grigia frequently, shutting the lift systems, and our last day was no exception. The long descent to Cervinia had to be down the pistes carrying all our bags and equipment. Poor David struggled – he could hardly ski on gentle slopes, never mind down a 1,500 m steep run over many kilometres, carrying equipment. He didn't join us again.

7. Aberdeen hypobaric chamber 1996: 26 May – 2 June

Expedition members: Maggie Beazley, Jo Bradwell, Ian Chesner, Tim Harvey, Peter Hillenbrand, David Lewis, Ian MacLennan, John Milles, Angela Shore, Sarah Walsh, Alex Wright.

The third of the three experiments on capillary leakage was in a hyperbaric chamber in Aberdeen. Having established that altitude exposure was associated with generalised vascular leakage, we wanted to know whether it was due to increased pressure or increased permeability at normal pressure. The first mechanism would imply blood pressure changes and the second a chemical process.

The study required the expertise of Dr Angela Shore from Professor John Tooke's team in Exeter. She was an expert on cannulating nail-fold capillaries and measuring their pressure. It was an exceptionally difficult technique, and few others in the world had the necessary skills. Using a binocular microscope, surface skin over the nail base was carefully shaved off to expose the underlying capillaries. An ultra-fine glass tube connected to a manometer was then inserted into an individual vessel so that beat-by-beat pressure could be measured.

Needless to say, it needed a lot of expensive equipment, which could easily be damaged in a mountain hut, so we chose to use a hypobaric chamber instead. The best in the country are at the National Hyperbaric Centre in Aberdeen, where they are used to prevent the 'bends' (gas bubbles in the brain) in North Sea divers. Although the chambers are primarily used to increase air pressure, one of them could be used in reverse, to reduce pressure. Furthermore, it was large enough to sleep several people. At the biennial Hypoxia conference in Banff, Canada, we met Dr Stephen Watts, a senior lecturer in the Department of Environmental and Occupational Medicine at Aberdeen Medical School. He was interested in our proposal and agreed to make the chamber available (figure 13).

Most of the recompression chambers at the centre were new and housed in fancy modern buildings but ours was the old-fashioned type with all the bells and whistles of a 1960s Meccano kit (figure 14). It was run by a giant of a man with huge hands, nose and prognathic jaw, but none of us had the courage to pry into the medical treatment of his acro megaly.

Overnight, in pairs, we decompressed to an altitude equivalent to 4,300 m. All the features of mountain sickness struck – headaches, nausea, weakness and dizziness; Ian Chesner and Alex Wright were particularly poorly. Next morning our nail-bed capillaries were lanced by Angela (figure 15). Results showed that capillary pressures were essentially normal, suggesting a chemical factor as the cause of mountain sickness.

With impeccable technical and scientific support, the chamber worked perfectly. The only problem was it overheated. It was an unusually hot sunny week in Aberdeen, far too hot for the depressurised victims. The solution was a fish market; fresh fish means loads of ice. We bought two hundred kilos and laid it on top of the chamber wrapped in towels. It worked, we worked and everyone was happy.

8. Testa Grigia 1998: 20–30 March

Expedition members: Maggie Beazley, Jo Bradwell, Steve Brearey, Ian Chesner, Tim Clarke, Martin Cooper, Jim Evans, Pete Forster, Dan Hale, Tim Harvey, Peter Hillenbrand, Chris Imray, Damian Mole, Andrew MacLennan, Ian MacLennan, Jon Morgan, John Simmons, Carl Tivas, Sarah Walsh, Dave Williams.

Arguments continued with the Swiss group, led by Peter Bartsch, over the role of CO_2 in improving cerebral oxygenation. Chris Imray bought his extensive clinical experience of vascular surgery to bear on the issue. When operating on blocked carotid arteries, he would monitor brain oxygenation using near-infrared spectroscopy (chapter 9). At the hut, he and a team of anaesthetists (Tim Clarke, Dan, Jon, Carl, Sarah and Dave) varied the amounts of O_2 and CO_2 inhaled to determine their effects on brain oxygenation. We were convinced that inhaling CO_2 was helpful.

We skied our hearts out, racing around the Zermatt and Cervinia slopes until we were exhausted. First onto the slopes in the mornings, last off in the evenings, then manic beers on the terrace of the hut. Medical studies started after dark. It was a great way to do research!

The return journey proved eventful. We were in two minibuses rented from Meteor Ford in Birmingham. Both were newish but one had a curious hum in the gears of the back axle. Not alarming, but definitely louder than in the other van. On the race back on the motorways through France, the noise increased, but over 80 mph it went quiet again. We presumed that it must be some sort of resonance with other parts of the back axle. Then disaster. After a huge bang, the van shuddered, lost all power, and expelled a half-shaft alongside a red-hot gearbox. It whizzed into the nearside hedgerow, setting it alight.

Vehicle rescue worked like a charm. Within the hour we were in a nearby hotel for a cosy meal and the first comfortable bed in a week. Much better than a sleepless overnight van journey with a midnight ferry crossing, we thought.

We had intended to travel together but now the vans were separated by a day, together with our personal bags and passports. We blagged our way through Her Majesty's border control with little difficulty and were home for midnight on Sunday.

9. Testa Grigia 2003: 25 April – 4 May

Expedition members: Maggie Beazley, Jo Bradwell, Alice Brockington, Colin Chan, Phil Collins, Pete Forster, Tim Harvey, Helen Hoar, Chris Imray, Brian Johnson, Kyle Pattinson, John Simmons. Canadians led by Joe Fisher: Takafumi Azami, Tali Fisher, David Preiss, Eitan Prisman, Ron Somogyi, Alex Vesely.

The experiments in Chacaltaya (chapter 10) were incomplete, so we revisited Testa Grigia to obtain more data. Joe Fisher and his group from Toronto joined us for similar reasons. We studied the effects of 50 mg Viagra on cerebral blood flow and oxygenation as well as end-tidal CO_2 and O_2 saturations. The seven Canadians kept themselves separate except when it came to skiing. Despite their skills, they failed to keep up with our mad-cap dawn-to-dusk racing, mostly off-piste. In the good weather, there was even time to climb the Breithorn (figure 8) and ski over to Castor and Pollux. Joe Fisher thought we were completely mad going out when the weather was particularly foul, but he joined us nevertheless.

10. Testa Grigia 2013: 5–14 April

Expedition members: Kimberly Ashdown, Maggie Beazley, Jo Bradwell, Susie Bradwell, Ian Chesner, John Delamere, Mark Edsell, Olivia Faull, Pete Forster, Jamie Goodhart, Nick Harris, Steve Harris, Chris Imray, Jack Kreindler, Alastair Miller, Angie Miller, Kyle Pattinson, Josephine Robertson, Barry Smith, Mark Wilson, Yash Wimalasena.

The 35th reunion of BMRES in Birmingham on 13 October 2012 was attended by over 50 members. We became rather jolly – old friends, ancient stories, re-lived heroics and happy memories. However, it had been six months since the Bhutan expedition and we were itching for a quick fix, an expedition to satisfy the mountain rat. Rather than wait two years for a big expedition, why not go back to Testa Grigia for a mini-trip? There was also unfinished business. Mark and Yash had shown that there was evidence of early pulmonary oedema on ultrasound lung scans (lung comets) following hard exercise at 4,000 m (chapter 13). Since acetazolamide reduced mountain sickness, perhaps it would also reduce lung comets. Together we hatched a study of exercise and acetazolamide. I announced the possibility of a trip at the end of the meeting, when minds were chirpy and the glow of old successes was in the air. Immediately, Pete Forster put up his arm in support, followed by numerous others. The game was on.

We proposed a double-blind trial of acetazolamide versus placebo using a standardised exercise test on the redoubtable Alticycle, intense enough, we hoped, to provoke lung comets. The bike had failed us in Bhutan for want of a good service, but Steve Harris, who had designed and built the bike, agreed to give it a thorough overhaul. Over the next few weeks, the details of the trial were agreed so we booked the Lombard Hut for 20 people for early April.

The exercise intensity had to be sufficiently long and hard to produce lung comets but not too hard that some failed to finish the test. Using a hypobaric chamber, Kimberly Ashdown (Steve Myers's PhD student) showed that a workload of 60% sea-level peak power for 15 minutes, at the equivalent altitude of Testa Grigia (3,459 m), was about right.

The next step was to determine sea-level peak power. Because of a busy schedule, Steve Myers didn't release the bike until a month before departure, and it still wasn't functional. Steve Harris had to work frantically to get it ready in time for a weekend of baseline studies at his house in Farnham shortly before departure. I hated those last-minute problems, which dogged us from time-to-time.

A second weekend of baseline studies was planned for Birmingham but we had the worst March snowstorm in Britain for years and the lowest March temperatures since records began. Rail services were massively disrupted, while parts of Yorkshire were cut off. Birmingham had ten inches of fresh snow. I could feel a disaster looming, since individuals had to come from as far north as Cumbria. Remarkably, after a series of phone calls and changed schedules, everyone managed to make it and we established everyone's peak power.

We hired two minivans, fixed up a Channel Tunnel crossing for 10 pm on Friday 5 April and off we went, collecting various participants on the way. By midday on Saturday, having driven overnight, we were in Cervinia, in good weather and ready for the mountain ascent. Euros handed out to willing hands helped move bags and equipment through the three lift systems to Testa Grigia, where we arrived at 4 pm to a warm welcome from the hut guardian. However, it is not a salubrious establishment. On this occasion, the showers were frozen and toilets only semi-functional, but there was cold running water and a helpful supply of red wine. The bunks, in crammed rooms, were rickety, with saggy boards and dubious cleanliness, but at least we were warm. We cleared one bunkroom for experiments while another became the 'aviary' – the girls' room. It smelt rather better than the men's bunkrooms. We went to bed happy after a jolly evening. The tests were planned for 7 am sharp next morning.

In research, results usually reveal themselves as planned, hypotheses are confirmed. Maybe not enough data, perhaps some technical failures or over-hyped outcomes, but rarely opposite to expectations. All our thoughts and prejudices had assumed that subjects on acetazolamide would perform better than those on placebo – but that was not what happened.

Participants were exercised in matched pairs of drug or placebo based upon fitness and hours since ascending the previous afternoon. Since the trial was double-blinded, those managing the Alticycle, Steve, Nick, Susie and myself, did not know individuals' medications. The first person, Angie Miller, managed the 15 minutes of hard exercise reasonably well. Perfect, we though, since it meant the exercise intensity was about right. Next up was Angie's husband Alastair. However, within a couple of minutes he was struggling – puffing, grunting and gasping with the effort. I looked on anxiously wondering if something was wrong with the bike settings, or perhaps with his heart or lungs. It was unlikely to be a medical problem as he was a strong cyclist, but by three minutes he was overwhelmed by the effort and had to stop. As his gasping slowed and his grim facial expression settled, he complained that the exercise was far too hard and he could not possibly have continued. After five minutes rest, we re-started him at 30% less workload, still hoping it would be enough to produce lung comets.

As he had failed the test, I presumed he was on placebo. Many years earlier, we had showed that acetazolamide improved exercise performance (chapter 4). Maggie, our doctor to the group, thought he might be on acetazolamide since he had complained of tingling (a common side effect). I didn't believe her. People on acetazolamide had higher oxygen saturations at rest – surely that translated into improved exercise performance?

The third subject completed the exercise test but the fourth failed. He was young – 31, considerably younger than Alastair (54) – so most unlikely to have a heart problem. Again, Maggie thought he was on acetazolamide. We ploughed on with testing everyone. My turn came. I could tell from lack of tingling that I was on placebo. How was I going to perform? I lay down on the bike, my feet strapped to the pedals, pulse oximeter attached and started. After a few minutes, I was gasping and puffing but the effort was sustainable. By five minutes I felt that I would complete the test; it was very hard but just sustainable. The countdown to 15 minutes was shouted out with each turn of the pedals. My legs ached, my chest ached, I was dizzy with the effort but made it.

In total, five failed to finish, their oxygen saturations plummeting at high exercise intensities. Because of the double-blind nature of the study we didn't know the drug allocation, but if our suppositions were correct, we had a problem. How could individuals on placebo possibly perform better than those on acetazolamide? Had we mixed up the capsules? Had the baseline tests been inaccurate? Had we paired the individuals wrongly? Full analysis would have to wait until we looked carefully at the results and broke the code – which, following our agreed protocol, was when we got home.

Apart from another day of exercise tests, we had four days skiing in front of us, which, of course, was largely why we were in the Alps. There had to be a strong lure to entice 21 people to leave their families, partners, jobs and home comforts for a week in a high hut to sleep in bunk beds crammed into tiny rooms. The research and experiments may be the bricks of the BMRES structure, but the high mountains with their skiing and climbing were the fire escapes from high pressure jobs in hospitals.

The second day of exercise tests never happened. While the snow was good early in the week, the weather was rather poor. As the day dawned for the second set of tests three days later, it was bright sun with 30 cm of fresh powder. We made all the excuses possible under the clear skies to avoid repeating the tests. Each person's daily exercise had been different and four people had left early because of prior commitments. A total of 20 people was close to the minimum required for useful statistical rigour – and we were now down to 17. All willpower for work evaporated.

I was itching to discover who was on which pill and whether acetazolamide had really affected exercise. We argued about breaking the code, eventually reaching a compromise. I would forgo a day of skiing to analyse the data and, in the evening, we would reveal the results. Over dinner, Maggie revealed each person's medication, one by one, comparing it with their exercise tests. The results were remarkable: acetazolamide had reduced exercise performance, not enhanced it. It was a huge surprise – no one would have taken a bet on that.

Breaking the code was one of those many memorable days on BMRES adventures; in this case, we found results that were the exact opposite of what we had expected. Acetazolamide was not as benign as we had always supposed. We celebrated with a jeroboam of Barbaresco.

Saturday, our departure day, arrived all too quickly. Highly organised, we shuffled our kit down the lift system then rescued the two vans from under the large snow fall for the race home. The vehicles may have been limited to 100 kph, but there were other important factors that determined who arrived back first. Ian got lost twice and ran out of diesel approaching Birmingham (which he grudgingly admitted after much cross-examination). Our van beat the competition by four hours.

Bradwell AR, Myers SD, Beazley M, Ashdown K, Harris NG, Bradwell SB, Goodhart J, Imray CH, Wimalasena Y, Edsell ME, Pattinson K, Wright AD, Harris SJ, and Birmingham Medical Research Expeditionary Society. Exercise limitation of acetazolamide at high altitude (3,459 m). Wilderness and Environmental Medicine. 2014; 25(3):272-277.

11. Margherita Hut 2014: 11–20 July

Expedition members: Kimberly Ashdown, Jo Bradwell, Patrick Cadigan, Alex Clarke, Tim Clarke, Mariano Cozzi, Johnny Dawson, John Delamere, Carla Gallagher, Charles Hand, Chris Imray, Adam Jordan, Abigail Letchford, Christopher Lewis, Lauren Lock, Will Malein, Steve Myers, Johnathan Manning, Charles Newman, Owen Thomas, Sergio Pagliarini, Alex Wright.

The observation that acetazolamide reduced exercise performance at altitude had been a great surprise (see above). I recalled a few days in Switzerland when acetazolamide had been particularly effective. With Neville, Ian MacLennan and Ian Chesner, I had climbed the Jungfrau on the first day of an Alpine trip. While Neville and I were normally quicker, on that occasion we struggled badly and finished nearly half a kilometre behind. A couple of days later we walked on lower paths around Grindelwald when our respective speeds were back to their normal pattern, with Neville and myself far in the lead. A subsequent climb on Finsteraarhorn again saw the two Ians in front. At the time it seemed rather odd but it was not until a week later that they confessed their crime. They had taken acetazolamide. This seemed to explain their surprisingly good performance at altitude.

However, there was also contrary experience. On both the Karakoram and Kanchenjunga expeditions, taking acetazolamide when fully acclimatised seemed to make people feel weak and lethargic. The scientific literature also gave a mixed message, with some research showing improved exercise performance on acetazolamide and others worse. The studies varied considerably in their design and the test altitudes, so no clear consensus was apparent. When climbers asked whether they should take acetazolamide to climb Mont Blanc or Kilimanjaro, we were unable to provide a clear answer.

This is no small question for the innumerable tourists who climb in the high mountains. On Mont Blanc alone (4,810 m), there are 30,000 attempts a year, with an estimated 200 people per day reaching the top in July and August. Approximately 30% fail in their quest. Reasons include poor weather and lack of fitness, while some take acetazolamide to help acclimatisation. If acetazolamide significantly reduced exercise performance, however, it would be a major reason not to recommend it.

These thoughts led to an exercise study at the Margherita Hut. We would have chosen Mont Blanc, but the huts are not high enough to mimic the final ascent.

A typical ascent plan for Mont Blanc is:

Days 1 and 2. Climb in the Chamonix valley (1,500 m – 3,000 m) acquiring basic climbing skills

Day 3. Climb to the Tête Rousse Hut (3,167 m)

Day 4. Climb to the Goûter Hut (3,835 m)

Day 5. Early morning ascent of Mont Blanc (4,810 m)

We could maintain a similar ascent profile on Monte Rosa by climbing it from the Italian side (see front map):

Days 1 and 2. Climb in the Gressoney Valley (1,800 m − 3,000 m) at the base of Monte Rosa

Day 3. Climb to the Orestes Hut (2,646 m)

Day 4. Climb to the Gnifetti Hut (3,647 m)

Day 5. Ascend to the Margherita Hut (4,559 m) and test exercise performance.

While each altitude on Monte Rosa was slightly lower than for an ascent of Mont Blanc, the exercise test altitude would be representative of climbing near its summit. Another favourable feature of Monte Rosa was the easy, well-marked route from the Gnifetti Hut to the Margherita Hut. Naturally, crampons, ice axes and ropes would be needed but we could safely climb with large numbers of relatively inexperienced individuals for exercise experiments.

We calculated that we would need 20 people for a study with sufficient statistical rigour. This was larger than the current active membership of the BMRES. However, there were several medical students who were regular attendees at our monthly meetings and some had been on our winter or summer walks, so we offered them heavily subsidised trips.

With that plan we soon acquired ten students, eight from Birmingham and Warwick Medical Schools and two (Kim and Carla, who worked with Steve Myers) from Chichester University. The majority of participants were under 25 years of age while the 'oldies' ranged in age from 45 to 67 (me) and 76 (Alex Wright).

We rented two minivans with ten to each van. They left Birmingham 24 hours apart so participants could be tested in two separate batches of ten as they arrived at the Margherita Hut. Final arrangements included hiring climbing guides to help the novices over the glaciers and helicopters to lift heavy experimental equipment to the Hut, but a lot rested on good visibility. We had a bad weather contingency of only one day.

After months of preparations, it felt like a real expedition. I was in the first van leaving the Medical School on the Friday evening, with the other leaving on Saturday. Only Steve, Chris and I were allowed to drive; the six students were too young and Alex was too old. Furthermore, the minivan, nice though it was, could not exceed 62 mph because of a speed governor. Slowly we made our way across France, in the rain, to the Mont Blanc tunnel. There we were stopped by a massive queue; it was the first day of the school holidays. One and a half hours later, we emerged into Italy for the short drive down the Aosta Valley in heavy rain. It bode ill for our trip.

Our first hotel was Chalet de Lys near Gressoney which, at 1,823 m, would allow some acclimatisation. Next morning, we looked out anxiously at the weather. It had rained heavily overnight and thick clouds still covered all the surrounding mountains. There were no helicopters flying so we fretted over the chances of the equipment being carried up. The rain stopped for a couple of hours, encouraging us to climb a ski trail, but as we jogged back down the rain started again. Afternoon storms seemed to be a regular pattern, but as staff at the hotel explained, the previous week's weather had been awful with no access to the Margherita Hut at all. By chance, we had recently changed the bookings to a week later. We could have completely wasted the £20,000 cost of the expedition.

Our second group arrived from Birmingham in the afternoon rain. They looked pretty knackered, as we must have done the previous day, but they had had mechanical problems with the van. While passing Dijon at 3 am, there had been a bang underneath and the van slowed to a crawl. Tim, who was driving, managed to coax it along at 15–20 mph to a petrol station where they contacted the emergency services. An engineer found that a jubilee clip holding the exhaust pipe to the back of the engine had broken. This had disconnected the turbo-charger, hence the reduction in engine power. The clip was replaced and on they sped at 62 mph.

Shortly after they arrived, we met Marco, one of the top mountain guides for the Gressoney Valley. He insisted that we needed four guides, since a maximum of five people were allowed on a single rope. As our numbers had increased to 22 (we had been joined by two Italian ophthalmologists, Sergio and Mariano, studying retinal oedema), it left Chris and me to climb separately.

The planned route over three days would be strenuous, as we would have to carry all our personal belongings, but the helicopter would carry all the medical equipment. A guide would fly in a second helicopter to unload it at the hut. By law he had to fly separately from the luggage. That meant two flights at £30 per minute for the 30-minute round trip: £900 a pop.

The next morning, we packed all the equipment into 12 boxes for John Delamere and Patrick to take them to the helicopter pad two miles down the hill. However, all flying was cancelled because of bad weather. The weather window for our experiments was looking perilously tight. Fortunately, the weather forecast for the following day was sunny with little wind.

As the second team departed for their training walk, we headed up Monte Rosa. We toiled in the warm morning sun carrying all our gear for the next few days – big boots, crampons, ice axes plus laptops and cameras. Those renting boots had been advised not to walk in them until the snow line or glacier since blisters would be a problem. And this proved to be the case. Sergio assured us he would be fine but by the time we stopped for lunch at Albergo del Ponte (2,380 m) he was well blistered. He was not fit and quite out of his comfort zone, but good company. We were up to the Orestes Hut (2,600 m) in three hours, which was good compared with the guide times of four hours, particularly with heavy rucksacks. The hut was modern and first rate – completed only four years earlier by the family who ran it for climbers in the summer and skiers in the winter.

Next morning, up came the sun in a perfectly cloudless sky – the weather forecast had been correct. After two weeks of bad weather in which the mountain had been unclimbable, it was now safe. Looking upwards, we could easily see the Mantova Hut in the morning sun, whereas in the swirling mist of the previous evening it had looked impossibly high.

We followed a broad path before reaching snow that required big boots, gaiters and ice axes, but at least the weight was off our backs and onto our feet. The snow was soft with deep footprints and could easily have been climbed in trainers, but I had to set a good example to the students. Some had never been on glaciers or even at that altitude before and were blown away by the whole experience.

Several helicopters whirled up the mountain, servicing the huts and hopefully carrying our equipment. From the Mantova Hut, we put on crampons, advising the novices about techniques and dangers, then filed up to the rather attractive Gnifetti Hut (3,647 m) (figure 16). We arrived to welcoming huge pots of tea and coffee with multiple refills. Sitting in the afternoon sun, we admired the impressive views across to Piramide Vincent and the massive Lys Glacier.

After rehydrating from the sweat loss on the hot climb, our guides for the morning, Alberto and Carrado, finally appeared, albeit six hours late. They explained that, after the helicopter had delivered our equipment, it gave them time to make more money guiding a group to the Margherita Hut – a baffling excuse, but it was not the time to complain.

Over dinner, Alex Clarke developed headache and nausea, and became anxious about his health. A few months earlier he had developed high-altitude cerebral oedema during a hypoxia experiment in Coventry. I discussed with Alex Wright what we might do in an emergency. It would be dexamethasone followed by an emergency descent. Even with a guide, it would take two to three hours. Fortunately, he improved after dinner.

We were awoken at 4 am to the usual early morning sounds in a mountain hut as climbers prepared for an early start. There was no hint of anxiety among the novices, with everyone remarkably well; even Alex Clarke felt better. Our first rope of five with Alberto guiding departed at 7 am, with the second roped group following an hour later. Ahead of us were at least 70 climbers heading along the side of Piramide Vincent.

We followed in a perfectly clear day. Huge seracs surrounded us in a frozen tumble from the ice cap, stretching from Monte Rosa to Testa Grigia. Cubic kilometres of water trapped for hundreds of years but now melting quickly from global warming. Massive crevasses gaped open on the Lys Glacier as it arched over concealed crags. Our route was clear of the widest fissures but a few crossed our well-used path. A 20-cm wide crevasse was the worse we saw, its innocent-looking aperture turned deep blue then black as it plumbed the depths. But it was a simple step across it. No danger there, we thought.

We ascended onto a broad ridge (figure 17) and past the east peak of Lyskamm, looking menacingly difficult. Along the top, a tiny trail was visible over a heavily corniced ridge, where a few ant-like figures were moving very slowly upwards. Then the north face of the mountain appeared, sloping at 45 degrees and covered in monstrous seracs.

The slow pace of the novices was frustrating, so Chris and I took the lead, despite the risk of crevasses. We counted 1,000 paces before a brief pause; two breaths per pace, four per pace on steep parts. Another 1,000 paces and we were at the bottom of the final pyramid to the hut, a steep ascent cut into the 30-degree slope by innumerable footsteps (figure 9). We gasped for breath, concentrating on careful crampon and ice-axe placements to the summit ridge. The hut rose above us, while below was a two-kilometre drop into Italy. It had been a hard last push.

The warmth and safety of the hut, the welcoming staff and the brightly decorated interior contrasted with the cold white of the ice cap with all its hidden dangers. Our first group were sitting having cups of tea, having only just arrived, but they had a reason for their slow ascent. Steve had fallen into a crevasse and Kim thought she had had a heart attack.

I mentioned that we had crossed a small crevasse in the ice fall of the Lys Glacier. In the height of summer, when the top layers of winter snow have melted, it can be 5–8 m wide. However, the weeks of unseasonal heavy summer snow had built up overlapping cornices, leaving a mere 20-cm crack that we had spotted and carefully stepped over. By contrast, Steve had found it with a boot and down he went. Thankfully, only as far as his waist as he was held by the rope, but his crampons were hardly able to reach the sides and it appeared bottomless. With a good pull he was out.

Kim also recovered from her heart attack. Unbeknown to her (and please remember, dear readers, for many of the team it was their first time on a glacier), the sleeves of her inner garments on her left arm had rolled up under her outer jacket. As we ascended and the air temperature dropped to well below freezing, her arm and hand gradually became cold, then numb and painful. Add in a hypoxic brain and chest-aching breathlessness, and the diagnosis became a heart attack. Fortunately, the medics on the rope made an accurate diagnosis before mouth-to-mouth resuscitation and cardiac massage were applied.

Now we had work to do. The dedicated experiments room on the top floor was full of Italian junk. Research workers from the University of Turin had not bothered to chuck out ancient apparatus from innumerable experiments. It was 2 pm before we were ready for exercise tests. It was a tight schedule to finish everyone by 10 pm when the generator was switched off for the night. Despite hypoxic brains and headaches, we pressed on with determination, so that by dinnertime at 6.30 pm we had completed six studies and accompanying ultrasound lung scans. Poor Charles, who had mountain sickness, had 16 lung comets, indicating early pulmonary oedema (chapter 13). He had struggled above 4,000 m with a bad headache, nausea and weakness. The altitude had slowly drained him of all his bravado and he lay in bed feeling poorly. Kim was similarly affected but doggedly helped with the exercise tests. Others, including Adam and Jonathan, were untouched by the altitude.

Sergio and Mariano were quite relaxed about starting their retinal studies, chatting to guides and wardens. They had hardly started by dinnertime, which was eaten leisurely, Italian-style. I fretted that they would never finish their experiment before lights out, but with typical Italian charm, Sergio persuaded the hut wardens to keep the generator running until we had finished.

I was second to last for the exercise test, with Steve last. It just worked out that way. I was started at 9 pm, nine hours after arriving, so not exactly mirroring an ascent of Mont Blanc, but it was the best we could do. We eventually finished everything at 10.30 pm and all the lights suddenly went out as the generator stopped. It had been a long day.

The ascent, the experiments, sick members of the group and the mountaineering afterwards were on my mind much of the night. So, despite being very tired, I slept poorly. A modest amount of mountain sickness with headache didn't help. Then the generator started at 4.30 am for the early-starting climbers. Charles and Kim were poorly overnight so we gave them 500 mg of acetazolamide. Within half an hour, Kim could feel tingling and by mid-morning both felt much better.

We lingered over an early breakfast, awaiting the arrival of our second group. At our pace, they would arrive around 9.30 am but at 8 am Owen and Will burst in. They had climbed up in a very fast time – 3 hours. They were manic from the ascent and felt very well. It was an impressive effort. Maybe when I was 25 years old I would have been as fast, I reflected. And they hadn't even noticed Steve's crevasse, but maybe snow in the night had covered it up. The second rope of six, guided by Guiseppi came up in less than 4 hours and included Lauren and Abigail, neither of whom had used crampons or ice axes before.

Their early arrival meant the studies were in full swing much earlier. Combined with the previous day's practice, six were completed before lunch. The final two exercise tests were on Patrick and John. Both had similar sea-level power on the bike so it was easy to compare their performance at altitude. Indeed, John was much weaker – and he was on acetazolamide while Patrick was on placebo. It seemed that the drug was having the same power-reducing effect that that we had observed at Testa Grigia a year earlier. All tests completed, we watched a glorious sunset over dinner (figure 18).

Finally, after seven days, we could enjoy a day of climbing in perfect weather. But first, the baggage. Our 12 medical boxes were bundled down the stairs and onto a small area of flat snow within a few metres of the hut, just where the ridge plunged over the precipice (figure 19). They were put into two huge white bags and tied to a rope lowered from a helicopter. Its engine strained in the thin air as it slowly rose, then plunged down the cliffs, banging our bags on a cornice as it went. It was heavier than on the ascent because many of us had stuffed the medical boxes with personal items. Chris had even added his garden gnome – a 20-cm, gold-painted plaster gnome that he had been awarded for carrying out research under difficult circumstances. Not places such as Testa Grigia or the Margherita Hut, as you might imagine, but at Coventry University Hospital. They were awarded as motivational tools by hospital managers for such feats as saving money and getting doctors to their clinics on time. Chris took it with him wherever he travelled so that on returning he could place 'gnome' pins on a world map alongside the pins of other winners. Such is modern management. Our helicopter plunged down to Gressoney, the extra weight of the golden gnome accelerating its descent.

Now to serious matters: we had to get 22 people down the mountain before the snow turned to slush. From our eyrie at 4,559 m, we could bag several 4,000 m peaks on the descent, including the Zumsteinspitze (4,561 m), Parrotspitze (4,436m) and Piramide Vincent (4,215 m). But the peaks were not for everyone. Theo, a guide from the second day's group, led a rope of Kim, Sergio, Alex and a very reluctant Charles directly to the Gnifetti Hut. Charles's macho view on climbing had come crashing down when he developed mountain sickness from which he had yet to fully recover.

Chris, Owen and I climbed together, starting with the Zumsteinspitze across the ice cap from the Margherita Hut. It was ascended by a steepening narrow snow ridge with a final rock scramble to the summit, a room-sized convex platform. Each side had sheer drops, one to huge crevasses on the Grenz Glacier and the other to green pastures via three kilometres of ice, rock and scree. Other climbers passed us on their route to the Dufourspitze (4,634 m), the second highest peak in the Alps. It has an even airier crest than the Zumsteinspitze and a steep rock climb to the summit. It was not for us.

Our next peak was the Parrotspitze. From views on the way up, we knew it was a sharp ridge, but they had not prepared us for what was in store. We climbed up a steep snow trail to emerge over the abyss – a 2.5 km drop into Italy and an even sheerer drop than from the Zumsteinspitze. The half-metre wide, crampon-marked track angled upwards, becoming more and more spectacular (figure 20): a knife-edge of pure alpine climbing bliss. Postcard perfection of what climbing is about. Several groups crossed our path, forcing us off the crest onto its steep loose sides. As they passed, we clutched the tops of ice axes pushed fully into the deep snow. There was hardly room to pass. The top traversed, with no widening of the route, we descended back to the ice cap. Chris, with all his climbing experience, including ascending Everest, had not come across anything quite so delightful. It was as good as it gets; glorious weather, no wind and visibility for 100 miles. A mini-classic.

The next treat was a small ice summit called Ludwigshöhe (4,342 m), which was a mere 50 metres above the glacier. It was another airy classic but just 100 metres long rather than the 750 metres of the Parrotspitze.

We then descended to a rocky peak with a small church perched on its side (Cristo delle Vette), but decided not to bother climbing it as it was a mere 20 metres of iron ladders. It hardly deserved the separate peak name of Balmenhorn (4,167m). I later found out that Alex, fearful of climbing, had been tethered like a dog at its base while the others went up.

We turned southwards down a sun-focused bowl of melting snow. Slushy, with foot-deep imprints, it was hard to descend without stumbling on the rotten soggy mush. From there, we turned towards the main route down, tripping as we went. We passed below Piramide Vincent (4,215 m) to see one of our groups high on its flank, struggling in the wet snow. We passed over the crevasse where Steve had fallen on the ascent. It was over 10 metres wide at its far end, narrowing towards us and completely covered over with hard snow. One could imagine that in late summer and occasionally in the skiing season it would require a huge detour.

The final hour was just one long slog in melting snow with deeply imprinted steps that occasionally gave way. And it was hot. But the Gnifetti Hut, our refuge for the night, was always visible, enticing us downwards in the perfect weather. We arrived around 1.30 pm, hot, tired and happy. Most of the group had already arrived, chatting excitedly about their wonderful climbing experiences, especially the novices. It was a happy group that had dinner that night. Because of our large numbers, we had private dining in the main bar with full service. Wine further flushed our sun-burnt cheeks, as we nattered contentedly.

The expedition was now largely over. We had a leisurely breakfast, then roped up for the last ice descent. Crampons were removed for the final contouring snow slope to the Indren ski-lift. There we bade farewell to the guides Guseppi and Theo as I pressed €50 each into their palms. Two more cable cars took us back to our hotel, Chalet du Lys. I tipped Corrado and Alberto with more €50 notes. The guides had been very accommodating and were perfect for our needs.

There were a few administrative details. Alex collected all the mountain sickness questionnaires, and we brought the remaining equipment back from the heliport. By midday, we were heading down to the Aosta Valley and pressed on to Birmingham with barely a stop, dropping everyone off en route: Steve, Kim and Carla at 2 am near the tunnel entrance, Chris, Charles and Alex at Warwick, and lastly Alex Wright at his house; I made it into bed at 5.30 am.

Analysis of the exercise test data confirmed our previous results. Acetazolamide had indeed reduced exercise performance, particularly in the older age group. We also elucidated the mechanism. The drug, in its role as an enzyme inhibitor, delayed the removal of CO_2 from exercising muscles, thereby reducing their efficiency. Furthermore, acetazolamide had a greater exercise-lowering effect in older people because of slower excretion rates. They would probably benefit from a reduced dose, but that would be an experiment for another day.

Bradwell AR, Ashdown K, Gallagher C, Delamere JP, Thomas OD, Lucas SJE, Wright AD, Harris SJ, Myers SD and Birmingham Medical Research Expeditionary Society. Acetazolamide reduces exercise capacity following a five-day ascent to 4,559 m on Monte Rosa. BMJ Open Sport Exerc Med. 2018;4(1):e000302. doi:10.1136/bmjsem-2017-000302

Photographs. AL: Abigail Letchford

***Fig 1.** Lombard hut at Testa Grigia*

***Fig 2.** Ski lifts at Testa Grigia*

***Fig 3.** Matterhorn from the Lombard hut*

***Fig 4.** Lombard hut view to Cervinia*

***Fig 5.** Testa Grigia or 'Grey Head', ice-cap*

***Fig 6.** Lombard hut in a blizzard*

***Fig 7.** Lombard hut dining room with John Simmons*

Fig 8. *Breithorn (4,164 m) opposite Testa Grigia*

Fig 9. *Margherita Hut on Gnifetti peak*

Fig 10. *Margherita Hut on Gnifetti peak (4,559 m)*

Fig 11. *Constructing the polystyrene box in Zermatt*

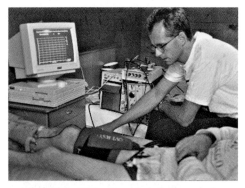

Fig 12. *David Lewis and limb plethysmography*

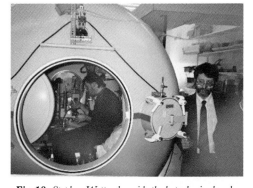

Fig 13. *Stephen Watts alongside the hyperbaric chamber*

Fig 14. *All the bells and whistles*

Fig 15. *Angela Shore measuring capillary pressure while breathing oxygen in the chamber*

Fig 16. Gnifetti Hut at 3,642 m

Fig 17. Zumstein, Gnifetti peak and Parrotspitz (Lt to Rt) (AL)

Fig 18. Sunset over Lyskamm and the Matterhorn from the Margherita Hut

Fig 19. View from the Margherita Hut into Italy (AL)

Fig 20. Parrotspitz and Lyskamm

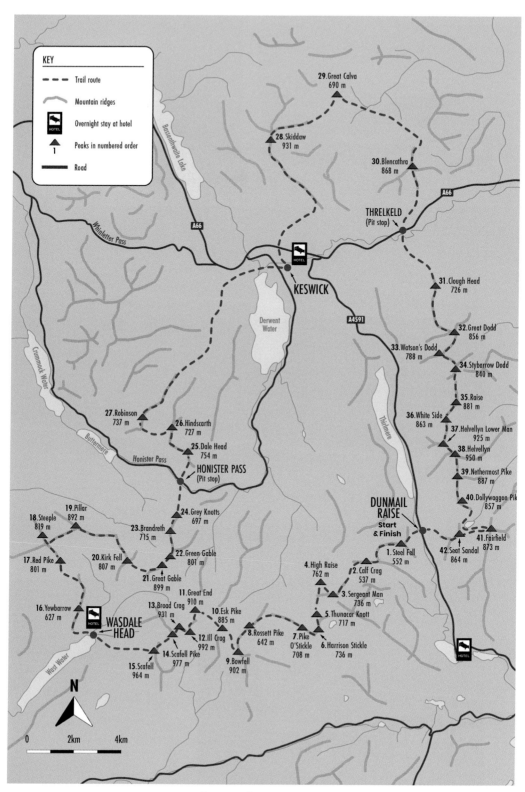

KEY

- - - - Trail route

Mountain ridges

🏨 Overnight stay at hotel

▲ Peaks in numbered order
1

Road

29.Great Calva
690 m

28.Skiddaw
931 m

30.Blencathra
868 m

Bassenthwaite Lake

A66

THRELKELD
(Pit stop)

A66

🏨

KESWICK

31.Clough Head
726 m

Whinlatter Pass

A4591

Derwent
Water

32.Great Dodd
856 m

33.Watson's Dodd
788 m

34.Stybarrow Dodd
840 m

Crummock Water

35.Raise
881 m

36.White Side
863 m

27.Robinson
737 m

26.Hindscarth
727 m

37.Helvellyn Lower Man
925 m

38.Helvellyn
950 m

Buttermere

25.Dale Head
754 m

Thirlmere

Honister Pass

HONISTER PASS
(Pit stop)

39.Nethermost Pike
887 m

40.Dollywaggon Pik
857 m

DUNMAIL
RAISE
Start
& Finish

19.Pillar
892 m

24.Grey Knotts
697 m

18.Steeple
819 m

23.Brandreth
715 m

41.Fairfield
873 m

1.Steel Fell
552 m

22.Green Gable
801 m

42.Seat Sandal
864 m

17.Red Pike
801 m

20.Kirk Fell
807 m

4.High Raise
762 m

2.Calf Crag
537 m

21.Great Gable
899 m

11.Great End
910 m

3.Sergeant Man
736 m

16.Yewbarrow
627 m

🏨

WASDALE
HEAD

13.Broad Crag
931 m

10.Esk Pike
885 m

5.Thunacar Knott
717 m

12.Ill Crag
992 m

8.Rossett Pike
642 m

7.Pike
O'Stickle
708 m

6.Harrison Stickle
736 m

🏨

Wast Water

14.Scafell Pike
977 m

15.Scafell
964 m

9.Bowfell
902 m

N

0   2km   4km

Bob Graham Round

Chapter 17
Big walks

Liathach in winter

Walking is the answer, who cares what the question is.

− Anon

Summary: Much of the Society's energies were targeted at major expeditions, while Alpine trips fulfilled skiing and climbing ambitions. As these were only occasional activities, it was the numerous summer and winter walks that welded members into a cohesive expeditionary force.

Typically they were based on a big Saturday walk and a smaller outing the following day. Summer walks were timed to be around midsummer when there were 18 to 20 hours of daylight. Although always ambitious, they gradually increased in intensity and duration until they became impossibly hard. Winter climbs were on the first or second weekend of February, hopefully to coincide with a decent amount of snow, and usually in Wales or the Lake District. They were more modest affairs because of limited daylight, but were always popular and often attended by 20 or more people.

The walks started in 1976 as the Society was forming but became regular events, leading to 80 or more trips in total. By their very nature they were highly social as we all jammed together in some small pub in the evenings and on coaches there and back. But on the walks themselves, it was different. Any group thins out based upon individuals' speeds, so the days were often spent with only one or two companions. My experiences are, therefore, more personal and do not necessarily reflect what was happening to others. Hence, this is a more autobiographical account than the expedition chapters.

The sheer number of walks makes it impractical to mention them all, but those of particular interest are described below.

1. The Three Peaks Race: September 1976
2. The Second Three Peaks: June 1977
3. The Welsh Fourteen: June 1978
4. The Lakeland Three Thousanders: June 1983
5. Two Torridons: Liathach and Ben Eighe: June 1986
6. An Teallach and the Wilderness Walk: June 1988
7. The Round of Glen Nevis: June 1989
8. Glen Coe and the Aonach Eagach Ridge: June 1990
9. The Cairngorm Four Thousanders: June 1991
10. The Cuillin Ridge: July 1991
11. The Round of Glenshiel: June 1992
12. Winter Walks and the Three Peaks of Yorkshire: February 2003
13. Monte Perdido: June 2010
14. The Bob Graham Round: June 2014

1. The Three Peaks Race: September 1976

Early in September 1976, we took on the challenge of the 'Three Peaks in 24 hours' race against time and police radar: Snowdon, Scafell Pike and Ben Nevis. Not from summit to summit but from car park to car park. Five of us – Tim Harvey, Neville Richardson, Gron Jones, Phil Gamlin (research chemist at ICI) and myself – set off in two cars from Birmingham for the exploit. Starting on the Friday evening, we knocked off Snowdon and then drove to Wasdale Head in the dark hours to ascend Scafell Pike. We pitched tents for a couple of hours to await the dawn in drizzle. Tired muscles, night-time sleepiness and excitability were a recipe for disaster. Nevertheless, we scrambled unharmed onto the summit of England's highest peak in the early hours of Saturday morning. The next section was the most dangerous, with unexpected traffic on the twisting Scottish roads. To help speed up the drive, we agreed a signal for overtaking. The lead car would stay on the right-hand side of the road if it were clear for the second car to pass slower vehicles. Blind corners were in the hands of the leaders. We dodged and weaved our way through Glasgow, overtook everything on the sweeping vistas of Rannoch Moor and watched the clock ticking by on the narrow roads up to Fort William. Frightened by the driving and fearing we were too slow, we arrived at the start of the Ben Nevis path with only four hours of our 24 hour deadline remaining.

By chance, it was the day of the annual fell race up Britain's highest peak. As we started, there was a crowd of race supporters looking at runners up the mountain and then at us in our dishevelled state from having slept rough overnight. Some commented that we were not fit for such a race but when we explained what we had already done they clapped us onwards. Surging up the lower slopes, Neville and I caught up the back markers as we entered the clouds. We teasingly offered them sweets and water, while the race leader, the legendary Joss Naylor, bounded down past us, leaping from rock to rock in 50 foot strides, winning in 1 hour 28 minutes. We reached the summit surrounded by fell runners and, jogging back, made it to the cars with 90 minutes to spare. But this was not an exploit for just the two of us; it was a team event where all had to complete the race. Looking back up the mountain, Phil and Gron could be seen below the cloud base and were soon down, but where was Tim? Mist had descended so it was hard to see far, but with 30 minutes remaining a lone figure was just visible high up. We walked up to encourage him over the remaining few hundred yards. Refusing all help with his pack, he stumbled in with 10 minutes left on the clock.

What a day! We celebrated our success in the appropriate manner in the pubs of Fort William. The dry conditions had been perfect and the timing excellent for the 4 month-long drought broke dramatically the following day (September 5). It was a marvellous climax to a wonderfully hot summer.

Highest peaks of Wales, England and Scotland
1. **Snowdon 3,560 ft (1,085 m)**
2. **Scafell Pike 3,209 ft (978 m)**
3. **Ben Nevis 4,409 ft (1,344 m)**

2. The Second Three Peaks: June 1977

The success of the Three Peaks Race set us thinking about a similar adventure for the second three highest peaks. We could climb successively lower ones each year, the third highest, the fourth highest and so on. As we aged, the peaks would become lower so that 50 years hence, when we were in our dotage, the fiftieth three highest peaks might still be attainable. Providence denied us our long-term goal in the following manner.

The second highest peaks are Crib-y-Ddysgl (Garnedd Ugain) next to Snowdon, Scafell in the Lake District and Ben Macdui in the Cairngorms. These summits have the benefit of 69 m less total height but, rather to our surprise, have longer road and walking distances. To add to the challenge, we agreed to start and finish at sea level. As it added even more to time to the schedule, this was unwise. Anyway, that was the plan as we set off from Birmingham on a Friday afternoon, Crib-y-Ddysgl our first target. We touched sea, or rather the Menai Straits at Caernarfon, and started the timers on our watches. We drove up past Llanberis to the car park at Pen-y-Pass, from where we took the Miner's Track, past the lakes and up the steep path to the standing stone near the Snowdon railway line. An easy slope on the right found us on the summit of Crib-y-Ddysgl. We touched its top then jogged down the same path to the car park.

The drive to the Lakes proved to be more dangerous. Six of us – Gron Jones, Tony Howell, Tim Harvey, Neville Richardson, Phil Gamlin and myself – were packed into three cars. Driving through the night, we took turns at the wheel. The route to Scafell was via the Hardknott Pass, Wast Water and Wasdale Head. It was a long tricky drive along country roads, with the inevitable competition. There was a natural tendency to try and be first. On one sharp corner, Neville was tricked by the darkness and slid off into a ditch.

Fortunately, no one was injured and miraculously the car could still be driven but it was badly damaged. As it was Phil's car, he quit the race to try and coax it back to Liverpool. Unaware of the accident, I had climbed Scafell with Tony and Tim, wondering whether the others were ahead or behind. Only on descent did we realise what had happened. I felt it was time to abandon the challenge. I had slept little overnight, and Tim's car had blown a cylinder head gasket driving to Wasdale. I quit with Tim for a return to Birmingham.

The three remaining adventurers, Gron, Tony and Neville, headed for Scotland – past Edinburgh, over the Forth Bridge and along the A9 to Aviemore then Loch Morlich and the path to Ben Macdui. With timing tight, it was a race for the top. Gron eased ahead as the clouds embraced them on the featureless Cairngorm plateau. It was not easy finding a remote summit in the mist (no satnav in those days). Having climbed to what appeared to be the highest mound, he headed back past Neville to the car. Realising that the 24 hours was almost over, and with Neville 20 minutes behind, he took the car and drove to Inverness as quickly as possible to touch the sea. Wishing to prove his successful timing, he went to the police station to get an official record that he had got there 5 minutes before the 24 hour deadline, justifying his decision to abandon the others.

They were pretty upset that the car had been taken, but there was worse. When questioned about Ben Macdui's summit and the location of the obvious triangulation point cairn, he was shocked. He had not seen one. The adventure had been a comprehensive failure.

Second highest peaks of Wales, England and Scotland
1. **Crib-y-Ddysgl (Carnedd Ugain) 4,494 ft (1,065 m)**
2. **Scafell 3,162 ft (964 m)**
3. **Ben Macdui 4,295 ft (1,309 m)**

3. The Welsh Fourteen: June 1978

Having failed to complete the second highest three peaks in Great Britain, we contemplated something more conventional – the Welsh 14. Snowdonia has 14 peaks over 3,000 ft on three mountain ridges – the Snowdon group, the Glyder range and the Carnedds – plus the two moorland peaks of Foel Grach and Foel-fras. The route had been immortalised by Thomas Firbank in his amusing autobiography, I Bought a Mountain. He was a Canadian farmer who, having married a Welsh girl, bought a farm that included the Glyder mountains. In his book, he beautifully described how he completed the route in 7 hours 30 minutes. Since then it has become a very popular challenge over 24 hours but the record stands at 4 hours and 10 minutes, and some have even completed it three times in a day. Our aim was a modest ten hours. A few of us had tried a couple of times but had been beaten by bad weather. The forecast for the midsummer weekend was good.

A dozen of us booked in at the Pen-y-Gwryd Hotel near Pen-y-Pass for Friday night, ready for the test. At 4.30 am on the Saturday morning, we left the hotel and dragged ourselves up the road to the car park and the start of the Pyg Track. Our first goal was to reach the summit of Snowdon, where we could start our watches. We arrived 90 minutes later to find many campers committed to the same adventure, or the three peaks race that we had completed two years earlier.

The route descended along the railway track to the stone monolith at the top of the Pyg Track, up Crib-y-Ddysgl then down to the pinnacles at the western end of Crib Goch. There were opportunities for jogging on level ground and the descents but we walked the ascents; we were not fell runners. Remarkably, they even ran the dangerous crest of Crib Goch. I have seen people clutching the ridge on hands and knees, yet the kings of the fells almost sprint along it. At the east end of the ridge, a narrow path leads down towards the Llanberis Pass; it is relatively easy but steep, with nearly 2,500 feet of descent. By now I had teamed up with Neville Richardson, my partner during the long night walk in the Himalayas nine months earlier. He is a downhill specialist, where I can't keep pace, while I am slightly faster uphill; between us, we were the fastest in the group. We reached the road and breakfast at the café leading to Elidir Fawr.

The route ascends through abandoned slate quarries onto a broad ridge. A series of false summits and 2,700 feet of ascent make it tiring but we still felt good. From the top, the panorama of the Snowdon ridge, the Glyders and Carnedds opened up, making almost the whole route visible. We jogged along a narrow moorland track to the bottom of Y Garn, then struggled up the stony path onto Glyder Fawr and Castell y Gwynt (Castle of the Winds). Our split time put us at a little over nine hours to complete the route, but we would get slower. There was no room for complacency.

There was a steep gully leading down from Glyder Fach to the col below Tryfan, then a boulder-strewn path to the standing stones of Adam and Eve on the very top. On a previous occasion, Neville had dared me to jump from one to the other. Seeing others performing this dangerous feat (figure 1), he had followed suit and for good measure had then done it backwards, despite the 500 foot precipice on the east side. I refused the dare. He was fearless while I had only a modest head for heights.

Others on the summit, attempting the Welsh 14, were impressed with our speed. Their target was 24 hours, but in fairness they had big packs and carried their own food. We were ultra-lightweight: trainers, shorts, food crammed into pockets and no spare clothing.

From the top of Tryfan, the car park at Llyn Ogwen looked a stone's throw away in the clear air but it was 2,300 feet of rugged descent. We took it direct, as the crow flies. Large angular boulders slowed us on the top section, then it eased to heather and finally grass. We were down in 20 minutes, struggling with fatigue, dehydration and weary legs.

A 20 minute stop at the café restored our strength for Pen yr Ole Wen. It was a straightforward climb with some loose rocks on the path but we were slow on that third big ascent of the day. We were losing time, but it was impossible to go faster. Next came Carnedd Dafydd, the outrider Yr Elen, followed by Carnedd Llewelyn, the largest peak on the third ridge, which gave views along to the final peaks. Our watches were suggesting we would just make the 10 hour mark. From the top, it was a long trek across moorland to Foel Grach and Foel-fras. Keeping a close eye on the time, we jogged intermittently but were slowing. Struggling on, we battled against the clock, desperately trying to maintain our speed to a distant triangulation point with its marker cairn. But our aching legs were against us; we finished in 10 hours and 4 minutes.

The final challenge of the walk was the descent from the high moorland. It was many miles to the road on weary legs, taking us another two hours to reach a roadside pub. A beery rehydration followed, with a taxi back to the bar in the Pen-y-Gwryd Hotel, where we watched others returning until nightfall. We had been out on the hills for over 14 hours, but were an hour ahead of anyone else.

The Welsh 14: peaks over 3,000 ft in Wales, in route order
1. **Snowdon (Yr Wyddfa) 3,560 ft (1,085 m)**
2. **Crib-y-Ddysgl (Carnedd Ugain) 3,494 ft (1,065 m)**
3. **Crib Goch 3,028 ft (923 m)**
4. **Elidir Fawr 3,028 ft (923 m)**
5. **Y Garn 3,107 ft (947 m)**
6. **Glyder Fawr 3,281 ft (1,000 m)**
7. **Glyder Fach 3,261 ft (994 m)**
8. **Tryfan 3,002 ft (915 m)**
9. **Pen yr Ole Wen 3,207 ft (978 m)**
10. **Carnedd Dafydd 3,425 ft (1,044 m)**

11. **Yr Elen 3,156 ft (962 m)**
12. **Carnedd Llewelyn 3,490 ft (1,064 m)**
13. **Foel Grach 3,202 ft (976 m)**
14. **Foel-fras 3,091 ft (942 m)**

4. The Lakeland Three Thousanders: June 1983

Our ambition for longer walks was gradually increasing. Having done the Welsh Three Thousanders a couple of times, including a winter ascent, we thought we should attempt the four peaks over 3,000 feet in the Lake District. According to Ken Wilson's Big Walks book, this covered 46 miles with 11,000 feet of ascent. The four 3,000 feet peaks are Skiddaw, Scafell Pike, Scafell and Helvellyn, with a start and finish at Moot Hall in Keswick. They were the basis of the 'Bob Graham Round' (see walk 14) but clearly much easier since the latter involved 42 peaks and 27,000 feet of ascent. Still, it looked challenging enough.

Midsummer found us at a hotel opposite Moot Hall with a weather forecast of partly sunny and no rain. We chatted over pints of beer in the hotel bar wondering when to start. We met several people attempting the 'Bob Graham' with plans to set off in late evening before dark. The first peak, Skiddaw, could be run in moonlight using a head torch. Should we do the same? I planned to partner with David Milles. He had recently run a marathon and was fit. Neville, my usual companion, and several others wanted to start that evening but even with the braggadocio of several beers, I was not tempted. A 4 am start was sufficient. As usual, it was to be a lightweight affair with 'pit stops' arranged in Borrowdale for 6 am and at the base of Helvellyn for midday. Barbara, my girlfriend of four years, and Helen Evans, John Delamere's girlfriend, were the cooks. Post-marriage, they were not so keen.

David and I were up at 4 am and out of the hotel 15 minutes later. We jogged out of Keswick, through the parks and towards Skiddaw. The morning was cold but conditions perfect as the dawn glow lit our route. We walked on the ascents but the flat parts and downhill were taken at a slow jog. We were back at Moot Hall by 6 am and off down the narrow road to Borrowdale and our breakfast stop an hour later. We felt strong running the eight miles along the tarmacked road. It was easy and David was good company. A 20 minute stop for breakfast, rehydration, some snacks for the next climb and we were soon striding up to Sprinkling Tarn, where we found John Milles (David's brother) having a bathe in a warm tarn. We passed a 65 year-old from the Ramblers' Association striding out, marvelling that he was attempting the same walk as us.

The climb to Scafell Pike was easy, with plenty of water to drink in the streams. Weaving our way through boulder fields, we were at the top by 11 am. We had views of all the Lake District and could see what a vast distance we would cover from Skiddaw in the north to High Raise and Helvellyn in the west. We were climbing right across the Lake District, yet this was trivial compared with the Bob Graham round of 42 peaks and Joss Naylor's round of 67 peaks, all in 24 hours. Our walk, mighty as it seemed, was trivial compared with theirs.

Our next steps were down to the saddle of Mickledore between Scafell Pike and Scafell, then along Lord's Rake. The direct route up Broad Crag was a little tricky and we were in no hurry The rake is a wide gully that ends below the top of Scafell. As we approached the summit cairn, we saw people asleep in the sun and then realised they were Nigel Hillman and Ian Chesner. How did they get ahead of us? Had they gone in a clockwise direction?

They awoke and were just as surprised to see us. They explained that they had started the previous evening with Neville but had been too early for the breakfast stop. Lacking food and fluids, and short of sleep, they had become too tired to go on. Offering a small amount of refreshment, we left them to sleep.

From the summit it was a long jog down to the base of High Raise. From there, it was a hard slog through heather on tired legs. Having been on the move for ten hours, we were starting to feel the effort. From the summit we had clear views down to our next pit stop at Helvellyn. On the way down, we met John Simmons walking slowly because of sore knees. He had also started the night before but had resisted sleeping with the others on Scafell. That meant only a few people were ahead. I wondered if we might catch them. David was more tired than I was so I left him chatting to John and jogged wearily down to the pit stop to meet Barbara and Helen and welcoming food and drinks. Nigel, another early starter, lay in the grass, so I joined him on the climb up Helvellyn. From the summit, we tracked north before the long descent at the far end of Thirlmere reservoir. This left six miles to the finishing line in Keswick.

By now it was impossible to jog. We slogged out the last few miles along the main road in the early evening heat, catching up with John Coote and Ginette Harrison. With sore feet, desperately tired legs, thirsty and generally worn out, I creaked into Keswick, arriving at Moot Hall 15½ hours after leaving early that morning.

Walking painfully across the street to the hotel, we found Neville and John Delamere at the bar. We tried to account for all the early starters but we had no idea about the later ones. After refreshments, I drove to the Helvellyn pit stop. A few of our friends were there, having decided to miss out Helvellyn. That left only Mike Winterborn unaccounted for. We tied a Mars bar to a branch with a note saying, 'see you later'. As the sun set, there was still no Mike and dinner beckoned. He could be anywhere. We left him to the wolves.

Lake District Three Thousanders
1. **Scafell Pike 3,209 ft (978 m)**
2. **Scafell 3,162 ft (964 m)**
3. **Skiddaw 3,055 ft (931 m)**
4. **Helvellyn 3,117 ft (950 m)**

5. Two Torridans: Liathach and Beinn Eighe: June 1986

The best big walks in North Wales or the Lake District had fallen to our feet so we needed to go further for our excitement. A walk from Peebles to Moffat a couple of years earlier had taken us to the Southern Uplands of Scotland. That was at the very limit of Friday evening drives that still allowed time for a decent supper at a hotel. But why not travel overnight in a bus for 10–12 hours instead? That could take us well into the Highlands and we could sleep with the help of an appropriate amount of alcohol or sedation. If we left from the Medical School early evening, we could get just about anywhere by 4 am the following morning, do a big walk and slump into a hotel that evening. The pain and tiredness of driving back would be taken by the bus driver while we recovered from our exertions.

A bus was booked, and at 6 pm on the closest weekend to mid-summer, 16 June, 24 of us left the Medical School for the 11 hour journey north to Liathach and Ben Eighe. These two titanic mountains stand as sentinels in the Western Highlands. They are colossal masses of Torridon sandstone with hard quartzite summits that have weathered for 200 million years. Monolithic, with few weaknesses in their southern walls to suggest an ascent, they became our next target. John Tavener, a general practitioner in Birmingham, advised us on sleeping medications for the night. Most of us thought beer was sufficient but he suggested Halcion (triazolam). It was a short-acting benzodiazepine, much like temazepam but more powerful. Half of us took his advice and hunkered down. The next thing we remembered was arriving at the west end of Liathach at 5 am, after a very restful sleep. We gathered our packs to set off up the mountain in the morning mist. Unfortunately, we hadn't quite recovered from the pills. Nigel Hillman and Phil Meredith, both experienced sailors, spent ten minutes arguing which way was north on a compass with a large red pointer on the needle. Norman Dorricott fell off the side of the path and dislocated a finger. Others fell into rhododendron bushes around the car park as they tried to orientate themselves. I had taken Halcion and, unusually for me, was last off the bus and last to start up the mountain.

The route was straightforward but not memorable. The mountain has an east/west orientation with steep vertical north and south faces. Before I knew it, we were on the first summit, Spidean a'Choire Leith. This was the first of two Munros on the mountain separated by a narrow crest and a series of airy pinnacles. The path climbed over these features to the second summit, Mullach an Rathain. The sun emerged intermittently providing good views but it was mostly cloudy with light drizzle. Near the top, I caught up with John Simmons but everyone else was invisible in the clouds.

Descent from Liathach was apparently tricky. There was only one way down and it was not easily found. It was unclear on the map, while the track we were following petered out above the eastern cliffs. Being nearly last, with mist obscuring the leaders and the mountain's sides, we were in trouble. Our only thoughts were to follow a northerly compass bearing to Beinn Eighe and hope for the best. The map showed steep sections but it lacked detail. Never having seen the north side of Liathach, we had no idea what to expect. As we descended below the cloud base, we realised our predicament. There was a series of small cliffs with intervening steeply sloping scree and grass. We could retrace out steps but that would take ages and we still might not find the correct route. We assumed everyone else was miles ahead and already half way up Beinn Eighe. We would be last home.

Cautiously, in light rain, we descended to the top of the first cliff. It was a ten metre drop, almost vertical, running in rainwater and covered in green slime. This north-facing side rarely saw any sun. At one end, the cliff had a right-angled corner with some small ledges and a narrow chimney. We crept over its upper lip being careful not to slip on the loose pebbles above the precipice. In the distance loomed Beinn Eighe, its quartzite top glinting in the sun from the recent rain. Gripping grass tussocks at the top, I climbed down the gulley with extreme caution. Dislodged rocks bounced onto the sloping ledges below and clattered into the abyss. It was most unlikely that anyone was below, unless it was our friends! John followed in his usual unflappable style and led the next cliff.

There are times to be gripped and times to keep calm. This was the latter. We were committed to a dangerous descent. There were five cliffs altogether, each with similar difficulties and dangers. One slip and we would fall 150 metres. Very slowly and with extreme caution, we worked our way down onto safer ground and finally the long gentle slope to the bottom. It had taken nearly two hours.

Imagining we were hopelessly behind everyone else and with no one in sight, we took a direct line to the north side of Beinn Eighe. We crossed the river, turning north past the triple buttresses of Coire Mhic Fhearchair, still full of winter snow (figure 2). The cliffs are the largest in Britain.

To reach the summit of Beinn Eighe, we climbed the mountain's northern spur. This steep ascent took us up to nearly 900 metres, from where it was a fairly flat route to the first of its two summit Munros, Ruadh-stac Mor. The quartzite rocks glistened under our trainers as we wearily ascended. The psychology of being first in the race, with adrenalin pumping, puts a spring into the step; being hopelessly last drained our legs of all strength. As we neared the top, we saw a crowd of people on a distant path below, north of the great cliffs and where we had been an hour earlier. I counted a dozen. How curious. Could they possibly be our group? We thought we recognised some but they were over a mile away. Dismissing the possibility that we had got ahead, we pressed onto the summit pinnacles. From there the route was due west along the quartzite ridge. It was like a huge whaleback, broad and simple with occasional steep pinnacles that we skirted around.

We reached the second Monro, Spidean Coire nan Clach, and then started the interminable descent. We were now very tired as it was past 6 pm and we had been on the move for 13 hours. We longed to reach the bus, which we had arranged to meet at 6 pm at Kinlochewe; it would probably wait a while. But the distance had deceived us. We reached the hamlet at 7 pm, so it was long gone. There were a few cars so we hitched a lift half-way back and then another to the Torridon Hotel. We walked wearily into the bar for a well-deserved drink and some food. John Delamere and Neville were sitting down with large beers in hand.

"Hi, what happened to you?" came their inevitable question. "We've been here for three hours."

"We got lost on the end of Liathach and descended the northern cliffs. It took over two hours," was our plaintive reply. "Where is everyone else, in the showers?"

"No one else has turned up yet. You're the first people we've seen," they responded, much to our amazement.

Slowly the truth dawned. The people we had seen below us from near the summit of Beinn Eighe had been our group. In some way we had got massively ahead. John and Neville had found a simple descent path from the south side of the summit ridge and jogged down the mountain. After completing the second Munro on Beinn Eighe, they had descended directly to the hotel and had not completed the agreed walk to the extreme east end. Contented, jovial and tired, we argued into the night about who should get the laurels for first home.

The others plodded their way in over the evening, with all back by dusk at 11 pm. The story of their descent then became apparent. The route that John and Neville took was the only easy way off and, although difficult to locate, they had found it immediately. The others had searched many false trails, eventually finding it after 2–3 hours.

A happy meal was followed by a walk along Loch Torridon in the midnight dusk with Peter Dykes and John Milles. Afterwards, I lay in bed reflecting on the day's climb, thinking through each section. The brain has an amazing capacity to temporarily retain all the details and drama of the climb, particularly the risky parts. Most details would fade over the next few days as work crowded in, so it was time to savour the best moments. Slowly

I realised I had little recollection of the first couple of hours. I remembered getting off the bus and people falling over, but had no memory of packing my day sack or who I had walked with. The first clear thoughts were on the pinnacles of Liathach's first summit.

Of course! It had been the sleeping pill, Halcion. It had erased my memories. We had taken the prescribed dose but it was clearly preventing retention of events. I then recalled another time when I took it on a returning transatlantic flight. Although I had departed from Gatwick, I had arrived back at London Heathrow Airport because of a change in landing arrangements. Later, driving back on the motorway past Oxford, I suddenly realised I had no memory of travelling between the two airports to collect my car from Gatwick. Halcion was the cause.

On the bus journey back to Birmingham the next day, we quizzed all those who had taken Halcion. Some fell into bushes, Norman dislocated a finger, there was a crazy argument about a compass and many of us had memory loss. We wrote an account of our experiences and sent it to the Medicines Agency, which collects details of drug side effects. Other doctors had noticed similar problems. It was withdrawn from use within the year.

Munros (peaks over 3,000 ft)
Liathach (the Grey One)
  1. Spidean a'Choire Leith (Peak of the Grey Corrie), 1,055 m
  2. Mullach an Rathain (Summit of the Row of Pinnacles), 1,023 m

Beinn Eighe (File Hill)
  3. Ruadh-stac Mor (Big Red Hill), 1,010 m
  4. Spidean Coire nan Clach (Peak of the Corrie of Stones), 993 m

6. An Teallach and the Wilderness walk: June 1988

An Teallach, remote, exotic and exciting, is arguably the most striking mountain in Britain. At 1,062 m, it towers over Dundonnell village like a huge alpine gendarme. Naturally, it was high on our list of Scottish peaks to climb.

Friday evening, 17 June, found 21 of us on a bus leaving the Medical School and heading for north-west Scotland, with huge excitement over expectations for the following day. The plan was to start walking at 5 am from the Dundonnell Hotel, climb south along the ridge of An Teallach, descend past Shenavall Bothy and then walk across 'the Great Wilderness' to Poolewe, taking in two other Munros on the way. The bus would wait at the end to drive us back to Dundonnell for dinner.

It was a clear night, raising our hopes for the following day as we chatted enthusiastically on the bus; many of us had not met since the Karakoram expedition a year earlier. It was a happy group that noisily disembarked from the bus in the hotel car park at 5 am. Thoughtlessly, we awoke some of the elderly guests, as we found out later.

The path started beside the hotel and abruptly ascended the north side of the mountain. Huge, forbidding and dangerous, An Teallach spreads over the landscape like some malign monster, its northern corries, leading to the very summit, black and stark. Its scale is hard to appreciate. We climbed towards the crest, which rises in a series of pinnacles to two Munro summits on a sharp edge (figure 3). Yet, despite appearances, it was not difficult. The track only occasionally moved to the top but was mostly a few feet below it and well cut into the turf. At one point, near Lord Berkeley's Seat, it went through a small tunnel on the very crest of the ridge. The views were massive. Nearby was the perfect peak of Beinn Dearg Mor; in the middle distance, the two Munros that were our next peaks; while west, shimmering in the sun, was the sea and Poolewe.

From the south end of An Teallach, there was a steep descent to Shenavall bothy. Normally, I am slow on descents as it favours shorter people with big muscles, whereas I am rather gangly. However, I had been in training. I had been living in southern California for three months and was cycling to the Scripps Research Institute in La Jolla every day – six miles each way. There were two steep hills and it was always a race. Americans wearing fancy Tour de France kit would whizz by. But over a few weeks I had gradually increased my speed and now could overtake some of them on the uphill sections. That meant big quads. Much to my surprise, I ran down to Shenavall bothy ahead of the others, even Neville. John Delamere kept up so we decided to stick together for the next two peaks.

We had a brief stop beside the stream leading to Loch na Sheallag, then jogged over a bridge to a wide grassy plain. We skirted east of Beinn Dearg Mor, to our third Munro, Ruadh Stac Mor. Looking back, we could see Neville and Nigel half a mile behind and others in the far distance.

The route took us to the col between Ruadh Stac Mor and A'Mhaighdean, so after climbing the first peak we ended back at the same place. At that moment the chasing two came round the corner intent on catching us up. It was easily possible. There was still 15 miles to go, right across 'the Wilderness'. We taunted each other as we started up the second peak going as fast as possible, only to meet them again on our way down. They were definitely getting closer.

The next section was a long downhill track past Carnforth, an Englishman's hunting lodge, and onto a flat bridleway to Poolewe. We looked back constantly, our pursuers inexorably closing in on us. The track crossed extensive peat bogs that were remarkably dry. Scotland can have periods without rain and this was one of those rare occasions. The sun shone, there was the occasional cloud and a gentle wind blew in our faces as we ran – as did they. We ran for miles, despite having already climbed four Munros. This was serious business. We ran till we could hardly run further. Then the race was suddenly over. The following two came to the top of a small bluff that we had just descended, perhaps 400 metres behind. Nigel stopped, bent over and vomited. Neville looked on in horror. They were beaten. We shouted across to each other and sped on.

By 4.30 pm we were in Poolewe, found our designated meeting place at a café and walked slowly in with the knowledge that we were the first home. But who should be sitting there drinking tea and eating biscuits? Ian MacLennan. We were astonished to see him, as he was us.

"You can't have done it," we complained. "How did you get here so quickly?" Upon cross-examination, it was apparent that he had not climbed the middle two Munros. He had missed two of the four peaks thinking they were not worth bothering with. Nigel and Neville arrived shortly afterwards, with the rest of the group coming in over the next three hours.

What a day! Perfect weather in wonderful mountains. Contentedly we took the bus back to the hotel. It was a noisy evening with bountiful excitement and lots of beer and wine. Unfortunately, we were a noisy lot in a rather nice hotel. An elderly lady came over, bitterly complaining about hooligans from the south, accusing us of being football thugs. And we had made an outrageous amount of noise at five o'clock in the morning.

Next morning, slightly worse for wear, both in heads and legs, we climbed into the bus for the long journey home.

Munros (peaks over 3,000 ft)
 An Teallach (the Forge)
  1. **Bidein a'Ghlas Thuill (Pinnacle of the Grey-Green Hollow), 1,062 m**
  2. **Sgurr Fiona (White Peak), 1,060 m**
 The Wilderness Walk
  3. **Ruadh Stac Mor (Big Red Stack), 918 m**
  4. **A'Mhaighdean (the Maiden), 967 m**

7. The Round of Glen Nevis: June 1989

The beauty and sheer scale of the Scottish walks enticed us north of the border for many more years. But the four following summers saw us trying bigger challenges until eventually they were too hard for anyone. We routinely bolted together two of the 'Big Walks' described in Ken Wilson's book. However, as no one wanted to walk through the night, we were limited to the 20 hours of mid-summer daylight in Scotland. Each walk followed an overnight bus journey and ended up in a local hotel.

In June 1989, we completed the round of Glen Nevis. This started with Ben Nevis, followed by the Aonachs, the Grey Quarries, across the valley then the Mamores. Not all of the peaks on the latter ridge are Munros because some are on spurs off the main track, but it was still 15 Munros in a day, 35 miles and 17,000 feet of ascent. Only Neville and I completed it. The weather was sunny for most of the day but a thunderstorm broke in the evening, thoroughly soaking us all.

I thought we were the toughest guys on the mountains that day, and proud of what we had achieved. But we were soon put in our place. I creaked into the hotel in Fort William at the end of the epic and asked for two pints of bitter shandy as the first part of the revival process. I explained to the barman that my poor physical condition was due to having just completed the round of Glen Nevis. A slight, fresh-looking man beside me declared in a broad Scottish accent: "Laddie, that's nothing. I've just run up from Glasgae on the West Highland Way, and that's 93 miles."

It was the day of the annual fell race and we were surrounded by the best runners in the country. The gods of the sport, where us mere mortals meekly dare to tread. Nonetheless, we hadn't done badly.

Munros (15 peaks over 3,000 ft – 914 m)
 North side (8)
  Ben Nevis (Cloudy Hill), 1,344 m
  Carn Mor Dearg (big Red Hill), 1,220 m
  Aonach Mor (Big Ridge), 1,221m
  Aonach Beag (Little Ridge), 1,234m
  Sgurr Choinnich Mor (big Mossy Hill), 1,094 m
  Stob Coire an Laoigh (Peak of the Corrie), 1,116 m
  Stob Choire Claurigh (Peak of the Brawling), 1,177 m
  Stob Ban (White Peak), 977 m
 Mamores (7)
  Binnein Beag (Small Peak), 943 m
  Binnein Mor (Big Peak), 1,130 m
  Na Gruagaichean (the Maidens) 1,056 m
  Stob Coire a'Chairn (Peak of the Corrie of the Cairn), 981 m

Am Bodach (the Old Man), 1,032 m
Stob Ban (White Peak), 999 m
Mullach nan Coirean (Summit of the Corries), 939 m

8. Glencoe and the Aonach Eagach Ridge: June 1990

In June 1990, we walked the round of Glencoe. Starting at the western end, we tackled Bidean nam Bian then Stob Coire Sgreamhach. This was followed by a long descent to the head of the valley and up the steep track to the Aonach Eagach Ridge. This most airy of climbs has to be carefully negotiated, particularly while rounding a series of pinnacles (figure 4). The final part was a strenuous scree descent in the rain to the famous Clachaig Inn, from where we watched the back-markers slowly descend. That evening, Helen Delamere's birthday was celebrated with a very professional band of Scottish pipers.

Munros (peaks over 3,000 ft – 914 m)
1. Bidean nam Bian (Pinnacle of the Hills), 1,150 m
2. Stob Coire Sgreamhach (Peak of the Dreadful Corrie), 1,072 m

Aonach Eagach ridge
3. Meall Dearg (Red Hill), 953 m
4. Sgorr nam Fiannaidh (Peak of the Fingalians), 967 m

9. The Cairngorm Four Thousanders: June 1991 (peaks over 4,000 feet – 1,219 m)

After the walk around Glencoe, we wondered about the Cairngorms. Why not try the peaks over 4,000 feet in the Grampians – the four biggest peaks in the country after Ben Nevis: Braeriach, Cairn Toul, Ben Macdui and Cairn Gorm. For good measure we added Beinn Mheadhoin (surprisingly pronounced 'Ben Vain') – less than 4,000 feet but still a Munro. The peaks lie on the huge Cairngorm plateau but are straddled by a deep gulley called the Lairig Ghru. The total distance was around 30 miles with 12,000 feet of ascent. An easy day out for an old lady.

We had the usual start from the Medical School by bus, at 6 pm on the Friday night, but we had an unexpected friend in the form of Mike Winterborn. He usually climbed with us but on this occasion, he was an escapee from the Queen Elizabeth Hospital isolation ward. Three years earlier he had developed chronic lymphocytic leukaemia. I had been in the unenviable position of personally informing him of his diagnosis. At the time I was in charge of the leukaemia diagnosis service at the Medical School and his abnormal blood results had been bought to my attention. With some anxiety I visited him in the hospital, where he had been admitted for other reasons, to give him the bad news. In retrospect, his diagnosis should not have been such a surprise. While at Testa Grigia in April 1988, three years earlier, we had noticed that his blood contained a large white layer when centrifuged. We had joked about it among ourselves, assuming it was due to lipids from a fatty breakfast of eggs and bacon. In retrospect it was not – it was the pre-symptomatic stage of leukaemia. In fact, no treatment was necessary at that stage, but there were no marks for diagnostic acumen among the 14 doctors on that trip. Unfortunately, the disease had later progressed unusually rapidly, with transformation to a Richter's lymphoma. That required urgent treatment in the form of bone marrow ablation with chemotherapy and an autologous (self) bone marrow transplantation. There followed six weeks in an isolation ward which would finish after our trip to the Cairngorms. I visited him a few days before our planned adventure.

Talking through the small glass hatch separating us in his isolation room, he expressed his extreme disappointment at not coming. His blood results had demonstrated a good recovery from the intense treatment, and he had only a week left before discharge. He was bored and miserable. Perhaps, I wondered, it would be possible to get him out early. I knew his consultant well, so we met to discuss the possibility. His residual low white-blood-cell counts would certainly make him vulnerable to cross-infections but he was recovering well. I suggested giving him a white-cell-promoting hormone. This would increase his white cell count towards normal for a day or two which would cover the weekend. He would still be at risk of infections so we would have to keep him socially distanced but, otherwise, open countryside and being with friends should do him good. The consultant agreed to my suggestions with my promise to take special care of him.

At 5.30 pm, on the Friday evening, I went over to the hospital; Mike signed a discharge form and out we marched, him in his pyjamas and me carrying his clothes bag. Everyone cheered as he came down the Medical School steps to the bus, marvelling at his courage and determination. He beamed back in pure pleasure and gratitude for being included. We isolated him in the back of the bus, gave him some beers and off we drove.

It was an 11 hour journey to the base of Cairn Toul on the south side of the Lairig Ghru. Dawn crept into a clear sky at 4 am as we drove up the A9, turned off at Aviemore, past our hotel at Coylumbridge and through the forest to the end of the road. The Cairngorms were resplendent in the early morning sun, with flecks of snow on their upper gullies.

As the bus neared the start of our walk, we ate our breakfasts of sandwiches, biscuits and cold drinks, packed our day sacks with the least amount of weight, and waited eagerly. As the bus stopped, there was a rush for the door and we hurtled up a steep path through the bracken. No discussions, no farewells, no "see you later": it was only, "let's go". It was the first big walk for my brother Martin, who was nine years younger than me. He had been training for some weeks in order to beat me, as he could on a 5 mile run, but he was not prepared for the start. It took him ten frantic minutes to organise his gear by which time the leaders were half a mile up the hill. He never caught up and had to be content with walking in the middle of the pack. Mike Winterborn was last off to avoid any personal contact and had to spend his day alone. Looking back, he was just visible walking in the direction of Cairn Gorm, our last peak of the day.

It was a steep climb to Braeriach, then a jog with Neville, Alex Wright, John Delamere and Nigel Hillman to the peaks of Sgor an Lochain Uaine and Cairn Toul. From the summit, a long descent led to the Corrour Bothy, where we arrived at 8 am. Some of its occupants were just getting up and were amazed to see us, especially as we had already summited two of the four big peaks. Across the Lairig Ghru, the steep ascent to the neighbouring plateau and Ben Macdui beckoned. Neville and I had been faster on the descent so, just as the others arrived panting, we set off in order to keep our lead. We climbed up the steep east side of the Lairig Ghru to Ben Macdui, its upper flanks and northern gullies still covered by large amounts of winter snow. The 2,500 foot climb was tiring; pausing to look back, we could see some of our group descending to the Corrour Bothy on the opposite side of the valley.

After Ben Macdui, with its summit cairn (see walk 2 above), we headed north-east to Beinn Mheadhoin at 3,878 ft. Our route through heather and bushes was tiring since it is rarely climbed in the round of the Four Thousanders. There followed a long descent and then the final summit of Cairn Gorm itself. As we looked up, we could see the triangulation point and a lone figure on top. Had we been beaten? Had we taken a slow route off Beinn Mheadhoin, allowing others to get ahead? As we approached, the individual looked most strange. He was small, had a fez on his head and was leaning on a walking stick and staring towards the western hills as if in a dream. It was Mike Winterborn! And all alone. I felt guilty. Had we done the right thing? We had brought him all this way to spend a day in self-imposed exile.

"Hi Mike, great to see you. How's it going?" I dared to ask.

"The best day of my life," was his enthusiastic reply. "I've never been so happy."

We reflected on how precious life becomes when faced with death. How the pleasures we take so much for granted become moments of magic. It had been a wonderful decision to bring him with us.

We bade farewell and jogged down the mountain, past the ski lifts with all their paraphernalia, to the woods below. There followed a rather tedious 10 mile slog along forest tracks to Coylumbridge Hotel. We arrived around 7.30 pm, quite exhausted. There to greet us were several of the group but none had climbed all the peaks. Worryingly, there were many still missing, including three students, Helen, Jim and Seamus. By 10 o'clock, with dusk approaching and dinner eaten, they had still not appeared. Some volunteered to go looking for them. Not me; I was too worn out. Eventually they were found several miles back along the trail but resolutely refused any help. They were keen to come on our trip to Everest but feared they would be rejected if they failed to complete the walk. We were most impressed. This was clearly a good way to select students.

Munros (peaks over 3,000 ft – 914 m)
1. **Braeriach (the Brindled Upland), 1,296 m**
2. **Sgor an Lochain Uaine (Peak of the Little Green Loch), 1,258 m**
3. **Cairn Toul (Hill of the Barn), 1,291 m**
4. **Ben Macdui (Macduff's Hill), 1,309 m**
5. **Beinn Mheadhoin (Middle Hill), 1,182 m**
6. **Cairn Gorm (Blue Hill), 1,244 m**

10. The Cuillin Ridge: July 1991

Later in the summer of 1991, Chris Imray suggested climbing again in Scotland but on some 'Worthless Hills' with names such as 'Smallpox' and 'Alexander'. We jumped at the opportunity for these are the most exciting mountains in Britain, with their names more recognisable in Gaelic as the Cuillins, Sgurr na Banachdich and Sgurr Alasdair.

The plot was typical of BMRES: a last-minute decision to go, no communication with others, little equipment and a race all the way to Skye (the Misty Isle). The competition was enhanced by Ian MacLennan (Mac) and me taking our BMWs. Charnock Richard motorway services was the first pit stop. I carried Tim Harvey, Chris and Andy but, in spite of driving fast, was easily beaten by Mac and Ian Chesner (Ches). As losers, we were convinced that Ian had been reckless. This was adequately confirmed when they beat us to the second rendezvous at Nevisport in Fort William, and they then pressed home their advantage by not waiting for us to arrive. While we ate and fumed at their unreliability, for we were not sure if they were ahead or behind, fate dealt us a hand that was to prove Mac's later undoing: we bought a climbing guide to the Cuillin ridge.

We arrived at the Sligachan Hotel (Place of Shells) at the base of the Cuillins at 6 pm, with the victors gloating over their beers at our slow performance. They had stopped only briefly at Fort William to buy what they considered to be an essential item – a bottle of insect repellent. Being Scottish, Mac had much experience of the awful mosquitoes and horse flies.

There followed what can best be described as an intellectual hijack by Mac (he was the professor). The original agreed plan had been for us to climb the Cuillin Ridge over two days, with a bivouac half way. But Mac was convinced that one day was plenty of time – a single easy push with a 3 am start. Despite it being five against one, Mac won the day. Acknowledging his greater knowledge of the route from two previous traverses (the ridge is a mere seven miles long, although it involves 3,000 metres of ascent), the five of us bent our heads in shame and slunk off for an early night, well soaked in beer and wine.

At this point, I should like to add a short digression on sleeping habits. When the night is short and the booze is long, sleeping partners are best chosen carefully. Or to cut a long story short: don't sleep with snorers. Ian snores like a chainsaw, while Mac is more akin to a supercharged Kawasaki; yet, incredibly, they never wake each other. They may rouse guests in neighbouring rooms or half the camp on an expedition but they sleep blissfully and awaken refreshed. This again proved true for, come 3.30 am, the four of us in our separate rooms were ready for our 'wee day on the hills', while the two snorers could hardly be shaken from their slumbers.

The six toughest men from the Midlands crammed into Mac's car ready for the kill. This proved literally true, as within minutes a rabbit was dispatched by precision driving. Another soon followed, and a flock of sheep had a lucky escape. Mac's bleary eyes and hangover were the only barriers to the extinction of all life forms on Skye. Fortunately, the most dangerous part of the whole day was soon over and we arrived at Glenbrittle to a murky start. We loaded the gear onto our backs, what little there was, and marched resolutely into the gloom and the embracing hordes of midges, having left behind our only bottle of insect repellent.

The Skye ridge route is usually attempted from the south, which requires a seven mile walk-in from Glenbrittle over trail-less bogs. The only reason we stayed in remotely the right direction was because of the sea on our right and the rising escarpment of the Cuillins on our left. The tourist guide for grannies says allow two hours – our heroes took slightly longer. Nevertheless, with a superb dawn beckoning over the misty mountains, we started climbing our first peak. Mac had disappeared behind and Ches ahead but, as if orchestrated from afar, we emerged as one on top of Gars-bheinn, our first peak. Our eyes feasted on the mountain and marine panorama that unfolded before us, while the switchback, knife-edge route alerted our aching legs to the pleasures and challenges ahead (figure 5).

In the swirling mist and the morning sun (7.30 am), we fell-in behind Mac at an exhilarating trot. The world fell away on each side in cascades of rock-walls, screes and cliffs to Loch Coruisk (Lake of the Corrie Waters) to the east and the sea to the west. The first part of the route is not particularly terrifying, and in rapid succession we knocked off Sgurr a'Choire Bhig (Peak of the Little Corrie) and Sgurr nan Eag (Peak of the Notches), our first and the most southerly Munro (figure 5). Our fourth peak was Caisteal a'Garbh-choire (Castle of the Rough Corrie) and it provided the first hint of forthcoming problems. The peaklet on the main ridge is the first rock climb. In slow succession, we climbed up and then abseiled back down to the path; 90 minutes were wastefully cast aside instead of taking the two minute walk around the base. Suddenly, our day ahead became a serious proposition as Sgurr Coir'a'Ghrunnda, backed by Sgurr Sgumain, Sgurr Alasdair and Sgurr Thearlaich, loomed ahead.

Peak five was Sgurr Dubh na Da Bheinn (Black Peak of the Two Mountain Ridges), an undistinguished mountain with broken rocks that leads to the famous Thearlaich Dubh Gap. This was the crux of the whole climb. From the rocky ridge a chasm opened at our feet that split the mountains. A 10 metre abseil leading to a chock-stone poised over the swirling mists hid a fathomless gulf, while opposite beckoned a 25 metre vertical wall. At this point, Andy came into his own. An E2 climber, he ascended the highly polished basalt chimney in a smooth flow with a dynamic mantle-shelf move followed by a straddle below an overhang. Within moments he was at the top and lowered a rope for us to follow. I looked upward fearfully from the wet shadows beside the chock-stone, wondering how impossible I would find it.

Mac sprang to the cord to show off his abilities. But the ascent proved hard; 16 years of Hebridean living, and kilos to match, made the slippery and narrow chimney a tight challenge. Tim and Ches fared better, as I carefully observed their moves and mistakes. My turn. What the hell! Encouraged by Chris, I edged across the bolder then pulled in the rope, hung on the belays and cheated my way to the top. Thank God that was over. Chris rapidly followed in the rear as we marched to the top of Sgurr Thearlaich (Charles's Peak). This is made up of magnificent cliffs, which were hardly visible in the mist, but we did get brief views of the great stone chute that connects Thearlaich to its higher neighbour, Sgurr Alasdair (Alexander's Peak), the highest of the Black Cuillins. Mac climbed this in the mist to demonstrate his knowledge of the route while the rest of us regrouped.

An airy ridge welcomed us to Sgurr Mhic Choinnich (MacKenzie's Peak), our second Munro. Girdling the summit on the west face is a narrow ledge discovered by Norman Collie in 1890. We sought this with difficulty as Tim and I, struggling at the back, became lost in the mist. The others' voices were clearly audible from below but were like sirens attracting us to our doom. Only with considerable effort did we retrace our steps to the main ridge and survival.

Peak eight was Sgurr Dearg (Red Peak, more commonly known as the Inaccessible Pinnacle), at 986 m our highest peak of the day and the third highest in the range. We reached it by skirting the scree to the west and then onto the ridge. We looked up at this difficult Munro as we waited for Tim and anxiously checked the time. We had been moving for eight hours and were not yet half way. Perhaps the hardest technical climbs were behind us but the next three miles were an unrelenting airy ridge, encompassing over a dozen separate peaks, each with its particular brand of terror.

On Sròn Bhuidhe we waited in vain for Tim, and after a little food pressed on to the top of Midget Ridge, followed by the south and main peaks of Sgurr na Banachdich (Smallpox Peak). We obtained brief dramatic views of Loch Coruisk down the 200 metre cliff from our mountain eyrie, as tiredness and repeated exposure overcame our vertigo. The next peak, Sgurr Thormaid (Norman's Peak, after Norman Collie), hardly stood out, although we traversed a huge unseen overhang as we avoided the summit ridge.

Peaks 14 and 15 were the south top and then the main top of Sgurr a'Ghreadaidh (Peak of Torment). The traverse of this sensational knife-edge has been described as the most enjoyable (or more appropriately the most terrifying) scramble in Britain. This led to An Dorus (the Door), which demarcates the peaks of Sgurr a'Ghreadaidh and Sgurr a'Mhadaidh.

We later found that Tim had reached this pass before finally deciding to descend. He chose a difficult route for there is a 5 metre vertical step to the top of a corrie followed by 1,000 metres of rubble. After that, there was just a ten mile walk to Sligachan.

Peak 16, Sgurr A'Mhadaidh (Peak of the Fox), is severed by basaltic dykes into four separate summits, which revel in the mundane titles of first, second, third and fourth tops. The gaps between are among the deepest on the ridge, with exposed rock climbing between each summit. Mac raced onward. We struggled in his wake. Yet slowly fate played its hand. While Chris, Tim, Andy and I had cursed Mac and Ches for not waiting at Fort William, our purchase of *Scrambles in Skye* by J Wilson Parker helped to keep the four of us on track. A series of false leads gradually wore down the big man, while us lesser breeds carefully checked every turn and conserved our strength. When Mac headed towards Sgurr Thuilm to the west, we correctly followed the main ridge, which takes a sharp turn to the east. But it was now 5.30 pm and we still had a long way to go. The route was becoming very serious and it was not the time to make mistakes. We were tired, thirsty and hungry, the midges swarming around us like vultures before a kill.

Ches and Andy were the next to crack. Andy's feet had been fighting his boots since the Thearlaich Dubh gap and finally succumbed. Ches was exhausted. They progressively slowed over the four peaks of Sgurr a'Mhadaidh and announced they were going to descend after the next summit. They generously offered their water, which Chris and I drank gratefully. Refreshed, we caught up with Mac on Bealach na Glaic Moire, leaving one of the ropes prominently on the route for our followers to carry down. We looked back to see the exhausted pair slowly descending.

The south-west, central and north peaks of Bidein Druim nan Ramh (Bi-sharp Peaks of the Ridge of Oars) shone ahead in the evening sun. The route is to the right and the guide says "rope-up". Mac led un-roped and I struggled to follow, turned the overhand, clung on up a basalt chimney and climbed a cracked block to an airy summit platform. If there had previously been doubt, the guidebook now proved its worth for there seemed to be no route down. We retraced our steps three times before descending vertical rocks past an awkward overhang. Having led, Chris kindly climbed back and gave me a rope. We were poised over 600 metres of rock cliffs with Loch Coruisk below. Un-climbable rocks with false leads surrounded the route. We continued to the lofty overhung end of the summit ridge and several platforms to complete the most complicated part of the ridge.

The details of peak 23, An Caisteal (The Castle), are forgotten in a blur of rock, apart from two narrow slits. A brave stride takes one over the void. Chris stepped boldly on. I crept down the dank crack and up the other side, back into a western sun descending into the sea. We then briefly saw Mac level with us but separated by a 10 m vertical drop, before we retraced our steps to an easy ledge.

Sgurr na Bhairnich (Limpet Peak) is not remarkable and was soon passed, followed by Bruach na Frithe (Slope of the Deer Forest). This 'easiest Munro' of the Cuillin received its first recorded visit in May 1845 by Professor Forbes, the pioneering scientist. The view is one of the most celebrated in Scotland, with fabulous views of the main ridge curling away into the distance. We were too knackered to care. Then, quite unexpectedly, Mac announced his departure. We were dumbstruck. Having led, or rather mis-led us, for 25 peaks, he had had enough. Ahead and below was a small spring at Bealach nan Lice. That was his destination, followed by Sligachan and a wee dram or more at the hotel. Chris and I were determined to finish the ridge and so resolved on a bivouac by the water-seep.

We picked our way slowly between broken rocks, with the sun setting behind rising clouds; a gloomy silence descended. After a long drink of mountain water and a good wash, we selected a flat spot of grass and nibbled at a sparse meal of naan breads and cheese. Chris, contrary to Mac's advice, had wisely carried a bivouac bag and some spare clothes. He lent me over-trousers and a rucksack for my legs while I covered my top half as best as I could with my day sack. I was fit for a storm. Which was fortunate, as by midnight we had one. The water clattered on the outside of the sacks, forming small rivulets that trickled down my neck and waist, and the wind moaned through the peaks. Exhaustion took us until 5 am when I awoke to a misty morning, shivering violently.

After a meagre breakfast, for it was all we had, we studiously missed out Sgurr a'Fionn Choire (Fair Corrie) and headed towards the Basteir Tooth. This was unclimbed until 1889 and was unclimbed by us. It dankly dripped following the night's rain and disappeared up into the clouds. The guidebook thankfully advised us that the tooth "cannot be entertained by non-rock climbers". Am Basteir (the Executioner) followed. These peaks, together with Sgurr A'Bhasteir (Peak of the Executioner), just off the main ridge, are the hardest climbs of the whole ridge, with the Basteir Tooth being the most difficult Munro summit in Britain.

Fortunately, there was an easy northern route that avoided all the problems, and this we took to the very last peak – number 29, Sgurr Nan Gillean (Peak of the Gullies), the Cuillins' best-known peak. The four summits of its famous Pinnacle Ridge dominate the view from the road. The traditional climb is via the west ridge but a fallen gendarme had made the route dangerous. An alternative route was via Nicholson's Chimney. This starts with a moderately graded shelf which leads to a 50 metre chimney and the summit. What with the mist, drizzle, hunger and cold, determination deserted me. After some minutes of deep conflict, I bottled out, leaving Chris to complete the route alone; 31 hours of terror had been enough.

For over two hours, I wandered listlessly back to Sligachan Hotel to meet Tim, Ches, Andy and Mac, who were astonished at my failure on the point of triumph. Chris came back jubilantly a few hours later as we recounted and exaggerated our adventures and tales of courage in the face of adversity. The first four to wimp out had returned safely to an evening meal at Sligachan and alcohol rehydration. Even Mac, who had predictably got lost and almost revisited Glenbrittle, made the bar rendezvous before closing time. For the rest of the day we recovered from our exhaustion by walking a mere 15 miles over Bla Bheinn and then raced back to Birmingham in the usual fashion.

Munros (peaks over 3,000 ft – 914 m)
1. **Sgurr nan Eag (Peak of the Notches), 924 m**
2. **Sgurr Dubh Mor (Big Black Peak), 944 m**
3. **Sgurr Alasdair (Alexander's Peak), 992 m**
4. **Sgurr Mhic Choinnich (MacKenzie's Peak), 948 m**

5.   **Sgurr Dearg (Red Peak, more commonly known as the Inaccessible Pinnacle), 986 m**
6.   **Sgurr na Banachdich (Smallpox Peak), 965 m**
7.   **Sgurr a'Ghreadaidh (Peak of Torment), 973 m**
8.   **Sgurr a'Mhadaidh (Peak of the Fox), 918 m**
9.   **Brauch na Frithe (Slope of the Deer Forest), 958 m**
10. **Am Basteir (The Executioner), 934 m**
11. **Sgurr Nan Gillean (Peak of the Gullies), 964 m**

11. The Round of Glen Shiel: June 1992. 15 Munros

The Glen Shiel ridges were our nemesis. We finally bit off more than we could chew. Ian MacLennan had egged us on to greater and greater exploits, some of which he had failed to complete himself. Nevertheless, we agreed to walk all the peaks around Glen Shiel – 15 Munros, nine on the south side from the Saddle to Cluanie Inn, followed by the Five Sisters of Kintail (figure 6). None of us completed it. There were not enough daylight hours, the weather deteriorated from overcast to heavy rain and many got lost. It was just too much. An abiding memory is seeing Ian walking down the trail off Sgurr na Carnach at dusk. No one had climbed the last of the five sisters.

Munros (peaks over 3,000 ft – 914 m)
  South Glen Shiel peaks
   1. **The Saddle, 1,010m**
   2. **Sgurr na Sgine (Peak of the Knife), 946 m**
   3. **Creag nan Damh (Rock of the Stags), 918 m**
   4. **Sgurr an Lochain (Peak of the Little Loch), 1,004 m**
   5. **Sgurr an Doire Leathain (Peak of the Broad Oak Grove), 1,010 m**
   6. **Maol Chinn-dearg (Bald Red Head), 981 m**
   7. **Aonach air Chrith (Ridge of Trembling), 1,021 m**
   8. **Druim Shionnach (Ridge of Foxes), 987 m**
   9. **Creag a'Mhaim (Rock of the Large Rounded Hill, 947 m**
  North Glen Shiel peaks – the Five Sisters of Kintail
   10. **Aonach Meadhoin (Middle Ridge), 1,001 m**
   11. **Sgurr a'Bhealaich Dheirg (Peak of the Red Pass), 1,036 m**
   12. **Saileag (Little Heel), 956 m**
   13. **Sgurr na Ciste Duibhe (Peak of the Black Chest), 1,027 m**
   14. **Sgurr na Carnach (Rocky Peak), 1,002 m**
   15. **Sgurr Fhuaran (peak of the wolf), 1,067 m**

12. Winter walks and the Three Peaks of Yorkshire: February 2003

Winter walks were organised for the first or second weekend of February, hopefully the snowiest days of the year, so we could hone our winter climbing skills. Because of few daylight hours, the walks were shorter, more leisurely events and none were in Scotland. Typically, we would drive to a base hotel on a Friday evening, have a 7 hour hike over the snow-covered hills next day, with a group dinner in the evening and perhaps a short walk on the Sunday. North Wales saw us on the Snowdonia hills, the Arans and Berwyns, while in the Lake District, Borrowdale and Langdale were favourite springboards for the surrounding peaks.

Many trips left abiding memories but none provided the drama of the huge summer walks, apart from the Three Peaks of Yorkshire in February 2003. This 26 mile walk, over the easy hills of Ingleborough, Whernside and Pen-y-Ghent is normally a summer event but becomes challenging in the short winter daylight hours, particularly if there is snow and ice.

Fifteen of us booked into the Crown Hotel in Horton-in-Ribblesdale on 6 February. A cold, clear weekend with light snow was forecast. We had a slow 9 am start outside the hotel. There was the usual faffing about as people changed their footwear or rushed back to bedrooms for additional clothes or to dump excess weight. Finally, we all set off for Ingleborough – all that is except Tim Harvey and Maggie Beazley. They decided to start with Pen-y-Ghent and go round anti-clockwise. Their argument was that they would see more of us that way. Since they expected to be last and would rapidly drop behind, they would meet us all as we walked the other way. Their logic had merit.

The day was partially cloudy but we could see all three peaks intermittently before the weather deteriorated. The snow-level was around 450 metres and, although fresh, it had frozen hard in the night. The group gradually thinned as we headed along the lanes and then up the side of Ingleborough into cloud. I found myself walking with John and David Milles, my 17-year-old son Edward, Alice Brockington, Ian Sutton, Kyle Pattinson and Alex Wright. Mostly people wore trainers and light clothes since the intention was speed but we did have two ice axes between us. Completing the long route before nightfall would be difficult with heavy gear.

The featureless summit of Ingleborough was covered in thick cloud, and treacherous underfoot on the icy limestone terraces. There was doubt about the path as we split into two groups each vying to be in the lead. The Milles brothers, Kyle and Alex disappeared into the clouds in what I thought was the wrong direction. We were right; the summit appeared nearby.

Next was Whernside, on a compass course. The trail back-tracked down our ascent route for 400 metres, followed by a steep descent on a rocky path made slippery with ice. In trainers, great care was needed to negotiate each step. It then levelled off along more than a mile of Yorkshire paving stones. We had joined the Pennine Way, with the slabs corralling walkers away from the delicate moorland flora. They were set into the ground with a slight slope to allow water run-off but now were covered in sheet ice. Each of us fell before we moved onto the neighbouring grass. This was firm from the frozen snow and safe. Lower down the ice had melted, so we ran on the slabs, looking over our shoulders to see the others emerge from the clouds.

They had realised their mistaken route at the top and could hear us talking about the descent but we were invisible. They had decided to take a compass bearing from the summit cairn, but had failed to backtrack 400 metres, so their route had taken them directly down the escarpment. David led over the edge and fell badly, grazing his legs. The others followed more cautiously and, as the cloud cleared, they saw us a mile away running down the slabs. They set off in pursuit.

Whernside is a great whaleback of a peak, with the path gradually ascending over its long crest. Ian and I led the ascent with Alice and Edward a little way behind. The top was covered in a couple of metres of wind-blown snow. As it was too cold and windy to stop, we gradually drew ahead of the following pair. The descent route was a long gentle path through heather and scrub, then onto a track that passed under the beautiful Ribblehead viaduct. From the summit of Whernside, Edward watched us running down the track but was reluctant to leave Alice alone. By the time they reached the viaduct, we were miles ahead. En route, we met Tim and Maggie, as they had predicted, and chatted for a few minutes. They had climbed Pen-y-Ghent and were determined to complete the route, however long it took.

From Ribblehead, it is a tedious six miles along the road. I jogged a little with Ian's encouragement, but he could easily have run on. A 25 year age gap makes a big difference. Pen-y-Ghent was the next and final summit. It is an attractive limestone hill with a sharp escarpment at the south end but is particularly famed for its limestone cavern, Penyghent Pot, one of the deepest in the country.

The ascent was straightforward but it was nearly 4 pm and getting dark. The mountain steepened towards the top and was covered in snow and ice. Ian had a head torch, which we needed to find the summit. There followed a treacherous jogging descent on tired legs and with hungry stomachs, but we were certain to finish. We should have started earlier to grab every daylight hour, but motivating 15 people early in the morning had been impossible.

As we came off the mountain and into the fields with their dry-stone walls, we saw Alex and Edward coming towards us. Brilliant, we thought, they had come from the hotel to give us food and drinks. Not a bit of it. They were also determined to complete the walk. We were amazed. They had no head torches, it was pitch black and they were going into the clouds to a snow- and ice-covered peak. Furthermore, where was Alice, who had been so close behind us on Whernside? We subsequently discovered that she and Edward had returned to the hotel and, while realising we were probably on Pen-y-Ghent, Alice was too tired to press on. Alex then turned up and persuaded Edward that they should not give up so easily, particularly since Ian and I were still out on the hills.

We returned to the hotel at 5 pm to meet Alice and the others, but a few had yet to return. At 6.30 pm Alex and Edward came in knackered. Route finding had been very difficult but fortunately the clouds had cleared a little and they could see their way by starlight. As they descended, they met John, David and Kyle, who likewise were unwilling to give up. They had better equipment, including head torches, but cocked up the descent. Rather than coming down the same path, which was easier, they traversed the summit onto its steep southern path. It was covered in ice and David fell again, this time fracturing his arm. Although not serious, it had slowed their return; they eventually appeared at 8 pm. As he was on anticoagulants, the whole side of his body was covered in deep blue bruises.

There was still no sign of Tim and Maggie. They had been last seen on Whernside at 3 pm, only an hour before dark. Knowing Tim's stubbornness, they would never give up. They had all the right equipment, were very experienced and were used to long slow days. The general feeling was that if they were not back when we had finished dinner, we should call out the mountain rescue. I had my doubts. Nothing would be more embarrassing than a night-time search for two people enjoying the hills. I advised caution, just as others advised a rescue. They turned up at 11 pm, shattered but happy. They had just completed the slowest ever round of the Three Peaks: 14 hours, when the record is under three. Tim was furious that anyone had even contemplated summoning a rescue team.

We all drank a little too much and it was Edward's first exposure to unlimited wine. He was drunk, fuelled by ample helpings of wine from Ian Sutton's girlfriend, and was still tipsy next morning. We had all had a thoroughly memorable weekend.

The Three peaks of Yorkshire
1.   **Ingleborough, 723 m**
2.   **Whernside, 736 m**
3.   **Pen-y-Ghent, 694 m**

13. Monte Perdido: June 2010

Participants: Maggie Beazley, Annie Bradwell, Barbara Bradwell, Edward Bradwell, Jo Bradwell, Susie Bradwell, Ian Chesner, Mary Chesner, Helen Delamere, John Delamere, Pete Forster, Roslyn Forster, Tim Harvey, Chris Imray, Barry Joseph-Lester, Graham Mead, Sheila Mead, John Milles, Kyle Pattinson, Jenny Richardson, Neville Richardson, John Simmons, Barry Smith, Alex Wright.

For a variety of reasons, there was a gap of many years before we had another really big summer walk: age was taking its toll; the long overnight bus journeys were not appealing; we had climbed the best mountains in Britain; and we had been drenched too many times in Scotland. You name it, we came up with an excuse. We certainly had summer walks but they were in Wales, the northern Pennines or the Lake District and were of modest intensity. What we needed was more imagination. This came about in midsummer 2010. We took on the challenge of a mountain in the Pyrenees, over a weekend.

I was approaching 65 and had plans to retire. I fancied a memorable day out to celebrate. Unpredictable weather excluded Scotland, wonderful though it might be on a sunny day, and we had climbed all notable peaks in England and Wales. What about France? The Alps could obviously supply any number of great walks or climbs but if we wanted reliable weather the Pyrenees would be preferable. I knew them reasonably well since I had spent several weeks climbing there 40 years earlier. I had even taken Barbara up to the top of Monte Perdido, the lost mountain, in the Central Pyrenees (its name derives from the fact that it is largely hidden by neighbouring peaks). It is the third highest peak in the Pyrenees (3,355 m) and at the head of the beautiful Ordesa Valley on the Spanish side. It has even been dubbed 'the Grand Canyon of Europe'. I thought this would be a wonderful objective.

To have a reasonable chance of climbing Monte Perdido, we would have to fly to Zaragoza in Spain, take a bus to the entrance of the Ordesa valley and start at dawn – 5 am. It would take 2–3 hours to walk the 12 km from the road head above the village of Torla to the top end of the valley, an hour of steep ascent to reach the refuge at Góriz and, from there, four hours to the summit and back. It was just possible during daylight hours if the weather was favourable and we ran down some of the way. We could recover the following morning and be back home for Sunday night. It was an ambitious plan but just within our capabilities if the mountain gods were on our side.

Friday 18 June at 5 pm saw 24 of us boarding a chartered plane in Birmingham bound for Zaragoza. Susie, my daughter, had an A-level exam in the afternoon and was then delayed by rush-hour traffic, so we were frustratingly late departing. Nevertheless by 6 pm we were in the air. Inevitably, there were lots of discussions about the likely outcome of the exploit. Among the group, it was clear that only a few would be successful because of its sheer scale. We would have to contend with high altitude, probably quite a lot of snow and maybe high winds. There was also the vexing question of what to take. There were the usual polarised schools of thought: to go light or to take full climbing equipment. Chris Imray, who had recently ascended Mt Everest, favoured the safe approach, as did Kyle Pattinson, while I preferred, as always, the lightweight 'dash for the summit'. This meant shorts, T-shirt and trainers. Neville, Graham Mead, Barry Smith and my son Edward followed my lead, trusting in my knowledge of the mountain. The debate went to and fro during the flight without resolution. Each must make their own decision. BMRES is a society of individuals. There are no leaders and there are no rules. However, half the group, particularly wives and girlfriends, realised the task was beyond them. Instead, they would take a serious walk along the lower levels of the canyon.

It was a three hour flight and, with an additional one hour time change, we landed at 10 pm. We had eaten on the plane so we tried to snatch some sleep on the three hour bus journey to the beautiful Monastery Hotel at Boltaña. At 1 am, we piled into reception, where thankfully they had been warned of our late arrival. Nevertheless, it took an hour to organise all the rooms so I didn't get to bed until 2 am, my head still full of indecision as to what to take.

The alarm went off at 4 am and I packed the minimal amount, hoping for good weather. I emptied the food contents of the mini-bar into my day sack and added sunglasses, a hat and a cagoule. Ice axe, crampons and big boots would be too heavy but I took them anyway so the decision could be delayed until the last minute on the bus. At breakfast, a dozen of us wearily ate as much and as quickly as we could and stuffed items into our packs. The bus departed at 4.30 am in the dark and a light drizzle. The portents were not good. The one hour journey past Torla to the end of the road allowed occasional views of big mountains blanketed in snow. While the summit of Monte Perdido was not visible, its lower slopes were white. The last time I had climbed it, which had been in August, there was hardly any snow. I left my climbing gear in the bus.

We were quickly off the bus and the race began – a race against time and among ourselves. It started as a beautiful woodland walk with the rush of water from the Rio Arazas alongside us. Above, pine forests led up to huge walls of limestone, tier upon tier, with snow at the very top.

The valley curved to the left, ascending in a series of steps, each marked with a large waterfall, full from the summer snow-melt. But there was no time to admire the views. The group thinned to 11 of us. Tim and Maggie dropped back, as did the mountaineers, Chris and Kyle. We crossed the bridge under the valley-end cliff and scrambled up a chain webbing to gain the first of several rock ledges. Alex Wright looked on in horror as we scaled the near vertical wall. He had no head for heights. It took an hour for him to follow the mule track so he was out of the hunt. We now saw the true scale of the task ahead. The snow line was just above the Refugio de Góriz (2,170 m). This was much lower than we had expected. There would be over 1,000 m of ascent in trainers on snow or ice. At least they were waterproof, I mused, as if that would make a difference.

We stopped briefly at Góriz for Ian and Barry to catch up but there was no sign of Chris and Kyle. That left six for the summit attempt. There were dozens of climbers all around us, huddling in the rain and sleet, recovering in the hut from their ascents. All were wearing full winter clothing, and those coming off the mountain carried ice axes and crampons. We were somewhat taken aback by their equipment. We had just walked up in trainers wearing only shorts and T-shirts. They were horrified by our lack of gear, especially when we told them we were going to climb Monte Perdido.

I was not quite sure of the route but there were lines of boot-prints across the rising snow fields. It was now 10 am, with the temperature slowly increasing as the summer sun burnt off the clouds. We were advised by the climbers hanging around the hut that we were crazy to attempt the mountain. They had experienced hard ice on the summit that would be dangerously steep without ice axes and crampons. Our planned attempt sent waves of consternation through the Spanish and French climbers. They feared for our safety but also wanted us to climb the mountain properly. They thought it should be taken seriously. It was a serious mountain and they were serious people.

Half an hour was enough stoppage time to allow us to cool off so we headed upwards. Ian was now weakening and by the time we reached the snow line he had dropped well behind. The snow was softened by the warming day while the sky had few clouds. The sun god was on our side. The route was cairned up to the small frozen Lake Helado at around 3,000 m. Descending climbers warned of the dangers higher up as they clanked past in their crampons. "It's hard ice and impossible in trainers. Very dangerous," many stated.

Graham and Edward who had climbed ahead paused with this serious news and wanted to turn back. "The snow is soft here," I retorted. "We should climb until it becomes dangerous, and it looks as though there are huge bucket steps on the steepest parts." (figure 7)

The five of us trudged slowly up the softening snow. There was only 350 m ascent remaining but the altitude was beginning to tell. None of us were remotely acclimatised, nor on acetazolamide. It was a long slow plod. As we ascended, the bright sun softened the hard snow from its overnight freeze. Bucket-sized steps, kicked by other climbers, were yielding with a firm base. Ideal for lightweight boots or even trainers. An hour earlier, it had been ice-hard but under the mid-summer sun it had softened rapidly. It was not surprising that the climbers we met at Góriz had experienced very different early-morning conditions.

We climbed steeply south-east up an open couloir leading to a saddle. I looked up to see Edward and Graham already on the summit. I panted desperately alongside Neville as we ascended the final ridge to the broad mountain top.

The view was magnificent – an immense panorama down the Ordesa Valley, across to the Posets Massif and the Breche de Roland in the north-west. But to the south a huge black cloud was bearing down on us, with an accompanying crack of thunder. The hot midday sun had brewed up a thunderstorm on the south face of the mountain.

We fled. Down the summit ridge, down the broad saddle and into the steep couloir with its bucket steps of snow and ice. It started to hail as lightning crackled repeatedly around us with elemental ferocity. The temperature plummeted and the snow froze. The soft bucket steps hardened, making the upper part of the couloir dangerously slippery. Then, who should we see coming up in full climbing gear, but Chris and Kyle, a full hour behind us.

Of the five of us who had already summited, four had a ski pole or stick; I was the only one without any manual support. I looked at Chris with all his gear and wondered if he would lend me an ice axe. "My kingdom for an axe," I pleaded.

He generously offered it and I accepted with great relief. I had been much slower than the others on the descent without a pole so they were now near Lake Helado. Moving away from the snow steps, I glissaded and slid on my back for 200 metres to reach the others who had descended in similar fashion. We looked anxiously back at the two black dots of Kyle and Chris ascending the final ridge. There were no others on the summit pyramid. The black thunder cloud descended to hide their progress and roared around them. There was no point in waiting – we would miss the 6 pm bus from the car park unless we moved fast. We ran, slithered, slipped and skidded down the snow slopes in light drizzle and bright sun, clouds growing ever larger on the summits. It was going to be a wet afternoon. By 1.30 pm we were at the Góriz Hut for refreshments and admiration from those who had seen us earlier. But it had been close, a fine judgement call. Half an hour earlier it would have been too icy and half an hour later there was a dangerous storm. We had been lucky.

We left the hut at 2.30 pm, tired but in high spirits: down narrow ledges to the chain-covered wall, down the face to the river, now in full fury from melting snow, for the long slog back to the bus. Our weary legs prevented us from running far and the distance seemed interminable; on the way up, it had seemed so easy. Finally, with five minutes remaining before the 6 pm departure, we saw our friends, the non-climbers, in a restaurant next to the car park. We told our tale, they told theirs. All had had a great day and all were safely back apart from Chris and Kyle.

The departure was set strictly for 6 pm and since we estimated that they were an hour behind it was sensible to leave. They would have to wait for the bus at 8 pm, but it was a mistake. They were only a few minutes behind because they had not stopped at Góriz on the descent whereas we had stopped for an hour. They just missed the bus. The driver dropped us at the hotel an hour later only to realise he would exceed his tachograph limit if he returned within the next two hours. They were eventually collected at 9 pm.

I sat next to Chris at our delayed dinner as he described the storm. He had never been so frightened, even above 8,000 m on Mt Everest and Cho Oyo. As they climbed towards the summit, the electric charges in the storm reached down to them, raising hair on their heads and arms. It then crashed down with a great shock wave. They had reached the summit at a dangerous time. Like us, they had fled down in the gathering gloom and hail but once off the summit pyramid it was safe and uneventful.

Hungry, exhausted and slightly tipsy, I reflected on the best day of the year and a great birthday treat. Welcome to retirement!

14. The Bob Graham Round. June 2014 (see front map)

Participants: Maggie Beazley, Barbara Bradwell, Jo Bradwell, William Bradwell, Ian Chesner, Mary Chesner, Amy Cogswell, Graham Cogswell, John Delamere, Jamie Goodhart, Charles Hand, Tim Harvey, Brian Johnson, John Keighley, Ruth Keighley, Hannah Lock, Will Malein, Ellie McCance, Alastair Miller, Angie Miller, Neville Richardson, Barry Smith, Owen Thomas.

For a few years, attendance at BMRES summer walks had become lacklustre due to busy schedules, aging bodies and lack of willingness to suffer. We did have walks in North Wales and the Lakes but they were usually modest affairs. For the few, Tim and Maggie had been hosts at Eden Brows, their beautiful house near Carlisle. From there, we walked the high peaks of the Pennines and the Lakes yet attendance was low, although not through lack of hospitality, which was always most welcoming. But they couldn't accommodate 20 people, so some camped or slept on the floor, while the youngsters were perhaps a bit shy or felt out of place and tended not to come.

We needed something special to re-invigorate our summer excursions. In Bhutan, during May 2012, while descending to the Dzong at Punakha, thoughts turned to a summer walk. We had completed the expedition and felt fit. Chris Imray asked me if I would like to do the Bob Graham Round with him. The answer was a firm, "No".

The Bob Graham Round is a mountain marathon in the Lake District, but that understates it. It is three mountain marathons in one, comprising 42 peaks, 66 miles, and 8,230 metres of ascent and accompanying descent – nearly the height of Mt Everest from sea level. Bob Graham was a famous Lake District fell runner in the 1920s and 1930s who first completed the round over a single day in 1932 on his 42nd birthday. The best descriptions of the joys and pains of trying to undertake his 24 hour challenge are included in Richard Askwith's engaging book *Feet in the Clouds*. The author succeeded on his fourth attempt. The current record of less than 14 hours is held by Mark Hartell, and there are nearly 2,000 members of the 'Bob Graham Club'.

I would have found it improbable when young and certainly ridiculous aged 67. I sought help from others in my determined rejection of the proposal. Sarah Walsh came to my aid. She agreed it was ridiculous for mortal men. Indeed, she was a fell runner and had accompanied someone on one section, finding the pace impossibly fast.

Nevertheless, the suggestion fell on fertile ground and a plan to tackle the mega-walk germinated. While it was not sensible for us to contemplate the Round in 24 hours, three days did seem possible. Indeed, it was a popular route over five days since it could be split into five sections that crossed roads. Some holiday companies sold vacations that dropped off walkers at a road intersection then collected them at the next while ferrying bags to nearby hotels. We wondered about a two day Round but realised that two 16–18 hour days would preclude overnight accommodation with meals.

Kyle Pattinson and I had a recce in the summer of 2013 to assess what a 3 day climb might entail, tackling the leg from Keswick to Threlkeld – just three peaks. This is a mere 14 miles with 1,980 metres of ascent. A 24 hour schedule required a completion time of four hours. We walked for eight hours and while they are the three most strenuous consecutive peaks in the circuit – Skiddaw, Great Calva and Blencathra – the weather was perfect, the ground reasonably dry and we did not slouch. We added to our time somewhat by losing our way out of Keswick and among the bogs between Great Calva and Mungrisdale Common. Furthermore, Hall's Fell Ridge leading down from the top of Blencathra slowed us as it is very exposed and impossible to run. For the next four days I was very stiff and struggled to walk down stairs.

The outcome of the reconnaissance identified several issues:
1. Completing the Round in 24 hours was indeed a fantasy – a dream, unless one was an experienced and fast fell runner. One would have to be capable of completing a marathon in under 3 hours.
2. Completing the Round in 48 hours was unrealistic for any member of BMRES, unless there was a good supporting team and the weather ideal. This would probably require people accompanying walkers through the night.
3. A 3 day attempt would be hard but possible provided there were carefully arranged logistics.
4. Any hint of bad weather would make route finding very difficult without intricate knowledge, particularly over the Langdales/Scafell section. Rain, high winds, mist or even hot sun would be problematic. It was likely to take 10–14 hours in good conditions for fit people to complete this section. Satnav on a phone should be considered.
5. Coordinating a BMRES walk would require planning. We would have to book hotels

a long time in advance. We would need a support team at Dunmail Raise, Honister Pass and possibly Threlkeld. Members would have to decide in advance which sections they would like to attempt each day and we might need to keep track of slower ones to ensure they arrived safely at destination hotels.

6. Extreme fitness would be essential. It was not a task to take on without a lot of training.

At one of our monthly meetings, I proposed the 3 day attempt. A lively discussion followed. Many thought it was ridiculous but Chris and I pressed our case until there was sufficient support. I agreed to book hotels.

Boldly, with a year to go, I put down a non-refundable deposit on every bed at the Wasdale Head Inn, 27 places in total. The Skiddaw Hotel in Keswick and Daffodil Hotel in Grasmere were more flexible, with deposits refundable if we cancelled nearer the date. I reserved similar bed numbers. We had little choice but to book early since we wanted to be at Wasdale Head on 21 June, mid-summer's day, when many other people would be booking accommodation for various mountain marathons. We all loved that hotel from previous big summer and winter walks. It is an iconic place, in the most remote part of the Lakes, with Kirk Fell, Great Gable and Lingmell providing magnificent backdrops to Wast Water in the evening sun.

The great challenge neared while I was in France for two months. Fearful of its demands, particularly the strenuous downhill sections, I trained on the high peaks. Pic du Canigou, Mont Ventoux, Le Dent de Crolles, the Jura and peaks of the Massif Central fell to my feet. Long days and running downhill gradually became easier and, after the last excursion, I had no muscle stiffness. I was as ready as reasonably possible, apart from my footwear: I had worn out my old Salomon 'Speed Cross 3s' and bought a new pair for the trip. Not very sensible.

As the date approached, the weather forecast was good, with final hotel bookings confirmed for 23 people at Wasdale Head, plus three students camping. Amy, my secretary, and her husband Graham hired a minivan that would transport our bags between hotels. We drove up with Owen, Will and Ellie, with whom I would be in close contact for the next three days. Chris, Barry and Neville would be my likely walking companions. We had climbed many peaks together and had a similar pace. On arriving at the Daffodil Hotel in Grasmere, I noticed some of the team at the bar nervously discussing the route and the likelihood of success. Twelve of us were ready for the start. Poor Chris Imray was unexpectedly on duty for transplantation surgery in Coventry and hadn't turned up, while a dozen others were walking simpler paths to Wasdale Head. We had our final discussions about water requirements for the predicted hot weather, plasters for blisters and sore toes, food and glucose supplements, and escape routes if storms came. There followed an edgy late bedtime for a 5.30 am breakfast.

Day 1: 15 peaks, 16 miles and 1,980 metres of ascent

At 6 am, Amy drove the first seven walkers up the two miles to Dunmail Raise, while Neville, Barry, Angie, Alastair and I had a 6 am start. I had slept fitfully, wondering if I was taking enough food and water. There are 15 peaks in the first section but few streams in dry weather to quench parched bodies. And I dreamt that my new trainers had rubbed my feet raw with blisters.

The first peak was Steel Fell (552 m), 300 metres above the road pass at Dunmail Raise. A severe grassy slope, steepening as it rose, confronted us. Barry, Neville and I, trying hard, were up in 25 minutes, emerging into the early sun as we neared the summit and surprisingly on the Bob Graham Round schedule for 24 hours. But it was an illusionary fast time. Fell runners would then speed on down the far side and run the next peaks of Calf Crag (537 m), Sergeant Man (736 m), High Raise (762 m) and Thunacar Knott (717 m). We, on the other hand, were already tired from our fast start and walked, albeit briskly, in the cool morning sunshine. Ahead, we could just make out seven friends, Owen, Will, John, Graham, Ellie, Jamie and Hannah. Gradually, they got closer. It was a measure of our good progress, since most were in their 20s. They climbed the undistinguished High Raise as their third peak while we climbed Sergeant Man, passing in the opposite direction as we climbed High Raise. A cool, misty summit greeted our feet. Four down; eleven to go. The clouds lifted as we approached Thunacar Knott and from there a glorious mountain panorama opened up. The route for the day was clearly visible, while the fells for Sunday and Monday were spread all around us on the skyline. How could it be possible to run all those peaks in a single day? Behind us we could make out the others on top of Sergeant Man.

Harrison Stickle (736 m) and Pike O'Stickle (708 m) are grand spires from the Langdale valley but from our northern side they were mere bumps on a high plateau and were soon completed. Rossett Pike (642 m) was visible in the distance below the peaks of Bowfell and Great End as we skirted around the high slopes above Langdale Comb and across Stake Pass. The grassy moor, firm underfoot following a week of dry weather, was a welcome surprise but there was little drinking water once we had swallowed what we were carrying. Bowfell (902 m) loomed up and, at its base, emanating from under some rocks by the path, a trickle of water allowed us to refill our bottles. We knew this would be the last natural water until Wasdale.

The 350 metre climb up the east buttress of Bowfell beckoned. Steep, uncompromising and ill-defined, it confused us despite our smartphone satnav. Or at least it confused Barry and me. Following a steep grassy slope, we ended with a difficult scramble in a narrow vertical rock gulley a short way below the summit ridge. Neville had made a better route decision and welcomed us at the summit with a big grin, having spent five minutes leisurely enjoying the views.

The remaining day's hike, comprising Lakeland's highest peaks, spread out ahead in the warm midday sun. A broad track led to Esk Pike (885 m), followed by a short climb to Great End (910 m). The boulders making up the path were warm and dry, their sandpaper-like surface providing perfect grip. I recalled times when they had been covered in treacherous ice and surrounded by deep pockets of snow ready to twist or break the ankle of an unwary walker. Conditions underfoot were ideal.

From Great End, Scafell Pike (977 m), an old volcanic summit, lay ahead along the highest ridge in England, which included Ill Crag (922 m), Broad Crag (931 m) and, beyond, Scafell itself (964 m), our fifteenth and final summit for the day. As we descended from Great End towards Ill Crag, five fell runners came alongside. They were on a recce for a future Bob Graham Round. Accelerating to their pace, we chatted with them up Ill

Crag but it was a struggle, and they were not even racing. For a few minutes we were in tune with the 'Kings of the Mountains'.

Numerous walkers were wandering among the ill-defined paths over the boulders on the lofty plateau, with the summit of Scafell Pike within reach. Straining our lungs to leave Barry flagging in our wake, Nev and I marched up the final slope to bag the highest peak in England. We were not alone. The hot dry weather, with perfect skies, had drawn out the day trippers. Over 100 people crowded the summit cairn and surrounding boulders. To my surprise, I appeared to be the oldest on the mountain. I recalled my first ascent aged 12, when I was the youngest. But, despite our vintage, we had made very good time – seven hours, with only one peak remaining.

The route to Scafell had yet to be decided. The classic way is a descent to the col at Mickledore followed by a simple rock climb up Broad Stand. For Bob Graham runners, accompanying supporters often lay a guide rope but we had no such luxury and the climb was not obvious. Although Neville had been up before, he was not certain of the line. There were two alternatives: a steep descent to Fox's Tarn followed by the return climb to Scafell summit, or a rough scramble along Lord's Rake, which runs below the crumbling Scafell Crag. We had been warned that this was currently dangerous because of rock fall and someone had died on it recently. However, walkers were visible at the far end so we took our chances. The narrow, shaded gully and steep scree were a welcome relief from the sunny mountain paths. We scrambled along the boulder-filled switchback, past the renowned leaning stone on the first crest, then down and up the following scree channels to emerge from the gloom, blinking in the bright sunlight on the northern flank of Scafell. From there it was a short walk to our final peak. It had been exactly 31 years to the day since I last stood on the summit during a BMRES walk of the four 3,000 foot peaks in the Lake District (walk 4).

We looked back in triumph at the crowds on Scafell Pike only a short distance away across the hidden chasm of Mickledore. To the north-west, bathed in the afternoon sun, lay Wasdale Head nearly a kilometre below us and the most formidable descent of the whole Round. The first part was the bolder-strewn trail we had ascended but it soon changed to a steep grassy path that was more easily jogged to save the knees, but the strain on the quads was painful. We turned left above Rakehead Crag then to the right below it. Here, the trail steepened further, with loose pebbles that required great care. We finally joined the broad path off Brown Tongue above Lingmell Gill. Fell runners bound down in a few minutes while we took 40. We were very tired but the thoughts of rest, beer and food pulled us along, over the remarkably dry beck at Wasdale, to the welcoming embrace of the Wasdale Head Inn at 3.30 pm. A total of 8 hours and 45 minutes, when we had predicted 10–14 hours. We had done surprisingly well.

With aching feet and legs, I rehydrated on three pints of bitter shandy and a litre of tea. Barry and Neville did likewise. Over the next few hours, others in our party arrived from all directions until we were eventually 25 sitting in the garden, with perhaps 100 other people enjoying the remarkably warm sunny evening. It was the Lake District at its very best. We all ate dinner around one big table in the residents' dining room, oldies at one end and students at the other, apart from Tim and Maggie who came in late from their own walk. It was a perfect setting for a BMRES dinner, and surrounded by large sepia photographs of Lakeland's climbing history.

Rehydrated and wine-soaked, we were in bed by 10 pm in preparation for an early start. Thankfully, Barbara and I were allocated a bedroom on the ground floor – Yewbarrow, the name of our first summit next morning.

Day 2: 12 peaks, 22 miles and 2,743 metres of ascent

I slept poorly, with aching legs and agitated excitement about the following two days. Eight of us met at 5 am for breakfast –Will, Owen, Ellie, Neville, Barry and me on the three day Round and Angie and Alastair on a four day assault. I carefully strapped my sore toes to prevent further chaffing; mercifully, I had no blisters, despite the new trainers. It was my 69th birthday.

While we were walking the four Lakeland Three Thousanders in 1983 with BMRES, the Ramblers' Association had organised a similar walk for its members. I was a mere stripling of 38 years, and while jogging down High Raise had passed an old man striding out with great vigour. He was on the same circuit and had already claimed Skiddaw, Scafell Pike and Scafell with only Helvellyn remaining. I had stopped to chat and commented on his remarkable vigour. It appeared extraordinary that he could be so fit and strong at his vintage. He proudly declared he was 65 years old. I could not imagine being able to undertake what he was doing at such an age. Now, here I was at 69 attempting even more, but I didn't need reminding that we were less than a third of the way round, with 27 peaks ahead.

Yewbarrow (628 m) was the first of the dozen peaks for the day. It shone to the west in the early light: a gruelling steep climb up a grass and scree slope. We discussed starting from its gentler southern end but that entailed an extra two mile walk past the tip of Wast Water. Instead, we chose to tackle it directly. South of the hotel, a dry-stone wall of a sheep enclosure led directly up the mountain. At 5.45 am, we ascended along its side, climbed over the wall at the upper end to enter the open fell. Grass and scrub gave way to scree as it steepened. Panting to our utmost and unable to speak for the effort, we struggled up the 500 metres to the skyline. Beyond, the angle eased off, the panorama opened on a perfect morning and dawn awaited. It had taken an exhausting 40 minutes. As for the day before, the ascent had taken the same time as the recommended 24 hour Round time but it was impossible to continue at that pace.

The summit path to Stirrup Crag was simple enough but the descent to Dore Head was steep and demanding. Then suddenly I noticed a painful blister on my right heel. Perhaps it was provoked by the damp grass or walking sideways on the sloping fell. I had no choice but to stop and protect it with layers of plasters. We imagined the experts running at high speed down this section, not stopping for mere blisters.

Red Pike (828 m) followed, then Scoat Fell (843 m) which, curiously, is not one of the 42 peaks. The highest point is marked by a few stones on a dry-stone wall. Steeple (819 m), our next peak, appeared as a small pinnacle to the north, yet from Ennerdale Water it stands proud as a huge spire.

On returning from its summit, Neville and I passed Barry, then the others on their way up. We slowed down to wait since we had a long day ahead.

The great whaleback of Pillar (853 m) shone ahead, while Kirk Fell and Great Gable were silhouetted against the morning sun. Three big peaks in a row and we were already low on water.

Following the ridge past Black Crag, down to Wind Gap and then to Pillar, we had a long high walk with Ennerdale beautifully mapped out below us, its blue lake and deep green woods so sharp they could almost be touched. Perfectly clear air and a blue-to-blue horizon were the very best that the Lake District could offer and there was barely a soul to be seen.

Beyond the rugged summit of Pillar, we dropped down to Black Sail Pass, searching the bog in vain for a drop of clean running water to refill our bottles. Now, starting to be compromised by dehydration, we marched up Kirk Fell (802 m) in the increasing morning heat. The descent to Beck Head followed, where we re-commenced our search for water. Just then we heard a shout and the sound of mocking voices coming from Gable Beck. It was a few of our group taking the short cut to Honister Pass from Wasdale Head. John Delamere taunted us on our slow progress. How could he? We had already climbed five peaks and he had only walked up from the hotel after a leisurely breakfast. But they were magnanimous and realising our plight, John Keighley jogged over with two litres of water and some food. We drained the bottles in moments and thanked them profusely, for they had surely saved our lives.

We then headed up the steep path to Great Gable (899 m). The scramble to the high point of the day became easier as the water slowly worked its way into our blood, together with calories from food scoffed on the move. On top we met a clutch of other walkers for the first time and rested for a few minutes as we described our mission. They were impressed.

Having rehydrated, I finally got the hang of the calorie requirements. Half a dozen jelly babies at the top of a peak took 20–30 minutes to work their magic on my muscles, so they needed to be taken on one summit in preparation for the next. Eating as I walked with Neville, I descended to the col and climbed Green Gable (801 m) with much more ease. There followed the steep descent to Brandreth (715 m) and Grey Knotts (697 m), hardly peaks in their own right. The path subsequently flowed down to Honister Pass (360 m) and a desperately needed pit stop. Helen Delamere, Barbara and Amy had set up a wonderful lunch: bacon sandwiches, cheese rolls, tea, juice, chocolates and even a birthday cake with a lone candle. Three litres of fluid later, I was in a good enough state to appreciate a chorus of 'Happy Birthday'.

After replacing all the bandages on my toes and heels, and a good 40 minutes of rest, the three of us walked across the road towards Dale Head (753 m). My son Will accompanied us, and fresh for the day, he carried my spare water and food. The ascent was easy enough, but false summits teased us one by one until the top, from where we could see Keswick and our evening route over Hindscarth (727 m) and Robinson (737 m). These high moorland peaks were in complete contrast to the rockier ancient volcanic tops of Great Gable and Steeple. Finally, we were on the long descent to High Snab and the six miles of road to Keswick. This is where many attempting the 24 hour round fail. It is usually the last section and it is a long way – not to be underestimated on tired legs. It needs to be run but that was impossible for us, even with our three day attempt, and it took nearly two hours. At 6.30 pm we dragged ourselves into the Skiddaw Hotel bar, just next to Moot Hall.

I tried to snatch an hour's sleep before dinner but was thwarted by the pain in my feet. Barry was in a sorry state and was doubtful about continuing but there was no stopping Neville. The others arrived over the following hour, with Owen and Will determined to complete the route even though they had started slowly. I was poor company at dinner and not able to eat much despite my huge calorie expenditure during the day. At 9.35 pm there were shouts of delight outside as two runners passed the hotel with their support team and kissed the main door of Moot Hall. They had completed the Round half an hour under the 24 hours. Wow.

Day 3: 15 peaks, 28 miles and 3,505 metres of ascent

The next day the alarm went off at 5 am for the longest day. I ate as much as I could, re-plastered my sore feet and with stiff, aching legs departed the Skiddaw Hotel guided by my iPhone satnav. The route across the river and up to the old railway line is not obvious and it was no time to get lost. The eight of us soon stretched out around Latrigg to the broad steep path up Jenkin Hill. Barry, unsure as to whether he was capable of finishing, dropped back with Angie and Alastair.

Inevitably, we were all markedly slower than on the previous two days and from the cool morning air of the valley we eased our way up into the sunshine and past Skiddaw Little Man. Owen, Will, Neville and I reached Skiddaw summit (931 m) in an hour, considerably slower than the split time of 45 minutes. When recce-ing the route last year, we had watched fell runners race to the top. We presumed this peak is normally taken at speed since it would be the first on the 24 hour circuit.

Once again, the sky was deep blue with postcard-perfect views across Derwent Water to the distant mountains and sea. A cold wind at the top encouraged us to press on at a jog down to the thankfully dry Candleseaves Bog and across the Cumbrian Way path to Great Calva (690 m).

This is the most remote of the peaks, straightforward but with a false summit. The subsequent route to Mungrisdale Common is poorly defined but again satnav came to our rescue. The narrow path, mostly hidden beneath spreading bilberry bushes, was dry and the River Caldew, which can be a torrent, was easily crossed. Following this was a long hard slog in a straight line up towards Atkinson Pike before a turn south to the top summit of Blencathra (868 m), which provided a clear view across to our final obstacle – the Helvellyn range. We looked back to see Barry struggling upwards then we continued south to Blease Fell for the descent to Threlkeld, fearing the more direct, steep ridge of Hall's Fell on weary legs. Awaiting us was our support team of Amy and Helen, ensconced in the village hall with full service laid on. Surprisingly, we had taken only six hours, despite our weariness, whereas it had taken eight hours on the reconnaissance a year earlier. For an hour, hot tea, burgers, sausage rolls and sweets slaked our thirst and hunger. Barry appeared and after a brief rest he was persuaded to continue.

Clough Head (726 m) rises 500 m above Threlkeld. The ascent starts gently through the village meadows but progressively steepens as it reaches the moors and up to Red Screes. With lungs bursting, legs crying in pain, we gasped our way to the top of our last big ascent. We now had a sense that we were going to complete the route. Apart from the sting of Fairfield at the very end, it was largely a high ridge walk. The next nine summits followed in fine style: Great Dodd (858 m), Watson's Dodd (789 m), Stybarrow Dodd (846 m) and, after Sticks Pass and the ski tow, the peak known as Raise (884 m). Then White Side (863 m), Helvellyn Lower Man (935 m) and Helvellyn itself (950 m), the third highest peak in England after the two Scafells. Briefly, we peered fearfully down the almost vertical northern edge to Red Tarn which Neville had bravely skied many years ago. John and

Ruth Keighley accompanied us for several peaks and shared their water bottles for the second time in two days.

Nethermost Pike (891m) and Dollywaggon Pike (858 m) were the final minor bumps on the long ridge. For the past three hours, looking north, we had seen approaching storms. Clouds covered the sky and a rain shower blocked the view north to Skiddaw. It gradually approached as we welcomed the cooling air with cloud cover and a few light spots of drizzle. But it cleared away as we descended the steep grassy path to Grisedale Tarn, turned anti-clockwise, and struggled up the crumbling path to Fairfield (873 m). What cruelty by Bob Graham to add such an uncompromising peak off the main ridge as a 42nd summit. From the top, we retraced our steps to the tarn and, in the evening sun, dragged ourselves up the short path to Seat Sandal (736 m), our final mountain. Emotional, weary beyond measure, legs and feet aching, we shook hands and grinned stupidly at each other (figure 8).

There remained the simple but painful descent to Dunmail Raise. Jogging down seemed easier on the quads, as Owen and I took the lead, initially over steep grass, then through bilberry bushes and finally high bracken. Neville, Will and Barry were close behind. Awaiting us were Amy, Helen and others with life-saving tea, biscuits, hot dogs, whisky and even deckchairs. It was 7.30 pm. It had taken 33 hours walking time. Perhaps as a youth, a 24 hour round would have been possible – but I doubt it. We drove to Birmingham and by 11.30 pm I was in bed contemplating one of the most extraordinary three days of my life.

Fig 1.
*Jumping Adam and
Eve on Tryfan*

Fig 2. *Coire Mhic Fhearchair on Beinn Eighe*

Fig 3. *An Teallach*

Fig 4. *Aonach Eagach ridge*

Fig 5. *Cuillin ridge*

Fig 6. *Five Sisters of Kintail*

Fig 7. *Monte Perdido summit climb*

Fig 8. *Bob Graham Round. Left to right: Owen, Neville, Jo
and Will (photo courtesy of Barry Smith)*

Epilogue

——

I am often asked to name my favourite expedition, for which I have a ready answer – the first. The reason lies with its novelty. Those initial sights of massive glaciated mountains in pristine environments, the charm of Kathmandu with its ancient buildings and cultures, camping in wild places, and the momentum of an expedition with dozens of Sherpas and porters. Subsequent expeditions had their own special features, spanning the first view of Everest, the race around Torres del Paine, fleeing a killer storm on Kanchenjunga, and the misery of diarrhoea and mountain sickness. But ultimately it is the camaraderie and deep friendship that makes all expeditions special; 'friends on the mountains are friends for life', as the saying goes.

As observed by Tim Harvey after a trip to the Margherita Hut in the Alps:

'There are so many grey days, months and years that slip by without leaving any mark on the memory, but those brief moments of adventure, peril, beauty, terror, exhilaration, achievement, trust, fellowship and friendship are etched on the soul forever.'

But I must not neglect the primary motivation for the expeditions, medical science. This has been a unifying theme on every trip as we have sought to understand the effects of high altitude on our bodies and minds. On the first trip it was easy to find projects – there was low hanging fruit waiting to be picked. Mountain sickness was new territory, little explored and poorly understood. Now its mechanisms are known, there are preventative strategies and numerous treatments. Safe ascent rates are discussed in every mountain guidebook, along with acetazolamide, dexamethasone, hyperbaric bags and the cost of helicopter rescues.

Our Society was formed by that rare combination of highly motivated people, unlimited opportunities and inspiration. The Society has nearly 250 publications to its name from 26 expeditions over 44 years. We started with an explosion of activity and are still very active scientifically. Nevertheless, most societies run a limited course. Our founding members are mostly retired. Alex Wright is still its secretary but at 83 has hung up his climbing boots, as have Tim Harvey, Neville Richardson and Pete Forster from those early years. However, young blood is taking over. The new generation may overleap the achievements of its predecessors.

Much remains to be studied and understood. For instance, what is the role of smaller doses of acetazolamide in older people and how should it be used in combination with other medications such as hypotensive agents? What is the effect of acetazolamide withdrawal and what is the optimal dose for treating mountain sickness acutely? How common is cognitive impairment, how much does it affect decision making and how can it be measured? There are unresolved questions about individual susceptibility to mountain sickness and how best to monitor people on treks. Should all tour guides use the Lake Louise scoring system for mountain sickness? Should finger pulse oximetry (measurement of blood oxygen saturations) be used on every trek? Should the role of mountain medicine societies include influencing trekking companies? Would it be helpful to have more medical first-aid posts at high altitude? And should mountain medicine be part of medical school curricula? These questions leave unfinished business.

As for me, I am still up for the next expedition. Annapurna in October 2021 sounds very enticing.

Obituaries

Michael H Winterborn FRCP (1939 – 1998)

In the early 1970s, Albert Einstein College in New York was an international focus for doctors training in paediatric nephrology. There Michael Winterborn, who was already committed to the speciality, made lasting friendships and found challenging ideas. He developed a special interest in metabolic disorders of the renal tubule, notably cystinosis. On returning to Birmingham he was among the first to pioneer long-term dialysis services for children in Britain. For this he required both perseverance and vision, as much medical opinion at the time was against exposing young children to invasive treatment. Michael knew that success could be claimed only if, beyond the limits imposed by dialysis, children perceived an attainable world of beauty, fun, and adventure. They did. Michael and the multidisciplinary team that he built up took children on challenging holidays, undertaking haemodialysis whether in an alpine chalet, a French farmhouse, or a Welsh cottage.

Not only did Michael relish outdoor life but he had an abiding love of mountains and took every opportunity to go climbing or skiing. He combined this with academic pursuits, being an active member of Birmingham Medical Research Expeditionary Society and participating in projects on the effects of altitude on vascular physiology. He was disappointed not to be able to return to the Himalayas earlier this year because of poor health.

Always quick to make acquaintances, Michael was a catalyst in any multinational gathering. Through the positions he held in the International Pediatric Nephrology Association and European Society for Paediatric Nephrology, he vigorously promoted the training needs of young nephrologist from developing countries and the former Soviet Union.

In 1966 Michael married Penny Stephenson; they had two boys, Simon and James. Later the marriage was dissolved, and he married Dr Mary Waldron, who is also a paediatric nephrologist, shortly before his death from chronic lymphocytic leukaemia. – C.M. Taylor

Michael Hugh Winterborn, a consultant paediatrician and nephrologist at the Children's Hospital, Birmingham, and honorary senior lecturer at the University of Birmingham, died 20 May aged 53. Born Oslo, 3 June 1939; educated Stonyhurst College and St Mary's hospital, London (MB, BS 1963). Senior registrar in paediatrics, Children's hospital, Birmingham, 1970-3; fellow in paediatric nephrology, Albert Einstein College of Medicine, New York, 1973-5; consultant paediatrician, East Birmingham Hospital 1975-91. Director of West Midlands Paediatric Dialysis Unit from its foundation in 1979. Secretary of British Association for Paediatric Nephrology 1980-5; member of council (1982-5), assistant secretary (1985-9), and secretary general (1989-92) of European Society of Paediatric Nephrology; and assistant secretary of International Pediatric Nephrology Association from 1989.

British Medical Journal 1998; 307

Ginette L Harrison (1958 – 1999)

"Dr Ginette L Harrison. English/American physician, died in an avalanche on Dhaulagiri.

Ginette Harrison, who has been killed in an avalanche in Nepal aged 41, was never overly concerned at becoming famous as a climber, despite her interest in the world's highest and best-known peaks. She would occasionally joke that she should stay in one place long enough to garner some sponsorship, but most of her expeditions she financed herself through her work as a doctor. Her quiet but fiercely determined personality may not have grabbed the headlines, but her achievements made her one of only a few British women to make an impact in high-altitude climbing.

She started while at school in Leeds and soon became hooked on rock-climbing. Studying medicine at Bristol allowed her to continue her new passion on the crags of the Avon Gorge. But it was in the mountains that she really made her mark, where her moderate technical ability was no handicap and where her prodigious stamina would keep her going in the thin air and searing light of high altitude.

Ginette had climbed Mount Kenya in 1982 [with BMRES], but her first big peak was Mount McKinley in Alaska at the age of 25. Completing her studies meant that trips to the mountains were irregular, although she joined a Bristol University expedition in 1986 to Bhutan, where she extended her experience of high altitude over the 7,000-metre mark.

She also developed a strong interest in the physiology of high altitude, spending two years in Denver studying high-altitude medicine at the University of Colorado, and throughout the 1980s she was often out in the field, including a stint at the Himalayan Rescue Post at Manang in Nepal.

But it was in the 1990s that her reputation as a climber was established. She became the second British woman to climb Everest after Rebecca Stephens in 1993, and seemed destined to play second fiddle when she repeated Stephens' next achievement of climbing the highest points of each of the seven continents [Aconcagua with BMRES in 1990].

"Part of my problem is that I am never in the right place at the right time," she joked in an interview with Stephen Venables. It was an enterprise that seemed curiously artificial for someone who had grown up a climber, and later Ginette admitted that she hadn't felt comfortable doing something that didn't ring true to her.

She used bottled oxygen on Everest simply because, as she put it, she had worked weekends and nights to raise the money and "wanted to make damned sure I got to the top". But the experience showed her she was strong enough to do without it. The trip changed her life in other ways. Gary Pfisterer was also on the team; he fell in love with her immediately, she confessed that her passion arrived a few days later, but they remained together from there on and reached the summit of the world, hand in hand, a practice they continued on every peak they climbed together.

Ginette settled in Massachusetts with Gary and together they set out on a series of remarkable expeditions to the world's highest peaks: Carstenz Pyramid in Papua New Guinea, Mt Vinson in Antarctica and Mt Logan in the Yukon. During the Logan expedition, a genuine and impressive achievement, she and Gary ran out of food still a week from civilization. She had done her preparation well.

In 1998, Ginette made the first ascent by a woman of the world's third highest mountain, Kangchenjunga, a vast massif first scaled by British climbers in 1954. Until that point, her long absences meant few in Britain knew of her achievements, but while that began to change, Ginette remained as open and friendly and well liked as ever. She watched in sorrow as other climbers she knew were lost – Alison Hargreaves, Chantal Mauduit – and wrote of her historic ascent: "Over the years four women had died while attempting to climb Kangchenjunga and it made me appreciate all the more how lucky I was to make the first female ascent and return safely."

The Guardian, Thursday 28 October 1999 by Ed Douglas

Frank Davies (1928 - 2014)

A keen climber, sailor, rally driver and philanthropist who founded The Climbers Shop in Ambleside has died, aged 86 (1928-2014). Frank Davies opened the store – one of the first outdoor shops in the UK – in 1959 and it remains a focal point in the town more than half a century on. He is survived by his son, Ben, and wife Cate. They paid tribute to him, saying they 'will miss him greatly'.

Born in Manchester in 1928, Mr Davies's first passion was cycling, and as teenager, he decided to take his bike off-road one weekend and carry it over Kinder Scout. This sparked a lifetime passion for the hills and, having had difficulty finding anywhere to buy walking and mountaineering gear himself, he decided that he would open a specialist shop.

Mr Davies was also a keen rock climber and, after learning to ski, he and friend Chris Bonington were members of one of the first British teams to tackle the Haute Route, from Chamonix to Zermatt. Back home in Ambleside, he became involved in mountain rescue, and was chairman of the Langdale and Ambleside team for a time.

In the '60s and '70s Mr Davies took part in rally's every weekend in his Mini Cooper S with friend and navigator Bod Redhead. In 1971, with the Wasdale farmer and fell runner Joss Naylor, Mr Davies established a Guinness record for the British Three Peaks that stands to this day. He climbed Ben Nevis, Scafell Pike, and Snowdon, in 11 hours and 56 minutes. Mr Davies drove the specially prepared Ford Capri while Mr Naylor ran, with his shoes stuffed with wool from his Herdwicks, to stop his feet from blistering.

Mr Davies was also a keen sailor, teaching himself astro-navigation, and crossing the Atlantic in December 1989. He and his wife Cate made many voyages together, in their Nicholson 43, Savoir Faire. Combining his love of the mountains and sailing Mr Davies competed in the Three Peaks races and Scottish Island Peaks races, winning the Three Peaks the year after its inception. Despite developing Parkinson's Disease in his 60s, Mr Davies continued to climb, sail, ski and walk in the mountains, with Cate, and their son Ben, until he was 80.

He was a quiet philanthropist and in 2005 set up the Frank Davies Family Trust – a charity that will now continue in his memory. The entire rental income for the Climbers Shop, which Mr Davies retired from in 1997, is given away each year to his favourite third world charities.

On Monday, nearly 100 people gathered at Mr Davies's Field Broughton home to celebrate his life, after he lost his battle with the disease on June 25.

Kate Dickinson, The Westmorland Gazette 12 July 2014

Ronald Frank Fletcher (1927 – 2016)

Honorary consultant physician Birmingham City Hospital (b 1927; q Birmingham 1950; MD, PhD, FRCP), died from disseminated bladder cancer on 19 June 2016.

Ronald Frank Fletcher ("Ron") was born Smethwick, in the West Midlands, on 30 January 1927. He was to live, study and work in Birmingham for nearly his entire life. His father and elder brother were engineers and medicine was suggested as a good alternative career.

He attended King Edward's school and moved from the sixth form to Birmingham University Medical School in 1944. He took a BSc in physiology, which stimulated his interest in both academic medicine, and endocrinology. Joining the university's mountaineering club (he was president in his last year) started his lifelong enthusiasm for hillwalking, scrambling and climbing. He qualified in December 1950, after retaking his surgical finals, and it was while doing a locum post at St Chad's Hospital that he met his future wife June Astill.

They married in the spring of 1954, immediately after Ron returned from national service as a medical office in the Suez Canal Zone and Libya. He then joined the newly opened metabolic and endocrine research unit at East Birmingham Hospital, under the mentorship of John Squire. Having obtained membership of the Royal College of Physicians and completed his MD thesis (on body composition measurement using skin fold callipers), he spent a year at John Hopkins in Baltimore in the US on an Eli Lilley fellowship, studying lipid analysis techniques.

After five years as a lecturer in medicine at the Queen Elizabeth Hospital, he took a consultant physician post at Dudley Road and St Chad's hospitals in 1965. He was able to establish a successful endocrine clinic, and took on a share in the diabetes services in the 1970s. Away from clinical practice, his affinity for committee work allied to a justified reputation for equanimity and calmness, led to his becoming chair of the hospital medical staff, vice chair of the West Birmingham Health Authority (1982-94), and a non-executive director at City Hospital Trust (1994-98).

Medicine and mountains combined in the 1970s, when Ron became a founding member of the Birmingham Medical Research Expeditionary Society, started by (now Prof) Jo Bradwell. He travelled with the society to Nepal, Ecuador, Kenya and the Alps to research (and at times experience) acute mountain sickness. Nearer home he rekindled his involvement in the Mallard Association of Mountaineers, and worked extensively to develop its facilities in north Wales.

Ron retired from his clinical post in 1991 but continued with some administrative work and a post as medical representative on war pensions appeals tribunals. With June, he travelled widely, and they frequently visited static caravans on the south French coast. Her early death in 1997 affected him badly, but he remained active in many spheres and adapted to life alone.

His last five years were dominated by physical and cognitive decline, but fortunately he was able to remain in the family home in Harborne, where he had lived for 50 years. He leaves three children and four grandchildren.

Martin Fletcher, Aesculapius No. 37 2017

John Coote (1936 – 2017)

Pioneering physiologist with a head for heights.

John Coote had two great passions. One was neurophysiology, the other was climbing, but his penchant for taking on dangerous challenges in the mountains almost brought a premature end to what would turn out to be a glittering career in research and teaching.

Coote was 33 when he and two other climbers set out to scale Pico Bolívar, the highest mountain in Venezuela. On their way down from the summit a rockfall snapped their descending rope and the three climbers fell.

Coote's Venezueluan companions were killed, and he ended up lying on a rocky ledge for ten hours next the body of one of the other climbers. He was rescued by a search party and taken to hospital, where he was found to have a fractured skull.

This was not Coote's first big injury. He had broken his pelvis after falling while rock climbing in England. He took fewer risks after getting married and having children, but continued to visit the Alps and Himalayas.

In 1988 he was able to combine his passions when a team from the Birmingham Medical Research Expeditionary Society carried out a study of Peruvian Indians living in the high Andes who are prone to chronic mountain sickness. When Coote and his colleagues arrived at the hospital that would be their base, in Cerro de Pasco, they found that the building was covered in bullet holes because of attacks by Shining Path guerrillas.

That night Coote and his team heard sounds of fighting for the first time, but continued with the mission. "We can always filter out the machinegun fire on the EEG [electroencephalogram – a device to test electrical activity in the brain]," he joked.

His focus in research was on the brains control of blood pressure in muscles. He and colleagues conducted path-breaking experiments in the late 1960s and early 1970s showing how muscles talk to the brain through nerve passages. They demonstrated that if a muscle is stimulated, the receptors inside the tissue feed back into the nerve and send signals back to the brain.

In his later research, collaborating with Professor André Ng at the University of Leicester, Coote focused on the way the brain and heart interact through the nervous system. His work showed – contrary to previous assumptions – that the vagus nerve plays a role in protecting the heart against rhythmic disturbances.

John Haven Coote was born in Enfield, north London, in 1936. His father, Albert Coote, was an electrical engineer who became a Pentecostal minister. His mother, Gladys, was from a mining family in south Wales and worked in domestic service. Coote first went to school in Enfield, but was evacuated with his mother and two sisters during the Blitz, first to Somerset then to south Wales, where he enjoyed his first taste of walking the hills.

On returning to London he went to Enfield Grammar School then began reading medicine and physiology at University College London. Even though National Service would have been phased out before he had finished his studies, Coote declared himself a conscientious objector in the mid-Fifties. As a result, he was sentenced to three years of farm work, which proved to be an eye-opener for a young man who had lived a fairly sheltered existence as the son of a clergyman.

Returning to his studies, he took a BSc in physiology and completed his PhD in 1964. It was at this time that he started to take an interest in the brain's control of circulation.

Coote joined the department of physiology at the University of Birmingham in 1967, working under Professor Sidney Hilton. He became the Bowman professor of physiology in 1983 and was also appointed visiting professor at the University of Leicester. Despite his earlier pacifism, he carried out advisory work for the Royal Air Force, some of which concerned the problem of hypoxia (oxygen deficiency) in jet pilots.

He was an honorary member of the Physiological Society and served as chairman of the editorial board of its monthly journal. He was awarded the Carl Ludwig Distinguished Lectureship of the American Physiological Society in 2003 and Paton Prize of the Physiological Society in 2005.

Modest and straight-talking – he abhorred jargon – Coote was an inspiration to hundreds of students. His department thrived. He loved nothing better than a brain-storming session over coffee and a piece of Fry's Turkish Delight. In 2013 Coote's colleagues honoured him with an all-day symposium in Birmingham that highlighted his academic contribution.

He met his future wife, Susan Hylton, an anaesthetist, on a blind date set up by one of her friends in 1974. It was love at first sight. They were engaged within two months and married later that year. She survives him with their three children: Edward, who became a dentist; Rachel, who is an aerospace engineer; and Naomi, who works in banking. Their father enjoyed DIY and supported charities that helped to send the children of Sherpas to school in Nepal.

During his inaugural lecture as the new professor at Birmingham in 1983, Coote faced the difficulty of addressing a diverse audience. His solution was to intersperse complex neurophysiology with "thinking time", when slides of soaring mountain peaks, ice ridges and azure skies would appear on the screen behind him. "Now," he advised those in the lecture theatre, "just rest your eyes on that and let it sink in."

John Coote, cardiovascular physiologist, was born on January 5, 1936. He died of a ruptured thoracic aortic aneurysm on November 27, 2017 aged 81.

The Times 27 January 2018

Peter William Dykes. FRCP, MD. (1928 – 2018)

Physician; scholar; researcher and loved by all.

Peter was born in New Zealand and qualified MB ChB at Otago University in 1951 coming to London in 1953 to work with Dame Sheila Sherlock. MRCP Australia and London followed in 1955 and FRCP of both colleges in 1968 and 1972 respectively. MD 1964 University of Birmingham. Registrar at the Queen Elizabeth Hospital, Birmingham in 1954. Consultant in General Medicine and Gastroenterology to the General Hospital, Birmingham in 1967 and to The United Hospitals Birmingham in 1969. He helped set up one of the earliest UK multidisciplinary gastroenterology units that included physicians, surgeons, radiologists, pathologists and dieticians that is now considered best practice. He was a particular expert on the management of gastrointestinal haemorrhage, and co-authored a book on the subject. Peter was first and foremost a clinician, who cared deeply about his patients and was loved by them in return.

In the mid '70's he developed research projects studying radio-immunodetection of tumours, especially of the bowel and only the second of such studies in the world. A rich seam of projects led to dozens of publications, innumerable lectures around the world and many PhD and MD graduates.

He joined the Birmingham Medical Research Expeditionary Society for three expeditions to the Himalaya including Everest. His work resulted in publications in The Lancet and other prestigious journals. Despite being the oldest on his first trip, aged 56, he had boundless energy, ran several research projects and was GP to the group but still found time to collect wild flowers, swim with the youngsters in freezing lakes at 4,000 m and always be charming and helpful. 'He looked at least 20 years younger than his age,' was Sheila Sherlock's comment.

Peter's last decade was troubled with coronary artery disease and chronic intestinal bleeding, yet he soldiered on, optimistic as ever, insisting to the inquirer that he was 'very well'. Despite numerous cardiac procedures, he died from heart failure after several years of poor health.

He is survived by his wife Mary (née Moss, MB ChB Birmingham 1955) and three children from a previous marriage.

Eulogy; Sandy McNeish, September 2018

Medical bag for Sikkim

(courtesy of Will Malein)

———

Equipment

Community dressing wound care pack - large – 7
Wound closure strip 3mm x 75mm (5 strips) – 4
Waterproof adhesive wound dressing 8cm x 6cm – 10
Waterproof adhesive wound dressing 10x8cm – 3
Fabric elastic pink tape 2.5cm x 4.5m – 1
Zinc oxide tape 2.5cm x 10m - White – 1
Transpore surgical tape 5cm x 9.14m – 1
Adult tongue depressor x 1 pack
Conforming bandage – 7.5cm x 4m – 5
Triangular bandage, 90 x 90 x 127cm - sterile – 2
Tough cut scissors 18cm – 1
Suture pack standard – 5
Ethilon suture 3.0 – 12
Sterile disposable scalpel No 11 – 10
Syringe 20ml – 2
Syringe 10ml –10
Assorted hypodermic needles
Wallace Cameron eye pods saline 25 x 20ml – 2
Eye bath plastic – 3
Insight urinalysis strips – 1 box
Digital thermometer – 1
Premier sterile powder free latex gloves large – 10
Premier sterile powder free latex gloves medium – 10
Catheter bags – 2
Foley catheter 14ch male – 1
Foley catheter 16ch male – 1
Normal saline 1000ml –10
Intravenous giving sets – 4
Intravenous cannula assorted
Optilube sachet – 10
Fabric plasters assorted box
Blister plasters assorted box
Stethoscopes – 2
Sphygmomanometer – 2
Otoscope – 1
Opthalmoscope – 1
BNF
Hand Gel
Oxford Handbook of Clinical Medicine
Oxford Handbook of Wild Env Medicine
Notebook and pens

Medications

2x Salbutamol Evohaler100cmg/dose
1x Compact spacer with large mask
56x Bisoprolol 5mg
28x Digoxin 250mcg
30x Nifedipine 10mg
112x Acetazolamide 250mg
28x Furosemide 40mg
1x GTN spray 400mcg/spray
56x Isosorbide Mononitrate 40mg
56x Prednisone 5mg
30x Dexamethasone 2mg
10x Oxybuprocaine 0.4% drops
56x Chlorphenamine 4mg
28x Naproxen 500mg
28x Naproxen 250mg
28x Lansoprazole 30mg
30x Ondansetron 4mg
28x Prochlorperazine 5mg
30x Cyclizine 50mg
60x Senna 7.5mg
1x 30g Fucidin cream
112x Amoxicillin 500mg
28x Erythromycin 250mg
112x Flucloxacillin 500mg
28x Co-Amoxiclav 500/125mg
2x Cefuroxime 1.5g powder for injection
6x Co-Amoxiclav 500/12 powder for injection
28x Clarithromycin 500mg
48x Clindamycin 150mg
2x Penthrox whistle
112x Ciprofloxacin 500mg
10x Lignocaine 1% 10mls
56x Doxycycline 100mg
56x Diclofenac 75mg
28x Metronidazole 400mg
28x Trimethoprim 200mg
1x Adrenaline 1 in 10,000 10ml
3x Chloramphenicol ointment 4g
28x Flecainide 50mg
2x Ibuprofen gel 5% 30ml
56x Aspirin 75mg
128x Paracetamol 500mg
128 x Ibuprofen 200mg
2x Deep Heat 30ml
20x Dioralyte sachets

Index

Expedition participants

———

Experiments

Mountains

—————

Medications

———

Medicine

———

People

———

Places

Miscellaneous

Ladha, Cassim (2)

Larcombe, Stephanie (1)

Letchford, Abigail (2)

Lewis, Chris (2)

Lock, Hannah (2)

Lort, David (1)

Lucas, Rebekah (1)

Lucas, Samuel (2)

Luks, Andy (1)

Lupton, Tom (1)

Mackintosh, John (1)

Maclennan, Andrew (1)

Maclennan, Ian (7)

Major, Robert (1)

Malein, William (3)

Mead, Graham (1)

Meech, Simon (1)

Milles, David (1)

Milles, John (10)

Mole, Damian (2)

Morgan, John (1)

Morrissey, Simon (4)

Mulholland, Seamus (1)

Myers, Steve (4)

Newman, Charles (1)

Olive, Ted (2)

Parker, David (1)

Patey, Susannah (2)

Pattinson, Kyle (4)

Preiss, David (1)

Prisman, Eitan (1)

Potokar, John (2)